Carboniferous and Permian Igneous Rocks of Great Britain

North of the Variscan Front

THE GEOLOGICAL CONSERVATION REVIEW SERIES

The comparatively small land area of Great Britain contains an unrivalled sequence of rocks, mineral and fossil deposits, and a variety of landforms that provide a geological record of a large part of the Earth's long history. Well-documented ancient volcanic episodes, famous fossil sites, and sedimentary rock sections used internationally as comparative standards have given these islands an importance out of all proportion to their size. The long sequences of strata and their organic and inorganic contents have been studied by generations of leading geologists, thus giving Britain a unique status in the development of the science. Many of the divisions of geological time used throughout the world are named after British sites or areas; for instance, the Cambrian, Ordovician and Devonian systems, the Ludlow Series and the Kimmeridgian and Portlandian stages.

The Geological Conservation Review (GCR) was initiated by the Nature Conservancy Council in 1977 to assess and document the most important parts of this rich heritage. The GCR records the current state of knowledge of the key Earth science sites in Great Britain and provides a firm basis upon which site conservation can be founded in years to come. Each GCR title in the 42-volume series describes networks of sites of national or international importance in the context of a portion of the geological column, or a geological, palaeontological or mineralogical topic.

Within each volume, the GCR sites are described in detail in self-contained accounts, consisting of an introduction (with a concise history of previous work), a description, an interpretation (providing geological analysis of the features of interest and assessing their fundamental scientific importance), and a conclusion (written in simpler terms for the non-specialist). Each site report is a justification of the particular scientific interest in a locality, of its importance in a British or international setting, and ultimately of its worthiness for conservation.

The aim of the Geological Conservation Review Series is to provide a public record of the features of interest in sites that have been notified, or are being considered for notification, as Sites of Special Scientific Interest (SSSIs). The volumes are written to the highest scientific standards but in such a way that the assessment and conservation value of each site is clear. The GCR Series is a public statement of the value placed on our geological and geomorphological heritage by the Earth science community and it will be used by the Joint Nature Conservation Committee, the Countryside Council for Wales, English Nature and Scottish Natural Heritage in carrying out their conservation functions. The three country agencies are also active in helping to establish sites of local and regional importance. Regionally Important Geological/Geomorphological Sites (RIGS) augment the SSSI coverage, with local groups identifying and conserving sites that have educational, historical, research or aesthetic value, enhancing the wider Earth heritage conservation perspective.

All the sites in this volume have been proposed for notification as SSSIs; the final decision to notify, or re-notify, sites lies with the governing councils of the appropriate country conservation agency.

Information about the GCR publication programme may be obtained from:

GCR Unit,
Joint Nature Conservation Committee,
Monkstone House,
City Road,
Peterborough PE1 1JY.

www.jncc.gov.uk

Copies of published volumes can be purchased from:

NHBS Ltd,
2–3 Wills Road,
Totnes,
Devon TQ9 5XN.

www.nhbs.com

Published titles in the GCR Series

Published titles in the GCR Series

———————

Carboniferous and Permian Igneous Rocks of Great Britain

North of the Variscan Front

D. Stephenson*,

S.C. Loughlin*,

D. Millward*,

C.N. Waters[+]

and

I.T. Williamson[+]

*British Geological Survey, Murchison House, West Mains Road, Edinburgh EH9 3LA.
[+]British Geological Survey, Kingsley Dunham Centre, Keyworth, Nottingham NG12 5GG.

GCR Editor: **D. Palmer**

Published by the Joint Nature Conservation Committee, Monkstone House, City Road, Peterborough, PE1 1JY, UK

First edition 2003

Typeset in 10/12pt Garamond ITC by JNCC
Printed in Great Britain by CLE Print Limited on Huntsman Velvet 100 gsm.

ISBN 1 86107 497 2

A catalogue record for this book is available from the British Library.

Recommended example citations

Stephenson, D., Loughlin, S.C., Millward, D., Waters, C.N. and Williamson, I.T (2003) *Carboniferous and Permian Igneous Rocks of Great Britain North of the Variscan Front*, Geological Conservation Review Series, No. 27, Joint Nature Conservation Committee, Peterborough.

Upton, B.G.J. (2003) Arthur's Seat Volcano, City of Edinburgh. In *Carboniferous and Permian Igneous Rocks of Great Britain North of the Variscan Front* (D. Stephenson, S.C. Loughlin, D. Millward, C.N. Waters and I.T. Williamson), Geological Conservation Review Series, No. 27, Joint Nature Conservation Committee, Peterborough, pp. 64–74.

Contents

Contents

Contents

List of contributors

William J. Barclay British Geological Survey, Kingsley Dunham Centre, Keyworth, Nottingham NG12 5GG.

Richard E. Bevins Department of Geology, National Museum of Wales, Cathays Park, Cardiff CF1 3NP.

Patrick J. Cossey School of Sciences, Staffordshire University, College Road, Stoke on Trent, Staffordshire ST4 2DE.

Kathryn M. Goodenough British Geological Survey, Murchison House, West Mains Road, Edinburgh EH9 3LA.

Susan C. Loughlin British Geological Survey, Murchison House, West Mains Road, Edinburgh EH9 3LA.

James G. MacDonald Department of Adult and Continuing Education, University of Glasgow, 59 Oakfield Avenue, Glasgow G12 8LW.

David Millward British Geological Survey, Murchison House, West Mains Road, Edinburgh EH9 3LA.

Alison A. Monaghan British Geological Survey, Murchison House, West Mains Road, Edinburgh EH9 3LA.

David Stephenson British Geological Survey, Murchison House, West Mains Road, Edinburgh EH9 3LA.

Brian G.J. Upton Department of Geology and Geophysics, University of Edinburgh, The Grant Institute, West Mains Road, Edinburgh EH9 3JW.

Colin N. Waters British Geological Survey, Kingsley Dunham Centre, Keyworth, Nottingham NG12 5GG.

Ian T. Williamson formerly British Geological Survey, Kingsley Dunham Centre, Keyworth, Nottingham NG12 5GG.

Derek G. Woodhall formerly British Geological Survey, Murchison House, West Mains Road, Edinburgh EH9 3LA.

V. Paul Wright Department of Earth Sciences, Cardiff University, Cardiff CF10 3YE.

Acknowledgements

This volume is the combined work of the 13 authors listed on page xi. Individual chapters have been compiled by the authors of the relevant chapter introductions and have been edited by D. Stephenson (chapters 2, 4, 5 and 6), K.M. Goodenough (Chapter 1 and introduction to Chapter 2), D. Millward (Chapter 3, introductions to chapters 4 and 5) and C.N. Waters (Chapter 7). Overall compilation and editing is by D. Stephenson and K.M. Goodenough. The GCR editor was D. Palmer and the referee was C.H. Emeleus, whose perceptive comments were responsible for much improvement during the later stages of preparation. The project was cofunded by JNCC and BGS and has been managed by N.V. Ellis for JNCC and D.J. Fettes and M. Smith for BGS.

The initial site selection and site documentation for this volume was by C.H. Emeleus, R. Macdonald, D. O'Halloran and I.T. Williamson and subsequent information and assistance has been provided by M. Murphy (for English Nature) and R. Threadgould, K.M. Goodenough and C. Bond (for Scottish Natural Heritage). Diagrams were drafted by S.C. White and C.F. Pamplin (J S Publications, Newmarket), the references were compiled by A. Muir and L.B. Gray, and the index was prepared by B.J. Amos. The production editor was E. Durham (JNCC). Photographs were scanned and prepared by T. Bain (BGS, Edinburgh). Photographs from the BGS collection are reproduced by kind permission of the Director, BGS © NERC; all rights reserved (PR/23–27).

Several people have helped with advice on the stratigraphical framework to the magmatism, notably M.A.E. Browne on the Midland Valley of Scotland, A.A. McMillan on the Solway Basin and B. Young on northern England. W.A. Read and M.A.E. Browne are also thanked for allowing sight of their text being prepared for the forthcoming fourth edition of *The Geology of Scotland*, which has been particularly useful for its summary of current ideas on palaeogeography and tectonic development. Several studies of radiometric ages were in progress at the time of compilation of this volume and the following are thanked for their permission to quote extensively from their unpublished work: M.A. Hamilton, A.A. Monaghan, D.G. Pearson, M.S. Pringle and M. Timmerman. D.T. Moffat allowed unpublished work on the diatreme at Golden Hill Quarry to be incorporated in that site report. B. Young provided information on mineralization associated with the Whin Sill-complex and contributed much helpful discussion on various aspects of the complex. Particular thanks are also due to B.G.J. Upton for his advice and inspiration over many years and for much discussion during the joint

Acknowledgements

compilation (with D.S.) of a contribution to *The Geology of Scotland*, some results of which will be inevitably duplicated in this volume.

Finally, on behalf of all of the site report authors, we would like to record our thanks to the owners and managers of land and quarries who have allowed access to the sites, either during previous work or specifically for the GCR exercise.

Access to the countryside

This volume is not intended for use as a field guide. The description or mention of any site should not be taken as an indication that access to a site is open. Most sites described are in private ownership, and their inclusion herein is solely for the purpose of justifying their conservation. Their description or appearance on a map in this work should not be construed as an invitation to visit. Prior consent for visits should always be obtained from the landowner and/or occupier.

Information on conservation matters, including site ownership, relating to Sites of Special Scientific Interest (SSSIs) or National Nature Reserves (NNRs) in particular counties or districts may be obtained from the relevant country conservation agency headquarters listed below:

Countryside Council for Wales,
Plas Penrhos,
Ffordd Penrhos,
Bangor,
Gwynedd LL57 2LQ.

English Nature,
Northminster House,
Peterborough PE1 1UA.

Scottish Natural Heritage,
12 Hope Terrace,
Edinburgh EH9 2AS.

Preface

There is such a diversity of rocks, minerals, fossils and landforms packed into the piece of the Earth's crust we call 'Britain' that it is difficult not to be impressed by the long, complex history of geological change to which they are testimony. But if we are to improve our understanding of the nature of the geological forces that have shaped our islands, further unravel their history in 'deep time' and learn more of the history of life on Earth, we must ensure that the most scientifically important of Britain's geological localities are conserved for future generations to study, research and enjoy. Moreover, as an educational field resource and as training grounds for new generations of geologists on which to hone their skills, it is essential that such sites continue to remain available for study. The first step in achieving this goal is to identify the key sites, both at national and local levels.

The GCR, launched in 1977, is a world-first in the systematic selection and documentation of a country's best Earth science sites. No other country has attempted such a comprehensive and systematic review of its Earth science sites on anything near the same scale. After over two decades of site evaluation and documentation, we now have an inventory of over 3000 GCR sites, selected for 100 categories covering the entire range of the geological and geomorphological features of Britain.

This volume, describing the Carboniferous and Permian igneous rocks of Great Britain, is the 27th to be published in the intended 42-volume GCR series. Not only does it contain the descriptions of key localities that will be conserved for their contribution to our understanding of the igneous of rocks of this age, but also provides an excellent summary of the petrological features and palaeogeographical significance to be found in them, and it outlines the research that has been undertaken on them. The book will be invaluable as an essential reference book to those engaged in the study of these rocks and will provide a stimulus for further investigation. It will also be helpful to teachers and lecturers and for those people who, in one way or another, have a vested interest in the GCR sites: owners, occupiers, planners, those concerned with the practicalities of site conservation and indeed the local people for whom such sites are an environmental asset. The conservation value of the sites is mostly based on a specialist understanding of the stratigraphical, palaeontological and sedimentological features present and is therefore, of a technical nature. The account of each site in this book ends, however, with a brief summary of the geological interest, framed in less technical language, in order to help the non-specialist. The first chapter of the volume,

Preface

---

used in conjunction with the glossary, is also aimed at a less specialized audience. This volume is not intended to be a field guide to the sites, nor does it cover the practical problems of their ongoing conservation. Its remit is to put on record the scientific justification for conserving the sites.

This volume deals with the state of knowledge of the sites available at the time of writing, in 1998–2001, and must be seen in this context. Geology, like any other science, is an ever-developing pursuit with new discoveries being made, and existing models are subject to continual testing and modification as new data come to light. Increased or hitherto unrecognized significance may be seen in new sites, and it is possible that further sites worthy of conservation will be identified in future years.

There is still much more to learn and the sites described in this volume are as important today as they have ever been in increasing our knowledge and understanding of the geological history of Britain. This account clearly demonstrates the value of these sites for research, and their important place in Britain's scientific and natural heritage. This, after all, is the *raison d'être* of the GCR Series of publications.

N.V. Ellis
GCR Publications Manager
May 2002

Chapter 1

Carboniferous and Permian igneous rocks of Great Britain north of the Variscan Front: an introduction

INTRODUCTION

D. Stephenson

Carboniferous and Permian igneous rocks

The Carboniferous and Permian igneous rocks described in this volume are widely scattered along the length of Great Britain, from the Bristol Channel in the south to the Orkney Islands in the north. By far the greatest concentration of outcrops is in and around the Midland Valley of Scotland, with significant but less extensive outcrops around the Solway Firth, along the England–Scotland border, and in Derbyshire (Figure 1.1). Small outcrops occur in the West Midlands of England, in the western Mendip Hills and in south-east Wales (Figure 7.1, Chapter 7). In addition, a concealed widespread volcanic field underlies younger rocks in the East Midlands, a sill-complex crops out and extends beneath a large area of north-east England (Figure 6.2, Chapter 6) and dyke-swarms extend across parts of the Highlands of Scotland (Figure 5.2, Chapter 5 and Figure 6.1, Chapter 6). Igneous rocks to the south of the Variscan Front, that is, south of the Mendip Hills, are described in the *Igneous Rocks of South-West England* GCR volume (Floyd *et al.*, 1993).

The chronostratigraphical distribution of the Carboniferous and Permian igneous rocks of Great Britain is shown in Figure 1.2, together with the radiometric timescale proposed by Gradstein and Ogg (1996), which is used throughout this volume. The more recently proposed timescale of Menning *et al.* (2000) is very close to that of Gradstein and Ogg for all of the system and series boundaries, with the exception of the Stephanian–Permian boundary, which is significantly older, at 299 million years (Ma). The earliest magmatism occurred during the Tournaisian Epoch and is represented mainly by volcanic rocks around the Solway Firth and the England–Scotland border. The volcanic rocks in the Mendip Hills span from late Tournaisian to early Visean times. The most voluminous and widespread igneous activity occurred during the Visean Epoch, resulting in vast lava fields in the Midland Valley of Scotland, lavas and sills in Derbyshire, and minor volcanic sequences around the England–Scotland border. During the Namurian and Westphalian epochs, volcanism became more localized in the Midland

Valley of Scotland and in the East and West Midlands of England, with an increasing tendency for the magma to be emplaced as sills, and all activity died out in late Westphalian times. Following a major change in tectonic conditions, a short-lived episode of regional dyke and sill intrusion occurred in north-east England and across central Scotland in early to mid-Stephanian times, and late Stephanian and Early Permian times saw the emplacement of widespread but localized lavas, sills and dykes that now extend from the eastern Irish Sea to the north-west Highlands. Evidence of Late Permian igneous activity in Britain is restricted to dykes in the Orkney Islands.

The Carboniferous and Permian magmatism in Great Britain was of typical intraplate type, largely controlled throughout the Carboniferous Period by back-arc extension to the north of the Variscan Front and, during Permian times, by major intracontinental rifting that heralded the eventual break-up of the supercontinent of Pangaea. In Scotland, the magmas were dominantly of transitional to mildly alkaline character, becoming generally more highly alkaline and silica-undersaturated with time. Some very primitive and compositionally extreme, alkali-rich lamprophyric and foiditic (feldspathoid-bearing) rocks characterized Early Permian lavas and intrusions of the Midland Valley as well as many of the dykes of the Scottish Highlands and Islands. However, many of the Tournaisian lavas around the Solway Firth and along the Scotland–England border are tholeiitic and the Visean lavas of Derbyshire are entirely tholeiitic. Some tholeiitic lavas also occur in the Westphalian rocks of the East Midlands, but other igneous rocks of central and southern England are alkaline. The principal exception to this overall pattern is the short-lived Stephanian event, which resulted in widespread intrusion of tholeiitic magmas as dykes and sills across much of central Scotland and north-eastern England.

Figure 1.1 (overleaf) Map of the British Isles, showing the main outcrops of Carboniferous and Permian igneous rocks and the major tectonic features that existed during Carboniferous times. Based on published sources, including British Geological Survey (Tectonic map of Britain, Ireland and adjacent areas) (1996); Cameron and Stephenson (1985); Chadwick and Holliday (1991); Chadwick *et al.* (1995); Corfield *et al.* (1996); Francis (1982, 1991); Guion *et al.* (2000); Leeder (1974); Macdonald *et al.* (1981); Read (1988); Rippon *et al.* (1996); and Smythe *et al.* (1995). See Figure 4.4 (Chapter 4) for outcrops in the northern Highlands.

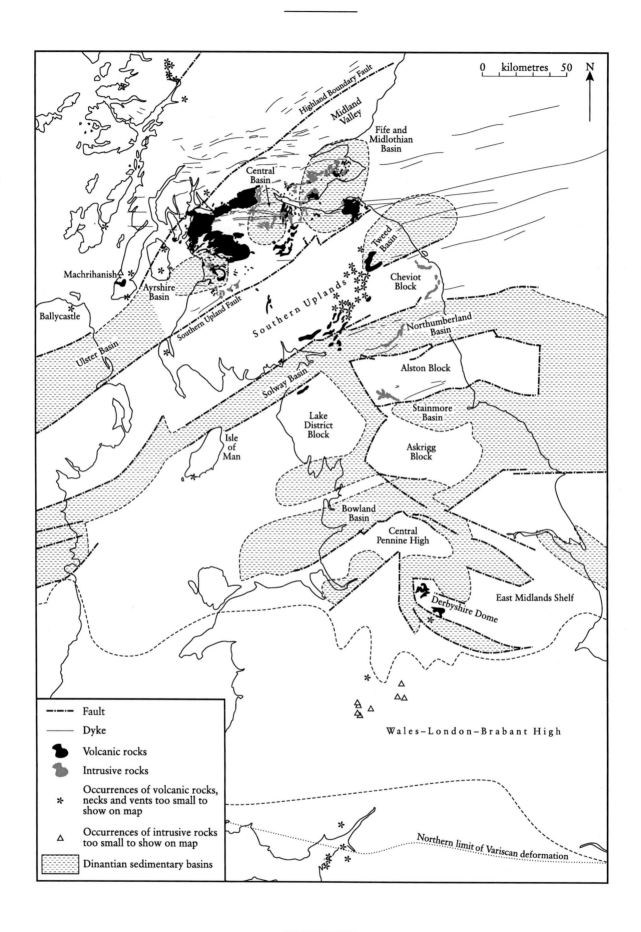

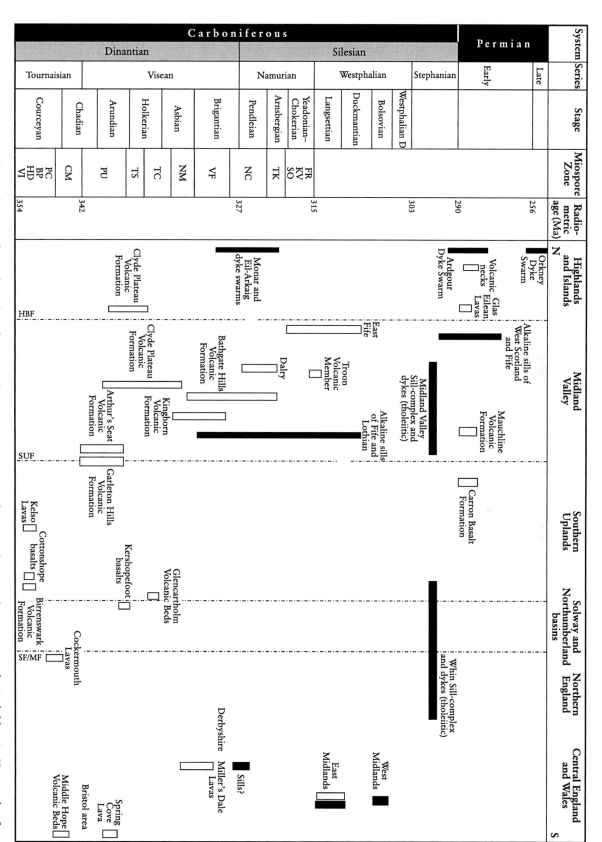

Figure 1.2 Stratigraphical distribution of British Carboniferous and Permian extrusive rocks (open bars) and intrusive rocks (solid bars). Timescale after Gradstein and Ogg (1996). See individual chapters for more detailed stratigraphical charts. (HBF = Highland Boundary Fault; SUF = Southern Upland Fault; SF = Stublick Fault; MF = Maryport Fault.)

Carboniferous and Permian magmatism was dominantly basic, resulting in basaltic to hawaiitic lavas and doleritic intrusions throughout Britain. However, during the Dinantian activity in Scotland, basic magmas were commonly accompanied by lesser amounts of more differentiated associates including mugearites, benmoreites, trachytes and rhyolites. Silica-undersaturated evolved compositions such as phonolitic trachytes and phonolites are found as intrusions, but only very rarely as lavas. In England and Wales during Dinantian times, and throughout Britain during Silesian and Permian times, batches of basaltic magma were volumetrically small and consequently significant differentiates are rare, other than as late-stage veins in some of the thicker alkaline and tholeiitic dolerite sills.

The classification and nomenclature of igneous rocks may seem complicated to the nonspecialist, and even people with long experience are commonly baffled by unfamiliar terms. In the Carboniferous–Permian Igneous Province of northern Britain this is compounded by the plethora of local names that were coined in early petrographical descriptions, which have been perpetuated until quite recently in literature and on [British] Geological Survey maps. In this volume we have tried to adopt a much-simplified, modern hierarchical approach (following Gillespie and Styles, 1999; and Le Maitre, 2002), which is explained with reference to some of the old terminology in the Glossary. Some old terms are retained in the text, *in addition to the modern terms*, especially where they enable comparison with existing literature.

Radiometric ages are quoted as in their original publications. However, the decay constants used for K-Ar determinations were changed significantly in 1976, resulting in an increase of about 2% in age values (Steiger and Jäger, 1977; Dalrymple, 1979). In the Carboniferous and Early Permian rocks, this amounts to an increase of 6 to 7 million years (Ma). Most pre-1977 determinations have been recalculated approximately in this volume, but the original values are also given to enable cross-referencing to previous literature.

Historical Review

Some of the earliest documented geological field observations ever made were by James Hutton in the course of formulating his *Theory of the Earth* (Hutton, 1788). Hutton lived in Edinburgh and was naturally influenced by the Early Carboniferous igneous rocks of Holyrood Park, Calton Hill and the Castle Rock (i.e. the **Arthur's Seat Volcano** GCR site). He correctly interpreted the contact features of the Salisbury Craigs Sill, and one locality, now known as 'Hutton's Section', was used as evidence for the 'Plutonist' theory that basaltic rocks had crystallized from magma (at this time, many 'Neptunists' maintained that all rocks had crystallized from a primeval ocean). Nearby at 'Hutton's Rock', dolerite is cut by a vein of haematite, which Hutton reputedly persuaded the quarrymen to leave intact in what was possibly the first ever conscious act of geological conservation. He also identified lavas of Carboniferous age in Derbyshire and Staffordshire. Influenced by Hutton's theories, James Hall conducted laboratory experiments to melt and recrystallize several samples of basaltic rock from Edinburgh, demonstrating the effect of cooling rate on grain size and comparing the resulting textures and minerals with those obtained from undisputed lavas (Hall, 1805). He thus showed that there was no difference between ancient basaltic rocks and those that had been observed to erupt from a volcano, a fact that many die-hard Neptunists had been stubbornly refusing to accept. These and subsequent experiments rightly earned Hall the title of the 'Father of Experimental Petrology' (Wyllie, 1999).

Even after the magmatic origin of igneous rocks had become generally accepted, doubts still existed over the mode of emplacement of sheets of basaltic rock. Most were thought to be extrusive lavas, until people began to recognize contact relationships at their upper margins, which showed that they were intrusive sills. Sills in the Edinburgh area were among the first to be recognized but it was the Great Whin Sill in northern England that generated the most controversy. Although it had been identified as an intrusion by Adam Sedgwick in 1827, others argued that it was a lava, before Tate (1867, 1871), Clough (1876) and, finally, Topley and Lebour (1877) established its intrusive nature beyond doubt and the Great Whin Sill became the internationally accepted type example of a sill.

Clearly the Carboniferous igneous rocks of central Scotland and northern England played a major role in the early development of geological principles and hence they rapidly

Introduction

attained international importance. Over a dozen accounts of aspects of the Arthur's Seat Volcano were published in the 19th century and the attention generated and knowledge gained no doubt prompted systematic studies of other areas. Most outcrops of Carboniferous and Permian igneous rocks are shown on MacCulloch's geological map of Scotland (1840), although there are few published accounts that date from this period, other than those of the Edinburgh district. Following the formation of the Geological Survey of Great Britain in 1835, mapping was concentrated in the coalfields and adjoining areas of central Scotland, so that between 1861 and 1879 memoirs were published that covered most of the outcrops of Carboniferous and Permian igneous rock in the Glasgow area, the central Midland Valley, the Lothians and Ayrshire. Memoirs for Fife followed in 1901 and 1902. A major author of all of these memoirs, and of several derivative papers, was Archibald Geikie who, in 1897, published *The Ancient Volcanoes of Great Britain*. This seminal work, in two volumes, includes remarkably detailed and accurate accounts of most outcrops of Late Palaeozoic extrusive rocks throughout Scotland and England, which still have use and relevance today.

Geological Survey memoirs of the 19th century also described most of the Late Palaeozoic igneous rocks of England, and more detailed descriptions of the lavas and sills of Derbyshire, the sills of the West Midlands and the extrusive rocks of the Weston-super-Mare area followed during the period 1894 to 1917. The notable exceptions were the Cockermouth Lavas of Cumbria, which were not described at all until 1928. Descriptive petrography had developed to a fine art during this period and the scientific deductions from such studies were being applied, along with field observations, to create a better understanding of the origin and evolution of igneous rocks. S. Allport's influential treatise on dolerites in 1874 included many Scottish and English examples and many first editions of standard petrographical textbooks appeared, such as J.J.H. Teall's *British Petrography* (1888), F.H. Hatch's *An Introduction to the Study of Petrology* (1891) and A. Harker's *Petrology for Students* (1895). All of these included examples of British Carboniferous and Permian igneous rocks, which continued to be used in subsequent editions to instruct generations of students.

The first half of the 20th century saw an explosion in detailed studies of individual lava fields and intrusions. In Scotland, the primary geological survey of the Midland Valley had been completed and more detailed second editions of the memoirs were prepared, many of which remain as definitive sources to this day, despite the publication of subsequent editions. Non-Geological Survey workers were also prolific. Scores of papers were published on the eastern Midland Valley, in particular by D. Balsillie, R. Campbell, T.C. Day and F. Walker. The Arthur's Seat Volcano continued to attract attention and was the subject of three books, by Peach (1911), Day (1933) and Black (1966); few ancient volcanoes of the world can possibly be so well documented and hence so well known to the general public. G.W. Tyrrell of Glasgow University published a series of papers between 1909 and 1952, mostly on the alkaline basic intrusions of the western Midland Valley, which became the basis for subsequent identification and classification. His most significant contribution was undoubtedly his work on the Lugar Sill of central Ayrshire (Tyrrell, 1917b, 1948, 1952), which became an internationally recognized type example of a layered and differentiated alkaline basic sill. The Whin Sill-complex also continued to attract attention with some classic petrological studies such as those by Holmes and Harwood (1928), Tomkeieff (1929) and A.C. Dunham and Kaye (1965).

As more information began to be accumulated, particularly in Scotland, it became possible to develop a wider appreciation of Late Palaeozoic magmatism and the first regional reviews were produced by S.I. Tomkeieff (1937) and A.G. MacGregor (1937, 1948). MacGregor contributed detailed petrographical accounts to most of the Geological Survey memoirs of this period and was largely responsible for a unifying but complex classification scheme that dominated Scottish maps, memoirs and other publications for well over 50 years (MacGregor, 1928). Unfortunately this scheme involved a plethora of locally derived names that confused generations of 'outsiders', but which has only recently been replaced by more modern, universally accepted terminology.

By the 1960s most of the igneous occurrences in Scotland and England had been described systematically in some detail and the whole province was already one of the best documented in the world. Between then and the present

General introduction

day, most of the key geological maps have been revised and the accompanying memoirs have described the magmatism in an updated stratigraphical and structural setting. During the same period, academic workers have turned to more specific problems, many of which have had international implications.

One of the first themes to be explored was the relationship between volcanism and sedimentation, and foremost in this was E.H. Francis, who drew upon wide experience of mapping and borehole logging for the Geological Survey in the eastern Midland Valley of Scotland. In addition to Geological Survey memoir contributions, Francis produced a dozen papers between 1957 and 1970 on this general theme and more specifically on the development of explosive volcanic vents within piles of wet sediments. Similar phenomena have been described more recently from the English West Midlands by Glover *et al.* (1993) and relationships between volcanism and carbonate sedimentation have been described from the Midland Valley, Derbyshire and south-west England (Walkden, 1977; Jameson, 1987; Faulkner, 1989b). On a broader scale, the presence of igneous rocks has had a major influence upon theories of Late Palaeozoic basin development, a theme that is explored more fully below (see 'Tectonic setting and evolution', this chapter).

Studies of the intrusive rocks have either concentrated upon detailed geochemical and mineralogical investigations (see below), or on mechanisms of intrusion. The most influential paper on the latter theme has been that of Francis (1982), in which he explained the emplacement of the large tholeiitic sill-complexes of northern Britain in terms of the impregnation of sedimentary basins by magma supplied from marginal dykes. Further work on alkaline basic sills of Fife led to the contrasting suggestion that many of these sills were intruded at higher levels into unconsolidated water-saturated sediments and may have been fed by magma emanating outwards from volcanic pipes after the route to the surface had become blocked (Francis and Walker, 1987). Work currently in progress is applying magnetic measurements to determine magmatic flow directions in the Whin Sill-complex, and related dykes, and this could have far-reaching applications (Liss *et al.*, 2001).

Prior to 1975, geochemical analyses were mostly confined to [British] Geological Survey publications, apart from specialist studies on various sills and the review of the 'petrochemistry' of Scottish Carboniferous and Permian igneous rocks by Tomkeieff (1937). Since then, the whole-rock geochemistry of the province has been well documented, initially as a result of R. Macdonald of Lancaster University and co-workers, who have published a series of papers covering most of the major suites in Britain, including Scotland (Macdonald, 1975, 1980; Macdonald *et al.*, 1977, 1981); the Whin Sill-complex (Thorpe and Macdonald, 1985); the Cockermouth Lavas (Macdonald and Walker, 1985); and Derbyshire (Macdonald *et al.*, 1984). A Lancaster University thesis and subsequent paper by Kirton (1981, 1984) investigated the geochemistry of lavas from the English Midlands and some geochemical details of lavas in south-west England were given in a University of Bristol thesis by Faulkner (1989a). The alkaline dyke-swarms of the Scottish Highlands were the subject of a comprehensive geochemical study by Baxter (1987) and the Lugar Sill was re-appraised by Henderson and Gibb (1987). A series of studies at the University of Edinburgh, led by B.G.J. Upton and J.G. Fitton, have produced a number of theses that are vital sources of data and have provided interpretations of magma genesis and evolution based upon trace-element, rare-earth-element and isotope data. These include Smedley (1986a, with subsequent papers 1986b, 1988a,b) on the Dinantian igneous rocks of Scotland, Wallis (1989) on the Silesian and Permian igneous rocks of Scotland, and Howard (1999) on the tholeiitic intrusions of Scotland and northern England.

Carboniferous and Permian igneous rocks have been recognized as key targets for radiometric dating since the very early days of the science, when Arthur Holmes was pioneering the 'Helium Method' (Lewis, 2001). He selected the Great Whin Sill for its proximity to the Carboniferous–Permian boundary during his early attempts to construct a geological timescale (Dubey and Holmes, 1929), and a dyke from Colonsay and one of the Clee Hills sills were selected as intrusions of problematic age for a later study (Urry and Holmes, 1941). Subsequently, K-Ar whole-rock determinations on a wide range of mainly intrusive rocks were determined by F.J. Fitch and co-workers (Fitch and Miller, 1964, 1967; Fitch *et al.*, 1969, 1970). Extrusive rocks were generally considered to be too prone to alteration and consequent argon loss for K-Ar determinations, but De Souza (1974, 1979, 1982) selected the freshest samples from Scottish lavas and intrusions and also performed determinations on separated minerals, which did produce seemingly more precise results. Other workers have also produced many K-Ar dates based on whole-rock and mineral analyses from various localities throughout Scotland, and Wallis (1989) has attempted to select and rationalize the most reliable Silesian and Permian data. However, few of the K-Ar results are satisfactory by modern standards. Clearly there is now much scope for more precise dating of crucial intrusions and, where possible, of lavas at key points in the stratigraphical succession using modern Ar-Ar and U-Pb methods. So far only one reliable U-Pb date, from a zircon megacryst within a volcanic neck (Macintyre *et al.*, 1981), and two Ar-Ar dates, have been published (Henderson *et al.*, 1987; Upton *et al.*, 1998). However, work is currently in progress to improve the situation (M.A. Hamilton, A.A. Monaghan and M. Timmerman, pers. comm., 2001).

One of the most productive lines of study has been the investigation of exotic fragments of crustal and upper-mantle material (xenoliths and megacrysts) that are commonly encountered in volcanic necks and minor intrusions, particularly in Scotland. Over two dozen publications have ensued so far, mainly since 1975. Of these, the vast majority have been by B.G.J. Upton of the University of Edinburgh and his co-workers such as P. Aspen, N.A. Chapman, A.N. Halliday and R.H. Hunter, and there have been several general reviews (Upton *et al.*, 1983, 1984; Hunter and Upton, 1987). This work has greatly increased knowledge of the origin of the Late Palaeozoic magmas and the structure and composition of the lithosphere beneath northern Britain, but it has also had widespread international impact upon crustal and upper-mantle models.

Carboniferous and Permian igneous rocks are responsible for many features that have been identified on regional gravity and aeromagnetic maps and on seismic profiles and hence have prompted many geophysical studies, particularly in the Midland Valley of Scotland. The gravity surveys of the western Midland Valley (McLean, 1966; McLean and Qureshi, 1966) and the seismic surveys of the Clyde Plateau lava field and the Central Coalfield Basin (Hall, 1971, 1974; Davidson *et al.*, 1984; Dentith and Hall, 1989),

all by researchers at the University of Glasgow, are particularly noteworthy. One feature that has attracted much interest and speculation over many years is the large magnetic anomaly in the Bathgate area, the most recent interpretation of which is given by K.E. Rollin (in Cameron *et al.*, 1998). The tholeiitic rocks of the Midland Valley Sill-complex, the Whin Sill-complex and their associated dykes are highly magnetic and this has not only proved to be a valuable aid to field mapping (e.g. Armstrong *et al.*, 1985), but it has also resulted in a number of magnetic surveys to elucidate their detailed form and structure (Cornwell and Evans, 1986; El-Harathi and Tarling, 1988; Goulty *et al.*, 2000). The tholeiitic intrusions have also been the main targets of palaeomagnetic studies, which have been a valuable back-up to radiometric age determinations (Creer *et al.*, 1959; Storetvedt and Gidskehaung, 1969; Giddings *et al.*, 1971; Torsvik *et al.*, 1989; Thomas *et al.*, 1995).

Field relationships have always been central to any study of these igneous rocks and for the past 200 years they have been the subjects of organized field excursions for educational and academic purposes or for general scientific interest. The role of geological societies in promoting this interest has been crucial, and the Edinburgh Geological Society, the Geological Society of Glasgow, the Yorkshire Geological Society and the Geologists' Association in particular have opened up many of the sites described in this volume to a wide audience through the publication of numerous excursion guides (Upton, 1969; Bluck, 1973; MacGregor, 1973, 1996; Johnson, 1973, 1997; McAdam and Clarkson, 1986; Lawson and Weedon, 1992; Scrutton, 1995).

As the overall knowledge of Carboniferous and Early Permian magmatism has increased there have been many reviews in a wide range of publications, both British and international. Most of these have been by E.H. Francis (1965, 1967, 1970a, 1978a,b, 1983, 1988, 1991, 1992), apart from chapters in D.S. Sutherland's *Igneous Rocks of the British Isles* (Upton, 1982; A.C. Dunham and Strasser King, 1982) and chapters in the *British Regional Geology* series of the British Geological Survey (e.g. Cameron and Stephenson, 1985). Such reviews have done much to raise international awareness of the province and have provided invaluable background for the preparation of this volume.

General introduction

GCR SITE SELECTION

D. Stephenson

Although igneous rocks and their contact relationships are on the whole less prone to damage than sedimentary rocks and fossil or mineral localities, they are nonetheless vulnerable to certain potentially damaging activities, some of which may not even be directly related to the igneous rocks themselves. In 1988 a farmer submitted a formal objection to the notification as a Site of Special Scientific Importance (SSSI) of one of the sites described in this volume, questioning the need for any protective measures on the grounds that the land was safe in the custody of his family ownership. He agreed with the need for conservation in general but wrote, 'I cannot imagine anything detrimental happening to this large rock mass, which has not altered one iota during my lifetime'. By 1997 his land was being encroached upon by one of the largest opencast coal sites in Scotland. Fortunately the operators had consulted with Scottish Natural Heritage under the terms of the SSSI notification, access to the igneous rocks was preserved and some exposures were actually enhanced in conservation value.

The greatest threat to igneous rocks is the possibility of them being obscured by artificial constructions or removed by excavations. Indeed their generally hard and resistant properties make igneous rocks an important source of construction materials and hence particularly vulnerable to large-scale commercial extraction. Whole igneous bodies can be lost in this way. Uses are many and varied; from large blocks formerly used for buildings, walls and coastal defences, to the crushed dolerites that make excellent roadstone and railway ballast, and the multipurpose aggregates that can be derived from less resistant igneous rocks. As demand changes with time, new uses are constantly emerging, so that no igneous body can be considered safe from future exploitation. However, with careful management, both disused and active quarries can provide highly instructive exposures, especially in areas of poor natural exposure, and there are many examples among the sites described in this volume. On a smaller scale, minerals and delicate cavity features are subject to the attentions of collectors and fine detail can be lost easily through injudicious hammering. Such damage is not necessarily malicious and there have been instances of delicate structures being removed for bona fide research purposes. Much of the value of the sites is derived from their research potential, but sampling does need to be controlled carefully and there is a clear need for better dissemination of information about protected sites.

The Geological Conservation Review (GCR) aims to identify the most important sites in order that the scientific case for their protection and conservation is fully documented as a public record, with the ultimate aim of formal notification as Sites of Special Scientific Interest (SSSIs). The notification of SSSIs under the National Parks and Access to the Countryside Act 1949 and subsequently under the Wildlife and Countryside Act 1981, is the main mechanism of legal protection in Great Britain. The origins, aims and operation of the review, together with comments on the law and practical considerations of Earth-science conservation, are explained fully in Volume 1 of the GCR series, *An Introduction to the Geological Conservation Review* (Ellis *et al.*, 1996). The GCR has identified three fundamental site-selection criteria; *international importance, presence of exceptional features* and *representativeness*. Each site must satisfy at least one of these criteria, many of them satisfy two and some fall into all three categories (Table 1.1).

The *international importance* of the British Carboniferous and Permian igneous rocks has already been discussed, highlighting significant contributions to the understanding of the origin and evolution of magmas, their mechanisms of ascent, intrusion and extrusion and the resulting diversity of igneous rock-types.

Exceptional features are commonly the reason for international importance, such as the well-preserved tuff-rings of the **North Berwick Coast** GCR site, the volcanic necks that represent the roots of small volcanoes on the **East Fife Coast** GCR site, the range of differentiated alkaline rocks in the layered sill at the **Lugar** GCR site, and the ropy flow structures within flattened amygdales at the **Holy Island** GCR site and Harkess Rocks (**Budle Point to Harkess Rocks** GCR site). In addition, many of the sites provide excellent examples of features and phenomena that, although seen better elsewhere, are invaluable for research and/or teaching purposes. Good examples of the latter include features formed by lava flowing underwater at the **Burntisland to Kinghorn Coast**,

GCR site selection

Table 1.1 Carboniferous–Permian Igneous Rocks Block: GCR networks and site selection criteria.

Site name	GCR selection criteria
Dinantian volcanic rocks of the Midland Valley of Scotland and adjacent areas Network, Chapter 2	
North Berwick Coast	Representative of the lower, basic members of the Garleton Hills Volcanic Formation. Exceptional examples of tuff-rings and small-scale volcanic vents. Internationally important for crustal and mantle xenoliths.
Garleton Hills	Representative of the trachytic upper member of the Garleton Hills Volcanic Formation and of Dinantian trachytic volcanism in general.
Traprain Law	Representative of the silica-undersaturated, highly evolved intrusions of East Lothian. Exceptional example of a laccolith.
Arthur's Seat Volcano	Representative of the Arthur's Seat Volcanic Formation. Exceptional examples of classic volcanic features that dominate the city landscape, influencing development and culture. Internationally important for the historical development of geology and understanding of igneous processes.
Burntisland to Kinghorn Coast	Representative of the Kinghorn Volcanic Formation. Examples of fragmented lava (hyaloclastite) with associated pillow lavas, formed in a marine lava delta.
Touch, Fintry and Gargunnock Hills	Representative of the north-eastern part of the Clyde Plateau Volcanic Formation. Exceptional example of a volcanic escarpment with 'trap' features.
Campsie Fells	Representative of the northern part of the Clyde Plateau Volcanic Formation and of the North Campsie Linear Vent System. Exceptional examples of volcanic vents, remnants of ash cones and plugs.
Dumbarton Rock	Exceptional example of a visually striking volcanic plug associated with the Clyde Plateau Volcanic Formation.
Dunrod Hill	Exceptional examples of composite hawaiitic lava flows with potential international importance. Representative of the dominant member in the western part of the Clyde Plateau Volcanic Formation.
Machrihanish Coast and South Kintyre	Representative of Dinantian volcanism north-west of the Highland Boundary Fault. Exceptional example of a trachyte lava dome.
Heads of Ayr	Exceptional example of a Dinantian volcanic neck, comprising the roots of a tuff-ring, with superb three-dimensional coastal exposures. Contains crustal and upper mantle xenoliths.
Dinantian rocks of the Northumberland, Solway and Tweed basins Network, Chapter 3	
Gill Beck	Representative of the Tournaisian Cockermouth Lavas.
Bothel Craggs Quarry	Representative of a tholeiitic andesite lava, rare in the British Carboniferous lava successions and providing evidence for fractionation of the tholeiitic magmas.
Little Mell Fell Quarry	Representative of dykes and pyroclastic rocks of a neck, both associated with the Cockermouth Lavas but well to the east of the main outcrop.
Langholm–Newcastleton Hills	Representative of the Tournaisian Birrenswark Volcanic Formation.
Lintmill Railway Cutting	Representative of the Tournaisian Kelso Lavas.
Hareheugh Craigs	Representative of the plugs associated with the Kelso Lavas. A rare composite example.
Cottonshope Head Quarry	Representative of the Tournaisian Cottonshope basalts.
Kershope Bridge	Representative of the Visean Kershopefoot basalts.
River Esk, Glencartholm	Representative of the Visean Glencartholm Volcanic Beds.
Silesian and Early Permian volcanic rocks of Scotland Network, Chapter 4	
Ardrossan to Saltcoats Coast (Chapter 5)	Representative of the Namurian Troon Volcanic Member and the Ayrshire Bauxitic Clay Member.
East Fife Coast	Representative of Late Carboniferous to Early Permian necks. Internationally renowned for cross-sections through the roots of phreatomagmatic tuff-rings at various structural levels. Exceptional examples of crustal and upper-mantle xenoliths.

Table 1.1 – *contd.*

Howford Bridge	Representative of the Early Permian Mauchline Volcanic Formation.
Carron Water	Representative of the Early Permian Carron Basalt Formation. Exceptional examples of volcanic rocks interdigitating with contemporaneous fluvial and aeolian sedimentary rocks.

Alkaline basic sills and dykes of Scotland Network, Chapter 5

Arthur's Seat Volcano (Chapter 1)	Representative of alkali dolerite sills of various ages in the eastern Midland Valley. Exceptional examples of both upper and lower contacts that have great historical significance and hence international importance. Spectacular part of the city landscape.
South Queensferry to Hound Point	Representative of alkali dolerite sills in the eastern Midland Valley. Internal mineralogical and textural variations are well displayed. Exceptional examples of hydrothermal alteration to 'white trap'.
Ardrossan to Saltcoats Coast	Representative of the composite alkali dolerite sills of the western Midland Valley. Exceptional examples of internal and external contacts and of metamorphic effects on the sedimentary country rocks.
Lugar	Internationally important example of a composite, alkaline basic sill, both historically and in recent times. Representative of the early Permian alkaline basic sills of the western Midland Valley, exhibiting a wide variety of rock-types from peridotite to spectacular late fractionates termed 'lugarite'.
Benbeoch	Representative of olivine-rich alkaline basic sills of the western Midland Valley. Exceptional examples of fresh, olivine-rich, nepheline-dolerite.
Craighead Quarry	Representative of the rare Late Carboniferous to Early Permian intrusions within the Southern Uplands. An exceptionally fresh and visually striking porphyritic nepheline-gabbro, formerly termed an 'essexite'.
Dubh Loch	Visually striking representative of the Late Carboniferous to Permian lamprophyric dykes of the western Highlands. Contains exceptional examples of mantle xenoliths and xenocrysts.

Tholeiitic sills and dykes of Scotland and northern England Network, Chapter 6

South Queensferry to Hound Point (Chapter 5)	Representative of the Midland Valley Sill-complex. Exceptional example of a basal contact, exhibiting multiple intrusive sheets and apophyses, chilled margins, thermally altered sedimentary rocks.
North Queensferry Road Cuttings	Representative of the Midland Valley Sill-complex exhibiting a complete section. Exceptional examples of many of the features that characterize large sills, including baked sediments on top of the sill that prove that it is an intrusion.
Wallstale	Representative of the Midland Valley Sill-complex. Exceptional example of a vertical transgression along a fault plane.
Lomond Hills	Representative of the Midland Valley Sill-complex forming a prominent scarp feature. Exceptional example of large-scale transgressive contacts and thermal effects above the sill. Equivocal relationships between the sill and alkaline basic plugs have generated much debate.
Gloom Hill, Dollar	Representative of the Ochil Fault-intrusion.
Mollinsburn Cuttings	Representative of quartz-dolerite dykes of the tholeiitic dyke-swarm of central Scotland. Exceptional examples of horizontal columnar joints.
Corsiehill Quarry	Representative of basalt dykes of the tholeiitic dyke-swarm of central Scotland. Exceptionally well-exposed vertical contacts and horizontal columnar joints.
Whin Sill Exposures in Upper Teesdale	Representative of the thickest part of the Great Whin Sill at its lowest stratigraphical level. Nationally important landscape features exhibit exceptional examples of many of the features that characterize large sills, including baked sedimentary rocks on top of the sill, which prove that it is an intrusion, transgressive upper and lower contacts, columnar jointing and a pegmatitic central facies.

Table 1.1 – *contd.*

Steel Rigg to Sewingshields Crags	Representative of the Great Whin Sill forming a major landscape feature of international historical importance. Exceptional features include offsets in the scarp attributed to transgression between stratigraphical levels and baked sedimentary rocks above the sill, which prove that it is an intrusion.
Longhoughton Quarry	Representative of the Great Whin Sill. Exceptional features include baked sedimentary rocks above the sill, and rafts of sedimentary rock in the upper part, which prove that it is an intrusion. The relationship of the sill to movement on the Longhoughton Fault is also clearly displayed.
Cullernose Point to Castle Point	Representative of the Great Whin Sill. Exceptional features include well-developed columnar jointing, rafts of baked sedimentary rock and late-stage veins.
Budle Point to Harkess Rocks	Representative of the Great Whin Sill. Exceptional for the large number of rafts of sedimentary rocks with varying orientations. Internationally important for the presence of miniature ropy flow texture on the insides of large vesicles.
Greenfoot Quarry	Representative of the Little Whin Sill.
Holy Island	Representative of the Holy Island dyke subswarm, which is related to the Whin Sill-complex. Exceptional example of an intrusion showing 'step-and-stair' transgression and numerous contact features. Internationally important for the presence of miniature ropy flow texture on the insides of large vesicles.
Wydon	Representative of the St Oswald's Chapel dyke subswarm, which is related to the Whin Sill-complex. A rare natural inland exposure of a simple dyke.

Carboniferous and Permian igneous rocks of central England and the Welsh Borderland Network, Chapter 7

Litton Mill Railway Cutting	Representative of the upper part of the Visean Upper Miller's Dale Lava of Derbyshire. Exceptional example of the brecciation of a lava flow that terminated in an aqueous environment.
Water Swallows Quarry	The Water Swallows Sill, representative of the alkali dolerite sills of Derbyshire, is intruded into the Visean Lower Miller's Dale Lava. Exceptional examples of columnar jointing and of mineral layering in the sill.
Tideswell Dale	The Tideswell Dale Sill, representative of the alkali dolerite sills of Derbyshire, is intruded into the Visean Lower Miller's Dale Lava. The sill shows chilled margins and thermal alteration of country rocks.
Calton Hill	The Calton Hill Volcanic Complex comprises the remains of a phreatic tuff-ring associated with the Upper Miller's Dale Lava, intruded by basanite sills. Internationally important as the only locality in England at which mantle xenoliths can be found.
Clee Hill Quarries	The Clee Hills Sill is representative of the West Midlands suite of Late Carboniferous alkali dolerite sills.
Barrow Hill	The Barrow Hill Complex is an exceptional example of a Westphalian volcanic vent with associated volcanic deposits. Internationally important for the presence of the oldest anatomically preserved conifers found to date.
Middle Hope	Representative of Tournaisian Middle Hope Volcanic Beds of south-west England. Exceptional examples of lapilli-tuffs and pillow lava. Nationally important for the association of igneous, sedimentological and palaeontological features that allow reconstruction of the growth and subsequent subsidence of a volcanic cone on a marine carbonate shelf.
Spring Cove	Representative of Visean volcanic rocks of south-west England. Exceptional example of a pillow lava erupted under water in a marine carbonate environment.
Golden Hill Quarry	Exceptional example of a monchiquite intrusion associated with a Visean volcanic pipe. Internationally important as the only locality in Wales at which mantle xenoliths are found.

General introduction

Litton Mill Railway Cutting, Spring Cove and Middle Hope GCR sites; the viscous trachyte lava dome at the Machrihanish and South Kintyre GCR site; and the external contacts, columnar jointing and numerous internal features seen in so many of the GCR sites representing alkaline and tholeiitic sills.

The criterion of *representativeness* aims to ensure that all major modes of origin and chronological and petrological groupings of Carboniferous and Permian igneous rocks are represented in the ultimate GCR site lists. It is difficult to do this whilst keeping the number of sites within reason. Hence there are some *regionally* important groups of rocks that are not represented, such as the Silesian volcanic rocks of the Midland Valley and the volcanic necks of the north-west Highlands. In some cases this is because there are no localities that show any exceptional features or there are none that exhibit the typical features of the suite any better than numerous other localities. However, it may be appropriate to designate 'Regionally Important Geological/Geomorphological Sites' (RIGS) to represent them so that, even though such status carries no formal legal protection, their importance is recognized and recorded, facilitating conservation at a local level. An attempt has been made in this volume to include, in each appropriate chapter introduction, a broad description of any group of rocks that is not represented by a GCR site, together with references to key publications. Hence, despite perceived gaps in the representativeness of the GCR site coverage, the volume does constitute a complete review of all Carboniferous and Permian igneous rocks of Great Britain.

Some sites are important in more than just an igneous context. For example, the Howford Bridge GCR site exhibits spectacular dune bedding in Lower Permian desert sandstones, and the oldest anatomically preserved conifers in the world occur in the volcanic vent at the Barrow Hill GCR site. The River Esk, Glencartholm GCR site is one of the most important Palaeozoic fish sites in the world and hence is also described in the *Fossil Fishes of Great Britain* GCR volume (Dineley and Metcalf, 1999). The River Esk GCR site also contains exceptionally well-preserved plant remains, and is described, along with two separate localities within the North Berwick Coast GCR site, also noted for their plant remains, in the *Palaeozoic Palaeobotany of Great Britain* GCR volume (Cleal and

Thomas, 1995). The Tournaisian limestones and interbedded volcanic rocks at the Middle Hope GCR site together allow a reconstruction of volcanism on a subsiding marine carbonate shelf and hence this site is also included in the *British Lower Carboniferous Stratigraphy* GCR volume (Cossey *et al.*, in prep).

Volcanic rocks within the stratigraphical column provide time markers and hence have potential international significance in the construction of geological timescales. They have been, and will continue to be, important targets for radiometric dating, in particular the Lower Permian volcanic successions (Howford Bridge and Carron Water GCR sites) that on palaeobotanical evidence are known to be very close to the Carboniferous–Permian boundary. Other volcanic successions provide key markers within the Carboniferous Series but the only available dates at the time of writing (2001) are K-Ar determinations of low precision and debatable accuracy. More reliable K-Ar dates have been obtained from numerous intrusions and some, notably the Stephanian Whin Sill-complex (numerous GCR sites) and the Early Permian intrusions (e.g. the Lugar and Dubh Loch GCR sites), have yielded precise Ar-Ar whole-rock and/or U-Pb zircon dates. Unfortunately intrusions are less precise stratigraphical markers than lavas; work is in progress to obtain more dates from volcanic successions using modern radiometric techniques (A.A. Monaghan and M.S. Pringle, pers. comm., 2002).

The GCR sites vary greatly in size and character, from large upland areas such as the Campsie Fells and the Touch, Fintry and Gargunnock Hills GCR sites that form part of the vast Clyde Plateau lava field, to small quarries such as the Craighead Quarry and Golden Hill Quarry GCR sites, exposing single small intrusions. There are also long coastal sections (North Berwick Coast, East Fife Coast GCR sites), disused railway cuttings (Litton Mill Railway Cutting GCR site), river sections (Lugar, River Esk, Carron Water, Howford Bridge GCR sites), working quarries (Benbeoch, Wallstale, Clee Hill Quarries GCR sites) and road cuttings (Mollinsburn Cuttings, North Queensferry Road Cuttings GCR sites). At many sites, the igneous rocks have resulted in spectacular landscape and geomorphological features such as those that dominate the city of Edinburgh (Arthur's Seat Volcano GCR site), the Clyde Plateau lava field that surrounds

14

Glasgow on three sides, the many craggy features formed by the Midland Valley Sill-complex, and the Great Whin Sill that controlled the siting of Hadrian's Wall (**Steel Rigg to Sewingshields Crags** GCR site) and is responsible for many of the scenic attractions in Upper Teesdale and the Northumberland coast (**Cullernose Point to Castle Point, Budle Point to Harkess Rocks, Holy Island** GCR sites).

Site selection is inevitably subjective and some readers may feel that vital features or occurrences have been omitted or that others are over-represented. However, the declared aim of the GCR is to identify *the minimum number and area of sites needed to demonstrate the current understanding* of the diversity and range of features within each block or network. To identify too many sites would not only make the whole exercise unwieldy and devalue the importance of the exceptional sites, but it would also make justification and defence of the legal protection afforded to these sites more difficult.

Features, events and processes that are fundamental to the understanding of the geological history, composition and structure of Britain are arranged for GCR purposes into subject 'blocks'. Carboniferous and Permian igneous rocks comprise a single GCR Block. Within each block, sites fall into natural groupings, termed 'networks', which in this volume are based upon petrological affinity, age and geographical distribution. The six networks, each represented by a single chapter, contain 52 sites, which are listed in Table 1.1 together with their principal reasons for selection. Some sites have features that fall within more than one network, for example the **South Queensferry to Hound Point** GCR site, which encompasses alkali dolerite sills (Chapter 5) and a tholeiitic sill (Chapter 6), and the **Ardrossan to Saltcoats Coast** GCR site, selected principally for its alkaline sills (Chapter 5) but which also includes Namurian lavas (Chapter 4). These sites are described in the chapters appropriate to their dominant features but are mentioned in the chapter introductions of any other relevant networks and are cross-referenced in Table 1.1.

Aspects of regional geology applicable to each network are given in the chapter introductions. However, space does not allow for more detailed accounts of country-rock successions or structures and the reader is referred to the *Geology of Scotland* (Craig, 1991; Trewin, in press), *Geology of England and Wales* (Duff and Smith, 1992) and volumes in the British Geological Survey's *British Regional Geology* series.

TECTONIC SETTING AND EVOLUTION

K.M. Goodenough, D. Stephenson and S.C. Loughlin

Following the end of the Caledonian Orogeny, in Late Devonian time (*c.* 370 Ma), the area of continental crust that now makes up the British Isles was part of the supercontinent of Laurussia (informally known as the 'Old Red Sandstone Continent'). This had formed during the orogeny by the amalgamation of several pre-existing continents. The crust of Scotland and the far north-east of England had lain on the margin of the continent of Laurentia, which included Greenland and most of North America, whereas England and Wales were part of the microcontinent of Avalonia (Figure 1.3). The junction between these two plates, now concealed beneath younger rocks, is called the 'Iapetus Suture' and trends approximately north-east from the Solway Firth to the coast of Northumberland, around Seahouses (Leeder *et al.*, 1989; Soper *et al.*, 1992).

From Late Devonian times onwards, the southern continent of Gondwana was in collision with the southern margin of Laurussia, leading to the Variscan Orogeny, and creating the supercontinent of Pangaea (Figure 1.4). The main orogenic belt associated with this collision was located far to the south of Great Britain in the Iberia–Armorica–Massif Central region (Leeder, 1982; Fraser and Gawthorpe, 1990). However, the northern limit of strong Variscan deformation, commonly known as the 'Variscan Front', migrated northwards during the orogeny and the final limit extends across southern Britain, between the Thames and Severn estuaries (Figure 1.1). To the north of this orogenic front, back-arc extension controlled structure, sedimentation and igneous activity in the British Isles throughout Late Devonian and Carboniferous times.

Five main depositional 'provinces', separated from each other by important palaeogeographical highs (Figure 1.1), have been recognized by Guion *et al.* (2000). These provinces are as follows:

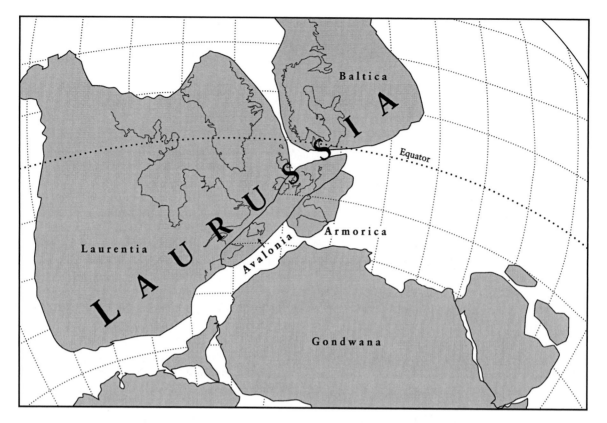

Figure 1.3 Continental dispositions in Late Devonian time (*c.* 380 Ma). Microcontinents including Avalonia and Armorica have collided with the margin of Laurentia, completing the assembly of the crust that now forms the British Isles. Gondwana lies to the south. The absolute positions of the continents on the globe at this time are still not known exactly, so the ocean between Laurentia and Gondwana may have been wider than is shown here. After McKerrow *et al.* (2000).

1. The Scottish Province, consisting essentially of the Midland Valley of Scotland, bounded by the Caledonian Highlands to the north and the Southern Upland High to the south.
2. The Pennine Province of central and northern England, bounded by the Southern Upland High to the north and the Wales–London–Brabant High to the south.
3. The Irish Province in the west.
4. The Southern Province, south of the Wales–London–Brabant High.
5. The Culm Basin of Devon and Cornwall.

The Scottish, Pennine and Southern provinces comprise the tectonic settings for the igneous rocks described in this volume. The Culm Basin, south of the Variscan Front, is the setting for those described in the *Igneous Rocks of South-West England* GCR volume (Floyd *et al.*, 1993).

Dinantian tectonics

At the beginning of the Carboniferous Period, Britain lay within low latitudes (*c.* 10° south) on the fringe of the southern arid climatic belt, and most of Britain north of the Variscan Front was made up of the eroded remnants of mountains that had been generated by rapid crustal uplift towards the end of the Caledonian Orogeny. During Late Devonian and much of Dinantian times, north–south lithospheric extension to the north of the Variscan Front brought about active continental rifting, which led to the development of a series of fault-bound basins. The majority of these basins were controlled by the re-activation of Caledonian faults and thrusts (Figure 1.1) (Leeder, 1982; Kimbell *et al.*, 1989; Fraser and Gawthorpe, 1990). Stable basement blocks, many of which were cored by Caledonian granitic plutons, separated the basins. The process of rifting and thinning of the lithosphere

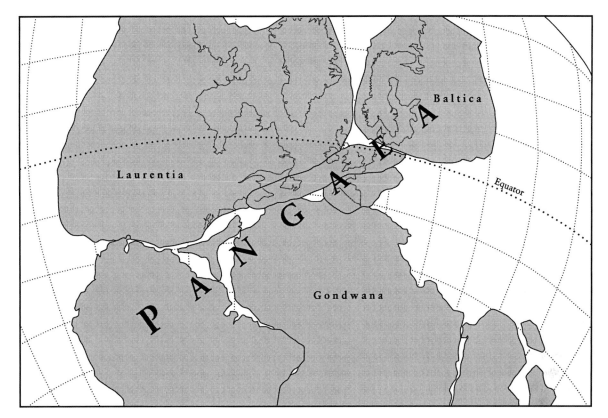

Figure 1.4 Continental dispositions in Late Carboniferous time (*c.* 320 Ma). Gondwana has collided with Laurentia, creating the supercontinent of Pangaea, and the crust of the British Isles lies close to the equator. After McKerrow *et al.* (2000).

led to high heat flow and thus promoted mantle melting (Macdonald *et al.*, 1977; Smedley, 1986b), producing basaltic magmas. The earliest volcanism began during the Tournaisian Epoch and was relatively local in extent, but much more extensive and persistent activity developed from early Visean times onwards.

Large volumes of alkali basaltic lavas were erupted across the Midland Valley of Scotland during the Visean Epoch, forming the Clyde Plateau Volcanic Formation in the west and the Arthur's Seat and Garleton Hills volcanic formations in the east (see Chapter 2). These volcanic piles subsequently formed topographical 'highs', which separated sedimentary basins to the east and west. In the western and central part of the Midland Valley, basin development was controlled by faults with a Caledonian (north-east–south-west) trend, and volcanic eruptions were focused along distinct NE-trending lineaments such as the Dumbarton–Fintry line (Figure 2.3, Chapter 2; Whyte and Macdonald, 1974). However, towards the end of Visean time, basins in

the eastern Midland Valley began to develop along north–south axes (Haszeldine, 1988; Read, 1988), and the margins of these basins became the focus of volcanism in the Burntisland area of Fife and around the Bathgate Hills.

In the northern part of the Pennine Province, volcanism occurred intermittently during Tournaisian and Visean times around the margins of the Northumberland, Solway and Tweed basins (see Chapter 3). Here, the basin-bounding growth faults typically follow northeast or ENE Caledonian trends, and volcanism has also been focused along those lines. In fact the Northumberland and Solway basins lie above the inferred line of the Iapetus Suture. Interpretations of deep seismic profiles across southern Scotland and northern England show these basins lying within the hanging-wall block of a set of northerly dipping crustal-scale shears (Chadwick and Holliday, 1991; Smith, 1992; Chadwick *et al.*, 1995). The rigid and buoyant, granite-cored Lower Palaeozoic massifs of the Southern Uplands, Alston Block and the Lake

District resisted subsidence during this early Dinantian extensional phase of basin formation, but gradually became submerged later.

In the southern part of the Pennine Province igneous activity did not start until late Visean times. The main centre of activity was in the Derbyshire Dome, with minor volcanism in the Wenlock area and in the East Midlands (see Chapter 7). Much of the activity occurred along lines of pre-existing basement lineaments that bounded the main blocks and basins (Francis, 1970a), many of which have a north-west–south-east trend, contrasting with the north-east–south-west Caledonian trend to the north.

To the south of the Wales–London–Brabant High, Dinantian tectonics were strongly influenced by the proximity of the Variscan Front. At this time, the Southern Province represented a back-arc seaway, in which carbonates and clastic sediments were deposited (Besly, 1998). Minor, largely submarine, volcanism occurred during late Tournaisian and early Visean times in the Bristol–Gloucester area and around Weston-super-Mare (see Chapter 7).

The driving mechanism for the Dinantian rifting has been a matter of debate for some time. Leeder (1982) proposed that rifting in Scotland and northern England could be explained by north–south to north-west–south-east tension, related to back-arc extension behind the Variscan Front to the south. A contrasting theory was put forward by Haszeldine (1984, 1988), who suggested that the north–south lineaments in the eastern Midland Valley could be attributed to long-lived east–west tension that was initiated in late Silurian times, and continued to influence sedimentation and volcanism through to the opening of the North Atlantic during Cretaceous and Palaeogene times. However, neither of these models could explain the contrasting extension directions in the Scottish and Pennine provinces, and more recent work (e.g. Read, 1988; Coward, 1993) has attributed the development of Dinantian basins to back-arc extension acting in conjunction with strike-slip shearing along major fault zones.

According to these last models, during Dinantian times Scotland lay within a zone of major sinistral strike-slip movement between the North America–Greenland and the European sectors of Laurussia. Most of this movement took place along re-activated NE-trending Caledonian fractures such as the Highland Boundary and Southern Upland faults. Coward (1993) pro-

posed that the strike-slip movement was due to the lateral escape of a large, wedge-shaped fragment of the northern European continental crust (Figure 1.5). The north-western margin of this fragment was bordered by sinistral shear systems, acting along the NE-trending faults, which were responsible for the east–west extension pattern in the eastern Midland Valley of Scotland. The model is supported particularly by observations on the N–S-trending late Dinantian to early Namurian structures of the Kincardine Basin (Rippon *et al.*, 1996). At the southern margin of the wedge, a dextral shear system along the northern margin of the Wales–London–Brabant High combined with the regional extension, to produce the NW-trending faults of the English East Midlands.

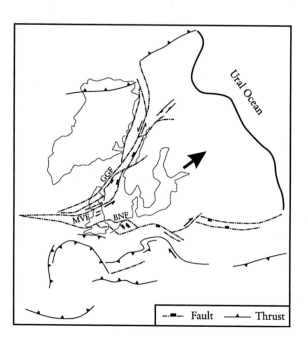

Figure 1.5 Early Carboniferous tectonics of Europe. A fault-bounded wedge of northern Europe was moving eastwards, creating strike-slip movements along pre-existing lineaments. (GGF = Great Glen fault system; MVF = Midland Valley fault system; BNF = Brabant–North Sea fault system.) After Coward (1993).

Namurian tectonics

By late Dinantian time, the part of Laurussia that was to become northern Britain lay in wet equatorial regions. The general land surface remained close to sea level throughout Namurian and early Westphalian times, although in the Midland Valley of Scotland, basins continued to subside rapidly until mid-Namurian times (Read, 1988), with patterns of sedimentation being strongly influenced by the existence of 'highs' formed by earlier volcanic rocks. In the western and central parts, Namurian sedimentation and volcanism were controlled by ENE-trending fault blocks between such structures as the Dusk Water, Inchgotrick and Kerse Loch faults, reflecting continued north-west–south-east tension (Read, 1988; Rippon *et al*., 1996). Farther east, the volcanism tended to concentrate upon hinge areas between basins and highs, such as the Bo'ness Line (extending from the Bathgate Hills into western Fife). The central basins were divided from those of Midlothian and East Fife by a complex high, developed from an amalgamation of the lava piles that now form the Bathgate Hills (late Dinantian to Namurian), the Burntisland area (Dinantian) and the Pentland Hills (Siluro–Devonian). Later in Namurian time, the Midland Valley basins gradually began to lose their separate identities as marine transgressions became more extensive and most of the earlier volcanic piles were submerged. The Highland and Southern Upland terranes generally acted as highs, though attenuated sedimentary successions began to accumulate in small basins at Thornhill, Sanquhar and Stranraer in late Dinantian times; the latter includes a thin Namurian lava.

McKenzie (1978) proposed a two-stage model for the development of sedimentary basins, in which a primary stage of active rifting, caused by lithospheric thinning and extension, is followed by a period in which the lithosphere cools and thickens through thermal conduction to the surface, causing thermal subsidence. The active rifting tends to be associated with mantle melting and abundant volcanism, whereas volcanic activity is less common during the thermal subsidence episode. This model has been applied to the evolution of Carboniferous basins in northern Britain by Dewey (1982), Leeder (1982) and Leeder and McMahon (1988).

The continuing importance of volcanic activity, combined with rapid basin subsidence, indicates that active rifting and lithospheric stretching were still the dominant controls on evolution of Midland Valley basins during early- to mid-Namurian times. Volcanism on the Bo'ness Line ceased in late Namurian times (end-Arnsbergian onwards), although volcanic activity continued farther east in Fife, and Rippon *et al*. (1996) suggested that it was at this stage that active extension in the Midland Valley gave way to the post-extension thermal subsidence phase.

Leeder and McMahon (1988) produced tectonic subsidence curves for basins in the north of England, and showed that active rifting in the Northumberland and Stainmore basins ended at the end of Brigantian (late Visean) time, at approximately the same time as the cessation of volcanic activity in the Northumberland, Solway and Tweed basins. Farther south, in the Bowland Basin, there was no volcanic activity but rapid subsidence continued into Pendleian or possibly Arnsbergian (mid-Namurian) times. On this basis, Leeder and McMahon proposed that the change from active extension to thermal subsidence occurred progressively later towards the south in the Pennine Province. This is supported by the fact that volcanism, characterized typically by small-scale explosive eruptions, continued intermittently in the English Midlands during Namurian time.

Overall, it is clear that during Namurian time active extension gave way to a thermal subsidence phase across the British Isles. The end of active rifting led to the cessation of the large-scale volcanic outpourings which characterized Dinantian times, so that during later Namurian times volcanic eruptions were relatively rare, sporadic and short-lived. To the south of the Wales–London–Brabant High, there was no volcanism at all during Namurian time. Basin subsidence in this region has been entirely attributed to flexural subsidence of the crust under the weight of Variscan thrust sheets to the south (Kelling, 1988; Maynard *et al*., 1997; Burgess and Gayer, 2000).

Westphalian tectonics

Thermal subsidence in the north, and flexural basin development in the south, continued from Namurian into early Westphalian times. The Variscan deformation front migrated northwards during this time and compressional tectonics began to dominate, so that the sedimentary rocks within the basins were deformed into large-scale folds. The compression also caused the direction of movement on basin-bounding faults to be reversed. This led to the sedimentary rocks within some basins being uplifted and eroded, whilst rapid subsidence occurred in previously high areas, so that regional unconformities developed within the sedimentary succession. This reversal process is known as 'tectonic inversion'.

In the Scottish Province, there was little volcanism during Westphalian time, and activity was mainly restricted to Fife and the Firth of Forth. One of the greatest areas of subsidence at this time, the Leven Basin of East Fife, was also the site of most known Westphalian volcanism (Read, 1988). The effects of Variscan compression and the consequent tectonic inversion also led to a reversal of lateral shear sense on pre-existing faults in the Midland Valley, so that the NE-trending major strike-slip faults, which had a component of sinistral movement during Dinantian times, now moved with a dextral shear sense. This dextral strike-slip produced a component of east–west compression, developing N–S-trending fold structures such as the Clackmannan Syncline (Read, 1988; Bénard *et al.*, 1990; Rippon *et al.*, 1996).

In the southern part of the Pennine Province, some igneous activity occurred in earlier Westphalian times, with the formation of dolerite sills and localized explosive volcanism in the East and West Midlands. In later Westphalian times, deformation (uplift, folding and faulting) occurred and, as in the Midland Valley, this has been attributed to a period of east–west compression that effectively marked the end of thermal subsidence (Bénard *et al.*, 1990; Waters *et al.*, 1994; Johnson and K.C. Dunham, 2001).

The model of Coward (1993) provided an elegant explanation for the episode of Westphalian tectonic inversion. He suggested that inversion occurred because the fault-bounded wedge of European crust that had 'escaped' from between Laurentia and Gondwana during Dinantian times (Figure 1.5) was being pushed back owing to plate collision in the Urals (Figure 1.6), thus reversing the movement generated in Early Carboniferous times. This re-activated the faults bounding the continental wedge in the opposite directions to those that had acted during Dinantian times, producing dextral movement on faults in the Scottish Province and sinistral movement on faults in southern and central England. Coward noted that at this time there must also have been an effect due to north-west–south-east compression associated with the Variscan Orogeny, and other workers, such as Maynard *et al.* (1997), have

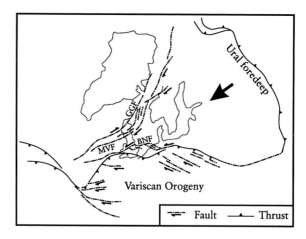

Figure 1.6 Late Carboniferous to Early Permian tectonics of Europe. Closure of the Ural Ocean led to the continental wedge being driven back to the west, reversing the directions of strike-slip movement. (GGF = Great Glen fault system; MVF = Midland Valley fault system; BNF = Brabant–North Sea fault system.) After Coward (1993).

preferentially emphasized the effects of the Variscan collision, rather than invoking collision in the Urals.

In the Southern Province, a rapidly subsiding foreland basin formed during Westphalian time owing to continued flexure of the crust in front of the Variscan Orogeny. The effects of loading of the Variscan thrust sheets spread northwards, and by Westphalian D time, the foreland flexural basin extended north of the Wales–London–Brabant High into the Pennine Province (Burgess and Gayer, 2000). Waters *et al.* (1994) suggested that earlier small-scale phases of localized extension and compression in the southern Pennine Province could also have been due to flexure of the crust under the weight of the Variscan thrust sheets, superimposed onto the thermally subsiding basin. However, since passive extension due to thermal subsidence is unlikely to have generated mantle melting, an alternative explanation is needed for the local Westphalian magmatism. Waters *et al.* suggested that melting during the localized extension was caused by movement on crustal thickness faults, which then acted as conduits for the transport of magma.

Igneous activity to the south of the Variscan Front is described in the *Igneous Rocks of South-West England* GCR volume (Floyd *et al.*, 1993). Possibly associated with this activity are thin felsic ash-fall tuffs (bentonites), which cover very large areas extending into the English Midlands. These are assumed to have been associated with Westphalian volcanic activity at a destructive plate margin to the south of Britain.

End-Carboniferous to Permian tectonics

During early Stephanian times, tholeiitic sills and dykes with a general east–west trend were emplaced into the sedimentary rocks of the Midland Valley and northern England (see Chapter 6). The arcuate dyke-swarm extends from the Atlantic margin as far as the Central Graben of the North Sea, and has been linked to lavas and dykes of similar age and composition in Scandinavia. These intrusions mark an end-Carboniferous period of approximately north–south extension (Read, 1988; Rippon *et al.*, 1996). Subsequently, in late Stephanian to Early and possibly later Permian times, alkaline basic magmas exploited fractures of similar trend over a wide area of western Scotland from Ayrshire to the Orkney Islands (see Chapter 5).

Francis (1978a) suggested that the short-lived tholeiitic event was a result of decompressive mantle melting caused by rotation of a micro-continental plate fragment involved in the Variscan Orogeny to the south. However, Russell and Smythe (1983) modified earlier theories (Russell, 1976; Russell and Smythe, 1978) to suggest that the intrusions formed as a result of extensional stresses associated with propagating rifts in the Rockall Trough (the proto-North Atlantic Ocean) and the eastern Norwegian Sea. They proposed that an area of ancient continental lithosphere between the rifts in the Faeroe region was resistant to extension, causing stresses to be offset to thinner litho-sphere around the Oslo Graben and in northern Britain. The short period of extension in north-ern Britain was halted when the lithosphere in the Faeroes region ruptured, forming the incipient Faeroe–Shetland Trough (Smythe *et al.*, 1995). This model predicts correctly the arcuate orientation of the regional dyke-swarm from northern Britain to the Oslo Graben and also accounts for thickening of the dykes in the western North Sea. However, it does not explain the intrusion of dykes in southern Sweden. More recently, Wilson *et al.* (2000) have suggested that the extension was caused by the impingement of a mantle plume on the base of the lithosphere beneath Scandinavia, and that

the tholeiitic magmas may represent laterally transported melts of plume material.

By Early Permian time, the crust that was to become the British Isles had drifted northwards into the northern semi-arid climatic belt, and the distant effects of the Variscan Orogeny had raised the land surface above sea level. The main Variscan fold belt in southern Britain may have created a mountainous barrier to possible 'monsoonal' moisture-bearing winds from the south, accentuating the arid conditions (Parrish, 1993). Regional tension with a general north-west–south-east orientation was giving rise to intracontinental rifting along the line of the Rockall Trough, the Faeroe–Shetland Trough and the Norwegian–Greenland Sea (Smythe *et al.*, 1995). Smaller, mainly half-graben structures developed in Britain, commonly on the site of Late Carboniferous basins. Anderson *et al.* (1995) argued that the geometry of most of these structures in the north-west of the British Isles was strongly influenced, in a variety of ways, by underlying Caledonian basement structures. Thus, in the Grampian Terrane, the largely offshore Rathlin Basin is orientated north-east–south-west, parallel to the general strike of the underlying Dalradian rocks. How-ever, in the Southern Uplands Terrane, small basins such as Thornhill, Dumfries and Stranraer are elongated perpendicular to the structural fabric of the underlying Lower Palaeozoic rocks. Anderson *et al.* (1995) argued that these Southern Upland basins originated by ENE–WSW along-strike crustal stretching and dip-slip re-activation of north–south or north-west–south-east Caledonian fractures that formed conjugate sets with the more obvious north-east–south-west structures. Basins in the onshore and offshore Midland Valley (e.g. Mauchline) have a less regular shape as they are sited on deep Carboniferous basins with little or no inherited Caledonian trend. They commonly have a general north-west to NNW elongation that has been attributed to structural control of subsidence and volcanism, possibly dating back to Early Carboniferous times (MacGregor, 1948; Mykura, 1967; Hall, 1974; McLean, 1978; Russell and Smythe, 1978). Fractures with this trend in the west of the Midland Valley have subsequently controlled the siting of Permo–Triassic major baryte vein mineralization and Palaeogene regional dyke-swarms (Cameron and Stephen-son, 1985). However, Rippon *et al.* (1996) cited E–W-orientated dykes with petrological affinity to the Mauchline Volcanic Formation as evidence that the Stephanian north–south extension continued during Early Permian development of the Mauchline Basin.

MAGMA SOURCE AND EVOLUTION

D. Stephenson, S.C. Loughlin, D. Millward and C.N. Waters

Although the geochemistry of all the various suites of Carboniferous and Permian igneous rocks in Great Britain has been studied in some detail, there is a considerable bias towards those of central and southern Scotland. Many theses and publications on the Scottish suites provide a wealth of data and interpretation, much of which has broad implications for magma genesis and the tectonic setting of the whole igneous province. The less voluminous suites of England and Wales have received less attention, usually only a single study on each area. These smaller studies too are of great value to the overall model, but their detailed conclusions are limited by geographical extent and compositional range. This bias is reflected unavoidably in the following discussions.

Dinantian magmas

In central and southern Scotland, Dinantian igneous activity mainly involved transitional to mildly alkalic basaltic and hawaiitic magmas, and the rocks are characterized by relatively small amounts of normative hypersthene or nepheline. Rare low-K tholeiitic basalts occur at Machrihanish and some basalts with normative quartz and therefore of tholeiitic affinity are recognized among the Birrenswark Volcanic Formation and the Kelso Lavas on the north-west margins of the Tweed and Solway basins. However, the Cockermouth Lavas on the southern margin of the Solway Basin and the lavas of Derbyshire are almost entirely tholeiitic. Most of the sills in the English Midlands are alkaline, as are the lavas of the western Mendip Hills.

Midland Valley of Scotland and adjacent areas (Chapter 2)

A major review of Dinantian lavas in Scotland by Macdonald (1975) identified the full range of compositions, classified the rocks in terms of established magma series, and divided the local

successions into geochemical 'lineages' and petrographical associations. The petrogenesis of the lavas was discussed and general trends were identified. Variations in major-element chemistry with time were explored in a subsequent paper (Macdonald *et al.*, 1977) and a study of trace-element variations led to conclusions regarding heterogeneity in the mantle source regions (Macdonald, 1980). The evolution of the Campsie Fells lavas was described by MacDonald and Whyte (1981), but otherwise much of the detailed geochemical data for the Midland Valley resides in unpublished theses (Whyte, 1963a; MacDonald, 1965; De Souza, 1979; Craig, 1980). Specific aspects of the magmatic evolution have also been investigated in theses by Boyd (1974) and Russell (1984). It was a PhD thesis by Smedley (1986a) that provided the most detailed review of Dinantian magmatism in northern Britain, and more general aspects of this work, mainly concerned with the mantle source and magma generation, have been published as papers (Smedley, 1986b, 1988a,b). Some aspects of the Dinantian magmas, based upon Smedley's data, were discussed subsequently in comparison with those of Silesian and Permian age from Scotland in a thesis by Wallis (1989).

The most basic lavas (those with MgO 4%) show trace-element enrichments and isotope ratios that are typical of within-plate magmatism (Macdonald, 1980; Smedley, 1986a,b, 1988a). Many rapidly accumulated continental flood-basalt sequences are associated with the rise of anomalously hot deep mantle in mantle plumes. However, geochemical and mineralogical evidence does not favour an unusually deep source for the Dinantian magmas, and the absence of any systematic change in the location of magmatism with time makes plume-generated melting unlikely (Smedley, 1986a,b). It seems more likely that all of the Carboniferous and Permian alkali basaltic magmatism in Britain was due to pressure-release melting of the upper mantle during extension related to subduction processes occurring several hundred kilometres farther south (see 'Tectonic setting and evolution', this chapter). The abundance of spinel lherzolite and the absence of garnet lherzolite in inclusion suites (see 'Xenoliths and megacrysts', this chapter) suggests that the magmas rose through an attenuated lithosphere that was too thin for its lower levels to be within the garnet lherzolite stability field (Smedley,

1988a). Hence, it is inferred that the rapid onset of widespread and voluminous igneous activity at a time of general subsidence, sedimentation and extensional faulting in the Midland Valley was a result of passive rifting and diapiric up-welling from the upper mantle during a period of lithospheric stretching (Smedley, 1986b).

It is generally agreed that the alkaline basic magmas of northern Britain were derived by small-fraction partial melting (less than 5%) of upper-mantle material at depths of 80–60 km (B.G.J. Upton, pers. comm., 2001). Light rare-earth-element enrichments in the Dinantian basalts imply that garnet was an important phase in the mantle source, which was therefore most likely to have been garnet lherzolite, present only in the sub-lithospheric mantle (Smedley, 1986a). The incompatible element patterns and isotope ratios do not allow unequivocal distinction between lithospheric and sub-lithospheric mantle sources, but data from the most basic rocks strongly resemble those from ocean island basalts (OIB), suggesting that interaction with continental lithosphere was minimal and that an asthenospheric or sub-asthenospheric origin was more likely (Smedley, 1986a,b, 1988a).

Smedley (1986b) showed that certain trace-element and isotopic values of the most basic Dinantian lavas are similar to those of the pre-ceding, late-Caledonian calc-alkaline lavas that were erupted in the Midland Valley some 60–70 Ma earlier (Thirlwall, 1982). She con-cluded that similar portions of mantle were melted in each event and hence that the Dinantian magmas could have come from a relatively shallow depth in the upper mantle, equivalent to the supra-subduction zone mantle wedge of the earlier event. In a later paper (Smedley, 1988b), she noted spatial variations in isotope ratios of Dinantian lavas across the Highland Boundary Fault that correlate well with a general increase in enrichment towards the north and north-west observed in earlier calc-alkaline lavas and granitoid intrusions. This is seen particularly in differences in Sr, Nd and Pb isotope ratios between Dinantian lavas of Kintyre and Arran and those of areas south-east of the Highland Boundary Fault. Such long-term spatial isotopic distinctions, implying differing styles of enrichment of the sources prior to partial melting, could suggest that the mantle sources were immobile, non-convecting and therefore lithospheric. However, the overall ele-ment and isotope variation within the Dinantian

basic lavas falls entirely within the range of OIB and hence Smedley (1988b) concluded that their principal source could have been within heterogeneous convecting asthenosphere as originally proposed (Smedley 1986b, 1988a).

Macdonald (1975) demonstrated that volcanic sequences from geographically separate areas produced distinctive magmatic lineages, each, to a greater or lesser degree, distinguishable in terms of silica-saturation, Fe/Mg and Na_2O/K_2O ratios, TiO_2 and P_2O_5. This geochemical provin-ciality was subsequently confirmed by the contrasting incompatible trace-element and isotopic characteristics of different areas that in some cases persisted throughout Silesian and into Permian times (Macdonald, 1980; Smedley, 1986a, 1988a). Although all authors have invoked a degree of mantle heterogeneity (see below), some of this variation could be due to varying degrees of partial melting. Wallis (1989) observed that Dinantian magmatism seemed to have been more productive in the west and that this is reflected by greater degrees of silica-saturation, implying a greater degree of partial melting (2–4%), as opposed to less than 2% for the eastern Dinantian and subsequent alkali magmatism. Anomalously low potassium in many of the Midland Valley basic lavas, particu-larly those with high contents of incompatible elements, suggests that a K-bearing phase such as phlogopite was present as an accessory in the sources of the magmas and that this was con-sumed only during higher degrees of partial melting (Macdonald, 1980; Smedley, 1986a, 1988a). Hence, the most silica-saturated west-ern lavas of Kintyre and the Clyde Plateau do not show K-depletion, having gained potassium from phlogopite as a result of greater melting.

However, these geochemical variations can-not be accounted for entirely by variable degrees of partial melting or by crystal fractionation of observed phenocryst phases, and they must be due in part to differing mantle compositions. Smedley (1988a) used Ce/Y and Zr/Nb ratios of the most basic rocks to show that the best model involves varying degrees of partial melting, superimposed upon slight heterogeneity of the source region. There is no isotopic evidence in any of the basic rocks for crustal contamination or for input from a relict lithosphere slab, so the heterogeneity is not related to either of these processes. Smedley (1988a) considered that the variation reflects to some extent the relatively high speed of northward migration of the lithospheric plate (15° of latitude in 40 Ma; Irving, 1977), during the course of which magmas could have been extracted from an enormous volume of varied convecting sub-lithospheric mantle over a wide area. However, in her re-assessment of the earlier data, Wallis (1989) suggested that the amount of enrichment observed in some areas could not be derived entirely from heterogeneous asthenosphere and invoked a small input from enriched mantle at the base of the lithosphere.

Subsequent evolution of the magmas was largely by fractional crystallization, as is suggested by a general close agreement between major elements, compatible trace elements and the phenocryst assemblages (Smedley, 1986a, 1988b). For example, the behaviour of Al and Ca in relation to Mg in whole-rock compositions demonstrates that fractionation of clinopyroxene played a major role and Macdonald (1975) suggested early crystallization of clinopyroxene only above 13 kbar or of olivine + clinopyroxene + plagioclase at slightly lower pressure (above 9 kbar). The complex zonation of clinopyroxene phenocrysts from basalts of the Castle Rock and Holyrood Park (**Arthur's Seat Volcano** GCR site) provides a classic illustration of polybaric crystallization commencing at pressures of up to 11.5 kbar, i.e. at sub-crustal depths (Clark, 1956; Russell, 1984; Smedley, 1986a). It appears likely that primitive picritic magmas were arrested at, or close to, the crust–mantle boundary as 'underplated magmas' where they resided until fractionation of olivine, clinopyroxene and subordinate spinel had reduced the melt densities sufficiently for further crustal ascent to take place. This interpretation is supported by the observation that primitive high-Mg melts are not represented among the Dinantian lavas and intrusions. Although some of the olivine-clinopyroxene-phyric rocks have bulk MgO contents of up to 12%, these almost certainly experienced concentration of both augite and olivine prior to eruption, the groundmass compositions (taken as indicative of melt compositions) being no more magnesian than c. 10% (Smedley, 1986a). Therefore, it may be inferred that olivine-clinopyroxene cumulates (wehrlites) and subsequent olivine-clinopyroxene-plagioclase cumulates (gabbros) were produced in abundance at depth during the interrupted ascent of the magmas. Fragments of such materials are found more commonly in Silesian and Permian vents and intrusions (see 'Xenoliths

and megacrysts', this chapter), but Clark (1956) drew attention to the presence of coarse clusters of crystals in some of the Arthur's Seat lavas that could be autoliths (cognate xenoliths) of gabbroic, anorthositic and pyroxenitic facies acquired at depth.

The strongly porphyritic nature of many of the Dinantian extrusive and intrusive rocks, together with their broad compositional range (Figure 1.7a), suggests that magma residence in sub-crustal and crustal magma chambers was general and widespread. High-pressure clinopyroxene-dominated fractionation was followed by fractionation of olivine + plagioclase ± magnetite at lower pressures (Macdonald, 1975; MacDonald and Whyte, 1981) and hence the bulk of the Dinantian magmas were erupted in a relatively fractionated condition. In some areas, basaltic hawaiites and hawaiites predominate over basalts proper. Further crystal fractionation (mainly of plagioclase) in small, near-surface magma chambers can be deduced from hawaiitic lavas in the Renfrewshire Hills and Campsie Fells that exhibit slight variations in composition during the course of a single eruption (Kennedy, 1931; MacDonald, 1967; Boyd, 1974). Such composite flows are particularly well illustrated in the **Dunrod Hill** GCR site. Macdonald (1975) noted that there is compositional continuity throughout the whole series, and the trachytes, phonolitic trachytes and rhyolites are all regarded as having been derived by further fractional crystallization from the mugearitic stage of magma differentiation. However, it is reasonable to suspect that genesis of some of the more highly siliceous magmas involved varying degrees of crustal contamination. Some evidence of this has been found in Kintyre, from the presence in basalts of quartz xenocrysts with complex reaction rims of clinopyroxene and from the isotopic composition of trachytic rocks (Smedley, 1986a).

Solway, Northumberland and Tweed basins (Chapter 3)

Collectively the Dinantian volcanic rocks of the Solway, Northumberland and Tweed basins are part of the transitional, mildly alkaline to tholeiitic suite that characterizes all of the Dinantian volcanism of northern Britain (Macdonald, 1975). The Tournaisian Cockermouth Lavas, Birrenswark Volcanic Formation and Kelso Lavas have similar compositions and hence the

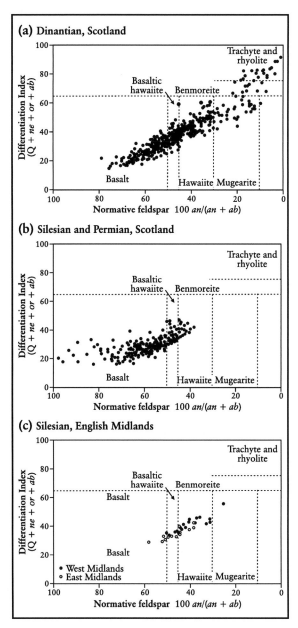

Figure 1.7 Range of compositions of Carboniferous and Permian igneous rocks, illustrated by a plot of Differentiation Index (normative % quartz + nepheline + orthoclase + albite) against normative feldspar composition (% anorthite/(anorthite + albite)), as used in the classification of Coombs and Wilkinson (1969); and Macdonald (1975). (a) Dinantian igneous rocks of Scotland, after Smedley (1986a); (b) Silesian and Permian igneous rocks of Scotland, after Wallis (1989); (c) Silesian igneous rocks of the English Midlands, after Kirton (1984).

juxtaposition of Laurentian and Avalonian lithosphere across the Iapetus Suture appears to have had no detectable influence on the geochemistry of the early Dinantian magmas (Macdonald and

Walker, 1985). Most of these rocks contain normative quartz and hypersthene and are thus tholeiitic, though some nepheline-normative lavas (hawaiite and mugearite) are present in the formations from the northern margins of the basins (Macdonald and Walker, 1985; Smedley, 1986a). Smedley (1988a) showed that, in terms of trace-element concentrations, such as Ce, Nb and Ba, these early basalts are some of the least enriched of the Dinantian volcanic rocks of northern Britain. However, despite their close proximity to the Birrenswark Volcanic Formation, the slightly younger Kershopefoot basalts have very distinctly different Ce/Y and Zr/Nb ratios. These and other geochemical characteristics were interpreted by Smedley (1988a) to have arisen from the partial melting of a chemically heterogeneous mantle. In contrast, the Cockermouth Lavas were interpreted by Macdonald and Walker (1985) as having formed by varying degrees of partial melting of homogeneous mantle, followed by fractional crystallization and equilibration at high crustal levels to produce some tholeiitic andesites. There is no evidence of significant crustal contamination.

Central England (Chapter 7)

The geochemistry of Derbyshire Carboniferous igneous rocks has been detailed by Macdonald *et al.* (1984). The bulk of the volcanism was tholeiitic, as is shown by normative hypersthene and typically tholeiitic trace-element abundances in the whole rock and by clinopyroxene compositions. However, some nepheline-normative alkaline compositions occur in sills. Incompatible trace-element data show a wide variation in Zr/Nb, suggesting derivation from a mantle source that was highly heterogeneous and that each lava or sill represents a discrete melting event. Most of the major-element variation can be attributed to varying degrees of partial melting, followed by fractional crystallization and final equilibration within the lower crust, with no low-pressure fractionation in higher level magma chambers. Crustal contamination, if it occurred at all, was only slight. There is no consistent relationship between compositional variations and time or geographical location. Macdonald *et al.* (1984) considered this to be consistent with relatively short-lived, small vents with each event derived from melts that passed through the crust via small unconnected conduits, dykes and sills.

General introduction

Silesian and Early Permian alkaline magmas

Scotland (Chapters 4 and 5)

Like those of the preceding Dinantian times, the Silesian and Early Permian igneous rocks of Scotland are typical of extension-related intraplate continental volcanism but also have similarities to ocean island basalts (OIB). The lavas and intrusive rocks range generally from hypersthene-normative transitional basalts to nepheline-normative mildly alkaline basalts and basanites, but the latest Early Permian assemblages are characterized by highly silica-undersaturated foidites and monchiquites (Macdonald *et al.*, 1977; Macdonald, 1980; Wallis, 1989). This range lies within a general trend from tholeiitic to transitional basalts in early Dinantian times in the Northumberland, Solway and Tweed basins, to transitional to mildly alkaline types in the Midland Valley in later Dinantian and Silesian times, to the highly silica-undersaturated rocks of the Permian basins and wider dyke-swarms. However, Macdonald *et al.* (1977) pointed out that the overall trend is seriously interrupted by the presence of hypersthene-normative, almost tholeiitic lavas in the Troon Volcanic Member, and proposed that volcanism in the Midland Valley was related to two magmatic or thermal cycles. Each of these began with the eruption of hypersthene-normative magmas, which then gave way through time to increasingly nepheline-normative types. The late Namurian to Early Permian rocks therefore define the second cycle.

This two-cycle model is almost certainly an over-simplification; it fails to take into account the voluminous injection of tholeiitic magma during early Stephanian times (see Chapter 6) and further analyses (Wallis, 1989) 'cloud' the geochemical trends proposed by Macdonald *et al.* (1977, fig. 1). However, there does seem to be a trend towards increasingly silica-undersaturated magmas with time in several individual areas (Upton, 1982) which may reflect progressively lower geothermal gradients and smaller degrees of partial melting at greater mantle depths, producing less magma in the later stages of each local thermal event. Macdonald (1980) showed that separate geographical areas of the Midland Valley retained

their own distinctive incompatible trace-element abundances and ratios over periods of up to 50 Ma. This he attributed to long-lasting heterogeneity in the underlying mantle from which the magmas were derived.

The alkaline dyke-swarms of the Highlands and Islands sampled some of the most primitive magmas in the whole Carboniferous–Permian Igneous Province of Great Britain. In a detailed review of their geochemistry, Baxter (1987) showed that these were generated by small degrees (0.5–2%) of partial melting of chemically heterogeneous garnet lherzolite. Spinel lherzolite commonly occurs as xenoliths in these rocks and hence presumably represents lithospheric mantle overlying the source. Within these dyke-swarms, monchiquites represent the most primitive nephelinitic mantle melts (see also Upton *et al.*, 1992), whereas alkali basalts and camptonites were generated by varying degrees of fractionation of olivine and clinopyroxene from variably hydrous alkali basalt or basanitic magmas, coupled with the loss of volatile material during ascent.

The most comprehensive investigation and summary of the petrology and geochemistry of Silesian and Early Permian igneous rocks in Scotland is that of Wallis (1989). According to Wallis, the post-Dinantian igneous rocks are remarkably coherent in terms of whole-rock geochemistry and she concluded that the main source region of the magmas was in heterogeneous, streaky, phlogopite-garnet-bearing asthenosphere. Incompatible trace-element and rare-earth-element variations were interpreted generally in terms of variable degrees of partial melting (from less than 2% to 15% melting, depending on how enriched the source may have been), and the lavas and intrusions were divided into two broad geochemical groups based on their content of incompatible trace elements.

The most enriched group included most of the Highland dykes, about half of the Fife and Lothian sills, the smaller basanitic intrusions associated with volcanic necks in the eastern Midland Valley and a few of the lavas of the Mauchline Volcanic Formation. These represent the smallest degrees of partial melting of the asthenosphere and show no evidence of lithospheric contamination. Clinopyroxene fractionation played an important part in their early evolution and the Al^{iv}/Al^{vi} content of clinopyroxene phenocrysts indicates the highest crystallization pressures of any in the suite (10–20 kbar). Wallis (1989) also noted a positive correlation between the maximum pressure recorded and the degree of alkalinity of the rock.

The less enriched group included the remainder of the Fife and Lothian sills, the Ayrshire sills, the Troon Volcanic Member lavas and most of the Mauchline Volcanic Formation lavas. These originated by larger degrees of partial melting of similar asthenosphere, but relatively high levels of incompatible elements and variations in Ce/Y and Zr/Nb in some of the Troon Volcanic Member lavas (and some sills of Fife and the Lothians) suggest an additional minor component from the overlying sub-continental lithospheric mantle, comparable with the source of earlier, Dinantian lavas. However, the overall similarity of incompatible element abundances and ratios to ocean island basalt (OIB) indicates that such contamination was only minor.

Subsequent variations in major elements and compatible trace elements were controlled by limited (less than 36%) polybaric fractional crystallization of olivine ± clinopyroxene as the magmas rose through the crust. The preservation of mafic xenocrysts and high-pressure phenocrysts, most notably high-Al clinopyroxene, indicates high rates of ascent and this would have allowed little or no residence time in high-level magma reservoirs. There was little opportunity for further fractionation and initial ratios of Sr and Nd isotopes suggest that crustal contamination was only minor. Consequently, rock compositions range only from foidites, basanites and basalts to hawaiites (Figure 1.7b).

Central England (Chapter 7)

The whole-rock major- and trace-element geochemistry of the Silesian volcanic rocks and associated sills of the East and West Midlands of England has been described by Kirton (1981, 1984). Both alkaline and tholeiitic magmas were recognized in the East Midlands, where compositions range from basanite and basalt to hawaiite. However, in the slightly younger sills of the West Midlands only alkaline rocks occur and these are a little more differentiated, ranging from basaltic hawaiite to hawaiite, with mugearitic late-stage veins (Figure 1.7c).

Stephanian tholeiitic magmas (Chapter 6)

The extensive tholeiitic sill-complexes and dykes of central Scotland and north-east England were all intruded during a relatively short time interval during the Stephanian Epoch and also show close geochemical similarities. The chemical composition of the basalts and dolerites is similar to those from Hawaii and to Fe-Ti basalts from the Palaeogene North Atlantic Igneous Superprovince and implies large degrees of shallow-level mantle melting. Such melting tends to occur in regions where active lithospheric spreading is taking place and there is excess basaltic discharge due to the influence of a mantle plume (Brooks and Jakobsson, 1974). Investigations by Pederson and van der Beek (1994) found no evidence of a plume associated with the Oslo Graben, but Ernst and Buchan (1997) suggested that a mantle plume in the Skaggerak area could be the centre of a giant radiating dyke-swarm, with the Whin Sill-complex and Midland Valley Sill-complex, the Oslo Rift and the Scania dykes marking the arms of a 'triple junction'. Wilson *et al.* (2000) supported this idea and suggested that magma could have been transported horizontally by dyke injection for great distances from the Skaggerak source region, so that any thermal anomaly need not have been widespread.

Slight geochemical variations across the Whin Sill-complex imply that it was emplaced as a number of pulses of tholeiitic olivine basalt magma (Thorpe and Macdonald, 1985; Howard, 1999). The variations may be due to a heterogeneous mantle source but, based on incompatible element abundances, Howard (1999) suggested that crustal contamination was also an important factor in the evolution of both the Whin Sill-complex and the Midland Valley Sill-complex. Systematic minor variations in both major- and trace-element geochemistry between the two sill-complexes suggest that they were not comagmatic (Howard, 1999). Similarly Macdonald *et al.* (1981) showed that although most dykes from the Scottish swarm fall within a restricted compositional range (which reflects the same compositional variation observed in the Midland Valley Sill-complex), there are also slight, non-systematic trace-element variations between dykes. In fact, some dykes were found to have a unique chemical 'fingerprint', which assists in the tracing of discontinuous dykes across the region. Macdonald *et al.* considered this to be proof that the dyke system was not fed by a single homogenous magma but that fissures were filled by a number of small, partly independent magma chambers reflecting a heterogeneous mantle source. They found no evidence for crustal contamination in the Scottish dykes.

The generation of tholeiitic magmas beneath part of the Midland Valley during Stephanian time may have had an effect upon later magmas by depleting the basal lithosphere in incompatible elements. Wallis (1989) argued that the basanitic intrusions associated with late Stephanian–Early Permian necks in Fife and East Lothian, together with some sills in the area, lack a lithospheric mantle signature because the enriched lithosphere had been 'swept clean' of the more easily melted phases by the tholeiitic melts. However, the Early Permian Mauchline Volcanic Formation lavas originated some 20–30 km to the south of the limit of tholeiitic intrusions, and here interaction of the magmas with the basal lithosphere is reflected by higher Sr and lower Nd initial isotope ratios.

XENOLITHS AND MEGACRYSTS

D. Stephenson

Many of the Carboniferous and Permian igneous rocks of the British Isles contain suites of xenoliths and related individual inherited crystals (megacrysts) that are valuable samples of the otherwise inaccessible underlying continental lithosphere. These bring added conservation value to many of the GCR sites as, apart from geophysical interpretations and indirect observations of geochemical features, they are the only direct source of information on the nature of the upper mantle and deep crust beneath the region. The majority of xenoliths occur either in pyroclastic rocks preserved within volcanic vents and necks or in fine-grained minor intrusions; they are rare within lavas. The minor intrusions include plugs, sills and inclined sheets but xenolith-bearing dykes are particularly common. These dykes are typically narrow (less than 1 m), with xenolith-free marginal zones and axial zones that are crowded with xenoliths; in inclined sheets, the xenoliths are typically concentrated at the base. Host magmas are predominantly the more silica-undersaturated, alkaline basanitic, lamprophyric and foiditic

varieties, and consequently xenoliths are most commonly associated with the Silesian and Early Permian magmatism; they are scarce in the transitional to mildly alkaline sequences that characterize the Dinantian rocks of Scotland and northern England.

Over 70 xenolith-bearing localities in the north and west of the British Isles collectively constitute the oldest documented basaltic 'nodule province' in the world, others being of Mesozoic or younger age. A general review of upper-mantle and deep-crustal xenoliths in the British Isles by Upton *et al.* (1983) includes a list of all occurrences known at the time of publication. Most of the localities are in the Midland Valley of Scotland or in the north-west Highlands, Inner Hebrides and Orkney Islands, with a scattering in the Southern Uplands; the Midland Valley and Southern Uplands localities have been reviewed by Upton *et al.* (1984). Notable localities in Scotland that are GCR sites are **North Berwick Coast**, **East Fife Coast**, **Heads of Ayr** and **Dubh Loch**. In England, mantle xenoliths are known only from Derbyshire (see **Calton Hill** GCR site report) and from boreholes in the East Midlands (Kirton, 1984). In Wales, Late Palaeozoic igneous rocks are rare but the occurrences near Usk both contain mantle xenoliths (see **Golden Hill Quarry** GCR site report).

The abundance of xenoliths and megacrysts, and the proportions of different lithologies, vary widely between sites but the reviews by Upton *et al.* (1983, 1984) have identified up to 11 categories. In addition to those of upper-mantle and deep-crustal origin, cognate xenoliths ('autoliths') associated with the evolution of the host magmas themselves and fragments of upper-crustal country rocks are commonly present. For descriptive purposes, the various suites will be described below in relation to their inferred site of origin.

Upper mantle

The nature of the upper mantle beneath the British Isles, as deduced from xenoliths, has been reviewed by Hunter and Upton (1987) and there have been numerous studies of xenolith suites from individual intrusions. A detailed trace-element and isotopic study of mantle material from Scotland by Menzies and Halliday (1988) identified lateral heterogeneity, with discrete domains of variably depleted or enriched mantle resulting from successive tectonomagmatic events. Mantle xenoliths are particularly relevant to discussions of Carboniferous and Permian igneous activity as they are representative samples from the possible source region of the magmas or provide information about the processes of magma generation. They are widespread, occurring in almost all of the known xenolith localities, and they are normally the most abundant 'deep-source' xenoliths at any locality. They are all ultramafic and can be divided into two main groups: (a) olivine-dominated magnesian peridotites, mainly spinel lherzolite but with some spinel harzburgite, and (b) clinopyroxene-dominated rocks, including wehrlites, clinopyroxenites, websterites, hydrous clinopyroxenites and rare garnet pyroxenites.

Xenoliths of spinel lherzolite (ol + opx + cpx + sp) and spinel harzburgite (ol + opx + sp) are generally less than 5 cm in diameter. Although fresh at some localities (Figure 1.8; and Figure 7.11, Chapter 7), they have commonly undergone low-temperature hydrous alteration to serpentine, carbonates and clay minerals. They exhibit a variety of textures that reveal a history of deformation and recrystallization and some have a pronounced foliation.

Clinopyroxene-rich ultramafic rocks commonly accompany peridotites in xenolith suites. They are generally slightly larger (5–10 cm), coarser grained and darker in colour than the peridotites (Figure 1.9) and their minerals are more Fe-rich. Metamorphic textures are absent but relict igneous textures, including cumulates, are commonly preserved and there is some evidence of mineral layering. A protracted cooling history is indicated by re-equilibration, recrystallization and unmixing of the clinopyroxene, with exsolution of orthopyroxene and spinel (Chapman, 1975). The most common varieties are wehrlites and clinopyroxenites, which contain varying proportions of clinopyroxene and olivine; some have spinel. Websterites (opx + cpx + sp) are less common. Mica pyroxenites are widespread and are abundant locally (e.g. **East Fife Coast** and **North Berwick Coast** GCR sites); virtually mono-mineralic mica rocks, known as 'glimmerites', also occur. Amphibole-rich pyroxenites are less widespread although these too are abundant locally, for example in East Fife (Chapman,

Figure 1.8 Peridotite xenolith with a thin rim of altered chilled basalt in the Weaklaw Vent, **North Berwick Coast** GCR site. The coin is 24 mm in diameter. (Photo: B.G.J. Upton.)

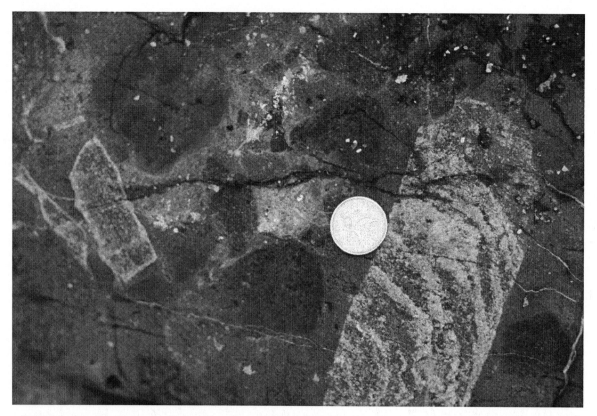

Figure 1.9 Xenoliths in an Early Permian olivine nephelinite dyke at Gribun, Isle of Mull; dark pyroxenites and pale-coloured granulite-facies gneisses. Note the folding in the large block of gneiss. The coin is 24 mm in diameter. (Photo: B.G.J. Upton, from Upton *et al.*, 1998.)

1976), and in Mull (Upton *et al.*, 1998). The hydrous ultramafic rocks tend to be enriched in Fe and Ti relative to the anhydrous equivalents and commonly contain apatite indicating an enrichment in phosphorous. Garnetiferous ultramafic rocks, possibly garnet websterites, are rare; these rocks have granoblastic equilibrium textures but the pyroxene is commonly altered and the garnet appears to have formed by reaction between clinopyroxene and spinel.

It is generally agreed that peridotitic xenoliths originated in the upper mantle and detailed mineralogical studies of lherzolites from Calton Hill (Derbyshire), the western Highlands and the North Berwick Coast (Donaldson, 1978; Praegel, 1981; Hunter *et al.*, 1984) have resulted in estimates of equilibrium conditions in the range 884–1200°C and 8–23 kbar, corresponding to depths of *c.* 30–70 km. The pyroxene-rich ultramafic rocks could be either from the upper mantle or the lower crust, although geophysical properties and phase equilibria studies favour the upper mantle. Elsewhere in the world, where tectonically emplaced upper-mantle is

exposed, lherzolites and pyroxenites are intimately associated, and rare composite wehrlite-lherzolite xenoliths from East Fife and North Berwick suggest that this is also the case beneath Scotland. The overall impression gained is of an extremely heterogeneous upper mantle consisting of deformed magnesian peridotites, cut by a stockwork of sheets or by larger bodies of younger pyroxenite (Upton *et al.*, 1983, 1984). The peridotites are probably residual mantle material ('restites') depleted by episodes of partial melting during the Proterozoic and Palaeozoic eras. It is not possible to determine when the deformation and recrystallization occurred but Hunter *et al.* (1984) speculated that it could have been due to solid flow associated with the initial stages of lithospheric rifting in Early Carboniferous times. The pyroxenites represent high-pressure crystallization products from basic magmas retained at depth, and their rare-earth-element patterns in particular suggest that they may have been related to their host basalts (Downes *et al.*, 2001). Many could have been side-wall cumulates in narrow magma conduits. It has also been argued that under-plated pyroxene-rich rocks form a substantial layer between peridotitic upper-mantle and feldspathic lower-crust (Menzies and Halliday, 1988; Upton *et al.*, 2001).

The hydrous, mica- and amphibole-bearing pyroxenites (and rare hydrous peridotites) pro-bably indicate local metasomatic enrichment of volatiles, K, Ti and P, probably from a volatile-rich alkali basalt melt rather than a fluid (Upton *et al.*, 1998). The local nature of the metasoma-tism is well demonstrated in the **North Berwick Coast** GCR site, where the change from domi-nantly anhydrous to dominantly hydrous xeno-lith assemblages occurs over a very short dis-tance from west to east. However, Chapman (1976) proposed a cumulitic origin for biotite- and kaersutite-pyroxenites at Elie Ness (**East Fife Coast** GCR site) as a result of high-pressure fractional crystallization of a primitive alkali basalt magma, trapped at uppermost-mantle and lower-crustal levels. In this model, the cumulate pyroxenites and their associated megacryst assemblages (see below) were comagmatic with the host intrusions of basanite and monchiquite, which represent middle to late stages of evolu-tion of the same primitive magmas.

Lower crust

Although the crust–mantle boundary (the Moho) is usually well defined in deep seismic profiles across northern Britain (e.g. Bamford, 1979), it is less distinct petrologically. At most of the xenolith localities, ultramafic clinopyroxenite and wehrlite cumulates, as described in the previous section, are associated with mafic granulite-facies meta-igneous rocks. The densities of the latter lithologies correlate well with seismic velocities observed above the Moho and mineral assemblages are consistent with equilibration at depths of 18–30 km (Hunter *et al.*, 1984). Hence they probably constitute the bulk of the lower crust. However, around the base of the crust the pyroxenites and mafic rocks are probably interleaved in a broad zone. They have similar rare-earth-element abundances and patterns and, together with their general similarity in mineralogy, this suggests that they may be genetically related as parts of cumulate complexes (Upton *et al.*, 1998, 2001; Downes *et al.*, 2001).

Xenoliths of mafic lower-crustal materials are less common than ultramafic rocks from the mantle but they are known from many of the localities in Scotland. Much detailed work has concentrated upon the Partan Craig Vent in the **North Berwick Coast** GCR site, which has yielded by far the most examples (Upton *et al.*, 1976; Graham and Upton, 1978), the Fidra Sill, also near North Berwick (Hunter *et al.*, 1984; Downes *et al.*, 2001), the Gribun Dyke on Mull (Upton *et al.*, 1998) and the Tingwall Dyke, Orkney and Duncansby Ness Neck, Caithness (Upton *et al.*, 2001). A detailed isotopic and geochemical study by Halliday *et al.* (1993) provided a review of all lower- and middle-crustal xenoliths in Scotland, and the influence of the host magma upon the trace-element and isotopic composition of the xenoliths was investigated by Lee *et al.* (1993).

The mafic lower-crustal xenoliths are mostly metagabbroic or metadioritic and are composed essentially of pyroxene (clino- ± ortho-) and plagioclase (labradorite to oligoclase), with com-mon magnetite. Biotite, amphibole and apatite are present in some. The more plagioclase-rich varieties grade into meta-anorthosite, and with the development of quartz, the compositions become meta-quartz-dioritic and metatonalitic. Garnet-pyroxene-plagioclase assemblages, com-mon in many other continental lower-crustal xenolith suites, are rare. Relict igneous textures are preserved but textures are more commonly granoblastic, with some gneissose mineral layer-ing (Figure 1.9), and there are indications of partial melting. These mineralogical and tex-tural features signify granulite-facies metamor-phism and the lithologies have been referred to collectively as 'basic granulites' in many publica-tions.

The detailed studies of lower-crustal mafic xenoliths by Hunter *et al.* (1984) and Upton *et al.* (1998) have both suggested that their parental magmas were of alkali basalt composi-tion, and Halliday *et al.* (1993) calculated that the average composition of all of the lower crust beneath Scotland is alkalic. The compositions of the principal minerals and regional whole-rock trace-element variations suggest that the xeno-liths represent high-pressure cumulates formed by crystal fractionation (Halliday *et al.*, 1993). These may have originated from the differentia-tion of basic magmas that were trapped at the crust–mantle boundary as part of a process known as 'underplating'. Here they probably formed layered mafic igneous complexes that were subjected to varying degrees of recrystallization, partial melting and possible local metasomatism as they became incorporated into the lower crust (Hunter *et al.*, 1984). The rarity of garnetiferous lithologies in the xenolith suites implies that these must represent only a minor component of the deep crust and/or upper mantle and hence that the crust was not much more than 30 km thick in Late Palaeozoic times (Halliday *et al.*, 1993).

Although the mafic gneisses resemble and have similar seismic properties to those of the Lewisian Gneiss Complex of the north-west Highlands, there are significant differences in whole-rock geochemistry (Hunter *et al.*, 1984; Halliday *et al.*, 1993) and, from various lines of evidence, it seems unlikely that the Lewisian crust extends for more than 20–30 km east of the Moine Thrust (e.g. Smythe, 1987). In fact, U-Pb dating of zircons in an anorthositic xenolith from the Gribun Dyke, Isle of Mull, has indicated a crystallization age of 1850 ± 50 Ma, which is considerably younger than the Lewisian and more like the Rhinns Complex on the Isle of Islay (Upton *et al.*, 1998). Less precise estimates of radiometric age, described by Halliday *et al.* (1993), indicate that many of the igneous protoliths of the mafic gneiss xenoliths were formed and metamorphosed during magmatic underplating in Late Proterozoic and Palaeozoic times. However, the stable isotope and trace-element data also show that a significant component of the Palaeozoic deep crust beneath Scotland is derived from recycling of Archaean and Palaeoproterozoic lithosphere through sedimentary processes, arc volcanism and subduction, the latter as recent as during the later stages of the Caledonian Orogeny.

Middle crust

Xenoliths of granulite-facies quartzo-feldspathic gneiss have densities compatible with mid-crustal layers that have been identified on seismic profiles across northern Britain (e.g. Bamford, 1979). They are much less common than the lower-crustal mafic rocks, probably because the more felsic compositions are more easily melted and hence less likely to survive in high-temperature basaltic host magmas. They have been described principally from Partan Craig by Graham and Upton (1978) and from eight other Midland Valley occurrences by Halliday *et al.* (1993). Typical mineral assemblages involve quartz, plagioclase, biotite and alkali feldspar,

but rutile, sillimanite, kyanite, graphite, magnetite, zircon and monazite also occur. Biotite is the only hydrous phase and that is scarce. Some xenoliths contain large porphyroblasts (up to 8 mm) of garnet (almandine–pyrope) with chloritic rims, and mineral layering of garnet-rich and garnet-poor layers is common on a centimetre to decimetre scale. Textures range from equigranular to gneissose and some are blastomylonitic. Whereas most of the quartzo-feldspathic xenoliths are considered to have had a metasedimentary origin, foliated quartz-plagioclase (trondhjemitic) xenoliths may be from meta-igneous segregations. Although these lithologies probably dominate mid-crustal levels, they may well be interleaved in subordinate proportions in the lower crust (Upton *et al.*, 1984).

The felsic (and mafic) gneisses are presumed to be representative of a high-grade basement, extending beneath the Midland Valley and the north-western part of the Southern Uplands. Whereas the top of this crystalline basement may be at a depth of no more than 7 km beneath the Midland Valley (Bamford, 1979), lithologies of this general type may characterize much of the middle crust down to depths of 18–20 km, where they grade down into rocks for which meta-igneous origins are more probable. Mineral compositions suggest that the pressure and temperature of metamorphism exceeded 11 kbar and 850°C in places (Graham and Upton, 1978). Although they have geochemical similarities to quartzo-feldspathic gneisses of the Archaean Lewisian Gneiss Complex (Graham and Upton, 1978), isotopic studies of xenoliths from Partan Craig have cast doubt upon such an old age (van Breemen and Hawkesworth, 1980; Halliday *et al.*, 1984). Combined U-Pb zircon and Sm-Nd whole-rock data from these studies suggest that the sedimentary protoliths of the granulite-facies gneisses were derived from crust of varying age, some older than 2200 Ma, but some no older than 1000 Ma. Both the sedimentation and the metamorphism of these rocks must therefore have occurred after *c.* 1000 Ma (Late Proterozoic). Similar isotopic characteristics of the gneisses to sedimentary rocks of the Southern Uplands have led Halliday *et al.* (1993) to suggest that they may have originated from Caledonian events, involving high-grade metamorphism of Lower Palaeozoic metasedimentary rocks that were underthrust beneath the Midland Valley.

Upper Crust

Xenoliths of upper-crustal origin are mainly of local derivation, either from earlier eruptive phases or from the immediately adjacent country rocks, and hence are specific to each individual vent or intrusion. Lithologies are many and varied and many examples are described in the GCR site reports. Some xenoliths of undeformed layered gabbroic rocks, diorites and syenites have been recorded and these are most likely to be the result of fractionation of the host magmas in middle- to upper-crustal magma chambers. Some necks also contain xenoliths of unfoliated granitic rocks that have been attributed to plutons of probable Caledonian origin (Upton *et al.*, 1983).

Megacrysts

In addition to xenoliths, many of the Carboniferous and Permian intrusions also contain single crystals or crystal aggregates of a wide range of minerals of igneous origin. Many are clearly out of equilibrium with the host magmas that carried them to current erosion levels and can be termed xenocrysts, but others are remarkably idiomorphic, suggesting that they grew as phenocrysts within the magma. Because of their commonly large size (up to 10 cm) relative to the grain size of the host rock, they have usually been referred to in the literature as 'megacrysts', a purely descriptive term that covers any mode of origin. The crystals include alkali feldspar (oligoclase, anorthoclase, sanidine), clinopyroxene (diopside, augite, ferrosalite), orthopyroxene, amphibole (kaersutite), mica (phlogopite, biotite), garnet (pyrope), magnetite, ilmenite, zircon, apatite and Nb-rich phases.

Some of the mafic megacrysts can be matched in composition with the component minerals of the ultramafic and mafic xenoliths and hence result from simple disaggregation (e.g. Alexander *et al.*, 1986). However, others have to be attributed to earlier (higher pressure) or later (lower pressure) stages of magmatic evolution than those represented by the xenoliths. At the Elie Ness Neck, Chapman (1976) showed from experimental studies that megacrysts of subcalcic augite and pyrope garnet (the 'Elie rubies'; see **East Fife Coast** GCR site report) could have coprecipitated at a depth of over 70 km from primitive alkali basalt magmas,

formed by partial melting of garnet lherzolite at still greater depths (over 100 km). Donaldson (1984) accepted the high-pressure origin of these phases, with some qualification, though he cast doubt on their coprecipitation. Chapman (1976) interpreted other megacryst phases as having formed from the same magma or from related more evolved magmas; kaersutite at low crustal levels and anorthoclase from small bodies of evolved alkaline magma trapped in the upper crust. A trace-element and stable isotope study by Long *et al.* (1994) confirmed the association of most megacryst suites with the host alkaline magmas and the Midland Valley volcanicity. Density calculations have shown that the evolved magmas must have been of trachy-andesite composition in order for the anorthosite crystals to remain suspended and grow to large sizes, prior to being picked up and transported by later surges of more basic magma that also carried the higher pressure phases (Chapman and Powell, 1976). A geochronological study of megacrysts from East Fife necks by Macintyre *et al.* (1981) supported this model by showing that the cumulus minerals (biotite, amphibole and pyroxene) plus zircon were formed at *c.* 315 Ma, contemporaneous with the local Namurian volcanism, but that the anorthoclase did not complete crystallization until 295 Ma, just before the eruption of the host basanite magmas at 290 Ma during the Stephanian Epoch.

There is increasing evidence that many of the megacrysts could not have been derived from the fractionation of basanitic, foiditic or lamprophyric magmas related to their host rocks. Much of this evidence comes from alkali feldspar megacrysts and feldspathic xenoliths, which are common in several of the East Fife Coast necks, at Fidra off the North Berwick Coast and at several other localities (Aspen *et al.*, 1990). A few composite xenoliths show that the feldspathic rocks may occur as pegmatitic veins traversing hydrous pyroxenites. The mineral phases are out of compositional and isotopic equilibrium with their host rocks, are not associated with any obvious more primitive parental lithologies, and Aspen *et al.* (1990) considered that they had crystallized from geochemically extreme low-temperature trachytic melts present in the upper mantle and/or deep crust at the time of the Carboniferous–Permian magmatism. They suggested that the melts may have originated through very small-scale partial melting of lithospheric mantle under the influence of volatile fluxes.

Of particular interest are anorthoclase-rich syenitic xenoliths (anorthoclasites) that also contain corundum and Nb-, Zr-, U-, Th- and rare-earth-element-rich minerals (Upton *et al.*, 1999). The very high content of incompatible trace elements and the presence of calcite vein-lets in these xenoliths suggest the possible involvement of asthenosphere-derived alkali-rich carbonatitic melts that permeated and inter-acted with the uppermost mantle to produce carbonated trachytic melts (as suggested by Long *et al.* (1994) for megacrysts in a Palaeo-gene dyke cutting the Lewisian craton). In the most extreme compositions, the presence of corundum reflects a highly aluminous melt that would have been almost impossible to achieve by fractional crystallization and hence some mechanism of alkali loss has to be suspected.

Upton *et al.* (1999) proposed that the alkalis could have been removed in a carbonatitic fraction that separated from the trachytic melt to leave an aluminous residuum.

With the exception of the far north-west, which was subjected to magma generation and ascent during Palaeogene time, the nature of the deep lithosphere of Great Britain has probably changed little since it was sampled by the Late Palaeozoic magmas. Hence the information gained from the xenoliths and megacrysts, and summarized in Figure 1.10, is as relevant to the present-day deep structure of Britain as it is to their time of emplacement. The extensive literature summarized above demonstrates the importance that has been attached to this subject already, and the xeno-lithic vents and intrusions of the GCR sites will no doubt continue to supply material for further studies.

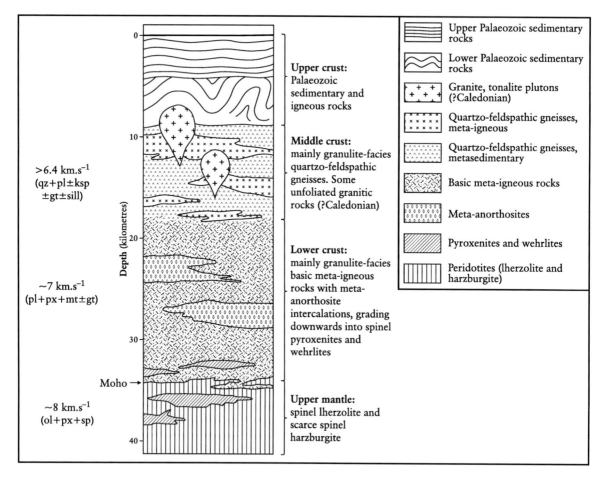

Figure 1.10 Generalized section through the upper continental lithosphere beneath the Midland Valley of Scotland. The left-hand column shows mean seismic velocities after Bamford (1979) and principal mineral assemblages (in brackets). (gt = garnet; ksp = potassium feldspar; mt = magnetite; ol = olivine; pl = plagio-clase; px = pyroxene; qz = quartz; sill = sillimanite; sp = spinel.) After Upton *et al.* (1984).

Chapter 2

Dinantian volcanic rocks of the Midland Valley of Scotland and adjacent areas

INTRODUCTION

D. Stephenson

In contrast to the Northumberland, Solway and Tweed basins, where local volcanism commenced during Tournaisian time (see Chapter 3), volcanism did not start in the Midland Valley of Scotland until earliest Visean time. However, the resulting eruptions rapidly built up vast lava fields, which are by far the thickest and most extensive in the whole Carboniferous–Permian Igneous Province of northern Britain and probably constitute over 90% by volume of its eruptive products. Tomkeieff (1937) estimated that almost 6000 km³ of magma was erupted during Dinantian times and some of the preserved volcanic successions are up to 1000 m thick (Paterson *et al.*, 1990). The most extensive lava fields are those of the Clyde Plateau, which dominate the landscape of the western Midland Valley to the north, west and south of Glasgow (Geikie, 1897). Possible outliers of these fields

occur just across the Highland Boundary Fault in southern Kintyre and on Ben Bowie, near Helensburgh. In the eastern Midland Valley, the largest lava field is centred upon the Garleton Hills of East Lothian, and small but prominent outcrops occur within the city of Edinburgh. Later in Visean time, volcanic activity became centred upon the Burntisland area of Fife and the Bathgate Hills of West Lothian. The stratigraphical range of each succession of Dinantian volcanic rocks is shown in Figure 2.1 and their distribution in and around the Midland Valley is shown in Figure 2.2.

The early Visean volcanic successions are dominated by lavas, although considerable thicknesses of pyroclastic rocks and volcaniclastic sedimentary rocks occur locally. Uniquely within the Carboniferous–Permian Igneous Province of northern Britain, they are characterized by a wide range of compositions and, although most successions are dominated by transitional to mildly alkaline basalts, hawaiites and mugearites, many include

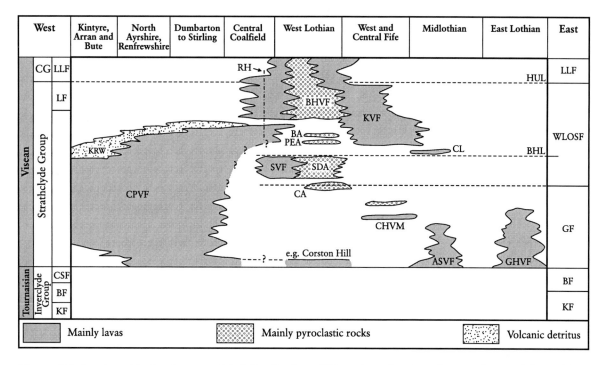

Figure 2.1 Stratigraphical and geographical distribution of Dinantian volcanic rocks in and around the Midland Valley of Scotland. Note that the diagram attempts to show stratigraphical range and not thickness of volcanic successions. (ASVF = Arthur's Seat Volcanic Formation; BA = Barracks Ash; BF = Ballagan Formation; BHL = Burdiehouse Limestone; BHVF = Bathgate Hills Volcanic Formation; CA = Crosswood Ash; CG = Clackmannan Group; CHVM = Charles Hill Volcanic Member; CL = Carlops Lava; CPVF = Clyde Plateau Volcanic Formation; CSF = Clyde Sandstone Formation; GF = Gullane Formation; HUL = Hurlet Limestone; KF = Kinnesswood Formation; KRW = Kirkwood Formation; LF = Lawmuir Formation; LLF = Lower Limestone Formation; PEA = Port Edgar Ash; RH = Rashiehill Borehole; SDA = Seafield–Deans Ash; SVF = Salsburgh Volcanic Formation; WLOSF = West Lothian Oil-shale Formation (equivalent to the Aberlady Formation in East Lothian).) Fife formation names omitted.

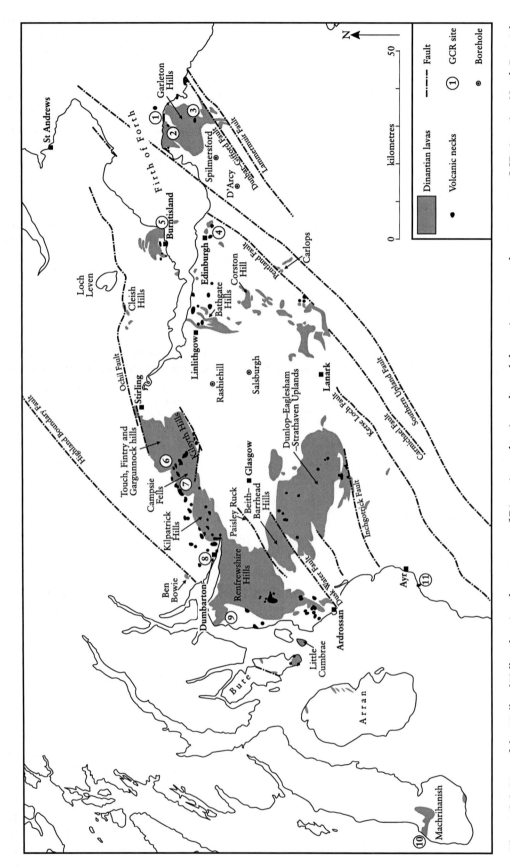

Figure 2.2 Map of the Midland Valley showing the outcrops of Dinantian volcanic rocks and the major structural components. GCR sites: 1 = North Berwick Coast; 2 = Garleton Hills; 3 = Traprain Law; 4 = Arthur's Seat Volcano; 5 = Burntisland to Kinghorn Coast; 6 = Touch, Fintry and Gargunnock Hills; 7 = Campsie Fells; 8 = Dumbarton Rock; 9 = Dunrod Hill; 10 = Macrihanish Coast and South Kintyre; 11 = Heads of Ayr. After Cameron and Stephenson (1985).

Introduction

trachytic rocks and some have rhyolites. Late Visean volcanism, in contrast, was exclusively basic in character.

The volcanism appears to have started approximately synchronously across much of the Midland Valley, around the Tournaisian–Visean boundary. In the east, the earliest volcanic rocks rest conformably upon the Ballagan Formation, and CM to PU zone miospores and plant remains have been found just below and within them (Davies, 1974; Bateman and Scott, 1990; Scott, 1990). In the west, the Clyde Plateau Volcanic Formation rests with regional unconformity on strata that range from the Stratheden Group (Upper Devonian) to the Clyde Sandstone Formation, which overlies the Ballagan Formation at the top of the Inverclyde Group (Paterson and Hall, 1986). However, in the south-west of the Kilpatrick Hills, thin sandstones occur in the lowest part of the Clyde Plateau Volcanic Formation, and below the northern escarpment of the Touch and Gargunnock hills tuffs occur in the top of the Clyde Sandstone Formation. In these areas, the boundary is clearly transitional and the volcanic succession is conformable with the Clyde Sandstone Formation.

The early Visean volcanic rocks are overlain more-or-less conformably in the east by strata of the Gullane Formation, which have yielded Asbian TC zone miospores (Neves et al., 1973). In the west, the Clyde Plateau lavas built up a considerable topographical feature that was denuded to produce volcaniclastic detritus, which overlies the lavas wherever the top of the sequence has been preserved. This highly diachronous Kirkwood Formation was then gradually overlapped by a range of late Visean strata, the oldest of which are from the lower parts of the Lawmuir Formation, of possible late Asbian age. Hence the early Visean activity is quite well constrained to the PU and TC miospore zones (Chadian to early Asbian). The major later Visean volcanic centre in the Burntisland area of Fife occurs within the Sandy Craig and Pathhead formations, which are well constrained elsewhere by miospore data to the Asbian–Brigantian interval (Brindley and Spinner, 1987, 1989; Browne et al., 1996). In the Bathgate Hills, volcanism commenced in latest Asbian time and continued well into Namurian time.

Radiometric ages obtained from Dinantian volcanic rocks of the Midland Valley are confusing, mainly because of a scarcity of suitable material, for which only K-Ar whole-rock determinations have been published. De Souza (1982), summarizing his earlier work, suggested that the bulk of the Clyde Plateau Volcanic Formation lavas were erupted between 335 Ma and 325 Ma and the De Souza (1979) data, adjusted for new constants, gave an age of c. 326 Ma for the Kinghorn lavas and 326–316 Ma for the Bathgate Hills lavas. These dates fit well with the biostratigraphical data and the Gradstein and Ogg (1996) timescale. The East Lothian phonolitic intrusions of Traprain Law and North Berwick Law gave dates of c. 328 Ma, suggesting that they were contemporaneous with the Visean activity. However, dates for the Arthur's Seat and East Lothian lavas (Fitch et al., 1970; De Souza, 1974), adjusted for new constants, ranged from 355 Ma to 345 Ma, suggesting an earlier, Tournaisian episode, which is inconsistent with the biostratigraphy. Recently obtained, more precise Ar-Ar dates from separated minerals have confirmed the age of the Clyde Plateau lavas at 335 Ma to 329 Ma and have also suggested that the East Lothian lavas may be slightly older (up to 342 Ma), though this latter date is close to the Tournaisian–Visean boundary and hence consistent with the biostratigraphy (A.A. Monaghan and M.S. Pringle, pers. comm., 2002).

Structural control

Structural controls of volcanism are inferred from NE- to ENE-trending lineaments that were particularly well developed during Dinantian times and are assumed to reflect Caledonian trends in the underlying basement. The lineaments are defined by elongate outcrops of proximal volcanic rocks, chains of plugs and/or volcanic necks and local linear dyke-swarms, all suggesting that the ascent of magma was probably controlled by planes of weakness in the deep crust that gave rise to faulting at higher levels.

The graben of the Midland Valley was clearly a major control, yet there is no evidence of volcanism directly associated with the Highland Boundary Fault. The most north-westerly extrusive centres on this side of the Midland Valley are concentrated on the NNW side of the main volcanic outcrops, within a 2–3 km-wide zone that extends ENE for some 27 km, from Dumbarton towards Stirling (Figure 2.3).

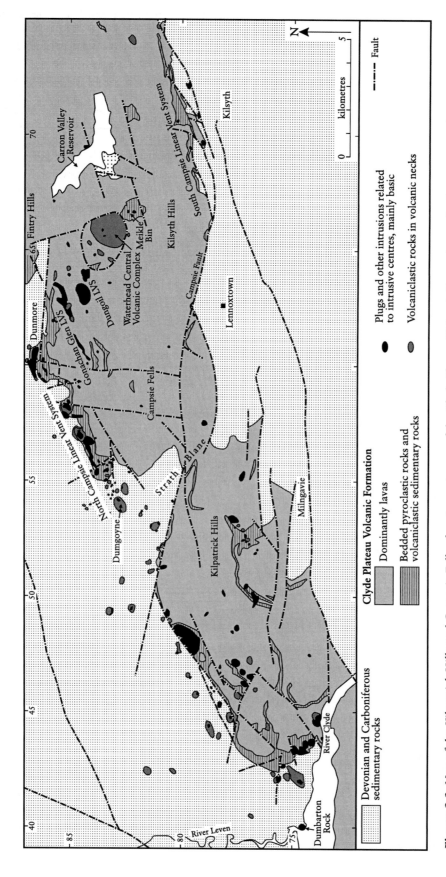

Figure 2.3 Map of the Kilpatrick Hills and Campsie Fells, showing outcrops of the Clyde Plateau Volcanic Formation and volcanotectonic lineaments defined by plugs, necks and proximal volcaniclastic beds. The most prominent lineament, along the north-west edge of the volcanic outcrops, is the Dumbarton–Fintry Line of Whyte and MacDonald (1974). Based on British Geological Survey 1:50 000 sheets 30W, Greenock (1990); 30E, Glasgow (1993); and 31W, Airdrie (1992).

Introduction

This lineament has become known as the 'Dumbarton–Fintry Line' (Whyte and MacDonald, 1974; Craig and Hall, 1975). It is marked by numerous intrusions (many of them forming prominent landmarks such as Dumbarton Rock, Dumgoyne and Dunmore), pipes occupied by fragmentary materials, and proximal bedded pyroclastic rocks that probably represent degraded tuff-cones. These features are particularly well seen in the **Campsie Fells** GCR site. A concentration of dykes along a similar trend to the south-west suggests that the lineament may continue through the Renfrewshire Hills to south Bute. The north-eastern end of the lineament comprises the North Campsie Linear Vent System, and two slightly younger linear vent systems form separate *en échelon* lines within the Campsie lava block to the south-east (Forsyth *et al.*, 1996). On the south side of the Campsie Block, the South Campsie Linear Vent System forms a 15 km-long lineament close to the Campsie Fault (Craig and Hall, 1975; Forsyth *et al.*, 1996).

Other lines of necks and plugs in the northern Clyde Plateau outcrop are aligned WNW–ESE to north-west–south-east and may reflect less extensive conjugate Caledonian fractures at depth. Notable examples occur at each end of the Kilpatrick Hills, at Dumbarton and Strath Blane, where their coalescing tephra cones may have acted as local barriers between adjacent lava fields during the earlier phases of volcanism (Hall *et al.*, 1998).

Other WSW- to nearly W–E-trending faults throughout the Midland Valley that may have been utilized by rising magmas, also probably formed active escarpments controlling local accumulations of lava. Consequently they are commonly marked by significant changes in thickness of the volcanic piles. These faults include the Paisley Ruck, and the Dusk Water and Inchgotrick faults in Ayrshire (McLean, 1966; Hall, 1974; Rollin in Monro, 1999), as well as the Campsie and Ochil faults (Rippon *et al.*, 1996) (Figure 2.2). The unconformity beneath the lavas in the west has been attributed to a localized mid-Dinantian east–west compressional event (Paterson *et al.*, 1990). However, a close association between the maximum excision of strata and the thickest developments of volcanic rocks led Monro (1982) and Forsyth *et al.* (1996) to suggest that it was due, at least in part, to magmatic updoming in advance of the Visean eruptions.

At the south-eastern limit of the Midland Valley, the north-eastern extrapolation of the main Southern Upland Fault, together with NE-trending splays to the south-east, in particular the Dunbar–Gifford Fault, are thought to pass beneath Carboniferous strata (Max, 1976; Floyd, 1994) and to have controlled the rise of magma throughout much of the Carboniferous Period (Upton, 1982).

Palaeogeography and styles of eruption

In the eastern Midland Valley, the earliest volcanic rocks seem to rest conformably on the mudstones, siltstones and dolomitic limestones of the Ballagan Formation. Therefore, they were probably erupted onto flat low-lying coastal plains and deltas, with semi-marine lagoons and sabkhas. The explosive interaction of magma with surface and ground water resulted initially in phreatomagmatic eruptions, evidence for which is well seen in East Lothian, particularly in the **North Berwick Coast** GCR site. Abundant small vent structures and bedded pyroclastic rocks with base-surge and ash-fall characteristics are interbedded with the sedimentary succession, suggesting the development of shallow tuff-rings, probably less than 1 km in diameter. Lacustrine sedimentary rocks in some of the vents suggest the presence of crater lakes (maars) and some preserve remnants of early terrestrial tropical vegetation.

Farther inland, generally to the west, were semi-arid floodplains, with outwash fans and playa lakes. This transition from coastal plain to the entirely terrestrial, fluvial environment, typified by the Clyde Sandstone Formation and indicating regional uplift, was probably diachronous across the Midland Valley and broadly coincided with the onset of volcanism. The plains may have been divided initially by NE-trending ridges and escarpments formed from pre-Carboniferous rocks but, with a rise in magma productivity, rapidly accumulating lava fields began to form major landscape features. These topographic highs dominated the late Visean palaeogeography and also had a long-lasting influence on subsequent basin development. In such areas, eruptions were almost entirely subaerial and lavas were usually of aa type, though rare pahoehoe features have been reported. Flow surfaces are rarely preserved and thick red-brown boles occur on the top of

Dinantian volcanic rocks of the Midland Valley

most flows, resulting from the development of tropical or sub-tropical lateritic soils, indicative of significant interludes of quiescence between eruptions. Basic to mugearitic lavas, typically between 5 m and 30 m thick, were erupted through relatively small shield volcanoes. Together with cinder cones of coarse pyroclastic rocks, these commonly coalesced along NE-trending lineaments, now marked by upstanding plugs and volcanic necks. This style of eruption is represented by the **Campsie Fells** GCR site.

The absence of volcanic necks and proximal pyroclastic rocks from some areas suggests eruption from fissure volcanoes. The **Touch, Fintry and Gargunnock Hills** GCR site represents one such area, and the lateral continuity of some flows for over 6 km in the escarpment of the Gargunnock Hills has been cited as further evidence of fissure eruptions (Read in Francis *et al.*, 1970). Regional dyke-swarms that may have acted as feeders to the fissure eruptions are not obvious in most lava successions. However, there is a marked concentration of ENE- to NE-trending dykes up to 12 m wide along a south-western continuation of the Dumbarton–Fintry volcanotectonic line, which can be traced beneath the thickest part of the Renfrewshire Hills succession (Paterson *et al.*, 1990), across Great Cumbrae (Tyrrell, 1917a) and into southern Bute (Smellie, 1916). Outwith the major lava fields, individual volcanoes such as Arthur's Seat and the Heads of Ayr were possibly up to 5 km in diameter and rose to heights of about 1000 m above the plain (Whyte, 1963b; Black, 1966).

More evolved lava compositions are common locally in the Dinantian lava fields, and the abundance of trachytic extrusive rocks in the southern crop of the Clyde Plateau Volcanic Formation between Greenock and Strathaven implies that higher stratovolcanoes may have developed in this region (MacPherson *et al.*, 2001). The best-documented example is the 8 km-wide Misty Law Trachytic Centre in the Renfrewshire Hills, which comprises trachytic pyroclastic rocks, massive lavas of trachyte and rhyolite, and trachytic plugs and necks (Johnstone, 1965; Stephenson in Paterson *et al.*, 1990). Trachyte lavas are also abundant in the upper part of the Garleton Hills Volcanic Formation and the **Garleton Hills** GCR site has been selected to represent this style of volcanism. They are also present in the upper

part of the Machrihanish succession (see **Machrihanish Coast and South Kintyre** GCR site report). Rhyolites occur locally in the upper part of the succession in the western Campsie Fells and near the base of the sequence in the Cleish Hills (Geikie, 1900). Flow banding in many of these evolved lavas indicates viscous flow; they probably never extended more than a few kilometres from their source and may even have formed steep-sided lava domes (e.g. the trachyte of Skerry Fell Fad, near Machrihanish and the rhyolite at Swinlees in the southern Renfrewshire Hills).

Calderas may have developed over some of the principal salic centres and the thick trachyte lavas forming the Garleton Hills of East Lothian may have been ponded in a caldera (B.G.J. Upton, pers. comm., 2001). However, the best-documented evidence occurs in the Waterhead Volcanic Complex of the Campsie Fells (Craig, 1980; Forsyth *et al.*, 1996). Here, a large multiple neck and several smaller necks, plugged by a wide variety of rock-types, occur within an oval ring-fault 2 km by 2.5 km. The complex is underlain by a positive gravity anomaly (Cotton, 1968) and the enclosed basic lavas show intense brecciation and hydrothermal alteration and are intruded by a variety of dykes (MacDonald, 1973). Some of the dykes are felsic, and trachytic pyroclastic rocks in the adjacent tephra cone of Meikle Bin have been attributed to the centre, although there are no felsic lavas preserved.

Despite the abundance of felsic volcanic rocks and the inferred presence of calderas in some areas, there is little evidence for pyroclastic flows, which are typical of such activity elsewhere. Well-bedded, carbonated and haematitized trachytic tuffs near the Weak Law Vent in East Lothian that were originally interpreted as welded ash-flow tuffs (Upton in Sabine and Sutherland, 1982), are now considered to be ash-fall material (see **North Berwick Coast** GCR site report). Welded trachytic lapilli-tuffs near Eaglesham have also been interpreted as ash fall (MacPherson and Phillips, 1998).

In the West Lothian oil-shale field, the land surface remained close to sea level during Dinantian times and similar conditions prevailed during most of Silesian time throughout the eastern Midland Valley. Relatively small basaltic volcanoes erupted onto coastal plains with lagoons and into shallow seas, locally building

Introduction

volcanic islands, fringed by reefs that were periodically eroded and submerged. Initial eruptions were explosive (phreatomagmatic), leading to widespread pyroclastic deposits, but later eruptions in any one area were dominantly of lavas. Pillow lavas and hyaloclastites at Kinghorn testify to local subaqueous eruptions, but most of the lavas were probably subaerial.

The eastern Midland Valley (early Visean)

Outcrops of the Garleton Hills Volcanic Formation of East Lothian lie entirely between the projected north-easterly continuation of the Southern Upland Fault at depth and NE-trending splays to the south-east, such as the Dunbar–Gifford Fault (McAdam and Tulloch, 1985; Davies *et al.*, 1986). They therefore overlie Lower Palaeozoic rocks of the Southern Uplands terrane at no great depth. Superb coastal exposures around North Berwick show the relationships of the basal basaltic pyroclastic rocks to associated necks and sedimentary country rocks (see **North Berwick Coast** GCR site report), and overlying basaltic to trachytic lavas form the **Garleton Hills** (see GCR site report). The sequence is up to 520 m thick. Thinner successions have been encountered to the south-west in the Spilmersford and D'Arcy boreholes and in a small outcrop near Borthwick, still within the same fault-bound block.

Some flows of analcime trachybasalt in East Lothian appear to have contained leucite originally (Bennett, 1945). Apart from one other flow in the Campsie Fells, which is phonolitic, these are the only known silica-undersaturated evolved lavas in the Dinantian lava successions. However, the East Lothian lava field is unusual because of its apparent association, backed by limited K-Ar whole-rock dates (De Souza, 1974, 1979), with several large high-level intrusions (plugs and laccoliths) of silica-undersaturated phonolitic rocks. The latter form the prominent landmarks of Traprain Law, North Berwick Law and the Bass Rock (e.g. see Figure 2.6 – **North Berwick Coast** GCR site report) as well as a sill at Hairy Craig (Bailey in Clough *et al.*, 1910; MacGregor and Ennos, 1922; Campbell and Stenhouse, 1933; McAdam and Tulloch, 1985). They are represented by the **Traprain Law** GCR site.

In Edinburgh, the lavas around Arthur's Seat and Calton Hill, together with associated intrusions such as the Lion's Head and Lion's Haunch vents and the basalt plug of the Castle Rock, dominate the city landscape, and the **Arthur's Seat Volcano** GCR site is one of the most widely appreciated geological localities in Britain. At least 13 lavas, ranging from olivine-clinopyroxene-phyric basalts to hawaiite and mugearite, form a succession 400–500 m thick (Clark, 1956; Black, 1966). A more restricted, 90 m-thick succession of tuffs and olivine-clinopyroxene-phyric basalts forms Craiglockhart Hill, 6 km to the south-west. Together these volcanic sequences comprise the Arthur's Seat Volcanic Formation.

Burntisland and Bathgate Hills (early Visean to Namurian)

In the Burntisland area of Fife, two volcanic developments within the Anstruther Formation are probably younger than the Arthur's Seat and Garleton Hills volcanic formations of the Lothians (Figure 2.1). At the base of the formation, the Charles Hill Volcanic Member consists of tuffs and olivine-microphyric basalts that crop out on the limbs of a shallow anticline centred upon the island of Inchcolm. The higher unit, of coarse tuffs and agglomerates, is known from boreholes and poor exposures onshore to the north. Major outcrops of late Visean volcanic rocks occur around the Burntisland Anticline, where up to 485 m of olivine-microphyric basalt lavas ('Dalmeny' and 'Hillhouse' types) with subordinate pyroclastic rocks and volcaniclastic sedimentary rocks constitute the Kinghorn Volcanic Formation. This formation, which is represented onshore by the **Burntisland to Kinghorn Coast** GCR site, is also well developed offshore to the east, as was seen underground in Seafield Colliery, and on the island of Inchkeith in the Firth of Forth. The succession is dominantly subaerial, but with periodic submergence beneath freshwater lakes or marine incursions during which some pillow lavas and hyaloclastites were formed.

Within and around the West Lothian oil-shale field, volcanic activity was of a distinctly different nature to the generally earlier Visean activity elsewhere in the Midland Valley. In contrast to the wide compositional variety within the Garleton Hills and most Clyde Plateau successions, this volcanism was entirely basaltic. Initial activity may have been contemporaneous with later phases of the essentially subaerial Clyde Plateau Volcanic Formation, but subsequently the terrestrial lava pile was overlapped and the volcanism continued to develop in a coastal-plain–lagoonal–shallow-marine environment that was a precursor to Silesian volcanic settings. The earlier phases of this activity are poorly exposed and much information has come from boreholes and underground workings (Mitchell and Mykura, 1962). Although later lavas are well exposed in parts of the Bathgate Hills, no suitable GCR site has been identified.

The Crosswood Ash, known from exposures and boreholes around Crosswood Reservoir, occurs at the base of the West Lothian Oil-shale Formation, and the 100 m-thick Seafield–Deans Ash of the West Calder area underlies the freshwater Burdiehouse Limestone that marks the base of the Hopetoun Member slightly higher in that formation. Other thin but widespread volcaniclastic beds occur within the Hopetoun Member (e.g. the Port Edgar Ash and Barracks Ash) and a basalt lava occurs at this general stratigraphical level near Carlops, in the Midlothian Basin. Farther west, in an oil-well at Salsburgh in the Central Coalfield, supposed Lower Devonian volcanic rocks are overlain by 100 m of basaltic tuffs and lavas with interbeds of limestone and mudstone that have been termed the 'Salsburgh Volcanic Formation' (Cameron *et al.*, 1998). These are succeeded directly by the Burdiehouse Limestone and hence are probably contemporaneous with the Seafield–Deans Ash.

Higher still in the Hopetoun Member, above the Houston Marls, thick and widespread pyroclastic rocks mark the base of the Bathgate Hills Volcanic Formation. Beneath the Central Coalfield to the west, in the Rashiehill Borehole, this major volcanic formation rests directly upon the Clyde Plateau Volcanic Formation. In the Bathgate Hills area it interdigitates with the Visean sedimentary succession and extends well into the Namurian, accumulating a total thickness of about 600 m of volcanic rocks (Cadell, 1925; Smith *et al.*, 1994; Stephenson in Cameron *et al.*, 1998). Rather than split the description between chapters, the formation is described in its entirety in the 'Introduction' to Chapter 4.

The western Midland Valley (early Visean)

The Clyde Plateau Volcanic Formation comprises the major part of the Strathclyde Group in the western Midland Valley. Its extensive main outcrop encircles Glasgow on three sides, forming the Touch, Fintry and Gargunnock hills, the Campsie Fells and the Kilpatrick Hills to the north, and the Renfrewshire Hills, the Beith–Barrhead Hills and the Dunlop–Eaglesham–Strathaven Hills to the south (Figure 2.2). The outcrop is divided by major faults into several discrete 'blocks', each with its own succession. Most have been described in some detail in Geological Survey memoirs and some attempt has been made to correlate parts of successions between blocks, although in some cases this is extremely tentative (Figure 2.4).

In the north-east of the outcrop the Gargunnock, Touch and Fintry hills form a coherent block (the Fintry–Touch Block, see Figure 2.4) with a volcanic sequence that is 300–400 m thick. The lavas are mainly of feldspar-phyric basalts and hawaiites ('Markle' and 'Jedburgh' types), with subordinate trachybasalts and mugearites (Read in Francis *et al.*, 1970). Volcanic necks and proximal volcaniclastic rocks are rare, so the **Touch, Fintry and Gargunnock Hills** GCR site represents part of the Clyde Plateau Volcanic Formation that may have originated mainly from fissure eruptions. The Campsie Fells, Kilsyth Hills and Denny Muir, forming the next block to the south-west (the Campsie Block), have a sequence in excess of 500 m thick. A wide range of lava compositions from olivine-clinopyroxene-phyric basalts to trachyte and a rare phonolitic trachyte are represented, though here too feldspar-phyric basalts and hawaiites are dominant and parts of the succession can be traced into the Touch Hills (Craig, 1980; Hall in Forsyth *et al.*, 1996; Hall *et al.*, 1998). Numerous volcanic necks are concentrated along four NE-trending 'linear vent systems' and the **Campsie Fells** GCR site has been selected to represent this multiple vent volcanism. To the east of the GCR site is the major Waterhead Central Volcanic Complex, which dominated the later extrusive phases and may have developed a caldera.

The sequence in the Kilpatrick Hills Block is separated from that of the Campsie Fells by the E–W-trending Campsie Fault, and correlations between these two blocks are only tentative.

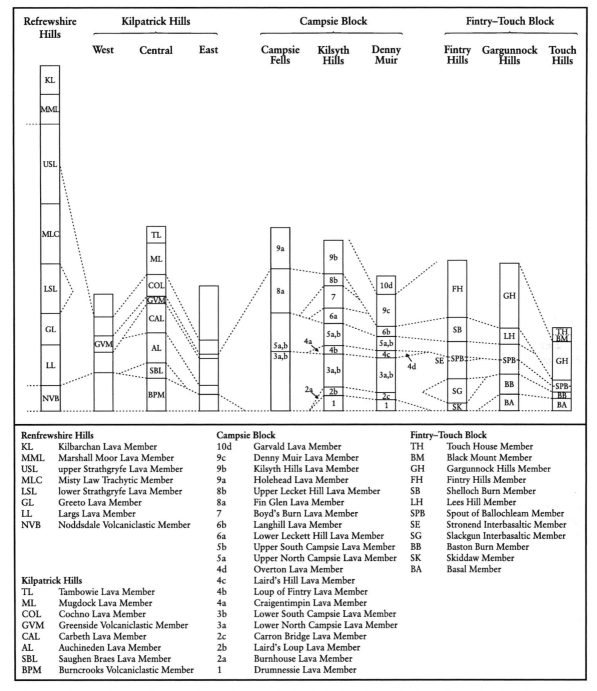

Figure 2.4 Correlation of composite sections in the Clyde Plateau Volcanic Formation. Based on information in Forsyth *et al.* (1996); Hall *et al.* (1998); and Paterson *et al.* (1990). N.B. formal designation of these units as members is currently in progress.

Renfrewshire Hills		Campsie Block		Fintry–Touch Block	
KL	Kilbarchan Lava Member	10d	Garvald Lava Member	TH	Touch House Member
MML	Marshall Moor Lava Member	9c	Denny Muir Lava Member	BM	Black Mount Member
USL	upper Strathgryfe Lava Member	9b	Kilsyth Hills Lava Member	GH	Gargunnock Hills Member
MLC	Misty Law Trachytic Member	9a	Holehead Lava Member	FH	Fintry Hills Member
LSL	lower Strathgryfe Lava Member	8b	Upper Lecket Hill Lava Member	SB	Shelloch Burn Member
GL	Greeto Lava Member	8a	Fin Glen Lava Member	LH	Lees Hill Member
LL	Largs Lava Member	7	Boyd's Burn Lava Member	SPB	Spout of Ballochleam Member
NVB	Noddsdale Volcaniclastic Member	6b	Langhill Lava Member	SE	Stronend Interbasaltic Member
		6a	Lower Leckett Hill Lava Member	SG	Slackgun Interbasaltic Member
		5b	Upper South Campsie Lava Member	BB	Baston Burn Member
		5a	Upper North Campsie Lava Member	SK	Skiddaw Member
		4d	Overton Lava Member	BA	Basal Member
		4c	Laird's Hill Lava Member		
Kilpatrick Hills		4b	Loup of Fintry Lava Member		
TL	Tambowie Lava Member	4a	Craigentimpin Lava Member		
ML	Mugdock Lava Member	3b	Lower South Campsie Lava Member		
COL	Cochno Lava Member	3a	Lower North Campsie Lava Member		
GVM	Greenside Volcaniclastic Member	2c	Carron Bridge Lava Member		
CAL	Carbeth Lava Member	2b	Laird's Loup Lava Member		
AL	Auchineden Lava Member	2a	Burnhouse Lava Member		
SBL	Saughen Braes Lava Member	1	Drumnessie Lava Member		
BPM	Burncrooks Volcaniclastic Member				

The 400 m-thick Kilpatrick sequence includes many olivine- and olivine-clinopyroxene-phyric basalts ('Dalmeny', 'Dunsapie' and 'Craiglockhart' types) and is generally more mafic than that of the Campsie Block. Many lavas thin eastwards towards Strath Blane, where Hall *et al.* (1998) suggested that high ground,

possibly formed by early tephra cones, formed a barrier. Later lavas, possibly emanating from the Waterhead Central Volcanic Complex, can be correlated across Strath Blane, suggesting that the barrier had become ineffective by this time. Many of the lavas in the Kilpatrick Hills originated from small central volcanoes, now represented by necks and plugs. Most of them lie on south-west continuations of the Campsie linear vent systems, and in the far south-west is **Dumbarton Rock**, selected for the GCR as representative of a volcanic plug associated with the Clyde Plateau Volcanic Formation.

Some of the upper lavas in the western Kilpatrick Hills appear to be continuous across the River Clyde and have been correlated with various higher parts of the Renfrewshire Hills succession. The maximum thickness of the Clyde Plateau Volcanic Formation, up to 1000 m, is attained in the Renfrewshire Hills (Stephenson in Paterson *et al.*, 1990), although this thins markedly southwards towards Ardrossan in the contiguous Kilbirnie Hills (Stephenson in Monro, 1999). Much of the succession consists of alternating flows of feldspar-phyric hawaiites ('Markle' type) and aphyric mugearites, and these two lithologies commonly occur together in composite flows, as represented by the **Dunrod Hill** GCR site. The Misty Law Trachytic Centre is a major feature in the middle of the succession (Johnstone, 1965) and minor trachytic rocks and rhyolites occur at higher levels. Across the fault zone of the Paisley Ruck, to the south-east, the lava sequence in the Beith–Barrhead Hills is probably less than 300 m thick, being arranged in a gentle SW-plunging anticline. The varied but essentially basaltic lavas may be equivalent to only the upper, more mafic part of the adjoining Renfrewshire Hills succession (Stephenson in Paterson *et al.*, 1990; in Hall *et al.*, 1998; and in Monro, 1999). This contrasts with the view of De Souza (1979), based on K-Ar age determinations (337 ± 7 Ma, or *c.* 344 Ma using new constants) and with the Ar-Ar date of 335 ± 2 Ma (A.A. Monaghan and M.S. Pringle, pers. comm., 2002), which both suggest that the Beith Hills include some of the oldest lavas of the Clyde Plateau Volcanic Formation. Farther south-east, across the Dusk Water Fault, lies a vast outcrop of poorly exposed varied volcanic rocks that form undulating high moorland between Dunlop, Eaglesham and Strathaven. Their stratigraphy and structure are difficult to determine but thickness estimates range from 500 m to 900 m and a full range of lithologies is present, from mafic basalts to trachyandesites, trachytes and rhyolites (Richey *et al.*, 1930; Paterson *et al.*, 1998; MacPherson *et al.*, 2001). Towards the east of this block, widespread proximal pyroclastic rocks and volcaniclastic sedimentary rocks, associated with trachytic lavas and plugs, constitute the Gowk Stane Member. Numerous other trachytic plugs and necks lie on NE- and NW-trending lineaments throughout the block, and there are several plugs or laccoliths of silica-undersaturated phonolitic trachyte, such as that which forms the prominent landmark of Loudoun Hill, near Darvel. Basaltic plugs are less common in this block.

The widespread volcanic outcrops terminate abruptly in the south-east at the Inchgotrick Fault, but the Heads of Ayr Neck on the south Ayrshire coast (Whyte, 1963b) may represent a small isolated volcano of similar age to the Clyde Plateau Volcanic Formation (see **Heads of Ayr** GCR site report).

It is probable that the original lava fields of the Clyde Plateau did not extend significantly farther to the north-west than the present outcrops (George, 1960; Whyte and MacDonald, 1974), although they do spill to a minor extent across the Highland Boundary Fault on Ben Bowie near Helensburgh (Paterson *et al.*, 1990). To the west, outlying lava successions on the islands of Little Cumbrae, Bute and Arran are thin, suggesting that there was dramatic attenuation westwards from the main outcrops. Significantly, on Bute and Arran, up to 16 m of fluvio-deltaic mudstones with sandstones and thin coals occur beneath the volcanic rocks, but with a sharp erosional base above the Clyde Sandstone Formation, suggesting that the onset of volcanism was a little later here than in the main outcrop. However, in south Kintyre a highly varied volcanic succession, ranging from mafic basalts to trachyte and up to 400 m thick, rests upon the Kinnesswood Formation, Lower Old Red Sandstone and Dalradian rocks, northwest of the Highland Boundary Fault (McCallien, 1927). The Kintyre succession is overlain unconformably by volcaniclastic detritus akin to the Kirkwood Formation and by Lower Limestone Formation strata and hence has been assigned to the Clyde Plateau Volcanic Formation, though it is likely that it constitutes an entirely separate lava field (see **Machrihanish Coast and South Kintyre** GCR site report). In fact it is closer to the Visean volcanic rocks at Ballycastle in Northern Ireland (Wilson and Robbie, 1966) than it is to the main outcrops of the Clyde Plateau.

East of Stirling, thin sequences of tuffs, basalts and felsic lavas close to the Ochil Fault near Dollar (Browne and Thirlwall, 1981) and in the

Cleish Hills (Geikie, 1900) are possibly contemporaneous with the Clyde Plateau Volcanic Formation, but separate from the main development. However, the formation is assumed to be continuous beneath the Central Coalfield Syncline and is present at the base of the Rashiehill Borehole, near Slamannan (Anderson, 1963). Seismic evidence suggests that it thins abruptly farther to the east, and is replaced by the thick sedimentary succession of the West Lothian oil-shale field (Hall, 1971). Around the southern rim of the oil-shale field, Francis (1991) suggested that the lowest lavas of the Clyde Plateau Volcanic Formation may be represented by thin sequences in poorly exposed ground around Carstairs and on the north-west flanks of the Pentland Hills (e.g. Corston Hill, Torweaving Hill, Cockburnhill), and that these impersistent outcrops may be contemporaneous with the volcanic rocks of Edinburgh (Mitchell and Mykura, 1962).

Highlands

In the northern Highlands, alkaline lamprophyre dykes with an approximate east–west trend (see 'Introduction' to Chapter 5) include some that have been assigned an age of *c.* 326 Ma (Baxter and Mitchell, 1984; Esang and Piper, 1984), making them contemporaneous with some of the Visean activity farther south. It is therefore possible that some of the diatremes in the northern Highlands that appear to be associated with these dykes are also of Visean age (see 'Introduction' to Chapter 4).

NORTH BERWICK COAST, EAST LOTHIAN (NT 496 858–NT 624 829)

B.G.J. Upton

Introduction

The North Berwick Coast GCR site, extending for some 17 km between Fidra and Dunbar along the coast of East Lothian, exposes a succession from sedimentary rocks of the Ballagan Formation up through the dominantly volcanic Garleton Hills Volcanic Formation to the unconformity with the overlying sedimentary Gullane Formation. The volcanic rocks form part of the East Lothian volcanic field that crops out between the extrapolation at depth of the main splay of the Southern Upland Fault and the Dunbar–Gifford Fault (Figure 2.2). This downfaulted area of Carboniferous strata lies within the Southern Uplands Terrane and is not strictly part of the Midland Valley (Max, 1976; see Chapter 1). However, the siting of the Carboniferous and Permian volcanoes, whose eroded relics form much of the scenic coastline, was almost certainly dictated by faulting related to the southern boundary of the Midland Valley. Volcanism was mainly of latest Tournaisian to early Visean age but with a probable recurrence in Permian times some 50 million years later.

In simplest terms, the Garleton Hills Volcanic Formation (520 m thick in the Garleton Hills; McAdam and Tulloch, 1985) consists of a basal sequence of bedded tuffs, tuffites and volcaniclastic sedimentary rocks (the North Berwick Member), overlain by predominantly basic lavas (the East Linton and Hailes members) which, in turn, are overlain by felsic (trachytic) tuffs and lavas (the Bangley Member) (see **Garleton Hills** GCR site report). The strata have a generalized dip towards the west so that the basic tuffs and lavas predominate in the east and the felsic products in the west. Whereas most of the basaltic tuffs were erupted through a large number of small volcanoes whose eroded relics are now seen as vents, larger volcanoes, from which the lavas and trachytic tuffs were erupted, developed at a later stage. Some 14 volcanic vents have been recognized along this coast and it may be supposed that many more lie both out to sea and inland beneath drift deposits.

Inland exposures, other than of trachytes in the Garleton Hills, are generally poor whereas the largely unspoiled and rocky coast affords excellent sections. Although some of the outcrops are above high-water mark, many lie in the intertidal zone. Four prominent islands lie off this coast and outwith the North Berwick Coast GCR site; these are, from west to east, Fidra, The Lamb, Craigleith and Bass Rock. Of these, the first three consist of alkali basalt or dolerite sills whilst the Bass Rock is made of phonolitic trachyte, probably forming a sub-cylindrical stock.

Studies of the East Lothian volcanic rocks have not made the same impact on the history of geology as those closer to Edinburgh (see **Arthur's Seat Volcano** GCR site report) or on the opposite side of the Firth of Forth (see **East Fife Coast** GCR site report). However, they are of first-order importance in presenting (1) a superb set of shallowly eroded Late Palaeozoic tuff-rings, (2) some remarkable welded ash-fall tuffs, and (3) inclusions of middle- to lower-crustal and upper-mantle material, allowing insight into the rock-types present at depth that have been sampled by rising magmas. The North Berwick Coast GCR site also includes two localities, Oxroads Bay and Weaklaw, where plant remains of international importance are preserved in the volcaniclastic rocks (Cleal and Thomas, 1995). The earliest descriptions of the volcanic rocks were in the Geological Survey sheet memoir (Howell *et al.*, 1866), but considerably more detail was given in the second edition (Clough *et al.*, 1910). The section was subsequently investigated by T.C. Day, who was responsible for the identification of many of the volcanic vents and published a series of detailed papers between 1916 and 1936. The most recent Geological Survey revision of the area led to an overall appraisal of the volcanism by Martin (1955), which synthesized the work of Day and formed the basis for the current maps and memoirs (McAdam and Tulloch, 1985; Davies *et al.*, 1986). More recent work has concentrated upon the inclusions of crustal and upper-mantle material that are common in many of the vents and intrusions (Upton *et al.*, 1976, 1984, 1999; Graham and Upton, 1978; Halliday *et al.*, 1984; Hunter *et al.*, 1984; Aspen *et al.*, 1990). The section is a popular venue for field excursions and is described in various field guides (McAdam *et al.* in Upton, 1969; McAdam in McAdam and Clarkson, 1986).

Description

Since there is a generalized younging of strata from east to west, the sites are described in this sequence (Figure 2.5).

Scoughall Rocks, at the south-east extremity of the GCR site (NT 623 829), expose the 'Pilmour Volcano', a 900 m-broad vent containing blocks of bedded pyroclastic rock, tuffite, marl and sandstone, up to 100 m across, together with several small basaltic intrusions (McAdam and Clarkson, 1986; Davies *et al.*, 1986). Between Scoughall Rocks and The Car peninsula (NT 610 850) are marls and sandstones with intercalations of fine-grained volcaniclastic sedimentary rocks and tuffites. The concentration of clasts of tuffite and lava increases and boulders of lava with big augite phenocrysts become abundant towards The Car. Igneous clasts, present in abundance along

particular horizons in the red marls outside the vents, give them the appearance of agglomerates but they were thought by Clough *et al.* (1910) to have been deposited from 'sheet-floods' of great violence. The bedded rocks are transected by two small vents known as the Scoughall and Seacliff Tower vents. The eastern part of the *Scoughall Vent* contains red unbedded tuffite, blocks of sandstone and basaltic bombs. The exposed eastern part of the *Seacliff Tower Vent* is occupied by red pyroclastic breccia. Large tuffite blocks are prominent in this vent, together with basaltic bombs and fragments of sandstone and dolostone ('cementstone').

Day (1930b) described two vents at *The Car*, which cut sandstones, tuffites and ostracode-bearing marls (Clough *et al.*, 1910). The older of the two vents forms the end of the tidal peninsula whilst the cross-cutting younger vent forms the eminence known as 'Great Car'. The older vent contains stratified tuffite and volcaniclastic breccias dipping uniformly towards the north-west at *c.* 50°. The younger vent is likewise occupied by stratified pyroclastic materials that dip inwards to the north or north-west at 30°–70°. The clasts in these vents are highly scoriaceous with conspicuous augite phenocrysts. Described by Day (1930b) as limburgitic, they were re-defined as leucite basanites by Balsillie (1936). The same rock-type also occurs as irregular masses intruding the northern vent and one of these forms the islet of St Baldred's Boat to the east of The Car. A third vent on the south-east side of the peninsula, partially exposed at very low tide, was recorded by Day (1930b).

Some 500 m south-west of The Car, further exposures of pyroclastic rocks form The Gegan (NT 603 848) and the headland at Seacliff Harbour. At the latter, red tuffites show large-scale cross-bedding. Immediately inland, on the steep coastal slopes, are two basaltic intrusions. Whereas the Primrose Bank body is an olivine-augite-phyric basaltic sill, it is unclear whether the aphyric basalt around the old quarry at Auldhame is part of a plug or a sill. The intrusion contains celestine-bearing veins.

Between The Gegan and Oxroad Bay is a down-faulted mass of mainly greenish tuffites with intercalated dolostones ('cementstones'), ripple-bedded sandstone and impure limestone that correlates with strata cropping out farther west near North Berwick. Bedding is highly disturbed by faulting, with dips of up to 60° in varying directions. The green colouration is due

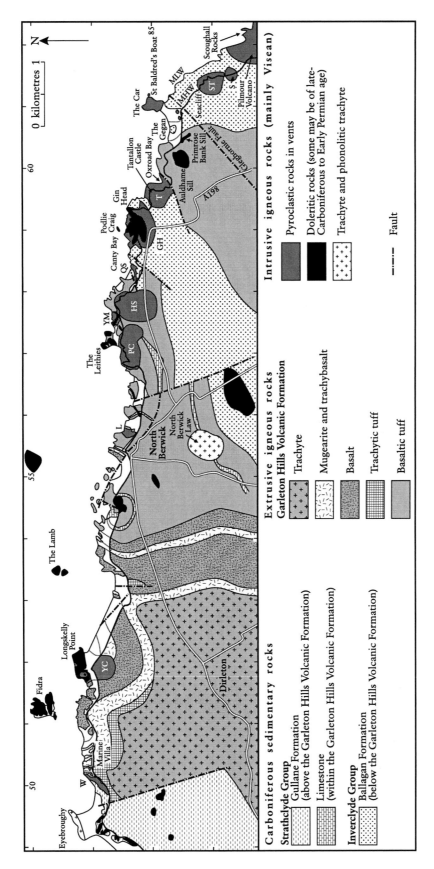

Figure 2.5 Map of the area around the North Berwick Coast GCR site. (GH = Gin Head Vent; HS = Horseshoe Vent; L = The Lecks Vent; PC = Partan Craig Vent; QS = Quarrel Sands Vent; S = Scoughall Vent; ST = Seacliff Tower Vent; T = Tantallon Vent; W = Weaklaw Vent; YC = Yellow Craig Plantation Vent; YM = Yellow Man Vent.) After McAdam (in McAdam and Clarkson, 1986); and British Geological Survey 1:50 000 sheets 33W, Haddington (1985); and 33E, Dunbar (1986).

to the presence of chlorite; more oxidized equivalents are red owing to the presence of haematite. At least some of the oxidation is believed to have been due to penecontemporaneous weathering. Several bedding planes in the reworked volcaniclastic sedimentary rocks at Oxroad Bay reveal important plant fossil assemblages indicative of a late Tournaisian to early Visean age (Bateman *et al.*, 1995). Some of these assemblages formed in lacustrine environments whereas another overlies a mass-flow deposit. An important SW-trending fault, throwing down to the south-east (the Oxroad Bay Fault), separates green tuffites from coarser pyroclastic breccias of the *Tantallon Vent*. This vent is filled with unbedded green tuffite and pyroclastic rocks containing small basanite bombs (Figure 2.6). A sandstone lens high in the cliff section may represent sedimentation within the vent during a dormant phase (McAdam and Clarkson, 1986). Beds below the volcaniclastic rocks are exposed locally as a result of faulting between Tantallon Castle and Gin Head where white sandstone is exposed.

To the west, cutting red and green tuffites, lies the *Gin Head Vent*, full of coarse pyroclastic breccia, rounded basaltic bombs, large masses of sandstone several metres across, and a fossiliferous limestone (Davies *et al.*, 1986). The pyroclastic breccia here is cut by an irregular sill of aphyric basanite that forms the Tapped Rock and Saddle Rock stacks and the Podlie Craig islet.

Farther west, green tuffites are a dominant component of the coastal outcrops for some kilometres between Canty Bay and North Berwick. They contain highly vesicular particles, originally of basaltic glass but now much chloritized. The basaltic clasts are accompanied by detrital quartz, mica and feldspar, much of the latter being microcline (Clough *et al.*, 1910). All are commonly cemented by calcite. They are intersected by numerous small reversed faults, slides and low-angled accommodation planes and have been folded into open dome and basin structures. Close to North Berwick the tuffites show various facies changes, the most important being due to the incoming of larger basaltic clasts (some over 1 m), which vary from

Figure 2.6 Tantallon Castle, on agglomerate cliffs of the Tantallon Vent, North Berwick Coast GCR site, with the phonolitic trachyte plug of the Bass Rock beyond. (Photo: British Geological Survey, No. D3665, reproduced with the permission of the Director, British Geological Survey, © NERC.)

rounded to angular. The interbedding of vocaniclastic and non-volcaniclastic sedimentary rocks is further evidence that the bedded rocks accumulated in an aqueous environment.

Some 500 m west of Canty Bay, the *Horseshoe Vent* is one of the larger vents on this coast section. It contains basanite bombs and coarse-grained, poorly bedded material. Blocks of highly scoriaceous basalt are characteristic (Day, 1928a), together with blocks of sedimentary and tuffaceous rock and fragments of wood. Intersecting the Horseshoe Vent on its north-west side is the small *Yellow Man Vent*, notable for its basanite bombs and the large size (up to 3 m) of its blocks of tuff (Day, 1925). Some layers of coarse-grained material within the vent may represent debris flows. The vent is transected by irregular basanite dykes (Figure 2.7).

Some 200 m north-west of the Horseshoe Vent lie The Leithies (NT 573 858), a group of small islets exposed at low tide that are formed by a columnar-jointed basanite sill. South of The Leithies and close to the western margin of the Horseshoe Vent is the *Partan Craig Vent* (Day,

1925), containing blocks of bedded tuffite, siltstone and dolostone together with bombs of nepheline basanite (Day and Bailey, 1928). This vent has been the most prolific source of lower- and middle-crustal xenoliths in Britain (Upton *et al.*, 1976; Graham and Upton, 1978) (see Chapter 1). A prominent debris-flow layer comprising blocks of bedded tuffite is well exposed on its west side. For approximately 1 km west of Partan Craig there are intermittent outcrops of bedded pyroclastic rocks (Figure 2.8) and intercalated sedimentary rocks, cut by the *Lecks Vent*. The Yellow Man is an irregular NE-trending dyke-like intrusion of olivine basalt that forms a rocky prominence above the beach. A wave-cut platform close by reveals a *c.* 3 m-thick sequence of dolostone with possible algal growths. This is a major stratigraphical marker within the North Berwick Member, separating green tuffites below from red tuffites above (Martin, 1955).

The overlying lavas of the East Linton Member, dipping west at *c.* 20°, are very well exposed between North Berwick harbour (NT 554 856) and the paddling pool some 100 m to the east. The lowest flow is *c.* 4 m thick and

Figure 2.7 Basanite dyke (left) cutting vent agglomerate of the Yellow Man Vent, North Berwick Coast GCR site. The cliff is about 6 m high. (Photo: British Geological Survey, No. D1113, reproduced with the permission of the Director, British Geological Survey, © NERC.)

Figure 2.8 Basaltic bombs (rounded) and blocks (angular) in red, bedded basaltic tuffs at The Lecks, North Berwick Coast GCR site. The hammer head is about 15 cm long. (Photo: British Geological Survey, No. D3044, reproduced with the permission of the Director, British Geological Survey, © NERC.)

intensively altered. It has been described as a 'kulaite', an analcime trachybasalt containing relict phenocrysts of both augite and hornblende. According to Bennett (1945), the analcime is secondary after leucite. Bennett also noted the presence of granitic xenoliths and fragments of quartz, orthoclase, microcline and oligoclase. This lava is overlain by tuffite, several metres thick, succeeded by a 7 m-thick basaltic lava containing phenocrysts of plagioclase, augite and pseudomorphed olivine as well as scarce inclusions (?autoliths) of gabbro.

The basaltic lava is directly overlain by a mugearite lava some 10 m thick with a well-preserved autobrecciated upper surface that marks the base of the Hailes Member (Figure 2.9). The vesicles (now amygdales) in this flow top have been stretched out into elongate, tubular forms, and individual lava blocks have been rotated during flow. The original surface clearly experienced minimal weathering before it was over-ridden by the next lava flow. The latter is *c.* 17 m thick and contains an abundance of plagioclase phenocrysts in association with smaller, scarcer phenocrysts of iddingsitized olivine. This flow is a hawaiite whose upper-most facies contains large (up to 20 cm) calcite-filled amygdales. This lava succession is repeated by faulting to the west at Cowton Rocks, where a porphyritic hawaiite overlain by a mugearite flow whose fissile nature and diagenetic ovoid structures, produced by concentric bands of haematite, are similar to those seen in the mugearite at North Berwick. The mugearite lava can be followed west as far as Marine Villa (NT 503 859) where the original rough and jagged flow top is perfectly preserved beneath bedded trachytic tuffs.

These lavas are cut by the *Yellow Craig Plantation Vent*, composed of poorly stratified tuffite with associated basanite intrusions, the more prominent of which form Longskelly Point (NT 522 863) and the hillock of Yellow Craig (Day, 1932c). Fidra island, lying north-west of the Yellow Craig Plantation Vent, consists of a thick, columnar-jointed basanite sill. The cobble beach on the mainland south-west of the island is largely composed of basanite pebbles, which are almost certainly derived from Fidra or its offshore extensions.

Figure 2.9 Mugearite lava at North Berwick, showing flow lamination in the main body of the flow and a slaggy, amygdaloidal flow top. The hammer shaft is about 35 cm long. (Photo: British Geological Survey, No. D3041, reproduced with the permission of the Director, British Geological Survey, © NERC.)

Bedded trachyte tuffs (*c.* 10–15 m thick) at the base of the Bangley Member crop out from Marine Villa westwards. Their original compositions have been largely obscured by later carbonation and oxidation to haematite. Mugearitic and trachytic clasts in these tuffs are mainly angular but some layers are rich in lenticular particles flattened parallel to the bedding. These lenticles were probably lapilli of very fluid pumice that were deformed beneath accumulating tuff layers above, i.e. they are welded ash-fall tuffs.

The *Weaklaw Vent*, which cuts the bedded trachytic tuffs, contains poorly bedded sandy tuffaceous breccia. Basaltic rocks in the vent have been intensely carbonated. Plant fossils are particularly well preserved (Bateman *et al.*, 1995) and Gordon (1935) considered that the plants grew on the flanks of an active volcano and were killed by ash flows. Immediately west of the vent a 5 m-thick flow of vesicular porphyritic trachyte overlies the bedded trachytic tuffs and is itself overlain by sedimentary rocks that mark the start of a prolonged period of magmatic inactivity.

Apart from shallowly derived fragments of volcanic and sedimentary rock, xenoliths representing rock-types present at deep levels in the crust and upper mantle are common within the East Lothian basanites. Xenoliths of granulite-facies quartzo-feldspathic gneisses occur in intrusions at Quarrel Sands, Canty Bay and Weaklaw but are most abundant in the coarse pyroclastic strata on the foreshore west of Partan Craig. Some of the xenoliths contain garnet, kyanite and rutile. The microcline recorded in the bedded tuffites (Clough *et al.*, 1910) probably came from disaggregation of these gneisses. Xenoliths of other, more basic granulite-facies gneisses, comprising plagioclase together with one or two types of pyroxene and subordinate magnetite, are also present, especially in the Fidra basanite.

Peridotite inclusions occur at Weaklaw and Fidra (Figure 1.8, Chapter 1). Those in the Weaklaw Vent are foliated, highly altered and up to 15 cm in diameter. Spinel is the only primary constituent in these that has not been altered by low-temperature processes. In contrast, the Fidra basanite contains abundant xenoliths of fresh spinel lherzolite, commonly foliated and with orthopyroxene porphyroclasts. Xenoliths of wehrlite grading to clinopyroxenite are also common here. The Fidra basanite is also remarkable for its content of large (up to 3 cm) discrete anhedral crystals (megacrysts), principally of anorthoclase but also of sanidine and magnetite. Rare xenoliths of related apatite-magnetite rock also occur. Peridotite xenoliths have not been found along the coast east of Fidra but xenoliths of biotite-rich ultramafic rock are known from Partan Craig and Beggar's Cap.

Interpretation

The chief distinction between the mapped vents and the surrounding tuffites and volcaniclastic sedimentary rocks is that the latter represent widely distributed (distal facies) fragmental material on and around the volcanic cones, which were subject to water-sorting and admixture with fluviatile detritus, whereas the vent material represents the generally coarser and more chaotic (proximal facies) material collecting as fall-out and talus on the steeper inward-facing slopes. Listric faulting and mass-flow (lahar) processes would have contributed to the complexity. The extreme alteration (dolomitization) of the pyroclastic rocks at Weaklaw may have resulted from extended exhalation of carbonated fluids from the post-eruptive vent.

In Early Carboniferous time the region lay within equatorial latitudes, with the evidence indicating a low-relief lagoonal landscape lying little above sea level, and supplied by fine clastic sediment from slow-flowing rivers. The vents probably represent shallowly dissected tuff-rings created by phreatomagmatic activity where rising magmas encountered wet sediment or standing water. The diameter of these tuff-rings, which would have been little wider than the vents, rarely exceeded 1 km and was commonly significantly less. Eruptions would have been short-lived and violent, yielding pyroclastic products composed mainly of broken fragments of near-surface rocks together with juvenile tephra, including at times lava bombs of substantial size. The identification of lacustrine sediment within some vents suggests the probability that lakes ('maars') formed within the craters. The presence of plant fossils

suggests that the emergent slopes were colonized by ferns, equisitales and club-mosses, fragments of which are common in the tuffites and which are well preserved in places, such as at Oxroad Bay and Weaklaw. Dolostone lenses (free of organic remains) within the green tuffs have been regarded as evaporites produced under more arid conditions. Martin (1955) divided the vents into a younger Green Group and an older Red Group, showing that the Red Group vents were active before the eruption of the lavas whereas those of the Green Group cut higher strata and contain fragments of the hawaiite and mugearite lavas. The Quarrel Sands Vent is representative of the older Red Group whereas the Yellow Craig Plantation, Partan Craig, Yellow Man and Horseshoe vents are among the younger Green Group.

The early magmas, represented by tuff fragments and 'bombs', all appear to have been strongly silica-undersaturated basaltic varieties. The compositions of many were primitive, with olivine as the sole phenocryst species. Ascent rates of these magmas were frequently high and uninterrupted, as is evidenced by the common occurrence of ultramafic xenoliths of probable mantle origin. However, some of the magmas contained both olivine and augite phenocrysts, as large and conspicuous crystals, indicative of stagnation and slower cooling (probably at deep crustal levels) during their ascent. It may be significant that the lowest lava in the succession, the analcime trachybasalt at North Berwick, is also silica-undersaturated. This, and a similar lava at the base of the lava succession farther south, are almost unique in the Dinantian lava successions of the Midland Valley in being relatively evolved silica-undersaturated rocks. They may be related to the nearby phonolitic intrusions of North Berwick Law, the Bass Rock and Traprain Law (for discussion, see **Traprain Law** GCR site report).

The overlying lavas at North Berwick and west to Marine Villa signify a situation different from that which produced the foregoing phreatomagmatic materials. They indicate larger volume eruptions under subaerial conditions and their less silica-undersaturated compositions point to greater degrees of melting at shallower mantle depths. The compositional variation (olivine basalt, hawaiite, mugearite and subsequent trachytes) implies extended crystal fractionation in magma chambers, probably in the deep crust. Since the greatest thickness of volcanic rocks in East Lothian is around Haddington (McAdam and Tulloch, 1985), it was probably in this area, some 20 km distant, that the principal volcanoes were sited. The thick trachyte lavas of the **Garleton Hills** (see GCR site report) may well be caldera-filling flows, and the thick trachytic tuff sequence at Marine Villa and Weaklaw could well signify a major pyroclastic eruption from a high-level magma chamber prior to caldera collapse. The disconformity above the trachytes heralded long-term volcanic quiescence in the region.

Basanite sills such as those at The Leithies and Fidra mark a later rejuvenation of activity. At Brigs of Fidra a small basanite sheet, believed to be correlative with that on Fidra Island, cuts hawaiite lava and may be assumed to post-date the trachyte episode. A recent K-Ar date on the Fidra basanite gave its age as 264 ± 10 Ma (Downes *et al.*, 2001). Other recent K-Ar dates include a dyke in the Gin Head Vent at 267 ± 5 Ma and the Yellow Man Dyke at 293 ± 7 Ma (Wallis, 1989). These all suggest early to mid-Permian ages. The younger 'Green Group' of vents (Martin, 1955) may also post-date the early phase of volcanism. These younger magmas may have been produced by depressurization melting of garnet lherzolite mantle sources in response to Variscan earth movements.

The xenoliths and megacrysts provide information concerning the rocks beneath the cover of sedimentary and volcanic rocks. Together with suites of inclusions from elsewhere in Scotland, they enable a detailed interpretation to be made of the composition, structure and history of the lower crust and upper mantle, which probably has not changed significantly from Late Palaeozoic times to the present day. A full account of this interpretation is given in Chapter 1.

Much work remains to be done and the physical volcanology of the shallowly dissected vents in particular awaits a modern study. Although many of the igneous rocks have been seriously affected by low-temperature alteration, they nonetheless offer wide scope for further petrological investigation. Additionally, many of the rocks, in particular the fresher basanites, could now be more satisfactorily dated by Ar-Ar techniques. Deep crustal xenoliths containing zircon invite more precise dating using the U-Pb method. Lastly, the petrology of the xenoliths within the volcanic rocks is being actively studied to learn more of the nature of the rocks at depth below this critical area, close to the junction of the Midland Valley and Southern Upland terranes.

Conclusions

The North Berwick Coast GCR site, covering the coast to the east and west of North Berwick is representative of the Visean Garleton Hills Volcanic Formation, but shows particularly the fragmental and intrusive products of numerous small basaltic volcanoes that characterize the earliest local volcanic activity, before the eruption of lavas and tuffs from larger volcanoes sited in the region of the **Garleton Hills** GCR site. Radiometric dates on later intrusions suggest that small-scale magmatism resumed in the Early Permian, possibly more than 50 million years later.

The rocks at this site provide an insight into an ancient tropical environment of sluggish rivers, lakes and lagoons subjected to short-lived, violent eruptions from small volcanoes that stood above an otherwise flat landscape. The wide variety of early land-plants that flourished on this landscape confers international palaeobotanical importance to the site.

The dissected volcanoes can be interpreted as small 'tuff-rings' of fragmental ejecta, formed as a result of the highly explosive interaction of magma with surface water, with groundwater and with water-saturated sediments. As such they complement the similar, but later volcanoes of the **East Fife Coast** GCR site and are possibly some of the best-preserved examples in Britain. As the chances of survival of such fragile structures are rare in the older geological record, there is potential for further study that could increase their international importance.

The intrusions and volcanic rocks of this section are renowned for the abundance and wide variety of exotic rock fragments that have been brought up from great depths by the magmas. These constitute a unique method of sampling the deeper levels of the Earth's crust and provide information of international value on the nature of the lower crust and the underlying upper mantle.

GARLETON HILLS, EAST LOTHIAN (NT 449 764–NT 520 763)

I.T. Williamson

Introduction

The upper part of the Garleton Hills Volcanic Formation in East Lothian, represented by the Garleton Hills GCR site, is the erosional remnant of a lava field, built up of evolved trachytic flows and associated pyroclastic rocks (Figure 2.10). The lower part of the formation, dominated by basaltic rocks, is represented by the **North Berwick Coast** GCR site.

Early Carboniferous volcanism in the Midland Valley of Scotland was dominated by the construction of basaltic and hawaiitic lava fields. However, mugearite, benmoreite and trachyte flows interbedded with the more basic rock-types also feature in many areas (see for example **Machrihanish Coast and South Kintyre**, **Campsie Fells**, and **Touch, Fintry and Gargunnock Hills** GCR site reports). Discrete trachyte-rhyolite centres were also formed in some areas, most notably the Misty Law Trachytic Centre in the Renfrewshire Hills (Johnstone, 1965; Paterson *et al.*, 1990). Studies of these more evolved members of the suite, such as those exposed in the Garleton Hills GCR site, are therefore important in modelling magma genesis and volcanic processes on a province-wide scale.

The Garleton Hills Volcanic Formation is the basal unit of the Visean Strathclyde Group; it is conformable with both the underlying Ballagan Formation (Inverclyde Group) and the overlying Gullane Formation. The underlying and over-lying sedimentary rocks have yielded good biostratigraphical evidence of age. In the Spilmersford borehole (NT 4570 6902), situated 7.25 km south-west of the Garleton Hills, sedimentary rocks from beneath the volcanic rocks have yielded (early Visean) PU zone miospores

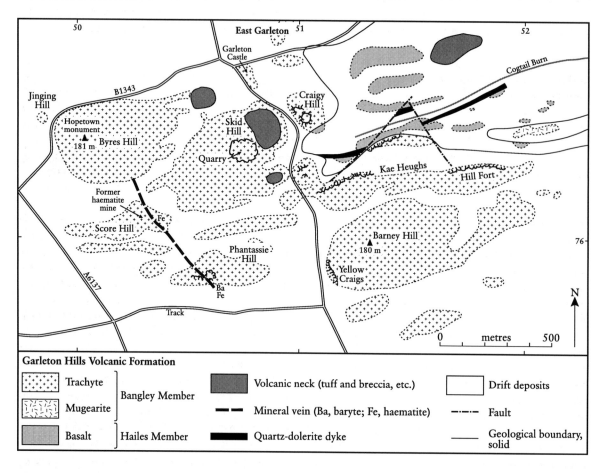

Figure 2.10 Map of the area around the Garleton Hills GCR site. Based on Geological Survey 1:10 560 mapping by M.F. Howells (1961) and A.D. McAdam (1964).

(Davies, 1974). However, Scott (1990) and Bateman and Scott (1990) reported late-Tournaisian (Courceyan–CM zone) plant assemblages from volcaniclastic rocks within the North Berwick Member at the base of the Garleton Hills Volcanic Formation. Sedimentary rocks above the volcanic succession have yielded Asbian–TC zone miospores (Neves *et al.*, 1973) and hence the volcanism can be fairly confidently assigned to early Dinantian time. Radiometric ages obtained by K-Ar whole-rock determinations from lavas at Skid Hill (349 ± 7 Ma) and Phantassie Hill (342 ± 5 Ma) are compatible with an early Dinantian age (De Souza, 1974). However these dates recalculate to *c*. 355 Ma and 348 Ma using new constants, suggesting an early Tournaisian age which is incompatible with the biostratigraphical evidence. A more precise Ar-Ar date of 342.1 ± 1.3 Ma on sanidine separated from a trachyte at Phantassie Hill is, however, compatible with the biostratigraphy (A.A. Monaghan and M.S. Pringle, pers. comm., 2002).

Early descriptions of these rocks are by Howell *et al.* (1866), Geikie (1880, 1897), Hatch (1892) and Clough *et al.* (1910). The geology of the area has been described more recently by McAdam and Tulloch (1985); accounts of the successions in the Spilmersford and East Linton boreholes are by Davies (1974) and Davies *et al.* (1986). Petrographical aspects of the rocks were described by McAdam (1974). Localities within the GCR site are used frequently for educational purposes and are included in excursion guides for the district (McAdam *et al.* in Upton, 1969; Upton and Macdonald in McAdam and Clarkson, 1986).

Description

The Garleton Hills form an area of low hills and escarpments up to 180 m above sea level, about 2.5 km north of Haddington, and in the south-west part of the outcrop of the Garleton Hills Volcanic Formation. The geomorphology is controlled strongly by the effects of both the strike of the rocks and glacial erosion (Figure 2.11). Former glacial drainage channels are a feature of the site with inferred water flow from west to east, parallel to the direction of ice movement.

Figure 2.11 Trap featuring in trachyte lavas, dipping to the right (south), modified by ice action and glacial drainage, at Kae Heughs, Garleton Hills. (Photo: British Geological Survey, No. D3262, reproduced with the permission of the Director, British Geological Survey, © NERC.)

The stratigraphy of the Garleton Hills Volcanic Formation is shown below.

Thickness (m)

Bangley Member
Trachyte, quartz-trachyte and augite-phyric
   quartz-bearing trachyandesite (formerly
   'quartz-banakite') lavas, trachytic tuffs   0–160
Hailes Member
Feldspar-phyric basalts ('Markle' type) and
   mugearites   25–70
East Linton Member
Mostly plagioclase-olivine-clinopyroxene-
   phyric basalts ('Dunsapie' type) and olivine-
   clinopyroxene-phyric basalts ('Craiglockhart'
   type), mugearites and analcime-bearing
   hornblende-phyric trachybasalts (formerly
   'kulaites')   10–90
North Berwick Member
Red basaltic tuffs and agglomerates, green basaltic
   tuffs and agglomerates, beds of freshwater
   limestone and dolostone   50–150

The Garleton Hills Volcanic Formation is divided into four laterally persistent members (see above). The Garleton Hills GCR site is situated mainly within the outcrop of the Bangley Member, but some of the upper units of the Hailes Member are also present. A few volcanic necks and minor basic intrusions cut the lava sequence. The thickness of individual lavas is difficult to assess because interflow junctions are not easily identified and any interbedded volcaniclastic rocks are not exposed. In addition, most of the flows have much the same characteristics, making correlation problematical even within this relatively small area. However, many of these lavas are probably more than 20 m thick (Upton, 1982). It is not known if, as seems quite likely, some of the units are shallow intrusions into the lava pile.

The oldest lavas within the area crop out in the relatively poorly exposed ground to the north-east of Kae Heughs (Figure 2.10). Scattered exposures there are of plagioclase ± olivine-phyric basalt belonging to the Hailes Member. Near the top of this unit is a thin unit of mugearite. The basalts are intruded by an ENE-trending quartz-dolerite dyke, interpreted by McAdam and Tulloch (1985) as part of the regionally persistent Prestonpans–Seton Dyke of the Stephanian Midland Valley tholeiitic swarm (see Chapter 6). The dyke is cut by later NW- and NE-trending faults (Figure 2.10).

At Craigy Hill (NT 511 765) the lowest trachyte lava of the Bangley Member seen in the GCR site rests directly upon a basaltic flow of the

Hailes Member. Successive trachyte lavas are well exposed on the elongate ridges, which display well-developed stepped or 'trap' features on their northern faces. A particularly fine example of this is exhibited by Kae Heughs (NT 512 762) (Figure 2.11), an E–W-trending ridge composed of two trachyte lavas that are less porphyritic than those higher in the sequence.

The disused quarry cut into the southern flank of Skid Hill (NT 508 763) appears to have been excavated through a single, 20 m-thick lava of massive, but well-jointed, quartz-trachyte. This unit is plagioclase-alkali feldspar-augite-apatite-phyric. A trachyte lava above that at Skid Hill forms Byres Hill (NT 500 764) (180.7 m) and has probably been used in the construction of the Hopetoun Monument, a prominent landmark on the summit. The escarpment at Phantassie Hill (NT 507 758) is composed of at least one thick flow of plagioclase-alkali feldspar-clinopyroxene-apatite-phyric trachyte. Internal structures include patchily developed vesicular facies and zones of alteration and reddening. Yellow Craigs (NT 5115 7585) and Barney Hill (NT 514 760) (179.8 m) expose similar rocks. All of these lavas have developed prominent dip-slopes to the south. Further trachytic lavas and a unit of trachytic tuff in the upper part of the formation crop out to the west of the GCR site. The highest lava is exposed in Bangley Quarry (NT 487 752), which is a GCR site in the Mineralogy of Scotland GCR Block. There, a lava of quartz-trachyte (formerly 'quartz-banakite') is cut by a dyke of trachybasalt that contains phenocrysts or xenocrysts of clear sanidine up to 5 cm long (Day, 1930e).

Near Skid Hill, three small areas (NT 5055 7660, NT 5080 7645, NT 5085 7625), up to 100 m by 200 m, of pyroclastic breccia and tuff, may represent volcanic necks cutting the trachytic lavas.

The volcanic rocks are extracted for road metal and were formerly used for building stone. Haematite and baryte veins that cut the lavas were once exploited commercially and traces of the old haematite workings can be seen north-west of Phantassie Hill, where working ceased in 1876 (Macgregor *et al.*, 1920; McAdam and Tulloch, 1985).

Published analyses of rocks from the Garleton Hills Volcanic Formation in general and their associated intrusions are few, the most recent, including stable isotope data, being those of

Smedley (1986a,b, 1988a). Analyses of trachytic rocks are included only by Livingstone and McKissock (1974), Macdonald (1975) and Smedley (1986a).

Interpretation

Max (1976) and Floyd (1994) have both noted that the Garleton Hills lava field lies over the sub-surface extension of the main Southern Upland Fault, and Upton (1982) suggested that this zone of weakness may have acted as a focus for the development of magma chambers large enough to evolve felsic magmas. Magmas of trachytic composition are considerably more viscous and volatile-rich than those of basaltic and hawaiitic composition. Consequently, the trachytes of the Garleton Hills GCR site are likely to have been erupted as viscous lavas of limited aerial extent, and some may have been emplaced as lava domes. Such eruptions are commonly associated with pyroclastic ash-flow and ash-fall deposits. Thin units of bedded tuff and welded tuff, and also some of volcaniclastic sedimentary rocks are present in the Garleton Hills Volcanic Formation, though none are seen in the Garleton Hills GCR site. The presence of the sedimentary rocks shows that volcanic activity was intermittent, and that during the quiescent intervals plant and animal communities were established (Bateman and Scott, 1990; Scott, 1990). Upton (1994) has suggested that the Holocene cinder cones and domes in the Massif Central of France are good analogues of both the basaltic and the trachytic volcanism in the Garleton Hills Volcanic Formation (see also **North Berwick Coast** GCR site report).

Most geochemical studies of Dinantian volcanic rocks of the Midland Valley of Scotland have concentrated upon the basaltic to hawaiitic members (Macdonald, 1975; Macdonald *et al.*, 1977; MacDonald and Whyte, 1981; Smedley, 1986a). This reflects not only their dominance in almost all sequences across the Carboniferous–Permian Igneous Province of northern Britain, but also that the more basic types are of most use in determining the composition and melting characteristics of the underlying mantle. However, understanding the evolution of the more evolved rocks from these suites, such as those seen in the Garleton Hills GCR site, is critical to our understanding of magmatic processes in the upper crust.

The Garleton Hills trachytes, like other more evolved Dinantian lavas of the Midland Valley, are regarded as the intermediate differentiation products of mildly alkaline and transitional olivine basalt magmas that underwent fractional crystallization in relatively high-level magma chambers (e.g. Macdonald, 1975; MacDonald and Whyte, 1981; Smedley, 1986a). Crustal contamination does not appear to have had a major influence, even in the evolved rocks (Smedley, 1986a). Intrusive rocks of even more evolved composition are represented nearby as the phonolitic trachytes of the Bass Rock and North Berwick Law, and the phonolite of Traprain Law. However, these highly evolved rocks are silica-undersaturated, in contrast to the silica-oversaturated trachytes and quartz trachytes of the extrusive sequence. They have been correlated traditionally with the trachytic rocks of the Garleton Hills, but their only likely extrusive associates are the flows of analcime-bearing hornblende trachybasalt that occur locally at the base of the lava sequence. The significance of this possible association is discussed in the **Traprain Law** GCR site report.

Conclusions

The volcanic rocks exposed in the Garleton Hills GCR site comprise the upper part of the Visean Garleton Hills Volcanic Formation, a sequence of trachyte lavas and minor pyroclastic beds overlying the mainly basaltic volcanic rocks that comprise the lower parts of the formation (see **North Berwick Coast** GCR site report). Though trachytic lavas are known from other Dinantian lava fields of the Midland Valley of Scotland, the Garleton Hills GCR site has been selected to represent this important group of geochemically evolved rocks and their style of volcanism. Individual trachyte lavas are probably more than 20 m thick, and were probably erupted as highly viscous flows or even as steep-sided domes. The extrusive rocks are cut by the remains of a few small volcanic necks that represent the feeders to the volcanoes.

The trachytes probably represent the magma that remained in magma chambers at relatively high crustal levels after the eruption, or crystallization at depth, of basalts (the process known as 'crystal fractionation'). Their abundance in East Lothian suggests that magma chambers of considerable volume were present beneath the lava field for considerable time in order to generate magmas of this composition. Such magma chambers may have been located along the projected continuation at depth of the Southern Upland Fault.

TRAPRAIN LAW, EAST LOTHIAN (NT 582 747)

I.T. Williamson and D. Millward

Introduction

The prominent rocky hill of Traprain Law in East Lothian is composed of phonolite, a rare, evolved, silica-undersaturated igneous rock. The phonolite forms a high-level intrusion, emplaced within the Ballagan Formation of the Inverclyde Group, and forming a marked structural dome beneath the Garleton Hills Volcanic Formation (Strathclyde Group; see **Garleton Hills** GCR site report) (Figure 2.12). The phonolite is believed to be associated with the development of the Garleton Hills Volcanic Formation and therefore of Dinantian age. A K-Ar whole-rock determination of 322 ± 3 Ma (*c.* 328 Ma using new constants) (De Souza, 1974) and a Rb-Sr isochron date of 342 ± 4 Ma (De Souza, 1979) appear to support this. The well-

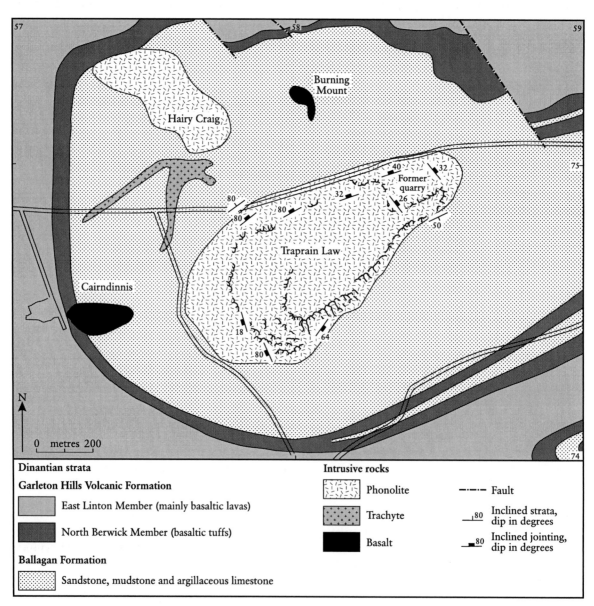

Figure 2.12 Map of the area around the Traprain Law GCR site. Based on Geological Survey 1:10 560 mapping by M.F. Howells (1963–1964) and A.D. McAdam (1964–1967 and 1974–1976).

documented dome-like outcrop is considered to be a particularly fine example of a laccolith, and is one of only a handful of examples of this form of intrusion in the British Isles. Although there are several phonolitic intrusions in East Lothian, rocks of this composition are extremely rare elsewhere in the Carboniferous–Permian Igneous Province of northern Britain and hence the Traprain Law mass provides an additional insight into the magmatic processes involved.

The Traprain Law intrusion was described first by Howell *et al.* (1866) as 'clinkstone', an archaic term for phonolite. Further descriptions are by Geikie (1897) and Bailey (in Clough *et al.*, 1910). Details of the petrography and chemical composition were presented by MacGregor and Ennos (1922), but the most recent descriptions of the intrusion, including details of its structure, petrography and age, are by McAdam and Tulloch (1985). British occurrences of this igneous rock-type are few, and petrographical descriptions of the Traprain Law example are featured in textbooks of igneous petrology such as Hatch's *An Introduction to the Study of Petrology* (1891), Harker's *Petrology for Students* (1895) and Sutherland's *Igneous Rocks of the British Isles* (1982). The considerable educational value of this GCR site is demon-

strated by its prominence in field guides to this part of Scotland (McAdam *et al.* in Upton, 1969; Upton and Macdonald in McAdam and Clarkson, 1986). The following description is based on these accounts.

Description

Traprain Law (221 m) rises abruptly from the fertile, undulating farmlands of East Lothian to dominate the surrounding countryside, about 3 km south-west of East Linton (Figure 2.13). The hill has a pear-shaped plan that is partially the result of glacial erosion, and measures about 1 km along its long axis. Its present-day, dome-like outline closely mirrors the original three-dimensional shape of the upper surface of the intrusion. The steeper slopes of the hill are craggy and are covered locally by talus cones. The crags on the south side are a popular rock-climbing venue. The surrounding terrain is formed by rocks of the Ballagan and Garleton Hills Volcanic formations, and a series of escarpments blanketed by till are present. In addition to abundant, glacially sculpted, weathered exposures scattered across the hill, the rock is well exposed in the former roadstone quarry at the north-east end of the hill (NT 5835 7495).

Figure 2.13 Traprain Law from the south-east. The shape of the hill probably reflects the laccolithic form of the phonolite intrusion. (Photo: P. MacDonald.)

Most of the sedimentary rocks covering the phonolite mass have been removed by erosion but, locally, exposures of bedded mudstone, calcareous sandstone and argillaceous limestone are tilted at up to 80° away from the hill (Figure 2.12). On the south-eastern side of the hill, sedimentary rocks are exposed well up the hillside and are steeply inclined at angles of about 50°. These demonstrate that strata are domed over the intrusion.

The phonolite mass is heterogeneous and shows considerable variation in texture and colour. The outer, glaciated surfaces of the intrusion exposed on the higher parts of the hill, most especially towards the summit, are variably vesicular, and there is an apparent increase in grain size towards the centre of the mass. Colour varies from pale pink and speckled through to darker grey, a feature that is exemplified by flow banding. This is clearly seen in the former quarry where the contact between dark and light rock is generally sharp and complex patterns are displayed. Towards the edge of the intrusion, the banding is more marked and is commonly sharply convoluted. Colour mottling is also noted. Bailey (in Clough *et al.*, 1910) and Tomkeieff (1952) both regarded the variations in colour as due to alteration of the feldspars, and Upton and Macdonald (in McAdam and Clarkson, 1986) attributed this to slight hydrothermal effects.

Jointing is prominent throughout the intrusion. In the former roadstone quarry a set of curvi-linear joints is orientated approximately parallel to the surface outline of the hill. These impart a coarse platy appearance to much of the exposure. The joints become more closely spaced towards the outer parts of the intrusion and are generally sub-parallel to, but locally cut, the flow banding. On the flanks of the hill, platy jointing is more-or-less conformable with bedding in the country rock and dips outwards at moderately high angles (Figure 2.12).

Baked xenoliths of sandstone and fissile mudstone are quite common, and several large masses, up to almost 3 m across, were noted in the quarry by Day (1930d, 1932b). Xenoliths of basic volcanic rock are small and less common (Bennett, 1945; Tomkeieff, 1952).

The rock of Traprain Law was described as a 'sodalite-bearing phonolitic analcime-trachyte'

in *Petrology of Igneous Rocks* (Hatch *et al.*, 1961) and as a 'phonolitic trachyte' by Upton in Sabine and Sutherland (1982). However, the former work noted the presence in the rock of about 20% analcime, 4% nepheline and a few crystals of sodalite, which along with the abundant alkali feldspar, indicate that it should be classified as an analcime phonolite after the scheme of Le Maitre (2002). Some parts of the mass are aphyric but others are sparsely porphyritic, containing phenocrysts, up to 5 mm long, of oligoclase and sanidine-cryptoperthite. Also present are opaque oxide pseudomorphs, up to 4 mm long, after amphibole and scattered crystals of augitic pyroxene. The pilotaxitic-textured groundmass is composed of abundant twinned sanidine laths, magnetite, anhedral aegirine-augite, fayalite, which poikilitically encloses alkali feldspar crystals, apatite and the feldspathoids mentioned above. The feldspathoids are wholly interstitial. Alteration of the phonolite is extremely patchy on a millimetre scale, with abrupt gradation from areas in which the alkali feldspar is intensely sericitized to other areas in which it is unaltered. Analyses have been published by MacGregor and Ennos (1922) and Day (1930c).

A number of unusual minerals have been collected from veins, druses and vugs in the phonolite. The most common species found include calcite and alkali feldspar, but Upton and Macdonald (in McAdam and Clarkson, 1986) list analcime, anhydrite, apophyllite, datolite, natrolite, pectolite, prehnite, selenite and stilpnomelane. Batty and Moss (1962) recorded powellite ($CaMoO_4$).

In the same general vicinity as the laccolith, there are a few other intrusions (Figure 2.12). A sheet-like body of phonolite is seen at Hairy Craig (NT 577 751) and small plugs of olivine-dolerite are noted at Cairndinnis (NT 573 745) and Gold Knowe (NT 580 752), all within about one kilometre of Traprain Law.

Interpretation

Early mapping of the area by H.H. Howell of the Geological Survey showed that strata adjacent to the Traprain Law phonolite are steeply inclined away from the hill (Howell *et al.*, 1866), a feature that has been regarded since as being associated with emplacement of the mass (see also Geikie, 1897, fig. 132). The domed outline of the intrusion, together with its contact relationships with the sedimentary rocks, and the arrangement of the flow-banding and jointing, suggested to Bailey (in Clough *et al.*, 1910) that emplacement as a laccolith was likely. This view was re-iterated by McAdam and Tulloch (1985). However, neither Bailey nor McAdam and Tulloch were entirely certain about the interpretation because lower contacts of the mass are not exposed. Nevertheless, there are several pieces of evidence to suggest the possibility of a concordant lower contact supporting the laccolith model. First, Clough *et al.* (1910) recorded vertical columnar jointing at one location on the deeply eroded western side of the mass. From this they inferred an approximately horizontal floor to the phonolite 'at no great distance below the surface'. The second clue is from a temporary excavation made at the entrance to the quarry in 1955 (examined by C.J.S. Stillman and cited by McAdam *et al.* in Upton, 1969). This exposed 12 m of bedded sedimentary rocks, with phonolite both above and below. The contacts were seen to be almost concordant and the bedding was inclined in a similar direction to that of sandstones in the adjacent fields, though at a shallower angle. Stillman concluded that the evidence present in the trench supported the long-held view that the Traprain Law mass has a laccolithic form. The complex patterns exhibited by the flow-banding at the north-eastern end of the outcrop suggest magmatic convection, and McAdam and Tulloch (1985) suggested that a feeder pipe to the laccolith may have been located in this area.

Further evidence for the three-dimensional form of the intrusion comes from ground magnetic profiles run by the Institute of Geological Sciences in 1965, which suggest very steep-sided contacts to the intrusion on the north-west and south-east sides of the hill. A pronounced, elongate aeromagnetic anomaly extends south-westwards from the phonolite outcrop at least as far as Whitelaw Farm (NT 567 720) and this too is compatible with a steep-sided igneous body with high magnetic susceptibility located at a shallow depth. The phonolite has the required susceptibility value to produce the observed anomaly, which is thus probably caused by a buried extension of the

exposed intrusion (McAdam and Tulloch, 1985). Whether or not the elongated shape of the intrusion in some way reflects a buried fissure, crudely parallel to deep-seated basement structures such as the Southern Upland Fault, is debatable. However, Upton (1982) has pointed out that the rocks of the Garleton Hills Volcanic Formation lie over the sub-surface extension of the main Southern Upland Fault.

Though the emplacement age of the Traprain Law laccolith, and a large number of other intrusions in East Lothian, cannot be fixed with certainty at present, their geographical association with the Garleton Hills Volcanic Formation suggests that many of them may be sub-volcanic components of this Visean volcanic field. The vesicular nature of the upper surfaces of the laccolith suggests emplacement at a high crustal level and it is possible that this, and other intrusions, may have acted as feeders to the lavas and pyroclastic rocks.

However, highly evolved silica-undersaturated rocks such as the Traprain Law and Hairy Craig phonolites and the nearby intrusive phonolitic trachytes of North Berwick Law and the Bass Rock are not represented within the Garleton Hills Volcanic Formation. Indeed, evolved silica-undersaturated rocks are virtually absent (there is one flow in the Campsie Fells) from all Dinantian volcanic successions of the Midland Valley, which evolve typically along a differentiation trend from alkaline or transitional olivine basalt to silica-oversaturated quartz-trachyte and exceptionally rhyolite. The Garleton Hills succession is unusual however, in that single flows of silica-undersaturated analcime-bearing hornblende trachybasalt (formerly 'kulaite') occur locally at the base of the earliest lava member, including one at Blaikie Heugh, only 2 km from Traprain Law. There are also xenoliths of analcime-hornblende trachybasalt in the Traprain Law phonolite, which both Bennett (1945) and Tomkeieff (1952) regarded as co-genetic with the nearby flow. Therefore, it is possible that the earliest magma chambers to form beneath the East Lothian area did evolve along silica-undersaturated lines, and that the phonolitic intrusions may represent their most extreme products. Almost all of the extrusive rocks erupted during this phase may have been removed by erosion, and the subsequent magmatism evolved entirely along a silica-oversaturated trend as seen in the preserved lava succession. The Traprain Law phonolite is thus potentially of great importance in showing that evolved silica-undersaturated rocks can be associated with a Dinantian basalt–quartz-trachyte series. It is one of only a handful of such examples within the Midland Valley of Scotland.

Conclusions

The Traprain Law intrusion is of national importance both for the form of the intrusion, a laccolith, and for its rock-type, a phonolite, which is rare in Britain. It is representative of a small group of intrusions in East Lothian of silica-undersaturated felsic igneous rocks, apparently associated with the Visean Garleton Hills Volcanic Formation. Other members of the group include the phonolitic trachyte intrusions of North Berwick Law and the Bass Rock. Rocks of these highly evolved compositions are not represented within the Visean extrusive rocks of East Lothian, which range in composition from basalt to quartz-trachyte (i.e. they are mostly silica-oversaturated). The presence of rare phonolitic rocks therefore adds considerable information to the understanding of the origin and evolution of Dinantian volcanic rocks in the Midland Valley of Scotland.

The shape of the upper surface of the intrusion is approximated by the craggy rounded outline of Traprain Law. Locally, around the lower slopes of the hill sedimentary rocks dip steeply away from the hill, indicating that these strata were arched up over the intrusion. The dome-shaped upper surface is mirrored within the intrusion by a characteristic set of curved joints, particularly in the outer part of the mass. The vesicular outer part, formed by gases and vapours escaping from the magma, indicates emplacement at shallow depth. Though the basal contact of the intrusion is not exposed, there are indications that it may be concordant with the sedimentary host rocks. Thus, the inferred form of the intrusion (a domed upper surface and a flat base) is that of a laccolith. Few laccoliths are described from Britain, and Traprain Law is featured in many geological textbooks as a typical example.

ARTHUR'S SEAT VOLCANO, CITY OF EDINBURGH (NT 266 733– NT 283 731, NT 262 742 and NT 251 735)

B.G.J. Upton

Introduction

Within Edinburgh, outcrops of Dinantian volcanic rocks occur at Craiglockhart Hill, Castle Rock, Calton Hill and Holyrood Park. Because each of these forms a high topographical feature, they have had a profound influence on the development of the city from at least Iron Age times to the present day. Edinburgh Castle and the Castle Rock on which it stands are world-famous. Calton Hill lying just north of the eastern continuation of Princes Street has provided sites for, among other things, the old astronomical observatory, Nelson's Monument, the Royal High School and St Andrew's House. Holyrood Palace is sited on a low-lying outcrop of lavas south-east of Calton Hill. The largest of these outcrops, however, is that mainly embraced by Holyrood Park to the south-east of the city centre and containing Edinburgh's highest prominence, Arthur's Seat. As with Castle Rock, the high ground within the park provided sites for human habitation some 6000 years ago.

The above-mentioned localities have major geological, as well as historical and cultural, importance. Castle Rock is the surface expression of a sub-cylindrical stock of basalt, almost certainly representing the infilled conduit of a surface volcano. The Calton Hill and Holyrood outcrops comprise lavas and tuff layers with numerous intrusions and vents occupied by fragmental deposits. The volcanic succession is some 200 m thick on Calton Hill, thickening to between 400 m and 500 m on Whinny Hill on the eastern side of Holyrood Park. These successions form part of the 20°–25° eastward-dipping limb of a synclinal structure occupied by the Midlothian Coalfield, whose eastern limb reveals the 600 m-thick East Lothian volcanic succession (see **North Berwick Coast** and **Garleton Hills** GCR site reports). The extrusive sequence is transected to the south by two major volcanic vents at the Lion's Head and the Lion's Haunch. The smaller Lion's Head Vent is cut by the Lion's Haunch Vent. A basaltic plug in the Lion's Head Vent forms the high point, Arthur's Seat.

Arthur's Seat Volcano

Within the western confines of Holyrood Park, the sedimentary sequence underlying the volcanic rocks consists of the Ballagan Formation (sandstones, marls, etc.) of the Inverclyde Group. This sequence contains two sills, the Heriot Mount–St Leonard's Sill and the Dasses Sill, which are regarded as contemporaneous with the extrusive activity. Approximately midway stratigraphically between these lies the much more prominent Salisbury Craigs Sill, which forms one of the most distinctive landmarks around Edinburgh. Although undated, the Salisbury Craigs Sill may be considerably younger than the igneous features mentioned above. Younger still are some (approximately) E–W-trending dykes that were intruded towards the close of the Carboniferous Period.

Following the Late Palaeozoic Earth movements that gave the easterly dip to the strata beneath Edinburgh, the geological record for the next 250 million years has been lost by erosion. The topography bequeathed to modern-day Edinburgh has been sculpted almost entirely by eastward-flowing ice during the past two million years. Among the most obvious results of this glaciation is the classic crag-and-tail topography exhibited by Castle Rock and the ridge of the 'Royal Mile' to the east (see cover photo, this volume), the steep west-facing escarpments of the Salisbury Craigs Sill and Whinny Hill lavas and their dip-slope tail towards Abbey Hill, and the analogous dip and scarp geomorphology of Calton Hill (see Figure 2.17). In each case the steep west-facing escarpments are formed by the igneous rocks, which presented more resistance to the glaciers that differentially eroded the softer sedimentary rocks and fault zones.

The rocks of the Arthur's Seat Volcano have played a major part in the history of geological science. The earliest geological reference appears to have been that of Atkinson in 1619, who mentioned the occurrence of 'Lapis haematite' in Holyrood Park (Clark, 1956). In the late 18th century, James Hutton realized that hot molten rock (magma) had injected sedimentary strata and that Salisbury Craigs represents a sill. Tradition maintains that Hutton used the site at the base of the sill ('Hutton's Section') to demonstrate the intrusive nature of the sill and to refute the widespread belief that 'whinstone' and basalt were marine precipitates as advocated by the popular Neptunist hypothesis. Samples of basaltic rocks from the park were used by Sir

James Hall (1805) for the earliest petrological melting experiments. Among the first accounts of the geology of the park are those by Townson (1799), Boué (1820), Maclaren (1834, 1839, 1866) and Howell and Geikie (1861). There was a subsequent burst of scientific interest in the area in the later part of the 19th century which saw publications by Zirkel (1870), Allport (1874), Judd (1875), Bonney (1878), Henderson (1880), Geikie (1880) and Teall (1888). Detailed mapping by the Geological Survey led to the appearance of a revision of Howell and Geikie's 1861 memoir by Peach *et al.* (1910) and the description of the Arthur's Seat Volcano in the memoir was also issued separately in the following year (Peach, 1911). Numerous early 20th century papers include those of Day (1912, 1923, 1933), Campbell (1914), Bailey (1923) and MacGregor (1936), but the definitive accounts that form the basis for most recent descriptions are those of Clark (1956) and Black (1966). Being so accessible, in the centre of a university city, the site must be one of the most popular geological excursion venues in Britain and has featured in all excursion guides to the area (e.g. Cox and Upton in Upton, 1969; Black and Waterston in McAdam and Clarkson, 1986; Land and Cheeney, 2000).

Description

The Arthur's Seat Volcano GCR site includes all the outcrops of Early Carboniferous igneous rocks close to the city centre of Edinburgh, namely Castle Rock, Calton Hill and Holyrood Park; the latter includes Arthur's Seat itself (Figure 2.14). A cross-section of Holyrood Park shows the relationships between many of the individual features of the Arthur's Seat Volcano (Figure 2.15).

Castle Rock (NT 251 735)

The rugged prominence crowned by Edinburgh Castle is composed of a steep-sided basaltic plug, 300 m by 200 m and elongated northwest–south-east in plan (see cover photo, this volume, and Figure 2.16). The plug cuts sandstones of the Ballagan Formation and the contact on the south-eastern side is visible from the road at Johnston Terrace. Castle Rock is an essentially homogeneous, fresh basalt ('Dalmeny' type) containing microphenocrysts of abundant olivine and less abundant augite and plagioclase.

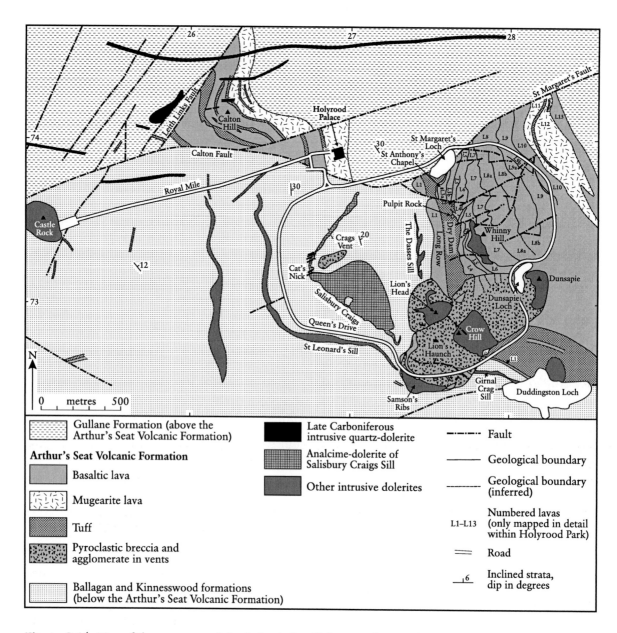

Figure 2.14 Map of the area around the Arthur's Seat Volcano. After Land and Cheeney (2000); and British Geological Survey 1:10 000 Sheet NT 27 SE (2000).

Calton Hill (NT 262 742)

The volcanic succession at Calton Hill is bounded on its north-west side by the NE-trending Leith Links Fault and on its southern and south-eastern margins by the Calton Fault and a WSW-trending fault that passes some 90 m north of Holyrood Palace. The succession comprises a number of lavas with subordinate tuffs, all with the regional eastward dip. As with the other two faulted outcrops of volcanic rocks (a) in Holyrood Park and (b) underlying Holyrood

Palace, there is a generalized progression with time from relatively primitive basalts through hawaiites ('Markle' type) to more highly differentiated mugearites. Cessation of volcanism was marked by an erosional disconformity followed by a relative sea-level rise and deposition of the Abbey Hill Shale. Basal tuffs to the west of Calton Hill are succeeded by a basalt flow c. 30 m thick, overlain by a tuff several metres thick. Above this are three flows ('Markle' type; probably hawaiites) with intervening thin tuff layers. The uppermost

66

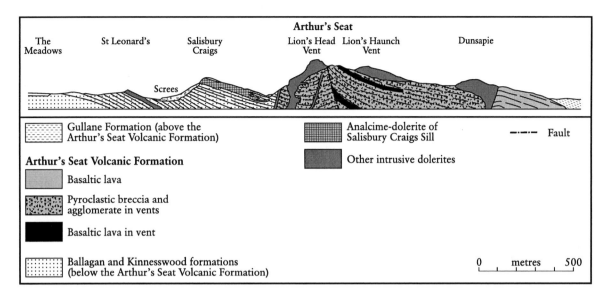

Figure 2.15 Cross-section of the southern part of Holyrood Park, Edinburgh, passing through the Arthur's Seat Volcano. After Mitchell and Mykura (1962).

of these tuffs forms the summit of the hill on which the old City Observatory stands (Figure 2.17). Overlying this are three highly weathered mugearite flows separated by thin tuffs on the north-eastern dip-slope, which are, in turn, overlain by the Abbey Hill Shale. Three E–W-trending Stephanian quartz-dolerite dykes traversing the northern part of the outcrop mark the youngest igneous events in the Calton Hill fault block.

Holyrood Park (NT 266 733–NT 283 731)

At Holyrood Park, as at Calton Hill, volcanism commenced with explosive activity, locally yielding a basal tuff (presently unexposed) immediately beneath the first lava. There have been different opinions concerning the number of lavas in the Whinny Hill succession in the northern area of the park (NT 278 734). Whilst Peach *et al.* (1910) reckoned that there are 19, Clark

Figure 2.16 Castle Rock from Princes Street Gardens, Edinburgh; a plug of olivine basalt within the Arthur's Seat Volcano GCR site. Note the glacial 'tail' to the left (east), protected by the plug. (Photo: British Geological Survey, No. MNS5624, reproduced with the permission of the Director, British Geological Survey, © NERC.)

Dinantian volcanic rocks of the Midland Valley

Figure 2.17 General view across Calton Hill (old observatory and monument on the summit), towards the Arthur's Seat Volcano and the Salisbury Craigs Sill, Edinburgh. (Photo: P. Macdonald.)

(1956) and Black (1966) concluded that there are only 13. Lava 1, approximately 30 m thick, forms a prominent cliff feature referred to as the Long Row (NT 276 735). It appears to be absent from the Calton Hill succession but crops out again south of the Lion's Haunch Vent in the vicinity of Duddingston Loch (NT 284 725). Lava 1 is compositionally similar to the basalt that forms the Castle Rock plug, although it is more porphyritic. Succeeding Lava 1 is a 30 m-thick sequence of tuffs and sedimentary rocks constituting 'the Lower Ash of the Dry Dam'. This comprises tuffs, fissile mudstones and a cherty limestone about 1 m thick, regarded as a lagoonal evaporite. The volcaniclastic mudstones and limestone contain plant fragments. At the top of this sequence, a tuff layer heralding the resurgence of volcanism is overlain by a highly porphyritic but severely altered basalt flow c. 8 m thick. This flow (Lava 2, of 'Craiglockhart'-type basalt) contains macrophenocrysts of pseudomorphed olivine, together with augite and plagioclase. The flow is highly amygdaloidal, with the amygdales occupied by calcite, chlorite, haematite and quartz. The long repose period that followed the Lava 1 eruption and permitted deposition of the Dry Dam mudstones and limestone was not repeated and, from here on

upwards, the succession is wholly composed of lavas and pyroclastic rocks. The 'Upper Ash of the Dry Dam', overlying Lava 2, is up to 7 m thick and contains fragments of plant and fish fossils.

Lava 3 consists of an (ankaramitic) alkali basalt ('Craiglockhart' type), with an outcrop confined to a restricted zone extending a little over 200 m south from the ruined St Anthony's Chapel (NT 276 738). This thick (c. 30 m) flow shows signs of 'colonnade and entablature' structure; massive columnar jointing in its lower facies gives way above to finer-scale jointing, and the uppermost facies, some 20 m thick, is more blocky with irregular jointing. Whereas the blocks are compositionally similar, they vary in degree of vesicularity, with some blocks evidently having accumulated in a highly scoriaceous condition. Abrupt changes of attitude shown by the jointing in the lower part of the flow, turning from perpendicular to its base to sub-horizontal a few metres above, testifies to a complex cooling history. A small columnar-jointed basaltic plug at Pulpit Rock on the western flank of Whinny Hill may be the source of Lava 3 (Clark, 1956; Black, 1966). Lava 4 (c. 8 m thick) is seen to the south of Pulpit Rock, overlying basaltic tuff. It comprises basalt ('Dalmeny' type) with abundant small microphenocrysts of fresh olivine. The flow has well-developed columnar jointing and forms the notable escarpment above the eastern flank of the Dry Dam (NT 277 735).

The higher part of the succession consists wholly of lavas. Lavas 5, 6 and 7 form distinct west-facing escarpments around the top of Whinny Hill. These basaltic to hawaiitic lavas ('Jedburgh' type) have microphenocrysts of olivine and plagioclase. They are overlain by lavas 8, 9 and 10, which are distinctly more porphyritic lavas of hawaiitic composition ('Markle' type). Lavas 11 and 12 are platy-jointed mugearites, overlain by Lava 13, a hawaiite of 'Markle' type, petrographically similar to those beneath Lava 11.

To the south of Arthur's Seat, the volcanic succession is seen on the north side of Duddingston Loch. Lava 1 and the Dry Dam volcaniclastic sedimentary layers can be readily correlated with those of Whinny Hill. Above these is a thick, coarse-grained pyroclastic unit in the vicinity of Duddingston village, within which two thin lavas can be discerned. This unit, which has no counterpart in the northern outcrops, is overlain by a series of hawaiitic and mugearitic lavas approximately correlative with lavas 8 to 13 in the Whinny Hill succession.

The lavas, in particular, have been extensively affected by relatively high-temperature hydrothermal alteration. Olivines have been pseudomorphed by calcite, iron-oxides and/or serpentine minerals. Pyroxenes are commonly chloritized and calcic plagioclases have been variously sericitized, albitized or analcitized. Amygdale and vein infillings include chlorite, haematite, calcite, chalcedony and prehnite.

The Crags (or Western) Vent forms an elongate outcrop (*c.* 200 m by 90 m) on the eastern dip-slope above the Salisbury Craigs Sill, close to the 'Camstone' sandstone quarries. It is filled with basaltic clasts, up to 40 cm across, petrographically identical to the basalts of lavas 1 and 2 (Clark, 1956). The clasts include highly amygdaloidal to scoriaceous types representing juvenile material.

The Lion's Head Vent would, prior to truncation by the Lion's Haunch Vent, have been approximately circular in plan, with a diameter of *c.* 300 m. It is filled with pyroclastic breccia, penetrated by a number of basaltic intrusions. The breccia shows crude bedding, defined by variation in clast size and dipping centrally. Clasts, up to *c.* 6 cm across, mainly of basalts

similar to those of the lower lavas, are accompanied by scarcer sandstone clasts. A plexus of 'Dalmeny'-type basaltic dykes in the lower exposures coalesces upwards to form a coherent mass in the centre of the vent, now forming the summit of Arthur's Seat. The latter consists of basalt with fairly well-developed, fine-scale columnar jointing.

The cross-cutting Lion's Haunch Vent (NT 275 729) has an ovoid plan, approximately 1200 m north-east–south-west by 500 m north-west–south-east. The vent includes Dunsapie Hill (NT 282 731) in its north-eastern extremity and the basaltic intrusion of Samson's Ribs in the south-west. A WNW–ESE fault, downthrowing to the north, traverses the south-western part of the vent. The pyroclastic breccia that occupies much of the Lion's Haunch Vent (NT 276 728) is, like that of the Lion's Head Vent, coarsely layered with the bedding dipping towards the vent interior. Much of it is very coarse relative to that of the Lion's Head Vent, with basaltic clasts up to 2 m across (Figure 2.18). Blocks of sandstone, mudstone and limestone are minor components. The breccia differs from that of the Lion's Head Vent in containing fragments of the feldspar-phyric hawaiitic ('Markle' type) lavas. There are several lavas within the vent, whose outcrops are predominantly towards the extreme south-west. Well-bedded sedimentary rocks intercalated between two of these may have been deposited in a crater lake (Black, 1966). A substantial but poorly exposed area between Arthur's Seat and Dunsapie Loch (NT 281 732) is also believed to be underlain by at least three lavas of relatively evolved feldspar-phyric basalt and hawaiite ('Dunsapie' or 'Markle' type).

Three substantial basaltic masses within the Lion's Haunch Vent are regarded as intrusive.

1. The Samson's Ribs mass, intruded along the south-western contact of the vent, shows spectacular columnar jointing. The columns, like those of Pulpit Rock, are curved (Figure 2.19). From the top of the *c.* 30 m-high cliff that forms the north wall of the road west of Duddingston Loch, the SSW-inclined columns steepen as followed down the cliff from *c.* 60° to 75° before turning outwards at much shallower angles to lie almost perpendicular to the rock face. As noted by Black (1966), the lower columns appear to have grown in response to cooling against an

Figure 2.18 Pyroclastic breccias, consisting of blocks of basalt in a matrix of red tuff, Lion's Haunch Vent, Arthur's Seat Volcano GCR site. The hammer shaft is about 35 cm long. (Photo: British Geological Survey, No. D3461, reproduced with the permission of the Director, British Geological Survey, © NERC.)

Figure 2.19 Spectacular columnar jointing of basalt in vent intrusion, Samson's Ribs, Arthur's Seat Volcano GCR site. (Photo: British Geological Survey, No. D3465, reproduced with the permission of the Director, British Geological Survey, © NERC.)

almost vertical side-wall whereas the upper portions grew in response to heat loss from a sub-horizontal upper surface.

2. Crow Hill, or the summit area of the Lion's Haunch Vent, consists of a mass of basalt with steep columnar jointing, surrounded by the vent breccia. The relatively fresh basalt ('Dunsapie' type) comprises approximately 30% phenocrysts of olivine, augite, plagioclase and subordinate magnetite in a finer-grained matrix. It is widely used for teaching purposes.

3. The third principal basaltic mass within the Lion's Haunch Vent lies at the north-eastern extremity where it forms Dunsapie Hill (the type locality for 'Dunsapie'-type basalt). It is crudely cylindrical in form and, like the Sampson's Ribs basalt, is thought to have been intruded along the contact zone of the vent, between the pyroclastic breccia and the Whinny Hill lavas.

The Duddingston plug lies outside the Lion's Haunch Vent and cuts the upper Duddingston tuff. It is ovoid in plan (*c.* 250 m across) and consists of olivine-clinopyroxene-felspar-phyric basalt ('Dunsapie' type).

Sills are a prominent feature of Holyrood Park. The lowest is the Heriot Mount–St Leonard's Sill. This is a composite body some 11 m thick, in which a 7 m-thick 'core' of porphyritic basalt ('Dunsapie' type) is surrounded by an envelope *c.* 2 m thick, of an aphyric hawaiite; there is a diffuse boundary, *c.* 85 cm wide, between the two varieties (MacGregor, 1936; Clark, 1956; Boyd, 1974).

The Dasses Sill, considerably higher up the sedimentary succession, is a more complex body, possibly consisting of several lenticular bodies, thickest in the south close to the Lion's Head pyroclastic breccia and pinching out northwards towards the St Margaret's Fault. Here too, a composite character has been shown by Oertel (1952) and Rutledge (1952). The compositional contrast is more extreme than in the St Leonard's Sill, involving a change from basalt to benmoreite (Boyd, 1974). The correlation of a section of sill at Girnal Crag (NT 280 726), farther east between the Lion's Haunch Vent and Duddingston Loch, has been contentious. Mitchell and Mykura (1962) considered the Girnal Crag Sill to be a continuation of the St

Leonard's Sill, but Boyd (1974) concluded on petrographical grounds that it correlates with the Dasses Sill.

Another small sill within Holyrood Park that probably accompanied the principal volcanic activity is that on Whinny Hill (NT 278 734). The Whinny Hill intrusion comprises 'a sill-like mass of Craiglockhart-type basalt' (Black, 1966), traceable for some 300 m and lying between lavas 6 and 7. A smaller body of identical basalt, with oval plan and vertical contacts, lying about 50 m to the west, was regarded by Black (1966) as the probable feeder to this sill.

The Salisbury Craigs Sill, attaining a maximum thickness of *c.* 40 m, presents a commanding feature in the park (Figure 2.20). Lying roughly midway between the Dasses and St Leonard's sills, it thins and cuts out south towards the contact of the Lion's Haunch Vent. Over much of its outcrop the sill is generally conformable with the sedimentary rocks into which it is intruded but it steps down northwards through the strata in the vicinity of the St Margaret's Fault. There are, however, some notable disconformities along the well-exposed lower contact,

Figure 2.20 The analcime-dolerite sill of Salisbury Craigs, Arthur's Seat Volcano GCR site. (Photo: British Geological Survey, No. D5403, reproduced with the permission of the Director, British Geological Survey, © NERC.)

including the famous 'Hutton's Section', where the magma has prized off a section of the underlying strata in a similar manner to that seen at the **South Queensferry to Hound Point** GCR site (see GCR site report). Towards its southern end, several thin sheets of hornfelsed sediment are intercalated near its upper surface. The contact with overlying sedimentary rocks is visible towards the north. The sill consists of analcime-dolerite (teschenite), which is coarse grained in the interior but fine grained in its marginal facies. Some large-scale layering in the sill, apparent from variations in the colouring, has never been investigated in detail but probably relates to variations in the modal content of olivine. The dolerite comprises plagioclase, olivine, augite, magnetite, apatite and analcime. Thin veinlets of microsyenite represent late differentiates in the southern part of the sill and there are some veins of haematite up to several centimetres wide, including one that has been preserved from quarrying, known as 'Hutton's Rock'.

Interpretation

The Upper Devonian to Lower Carboniferous sandstones, marls and mudstones of the Edinburgh region are mainly terrestrial clastic deposits laid down in intraplate fluvial, lacustrine and/or lagoonal environments. One may envisage an equatorial lowland terrane whose surface lay close to sea level and in which volcanism commenced at around 340 Ma. At the onset of volcanism, rising magmas encountered either standing water or waterlogged sediments at, or close to, surface level and Surtseyan-type phreatomagmatic eruptions resulted.

At near-surface levels the rising magmas would have reached levels of neutral buoyancy (particularly in the low-density Lower Carboniferous sediments) where they spread laterally as sills. Some batches, however, clearly reached surface level and erupted as small basaltic volcanoes. Initial gas release, largely of steam from heated meteoric water, drilled sub-cylindrical conduits that were followed and enlarged by rising magma. Castle Rock probably originated in this manner; a small cinder cone a few hundred metres high and with an external diameter of about 2 km has been eroded away, but the central plug of basalt remains. It has not been dated. Lava 1 contains quartz xenocrysts mantled by augitic reaction zones, and although such fea-

tures are rare in the other basalts of the region, they are typical of the Castle Rock basalt. This led Black (1966) to conclude that Lava 1 erupted from the Castle Rock volcano and flowed eastwards. If this is correct, it places activity at Castle Rock as the oldest in the north-eastern part of Edinburgh (although it is probably younger than the lavas at Craiglockhart). Black (1966) suggested, on slender evidence, that Lava 2 flowed from a southerly source within the Lion's Head Vent, whereas Lava 3 is inferred to have been supplied through a subsidiary centre to the north at Pulpit Rock (Clark, 1956; Black, 1966). Since the columnar joints of Lava 3 are presumed to have grown normal to the isothermal surfaces as cooling proceeded, the geometry of these surfaces was subject to continuous change, possibly through the action of percolating water. The blocky and scoriaceous nature of the uppermost part suggests proximity to a vent, and a lava fountain may have played above the columnar-jointed Pulpit Rock Vent. Flow 4 is correlative with the basalt plug occupying the core of the Lion's Head Vent and it was inferred that the lava erupted from this vent and flowed northwards until diverted by a lava cone around the Pulpit Rock Vent (Black, 1966). Lavas 5, 6 and 7, however, probably flowed northwards from the Lion's Haunch Vent (Black, 1966).

Interaction of hot rocks and/or magma with near-surface water would have played a major part in the formation of all the tuffs and pyroclastic breccias of Calton Hill and Holyrood Park. Most of the volcaniclastic rocks appear to show signs of some subaqueous reworking, although those of the Crags, Lion's Head and Lion's Haunch vents may have been largely ash-fall tuffs and scree (talus) deposits within the confines of steep-walled craters. The nature of the thick pyroclastic deposits at Duddingston, however, is scarcely known because of lack of exposure. There is a strong asymmetry in the stratigraphy north and south of the Lion's Haunch Vent, with pyroclastic beds to the south taking the place of the dominant lavas in the north. To explain this, Black (1966) surmised that strong northerly winds were responsible for the concentration of ash-fall deposits on the southern side of the main vents. At its maximum development the volcano may have risen to about 1000 m above sea level, with a cone-base of up to 5 km diameter.

Intrusion of sills is likely to have been instrumental in the episodic inflation of near-surface sedimentary strata, leading to emergence and allowing subaerial weathering and plant growth. Since plant fragments are commonly encountered in the volcaniclastic rocks, we may envisage the volcanic hills as having been forested for long periods between the occasional eruptions. The Dasses, Girnal Crag and St Leonard's sills may have been emplaced very early in the volcanic history 'into soft, pliable sediments' (Oertel, 1952). Subsidence and inundation following Lava 1 allowed deposition of the well-bedded ashes with intercalated lagoonal sediments seen in the lower part of the Dry Dam to the north and the lower part of the lower ash at Duddingston. The plant fragments within the Dry Dam sequence are inferred to have been washed down into shallow waters from the adjacent forested volcano flanks. The Dry Dam volcaniclastic mudstone unit thickens south towards the Lion's Head Vent, which may have been growing at the time through explosive action. The Crags Vent, which was probably surmounted by a basaltic cinder cone approaching 1 km diameter, may have developed fairly early, possibly contributing to the ashes of the Dry Dam (Black, 1966). The whole of the Whinny Hill–Lion's Head–Lion's Haunch area is clearly very shallowly dissected, and the larger basaltic outcrops within the two vents probably had surface expressions as confined lava lakes (cf. Oertel, 1952). Lava 4 may have been a northward overflow from the Lion's Head lava lake.

The Duddingston plug was possibly a feeder conduit for a parasitic basaltic volcano developed at a late stage in the volcanism on the south-eastern flanks of the main edifice. The Edinburgh volcanoes may thus have been distributed along a WNW–ESE lineament, *c*. 2.5 km long, exhibiting a very generalized migration of activity over time from Castle Rock in the WNW to the Duddingston plug in the ESE.

The younger products associated with the Lion's Haunch Vent tended to have more highly fractionated hawaiitic and mugearitic compositions, suggesting that magma ascent rates generally decreased with time, allowing time for fractionation to occur. However, analogous compositions did appear earlier if the surmise is correct that the Dasses, St Leonard's and Girnal Crag sills were early intrusions. The observation that these sills are composite, with more highly fractionated magma having been intruded ahead of more primitive basaltic magmas, suggests that they were fed from compositionally stratified chambers (dykes?) at depth (Boyd, 1974).

Basanitic magma originating from comparatively small-fraction melting, at greater mantle depths than the preceding activity, arose to form the Salisbury Craigs Sill. Although the depth at which the sill was intruded is uncertain, the vesicularity near the upper surface makes it unlikely that it was intruded at much more than a kilometre or two beneath a cover of sedimentary and volcanic rocks. Whilst the layering features could be due to in-situ differentiation they more probably reflect differences in the crystal content of successive magma batches as the sill inflated.

Although the Salisbury Craigs dolerite has not been dated, it may be significantly younger than the volcanic rocks. The principal reasons for so thinking are (a) the observation that it thins towards the main Holyrood Park vents and (b) that it is notably more silica-undersaturated than the other rocks (Peach *et al.*, 1910). It is cut (at 'the Cat's Nick') by a thin (*c*. 1 m) E–W-trending quartz-dolerite dyke of the late Stephanian swarm (see Chapter 6). This dyke provides an upper time limit for the Salisbury Craigs Sill, which is probably of Late Carboniferous age.

Whereas some of the secondary mineralization affecting the igneous rocks probably accompanied hydrothermal activity associated with the volcanism, further modification would have taken place in association with deep burial and deformation during the Variscan Orogeny. The Lower Carboniferous rocks revealed at the surface today would formerly have lain at a depth of several kilometres beneath Upper Carboniferous, Permian and possibly younger formations prior to uplift and erosion.

The rocks described above are still not precisely dated. Several of the fresher intrusive bodies could be dated by Ar-Ar methods. Dating of the Salisbury Craigs Sill, while highly desirable, is likely to present difficulties on account of secondary alteration. There is ample scope for further research within the site, such as a proper petrological investigation of the Salisbury Craigs Sill, for which a continuous drill-core would be desirable, and a modern volcanological study of the various volcaniclastic rocks.

Conclusions

The outcrops of igneous rocks forming the Castle Rock, Calton Hill and much of Holyrood Park constitute one of the prime geological sites in Scotland if not in the whole of Great Britain.

The site is representative of (1) early Visean volcanism and (2) the Late Carboniferous suite of alkali dolerite sills in the east of the Midland Valley. The various outcrops of igneous rocks that constitute 'Arthur's Seat Volcano' dominate the landscape of the city and are a vital part of its cultural heritage (the site of the Scottish Parliament is on the edge of the GCR site, as is the architectural World Heritage Site of the 'Old Town'). Splendid examples of many classic volcanic features are easily accessible to the specialist and general public alike, all within the confines of the inner city. These include the lavas and intervening tuffs, penecontemporaneous sedimentary strata, intrusions of various forms (plugs, sills and dykes), as well as volcanic vents infilled with pyroclastic breccia.

The site has great historical significance in the development of geological science and has played a continuing role in the evolution of ideas on volcanic rocks since the days of Hutton and Hall in the late 18th and early 19th centuries. It is undoubtedly of national importance and, from the worldwide interest that it has generated over two centuries, it can be argued that it is also of international importance. In brief, the value of this site, historically, scientifically and scenically, cannot be over-emphasized.

BURNTISLAND TO KINGHORN COAST, FIFE (NT 252 864– NT 280 891)

D.G. Woodhall

Introduction

The Burntisland to Kinghorn Coast GCR site incorporates one of the best-exposed successions of Visean volcanic rocks in the Midland Valley of Scotland. The 485 m-thick succession consists of basaltic lavas with subordinate volcaniclastic rocks (hyaloclastite, pyroclastic rocks and volcaniclastic sedimentary rocks).

Notable aspects of the site are the well-exposed internal structures of individual lava flows, a hyaloclastite unit, and occurrences within some lavas of sedimentary inclusions that locally contain important Early Carboniferous floral assemblages. The latter are described in the *Palaeozoic Palaeobotony of Great Britain* GCR volume (Cleal and Thomas, 1995) from two sites, Kingswood End and Pettycur, which fall within the area of the GCR site described here.

A detailed log of the volcanic succession by Geikie (1900) has formed the basis of most subsequent descriptions (Allan, 1924; MacGregor, 1996). The site was included in a recent re-survey of the Kirkcaldy district by the British Geological Survey (Woodhall, 1998; Browne and Woodhall, 1999, 2000). As a result of this re-survey, the volcanic rocks have been formally designated as the Kinghorn Volcanic Formation, and the exposures at this GCR site constitute the type section. Previously the volcanic rocks were either unnamed or referred to as the 'Burntisland Volcanic Formation' (Francis, 1991). Only a few geochemical analyses of the lavas have been published (Allan, 1924; Macdonald *et al.*, 1977; Smedley, 1986a, 1988a).

Description

The Early Carboniferous age of the succession at the Burntisland to Kinghorn Coast GCR site is constrained, outside of the site area, by Asbian to Brigantian miospore assemblages from fluviodeltaic, lacustrine and marine sedimentary rocks of the Sandy Craig and Pathhead formations (Strathclyde Group) (Brindley and Spinner, 1987, 1989; Browne *et al.*, 1996). Within the site, these same strata underlie, interdigitate with, and overlie the volcanic succession (Figure 2.21).

Lavas dominate the succession, and range in thickness from 5 m to 30 m. They are typically greyish- or brownish-green-weathered, olivine- or olivine-clinopyroxene-microphyric alkali olivine basalts. Amygdales of dark-greenish-grey chlorite and/or pale-yellow calcite are typically most abundant in the lower and upper parts of individual lava flows. Brecciated flow bases and/or tops are apparent locally, but in many cases have been obscured by weathering. Some of this weathering may have taken place soon after the emplacement of the flow, but it is indistinguishable from Quaternary weathering. Many lavas rest sharply on intercalated volcaniclastic and/or siliciclastic sedimentary rocks, and have a regular basal contact. However, those resting on mudstone tend to have an irregular contact owing to the presence of load structures, and some of these lavas contain inclusions of sedimentary rock that were probably derived from the underlying sediment during the emplacement of the flow. At Pettycur (NT 2608 8625), limestone inclusions have yielded an important Early Carboniferous flora dominated by lycopsids and ferns (Gordon, 1909; Scott *et al.*, 1984, 1986; Rex and Scott, 1987).

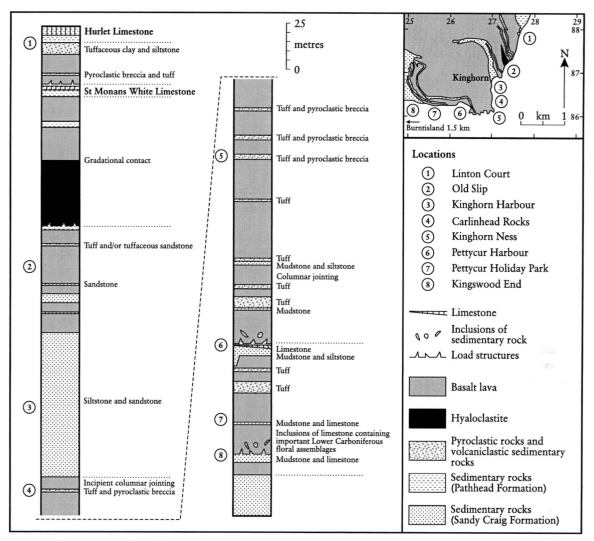

Figure 2.21 The volcanic succession exposed in the Burntisland to Kinghorn Coast GCR site.

The middle parts of the flows are the least weathered, contain the fewest and smallest amygdales, and commonly display cooling joints, which are locally columnar. Columnar jointing occurs in some of the flows exposed in the crags at Kingswood End (Allan, 1924), and on the coast, between Pettycur Harbour and Carlinhead Rocks (e.g. NT 2677 8611). Geikie (1900) described occurrences of pillow lava between Kinghorn Ness and Linton Court (e.g. NT 2751 8728, NT 2753 8740). However, these polyhedral, pillow-like masses lack chilled margins, which would be expected in true subaqueous pillows, and have been produced by weathering along intersecting planar and curvi-planar, horizontal and vertical cooling joints (MacGregor, 1996). In places the joint pattern is enhanced by vein-calcite along joint planes (e.g. NT 2753 8740).

Hyaloclastite, 35–40 m thick in the upper part of the succession, is exposed along the coast northeast of Kinghorn where it forms a 100 m-long wave-cut platform (NT 2734 8717–NT 2744 8722) (Woodhall, 1998). The base of the hyaloclastite is exposed at the southern end of the platform, where it rests on an intercalation of siliciclastic and volcaniclastic sedimentary rocks. The contact is in part irregular due to loading, but in places it truncates bedding in the underlying strata (NT 2734 8717). The hyaloclastite consists of green- to brownish-green-weathered, structureless breccia made up of angular clasts up to 30 cm across, many of which are pillow fragments. It also contains numerous basaltic pillows and pillow fragments, 0.5 m to about 1 m across, which are green with distinctly paler-green or brownish-green chilled margins (e.g.

NT 2735 8717, NT 2739 8723) (Figure 2.22). At the north-eastern end of the wave-cut platform (NT 2744 8722), a transition takes place, within a 5 m- to 10 m-thick zone, from hyaloclastite breccia to a coherent basalt lava, about 20 m thick. The base of the transition zone is marked by the appearance of lenticular sheets of green-weathered amygdaloidal basalt. Within the zone, these basalt sheets are separated by hyaloclastite breccia, but the thickness of intervening breccia decreases upwards (NT 2744 8722).

The volcaniclastic intercalations include primary and/or reworked pyroclastic rocks, up to about 5 m thick, in the form of various combinations of tuff, lapilli-tuff, lapillistone, and pyroclastic breccia (e.g. NT 2532 8651, NT 2676 8608, NT 2708 8633). These deposits were probably produced by mildly explosive volcanism, which accompanied the eruption of the lava flows. A number of intercalations display a distinctive reddish-brown colouration at the top, which is interpreted as a result of baking and oxidation by the overlying lava (e.g. NT 2540 8647, NT 2703 8616). Subaqueous accumulation of some pyroclastic deposits is implied where they occur interbedded with siliciclastic sedimentary rocks (e.g. NT 2528 8651). There are some intercalations of volcaniclastic sedimentary rocks, up to about 5 m thick, in the form of tuffaceous siltstone, sandstone and/or conglomerate, made up of basalt clasts derived from the erosion of pre-existing rocks (e.g. NT 2542 8646, NT 2536 8650).

Interpretation

The basaltic lava flows at the Burntisland to Kinghorn Coast GCR site are interpreted as the products of subaerial, effusive volcanism that probably involved hawaiian- and/or strombolian-type eruptions. Both types of eruption are dominated by effusions of low-viscosity, gas-poor magma, typically basaltic in composition, and they differ only in that magma discharge is more intermittent during strombolian eruptions (Walker and Croasdale, 1972; Blackburn *et al.*, 1976; McPhie *et al.*, 1993). During these types of eruption, only small amounts of pyroclastic material are produced, and most of this accumulates close to the vent, forming a cone of scoriaceous lapilli and blocks, with some bombs. No such cones are preserved within the volcanic succession of this site. Therefore, the abundance of tuff in the succession is indicative of more distal accumulations of ash and/or small

Figure 2.22 Basaltic pillows with hyaloclastite in the Kinghorn Volcanic Formation on the shore at Bellypuff, north-east of Kinghorn (NT 2740 8725). (Photo: British Geological Survey, No. D5217, reproduced with the permission of the Director, British Geological Survey, © NERC.)

lapilli, which were probably deposited downwind from vents. There are only a few occurrences of coarser-grained deposits (e.g. lapillistone and pyroclastic breccia), which may have accumulated more proximally.

Depositional environments during the volcanism probably varied from subaerial, with scattered swamps and shallow lakes, similar to those envisaged by Rex and Scott (1987), in the Pettycur area, to shallow subaqueous lacustrine, deltaic and marine. Although many of the lavas are interbedded with sedimentary rocks, the infrequency of evidence for magma–water interaction (e.g. hyaloclastite and/or pillow lava) is consistent with dominant subaerial eruption. However, the presence of load structures at the base of, and sedimentary inclusions within, some flows indicates that some of the lavas were erupted onto a substrate of semi-lithified, possibly wet, sediment. The inclusions are considered to represent masses of sediment isolated from the substrate as portions of the basalt sank into such sediment. The presence of interbedded sedimentary rocks can be explained by a combination of regional tectonic subsidence and eustatic sea-level changes, which repeatedly drowned newly erupted lavas.

Evidence that some lavas did encounter significant bodies of water is indicated by the presence of hyaloclastite. This has formed by the non-explosive quench fragmentation of magma (McPhie *et al.*, 1993). That exposed along the coast north-east of Kinghorn is capped by basalt lava, which displays no evidence of subaqueous emplacement. This relationship is similar to that present in lava deltas, formed as subaerially erupted lava flowed into water (Jones and Nelson, 1970; Moore *et al.*, 1973; Furnes and Sturt, 1976; Cas and Wright, 1987). Consequently, the hyaloclastite north-east of Kinghorn is interpreted as having formed the lower, subaqueous part of a lava delta. The transition upwards from hyaloclastite to basalt lava marks the approximate water level during delta formation, and consequently the 35–40 m thickness of the hyaloclastite provides an indication of minimum water depth. The presence of the trace fossil, *Rhizocorallium*, in siliciclastic sedimentary rocks immediately beneath the hyaloclastite, suggests that the delta formed during or soon after a marine transgression. The thickness (5–10 m) and complexity (alternating sheets of lava and hyaloclastite) of the transition zone is possibly due to the combined effects of tidal variation

and subsidence of the lava delta (Furnes and Sturt, 1976). The overlying coherent basalt lava forms the subaerial part of the delta.

Conclusions

The Burntisland to Kinghorn Coast GCR site is representative of the late Visean Kinghorn Volcanic Formation and provides a well-exposed, almost complete section through an Early Carboniferous volcanic field. The volcanism took place predominantly on land close to sea level. It probably involved the production of many small volcanic cones from which extensive basaltic lavas were erupted, although none of the volcanic cones are preserved within the site. Periodically, parts of the volcanic field were submerged, either by freshwater lakes, areas of brackish water, or the sea, within which mudstone, siltstone and sandstone were deposited. During one such period of partial submergence, possibly brought about by a rise in sea level, a lava flow encountered the sea. Abrupt cooling of the lava, as it came into contact with the water, caused it to fragment and the angular lava fragments accumulated by continuous avalanching from the edge of the lava to form a delta on the seabed. However, not all of the lava was fragmented; some formed elongate pillow-like masses (pillow lava) surrounded by narrow 'skins' of rapidly cooled lava. This occurrence of fragmented lava, with associated pillow-like masses, is one of few within the Carboniferous–Permian Igneous Province of northern Britain.

TOUCH, FINTRY AND GARGUNNOCK HILLS, STIRLING (NS 650 867– NS 626 895–NS 730 934)

I.T. Williamson

Introduction

The Touch, Fintry and Gargunnock hills between Fintry and Stirling comprise the most north-easterly fault-bound block of the Dinantian Clyde Plateau Volcanic Formation. The GCR site representative of this fault block comprises the whole of the spectacular, NNW-facing escarpment of the Touch and Gargunnock hills and the WNW-facing scarp of the Fintry Hills to the west (Figures 2.23 and 2.24). Prominent high points are Stronend (NS 629 895) (511 m), Lees Hill (NS 660 910) (411 m) and

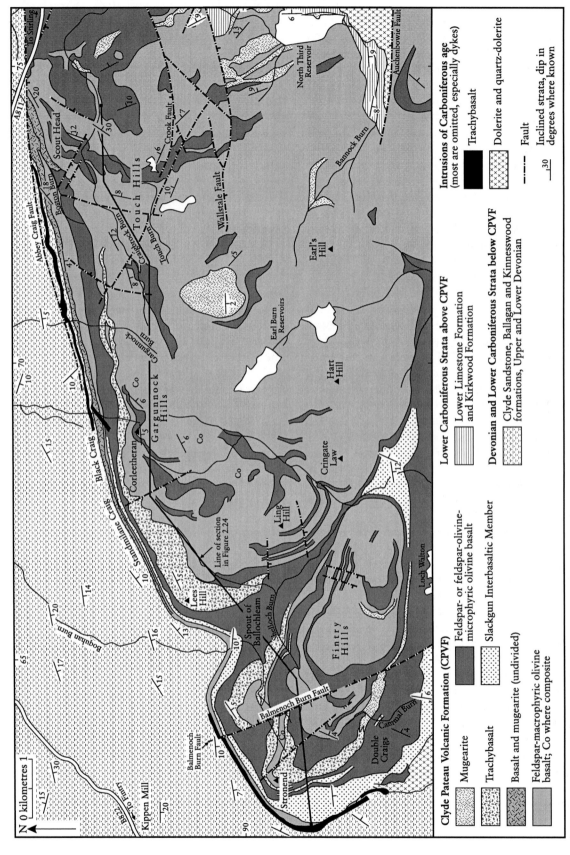

Figure 2.23 Map of the area around the Touch, Fintry and Gargunnock Hills GCR site. Based on Geological Survey 1:50 000 Sheet 39, Stirling (1970).

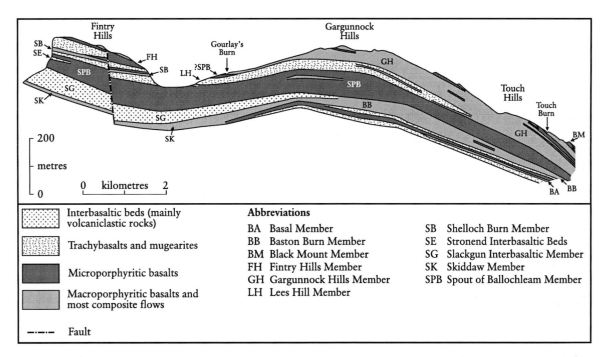

Figure 2.24 Cross-section of the northern part of the Touch, Fintry and Gargunnock Hills GCR site showing the dominant lava-types and boundaries between members of the Clyde Plateau Volcanic Formation. After Francis *et al.* (1970).

Carleetheran (NS 688 919) (485 m). A terraced, or 'trap', topography is particularly well developed along parts of the escarpment and the slopes immediately above (Figure 2.25). The highest ground and dip-slopes form an undulating and relatively poorly exposed moorland plateau. This terrain is mainly covered by a veneer of peat, though streams have cut through this and underlying glacial deposits, locally exposing bedrock. The Touch Hills have less cover of superficial deposits. Landslips are a major feature of the escarpment face, and talus and small alluvial cones have developed in many places.

The volcanic rocks were not sub-divided on early geological maps of these hills and only brief descriptions were given by Geikie (1897), who included them within the Clyde Plateau. Dixon (1938) was the first to give more details and to sub-divide the lavas. Little, if any, advance on this was made prior to the Geological Survey's re-mapping during the 1950s, almost entirely by W.A. Read, and the subsequent publication of the accompanying memoir (Francis *et al.*, 1970). That work remains the most detailed study of the district.

Description

The Clyde Plateau Volcanic Formation exposed along the northern escarpment of the Gargunnock Hills and Fintry Hills is conformable upon the Clyde Sandstone Formation of the Inverclyde Group (Paterson and Hall, 1986). This is predominantly composed of fluvial sandstone and conglomerate (Read and Johnson, 1967) and it is probably of late Tournaisian (Chadian) age. The Gargunnock Burn (NS 7072 9298 to NS 7067 9333) is also selected as a GCR site for the Dinantian strata below the lavas (see Cossey *et al.*, in prep.).

The upper age of the Clyde Plateau Volcanic Formation is less easily defined than its base as, outwith the GCR site, the highest lavas are separated from overlying volcanic detritus by a markedly diachronous erosional regional unconformity (Dinham and Haldane, 1932; Francis *et al.*, 1970). This unit of conglomerates, sandstones and mudstones, derived from the weathering of the volcanic formation, is similar to the Kirkwood Formation in the western blocks of the Clyde Plateau Volanic Formation (Paterson and Hall, 1986) and is probably of late Visean age.

Dinantian volcanic rocks of the Midland Valley

Figure 2.25 Trap-featuring on the northern escarpment of the Gargunnock Hills, around Carleetheran; Fintry Hills beyond. (Photo: P. Macdonald.)

Evidence for Dinantian volcanism prior to eruption of the earliest lavas is contained in beds of reworked volcaniclastic detritus below the oldest flows at several localities. Francis *et al.* (1970) included these within the uppermost part of the Clyde Sandstone Formation and noted increasing amounts of volcaniclastic detritus upward in the formation. Near Craigend, on the northern slopes of the Fintry Hills (NS 6229 8953), for example, 'white pebbly sandstones are reported to grade up into yellowish and greenish volcanic detritus which locally contains plant impressions'. Some beds closely resemble sedimentary units intercalated with the lava succession. In the Gargunnock Burn (NS 7072 9295) dark-red mudstones underlie the lavas and contain grains of plagioclase, pseudomorphs after olivine and decomposed basalt. These were derived either from pre-existing volcanic rocks or from ash-fall deposits.

The lava-dominated main volcanic sequence is 300–400 m thick and thins northwards and eastwards. The lavas are mainly plagioclase-phyric basalts described traditionally as olivine basalts of 'Markle' (macroporphyritic) and 'Jedburgh' (microporphyritic) types. They are more comprehensively described as plagioclase ± olivine ± Fe-oxide-phyric basalts, basaltic hawaiites and hawaiites (Macdonald, 1975). Some flows may be composite. There are also subordinate trachybasalts and mugearites, the latter mainly in the upper half of the succession.

Most of the lavas comprise a central massive facies between marginal rubbly, clinkery and amygdaloidal facies suggesting that they are aa lava. However, many show structures transitional between aa and pahoehoe lava types. Some, for example, exhibit rounded or elliptical masses of either massive or crudely columnar lava enveloped within less structured amygdaloidal lava and autobreccia. These structures may be considered as auto-intrusive features, perhaps representing cross-sections through infilled lava tubes. Such features are more common in pahoehoe lava fields. Some flows are clearly traceable along strike for several kilometres whereas others are more localized, perhaps only a kilometre or less in section. This probably reflects varying volume, viscosity and effusion rates as well as local topographical control during eruption. The lateral persistence, uniform stratigraphy and relatively constant thickness of most of the flows, as seen on the comparatively well-exposed northern escarpment, are typical of continental flood-basalt terrains. Many of the lavas have irregular weathered tops, and lateritic palaeosols (boles) are developed on some. These are seen particularly well at Double Craigs in the Fintry Hills, for example. A thick intercalation of laterite, detrital volcaniclastic sedimentary rocks and possible beds of reworked tephra (the Slackgun Interbasaltic Member), occurs in the lower half

80

of the sequence. This marks a prolonged episode of weathering and the re-distribution of weathered and unconsolidated volcaniclastic materials.

In marked contrast to most of the other regional blocks of the Clyde Plateau Volcanic Formation, there are no agglomerate-filled necks cutting the volcanic sequence in the Touch, Fintry and Gargunnock hills, but there are rare plugs. A good example is the irregular intrusion of microporphyritic olivine basalt within the Slackgun Interbasaltic Member at the Dun, north-east of Fintry (NS 628 873). However, several basaltic and doleritic dykes cut the volcanic sequence and the underlying strata. Most are thin, nearly vertical bodies trending a few degrees either east or west of north. Two major sills intrude the upper parts of the Clyde Sandstone Formation. The Skiddaw Sill, composed of trachybasalt, is confined to the northern and western slopes of the Fintry Hills. The distinctive Downie's Loup Sill, exposed below the northern escarpment of the Touch Hills, is a composite mass of trachybasalt with abundant large feldspar phenocrysts in its lower part, but is aphyric and finer grained in its upper part.

In the west of the GCR site the lavas dip generally between 4° and 8° towards the southeast and south, but farther east the strike swings round so that they generally dip eastwards and north-eastwards at 5° to 15° (Figure 2.23). Along the northern escarpment of the Gargunnock and Fintry hills, the dips of the lower lavas are greater than the dips of those higher in the sequence. There are some large open fold structures, but it is not clear to what extent these reflect major palaeosurface irregularities, volcanotectonic activity, or later tectonic events.

There are relatively few faults in the Gargunnock and Fintry hills. A number trend either north-west or NNW, generally with small throws down to the north-east. One of the largest is the Balmenoch Burn Fault which throws down to the ENE by at least 30 m. In other parts of the GCR site, some of the very large, approximately E–W-trending structures that affect the Stirlingshire Coalfield (e.g. the Wallstale and Auchenbowie faults) also cut the Clyde Plateau Volcanic Formation.

A few major- and trace-element analyses of lavas from the Touch, Fintry and Gargunnock hills have been published in papers by Macdonald (1975), Macdonald *et al.* (1977) and

Smedley (1988a), with additional data available in theses by Craig (1980) and Smedley (1986a). As with the Clyde Plateau Volcanic Formation in general, the lavas are mildly alkaline to transitional in character, meaning that basic members of the suite comprise both nepheline- and hypersthene-normative types. They can be assigned to the differentiation series ankaramitic basalt–basalt–hawaiite–mugearite–benmoreite–trachyte–rhyolite, although rocks more evolved than mugearite are not recorded from this GCR site.

The detailed lithostratigraphy of the Clyde Plateau Volcanic Formation in the Touch, Fintry and Gargunnock hills was established by Francis *et al.* (1970). Eleven lava 'groups' were recognized and these are now regarded as members of the formation. The members interdigitate in part and their boundaries may be diachronous (Figure 2.24). There are important lateral variations, with slightly different sequences in the north and east forming the Touch and Gargunnock hills and in the south and west forming the Fintry Hills. Correlation between the Touch, Fintry and Gargunnock hills sequence and the volcanic sequences in the Campsie Fells, Kilsyth Hills and Denny Muir has been established by Forsyth *et al.* (1996) (Figure 2.4). The succession exposed in the GCR site is as follows (Table 2.1).

Basal Member

The Basal Member is only present in the eastern area of the Touch and Gargunnock hills, where it forms minor cliffs at the foot of the main escarpment. It comprises a thin sequence of varied lava types with trachybasalt being the most common. In the Baston Burn, (between NS 7311 9352 and NS 7315 9340), Francis *et al.* (1970) recorded a 31 m-thick section comprising at least four flows. A basal, thick and laterally persistent mugearite is overlain by plagioclase-macrophyric and plagioclase-microphyric flows.

Baston Burn Member

The Baston Burn Member comprises mainly plagioclase-macrophyric flows but, as Francis *et al.* (1970) only refer to them as 'Markle basalts', the sequence may also include basaltic hawaiite and hawaiite. Rare plagioclase-microphyric units may represent parts of localized composite flows. From Baston Burn to Gargunnock Burn, both the thickness and the number of flows increases.

Table 2.1 Succession of the Clyde Plateau Volcanic Formation in the northern part of the Touch, Fintry and Gargunnock hills. (After Francis *et al.*, 1970, table 7.)

Fintry Hills	Touch and Gargunnock hills
Kirkwood Formation Conglomerates, sandstones and mudstones derived from weathering of Clyde Plateau Volcanic Formation	
Regional diachronous erosional unconformity	
	Touch House Member (thickness not known) Feldspar-macrophyric olivine basalts
	Black Mount Member (>24 metres) Microporphyritic basalts and subordinate trachybasalts
Fintry Hills Member (>122 metres) Feldspar-macrophyric olivine basalts with a high proportion of microporphyritic basalts and rare trachybasalts	**Gargunnock Hills Member** (91–>152 metres) Feldspar-macrophyric olivine basalts and composite basalts with subordinate microporphyritic basalts and rare mugearites
Shelloch Burn Member (40–60 metres) Trachybasalts, microporphyritic basalts and feldspar-macrophyric olivine basalts	**Lees Hill Member** (0–40 metres) Trachybasalts
Spout of Ballochleam Member (24–92 metres) Feldspar-microphyric basalts; Stronend Interbasaltic Beds in middle part	
Slackgun Interbasaltic Member (0–79 metres) Tuff (possibly volcanic detritus), laterites and weathered lavas	
Unconformity	
Skiddaw Member (0–37 metres) Feldspar-macrophyric olivine basalts and composite basalts	**Baston Burn Member** (9–67 metres) Feldspar-macrophyric olivine basalts
	Basal Member (30–46 metres) Trachybasalts, feldspar-macrophyric olivine basalts and feldspar-microphyric basalts
Clyde Sandstone Formation Fluvial sandstones and conglomerates; some reworked volcaniclastic detritus in upper part	

The Gargunnock Burn section (NS 7073 9320–NS 7234 9297) shows the maximum development of the sequence, with at least ten flows, totalling about 67 m. Farther west, successive flows are truncated by the overlying Spout of Ballochleam Member, and at Standmilane Craig (NS 6760 9214–NS 6683 9176), the section is reduced to only two flows, totalling 12 m.

Skiddaw Member

From the western end of the Gargunnock Hills into the Fintry Hills, the earliest lavas of the Clyde Plateau Volcanic Formation are assigned to the Skiddaw Member. The lavas are plagioclase-macrophyric types, similar to those of the Baston Burn Member, along with some composite basalt and microporphyritic basalt flows. At Slackgun (NS 6572 9122), below Lees Hill, Francis *et al.* (1970) recorded a 34 m-thick section. Partial sections are seen in the nearby Boquhan Burn and there are intermittent exposures along the western slopes of the Fintry Hills below Stronend. South of Skiddaw (NS 6210 8905), the member appears to be absent, so that the succeeding Slackgun Interbasaltic Member and beds within the upper part of the Clyde Sandstone Formation possibly merge and are difficult to distinguish from each other.

Slackgun Interbasaltic Member

The Slackgun Interbasaltic Member is a heterogeneous unit. There are intermittent exposures along parts of Standmilane Craig, but the best are at Slackgun (NS 6576 9118–NS 6577 9112), where Francis *et al.* (1970) recorded some 34 m. There are scattered exposures along the northern and western slopes of the Fintry Hills. Here there are three important sections: volcaniclastic rocks occur in the Boquhan Burn (NS 6526 8994–NS 6523 9014) (48 m), and the Cammal Burn (NS 6433 8697) (probably in excess of 61 m), at much the same stratigraphical level as thick and massive red laterite in the Balmenoch Burn (NS 6482 8694). The Slackgun Interbasaltic Member is not present in the eastern Gargunnock Hills nor in the Touch Hills, where an unconformity separates the Baston Burn and Spout of Ballochleam members.

There are two main lithofacies associations. The lower part is characterized by thick lateritic deposits and rare, thin and laterally impersistent olivine-phyric basaltic lavas, whereas the upper parts form a stratified sequence composed of tuff and volcaniclastic sedimentary rocks. Some of the coarser-grained beds may be cross-bedded and some contain large spindle-shaped clasts that may be volcanic bombs. The lateritic deposits mostly derive from deep subaerial weathering of volcanic rocks *in situ*, but locally may show evidence of reworking. The member possibly formed, at least in part, during a relatively quiescent interlude in the development of the lava field. Craig (1980) interpreted it as the degraded remains of a line of ash cones.

Spout of Ballochleam Member

The type locality for the Spout of Ballochleam Member is the Boquhan Burn at the Spout of Ballochleam (NS 6490 8963–NS 6526 8994),

where there are nine lavas, totalling 85 m. At least eight flows are exposed in the cliffs of the western Fintry Hills. All but the lowest lava are plagioclase-microphyric basalts and hawaiites. At NS 6425 9047, the lowest lava, scoriaceous olivine-microphyric basalt up to 20 m thick, envelops large rounded bodies of massive basalt interpreted as infilled lava tubes. A similar sequence, more than 100 m thick, occurs in the southern Fintry Hills. In the eastern Touch Hills there are fewer flows, totalling about 30 m, but farther west both their number and thickness increase. At Easter Blackspout (NS 6912 9252–NS 6911 9242) and east of Standmilane Craig the sequence is more than 80 m thick.

The Stronend Interbasaltic Beds, comprising a laterite up to 2.75 m thick, occur in the middle part of the member and are seen best below Stronend at NS 6288 8885 and in a tributary of the Cammal Burn at NS 6399 8764.

Lees Hill Member

The Lees Hill Member generally forms the crest of the Gargunnock Hills escarpment at the top of cliffs formed by the Spout of Ballochleam Member. There are a few rare olivine-plagioclase-macrophyric flows, but otherwise the Lees Hill Member is dominated by trachybasalt. Francis *et al.* (1970) recorded a 40 m section of at least two thick trachybasalt flows in the Gargunnock Burn (between NS 7065 9249 and NS 7059 9222).

Shelloch Burn Member

The Shelloch Burn Member comprises a variable sequence of trachybasalts and mugearites, along with olivine-plagioclase-macrophyric basalts ('Markle' type) and microporphyritic basalts. Its fullest development is in the northern Fintry Hills where it varies in thickness from 40 m to 60 m. Representative sections are exposed in the Shelloch Burn (NS 6509 8913–NS 6523 8924), the Boquhan Burn (NS 6468 8967–NS 6490 8963) and in the crags along the western side of the Fintry Hills (NS 6281 8910–NS 6304 8870).

The Shelloch Burn and Lees Hill members cannot be correlated despite their similar stratigraphical positions, their lithological similarities and their close proximity. Regionally, they probably correlate with the Langhill and Lower Lecket Hill lavas in the Campsie Fells block (Craig, 1980; Forsyth *et al.*, 1996).

Gargunnock Hills Member

The Gargunnock Hills Member forms the greater part of the dip-slope of the Touch and Gargunnock hills. It comprises mainly plagioclase-macrophyric ('Markle' type) basalt (at least four flows of which are composite), several microporphyritic basalt lavas and rare mugearite. There are also significant lateral variations in the sequence, with microporphyritic basalt more common towards the Fintry Hills and the local development of the composite flows. In the eastern Touch Hills the member is more than 90 m thick, but it may have originally exceeded 150 m in the Gargunnock Hills. It can be divided into two units. Part of the upper unit is well exposed on Craigbrock Hill (NS 7385 9295) and in the Touch Burn below Gilmour's Linn (NS 7395 9252). The remainder is seen in the area around Scout Head (NS 7354 9337–NS 7350 9313), where Francis *et al.* (1970) recorded a 75 m-thick section.

Fintry Hills Member

The Fintry Hills Member is the youngest unit of the Clyde Plateau Volcanic Formation in the western parts of the Touch, Fintry and Gargunnock Hills GCR site, where it forms the highest ground of the Fintry Hills, south-east of Stronend. The sequence consists of plagioclase-macrophyric ('Markle' type) lavas intercalated with a high proportion of microporphyritic basalts and rare mugearites, and is at least 122 m thick. It may be equivalent to the Gargunnock Hills Member in the Gargunnock and Touch hills, and regionally may correlate with the Denny Muir, Kilsyth Hills and Holehead lavas in the Campsie Fells block (Craig, 1980; Forsyth *et al.*, 1996).

Black Mount Member and Touch House Member

The youngest flows of the Clyde Plateau Volcanic Formation in the Touch, Fintry and Gargunnock hills are not seen within the GCR site. The Black Mount Member comprises at least 24 m of microporphyritic basalt and subordinate trachybasalt and the Touch House Member is composed entirely of plagioclase-macrophyric lavas.

Interpretation

Correlation of the Touch, Fintry and Gargunnock hills sequence with other sequences in the Clyde Plateau Volcanic Formation is illustrated in Figure 2.4. The lower members are not easily correlated with sequences in the Campsie Fells and are perhaps localized developments. Although substantial fragmental deposits occur at the base of the formation in the Kilpatrick Hills, they thin eastwards and are not seen to continue into the Campsie Fells block. In the Kilsyth Hills and Denny Muir area of the latter, the lowest member comprises interbedded proximal facies lavas and thick tuffs, the latter comprising up to half the total thickness. It is possible that the volcaniclastic beds within the upper parts of the Clyde Sandstone Formation in the Fintry and Gargunnock hills, are distal equivalents of these tuffs.

Evidence for the existence of small shield volcanoes, vents and caldera structures is abundant throughout the northern Clyde Plateau; many eruption sites lie along linear features. However, unlike the sequences in the Campsie Fells and the Kilsyth, Kilpatrick and Renfrewshire hills, there are only rare plugs and no recorded agglomerate-filled vents or calderas within the Touch, Fintry and Gargunnock hills block. Also, the dykes present seem to be too few and insignificant to be considered the main sources of the lavas. Hence, it is more likely that most of the laterally continuous pahoehoe flows with 'continental flood-basalt' characteristics are the distal products of eruptions along the linear vent–fissure systems in the Campsie and Kilsyth hills (Whyte and MacDonald, 1974; Craig and Hall, 1975; Hall *et al.*, 1998). Other flows, exhibiting proximal features and interbedded tuffs, may have been derived more directly from less voluminous eruptions centred upon small composite shield volcanoes south-west of the area.

Some members of the Clyde Plateau Volcanic Formation apparently thicken south-westwards from the Gargunnock Hills towards the Campsie Fells. This is especially clear in the Spout of Ballochleam Member and its proposed equivalent, the Campsie lavas, as illustrated in Figure 2.4. This could suggest the existence, in addition to the vents and structures such as the Waterhead Central Volcanic Complex (Craig, 1980; Forsyth *et al.*, 1996), of at least one major volcano in the Campsie Fells. However, there is considerable evidence to support, at least locally, the views of Tyrrell (1937) that the Clyde Plateau was more the result of coalesced lava flows erupted from a large number of small, closely spaced volcanoes. The absence of clear evidence of vent structures in the Touch, Fintry and Gargunnock hills block is in stark contrast to the well-documented **Campsie Fells** block to the south-west (see GCR site report).

Conclusions

The Touch, Fintry and Gargunnock Hills GCR site represents the most north-easterly of several large, fault-bound blocks that make up the overall outcrop of the Visean Clyde Plateau Volcanic Formation, by far the thickest and most extensive outpouring of Carboniferous or Permian volcanic rocks in the whole of Britain. Sub-parallel terracing, or 'trap' topography, is well developed and is seen particularly well on the long, spectacular, north-facing escarpment of these hills. The GCR site includes rock-types ranging from basalt to mugearite in composition, and there are several examples of ash-fall tuffs, probable remnants of ash cones, interflow sedimentary deposits derived from the reworking of the volcanic rocks, and soils that developed between eruptions. A detailed stratigraphy has been established, enabling comparisons with other blocks within the outcrop of the Clyde Plateau Volcanic Formation, thus allowing realistic three-dimensional models to be constructed for the evolution of the entire lava field through time.

CAMPSIE FELLS, STIRLING and EAST DUNBARTONSHIRE (NS 572 800–NS 535 825–NS 609 867)

J.G. MacDonald

Introduction

The Visean lavas and pyroclastic rocks of the Clyde Plateau Volcanic Formation, together with associated vents and intrusions, form the hilly areas that lie to the north, west and south of Glasgow. In the northern part of the Clyde Plateau the steep slopes that bound the Campsie Fells provide extensive exposures (Figures 2.26 and 2.27). Glacial erosion has produced escarpments, which afford well-exposed sections

through the lower part of the lava succession. The spectacular escarpment on the north-western margin of the Campsie Fells is carved out of the largest concentration of vents and intrusions in the Clyde Plateau, the North Campsie Linear Vent System (Figure 2.28).

The Campsie Fells GCR site extends for 8 km along the NW-facing escarpment, from Dunmore, above the village of Fintry, as far as the twin volcanic plugs of Dumgoyne and Dumfoyne. From there it continues south-eastwards along a 4.5 km stretch of the SW-facing escarpment of the Strathblane Hills between Dumfoyne and the Spout of Ballagan. As well as the volcanic features of the area, localities of stratigraphical and palaeontological interest have been notified at the Balglass corries in the north and at Ballagan Glen in the south (see Cossey *et al.*, in prep.).

The earliest detailed description of the geology of the Campsie Fells by Young (1860) proved to be so popular that it was reprinted in 1868 and 1893. More recent sources of information (Clough *et al.*, 1925; MacDonald, 1967; Whyte and MacDonald, 1974; MacDonald and Whyte, 1981; Hall *et al.*, 1998) provide a general picture of the petrography and geochemistry of the volcanic rocks, which vary in composition from mafic basalt to trachyte. Most of these accounts draw upon more detailed information in PhD theses by MacDonald (1965) and Craig (1980). Excursions to parts of the Campsie Fells outwith the GCR site are described by MacDonald and Whyte (in Upton, 1969) and MacDonald (in Lawson and Weedon, 1992). The mildly alkaline chemistry of the rocks, their range of composition, the relationships of vents to lava flows, and the presence of a flow of relatively fresh hawaiite that exhibits interesting internal variations, afford a potential for further research in the area, which could be of international significance.

Whole-rock K-Ar radiometric dates from vent intrusions in the western Campsie Fells (De Souza, 1979) include 329 ± 7 Ma (Dumgoyne) and 316 ± 5 Ma (Dunmore) (*c.* 336 Ma and 323 Ma respectively using new constants). Ages in the range 315 ± 7 Ma to 303 ± 7 Ma were obtained from lavas farther east but De Souza considered that, given the probability of argon loss during alteration, the age of eruption is likely to be in the vicinity of, or older than, 330 Ma (*c.* 337 Ma using new constants).

Figure 2.26 Corrie of Balglass on the northern escarpment of the Campsie Fells, with the Fintry Hills in the background. Largely microporphyritic basalts and hawaiites of the Lower North Campsie Lava Member forming the steep wall of the corrie, overlie volcaniclastic rocks derived from the North Campsie Linear Vent System. (Photo: P. Macdonald.)

Figure 2.27 The western end of the Campsie Fells viewed across Strath Blane from the south-west. The Dumfoyne Vent is the feature in the centre of the photograph; the Dumgoyne Vent is to the left of it. The high ground on the skyline above Dumgoyne marks the south-west end of the North Campsie Linear Vent System. (Photo: J.G. MacDonald.)

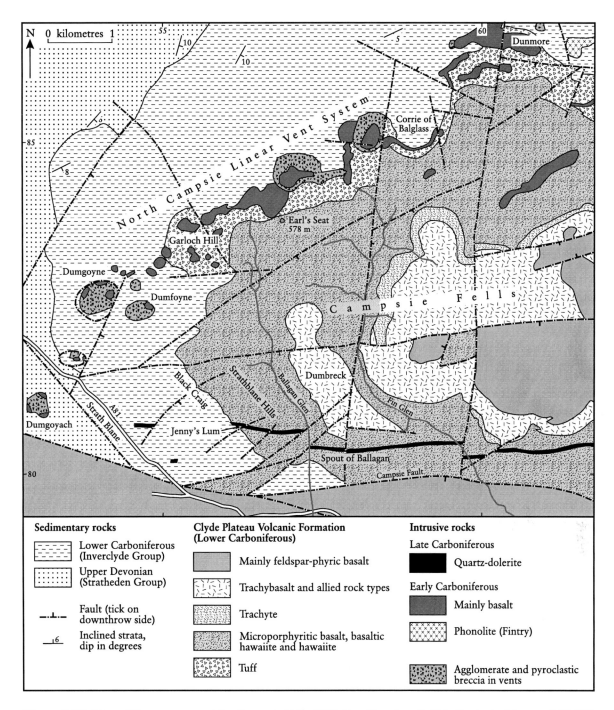

Figure 2.28 Map of the area around the Campsie Fells GCR site. Based on British Geological Survey 1:50 000 Sheet 30E, Glasgow (1993).

Description

The lava succession

Throughout the Campsie Fells the lavas rest directly upon the Clyde Sandstone Formation, the topmost division of the Tournaisian Inverclyde Group (Figures 2.4 and 2.28). The lavas form a plateau, dipping gently to the south-east and deeply dissected by Ballagan Glen (NS 565 830–NS 573 795) and Fin Glen (NS 583 833), where exposures of extensive parts of the succession supplement a continuous section in the steep cliffs at Black Craig

(NS 552 818), above Strath Blane. The overall succession is shown in Table 2.2. The lava plateau is cut by ENE-trending normal faults, which are displaced by a set of N–S-trending faults. To the south, the E–W-trending Campsie Fault downthrows to the south by some hundreds of metres, bringing the top of the Kilpatrick Hills succession into juxtaposition with the lower part of the Campsie succession (Figure 2.28).

The lavas vary in thickness from flow to flow and within flows, averaging about 10 m but in some instances exceeding 20 m. They generally take the form of single flow units, vesicular on top and in some cases displaying well-developed red bole between flows, the product of lateritic weathering. There are no clear indications of the development of multiple flow units or of other features typical of pahoehoe, so it is likely that the lavas were erupted as aa. The upper parts of the three lowest flows at Black Craig are particularly vesicular and slaggy, with drusy cavities, calcite veining, chalcedony veins and jasper lenses. The latter were at one time exploited as a source of material for the manufacture of jewellery in Edinburgh.

The basal lava at Black Craig is the most basic in the western Campsie sequence, being an olivine basalt containing abundant, randomly orientated, laths of labradorite (An_{66}), which comprise 55% of the rock. Olivine (12%) has been completely replaced by secondary minerals. A microcrystalline mesostasis contains small amounts of nepheline. The remainder of the succession in the Strathblane Hills is made up of flows that vary in composition from basaltic hawaiite to hawaiite. They are characteristically feldspar-rich, commonly display marked flow orientation of the feldspar, and contain variable amounts of augite which generally comprises less than 10% of the rock.

Studies of the petrology of the lavas are complicated by the almost ubiquitous replacement of olivine by secondary minerals such as 'serpentine', green pleochroic bowlingite and, in extreme cases, calcite. The oxidation state of the opaque oxides has also been affected to varying degrees so that titanomagnetite, which in some flows exceeds 9%, has undergone alteration resulting in the transformation of exsolved magnetite to maghemite (Goswami, 1968). This has the effect of distorting the ratio of ferrous to ferric iron in wholerock chemical analyses to the extent that some nepheline-bearing rocks appear to be silica-oversaturated in their normative composition. Most of this alteration can be explained by reaction of the early-formed minerals with the volatile fraction of the magma during the late stages of crystallization.

The distinctive texture of a hawaiite flow that occurs near the base of the succession in the Strathblane Hills allows it to be traced along the Campsie escarpment for at least 2.4 km (MacDonald, 1967). At Jenny's Lum (NS 562 806) it has a thickness in excess of 18 m of which the lowest 15 m are fresh, almost free of vesicles and display better developed columnar joints than is normal in the Campsie lavas (Figure 2.29). It is rich in andesine feldspar, much of it in the form of platy microphenocrysts; it has a small amount of nepheline in the mesostasis, and has both normative andesine and nepheline. Augite occurs only as microlites in the groundmass. It displays an unusually systematic gradational variation in its petrography, geochemistry and texture. This is most marked at Jenny's Lum where there is an overall tendency towards increasingly basic compositions in successively higher parts of the flow. There is a corresponding upward increase in the amount of augite and in the calcium content of the plagioclase,

Table 2.2 Succession of the Clyde Plateau Volcanic Formation in the western Campsie Fells. (After Hall *et al.*, 1998, table 4)

	Lava types	Source
Holehead Lava Member	Mainly feldspar-macrophyric basalt ('Markle type')	Waterhead central volcano
Fin Glen Lava Member	Microporphyritic basalt, mugearite, trachybasalt and a persistant phonolitic trachyte	Local centres and North Campsie Linear Vent System
Upper and Lower North Campsie lava members	Microporphyritic basalt, basaltic hawaiite and hawaiite	North Campsie Linear Vent System

Figure 2.29 Hawaiite lava at Jenny's Lum, western Campsie Fells. Note the flat-lying joints, particularly in the upper part of the flow, which are parallel to the flow texture of platy andesine microphenocrysts. The height of the cliff is over 15 m. (Photo: J.G. MacDonald.)

Renfrewshire Hills. One could argue that the Jenny's Lum and Dunrod Hill hawaiites are not truly composite but display gradational variations in composition, suggesting an orderly mode of emplacement of a magma that progressively changed in composition during the course of eruption. Such progressive variation in the composition of lava during the course of an eruption has been observed in historical activity in Iceland (Thorarinsson and Sigvaldason, 1972).

A distinctive phonolitic trachyte flow to the east of Fin Glen has petrographical similarities to an irregular intrusion of phonolite near Fintry (Hall *et al.*, 1998). This flow and a few analcime trachybasalts near North Berwick are the only silica-undersaturated evolved lavas known within the Carboniferous and Permian volcanic sequences of Britain. Elsewhere, any more evolved compositions trend towards quartz-trachytes and rhyolites (for discussion see **Traprain Law** GCR site report). The phonolitic trachyte marks the base of the Fin Glen lavas, which are, on average, more felsic than the underlying flows; in addition to basalt they include trachybasalt and mugearite. The topmost part of the succession in the western Campsie Fells consists of feldspar-macrophyric basalts ('Markle' type) of the Holehead Lava Member.

The North Campsie Linear Vent System and associated intrusions

Within the area of the Campsie Fells GCR site there are four major agglomerate-filled vents, a number of smaller ones and many associated intrusions that together form a continuous 7 km-long linear feature. This North Campsie Linear Vent System trends WSW from Dunmore (NS 606 865) to Garloch Hill (NS 553 836) (Figure 2.28). The volcanic plugs of Dumgoyne (NS 542 828) and Dumfoyne (NS 547 825) (Figure 2.27) are situated on this trend, which continues beyond the confines of the GCR site, through Dumgoyach, and to the WSW through the Kilpatrick Hills as far as Dumbarton (the Dumbarton–Fintry Line of Whyte and MacDonald, 1974; Figure 2.3; see **Dumbarton Rock** GCR site report). In close proximity to the vents, outcrops of bedded tuff and scoria represent the remains of cinder cones produced by lava fountaining.

matched by a systematic increase in the size of the feldspar microphenocrysts. In the upper part of the flow especially, the feldspar crystals impart a pronounced platy fabric, parallel to strongly developed flat-lying joints (Figure 2.29). In the very top of the flow these trends are partly reversed.

The gradational variations and apparent absence of internal discontinuities are very similar to those observed in hawaiitic flows in the northern part of the Renfrewshire Hills (Kennedy, 1931; see **Dunrod Hill** GCR site report). However, they are in contrast with composite lava flows involving two markedly different components, such as those described by Kennedy (1933) from elsewhere in the

The intrusive rocks associated with the vents vary in composition from basalt to hawaiite and mugearite. The basaltic types most commonly include microlitic and feldspar-microphyric varieties ('Jedburgh' type), and less commonly feldspar-macrophyric 'Markle' types. The more mafic varieties, rich in phenocrysts of olivine and augite, which occur in vents in the Kilpatrick Hills to the south of the Campsie Fault, are not represented in the Campsie vents. In general, the basalts and related rocks of the vent intrusions have suffered less immediate post-eruptive alteration than the lavas; olivine is much more commonly preserved, for example (see **Dumbarton Rock** GCR site report). It is likely that many vent intrusions represent fractions of magma that were emplaced at a late stage in individual eruptive sequences. As such they would commonly have been depleted in volatile constituents that had escaped to the surface through the open vent or had risen as gas bubbles to higher levels, now removed by erosion.

Whereas the North Campsie vents have an almost continuous outcrop that forms the north-western boundary of the lava plateau, Dumgoyne, Dumfoyne and a number of smaller vents and intrusions lie to the west of the main mass of lavas, forming isolated features. These plugs cut sedimentary rocks of the Ballagan Formation and, in the case of Dumgoyne, the underlying red and white cross-bedded sandstones of the lowermost Carboniferous Kinnesswood Formation. No part of the sub-aerial cone of these volcanic edifices is preserved *in situ* but both Dumgoyne and Dumfoyne are composed mainly of agglomeratic material, some of which may have slumped back into the volcanic conduit from higher levels at the end of eruptive episodes. At Dumgoyne, basaltic intrusions cut the agglomerates, especially on the eastern side of the vent where a major dyke-like mass occurs. Dumfoyne has only one small vent intrusion on the north side.

Within the western Campsie Fells a number of dykes have trends similar to that of the North Campsie Linear Vent System and coincide with ENE-trending normal faults. Some of these dykes are of feldspar-macrophyric ('Markle' type) basalt. Whyte and MacDonald (1974) have suggested that these could have been feeders for fissure eruptions of feldspar-phyric lavas, the latter having been subsequently removed by erosion of the top of the succession in the western Campsies.

Interpretation

The underlying structural control of the ENE-trending North Campsie Linear Vent System is probably related to a Caledonian lineament in the pre-Carboniferous basement (see 'Introduction' to this chapter). This trend is sufficiently similar to that of the feldspar-phyric dykes and associated normal faults to suggest that all three features are related to a common stress system. The high concentration of magmatic activity along the linear vent system is likely to have been accompanied by corresponding local swelling of the Earth's crust during periods of maximum magmatic activity. Such conditions are conducive to normal faulting, facilitating the intrusion of dykes, parallel to the elongation of the vents, as is seen in many areas of recent active volcanism. The swelling could also have created the palaeo-slope, down which the lavas flowed away from the vents.

The similarity in petrography and geochemistry between the vent intrusions and the lavas of the western Campsie Fells (MacDonald and Whyte, 1981) make it appear likely that the bulk of the succession, comprising the Fin Glen Lava Member and the Upper and Lower Campsie lavas, were derived from the North Campsie Linear Vent System and its continuation in Dumgoyne and Dumfoyne. It is difficult to correlate individual lavas precisely with particular vents, but Dumfoyne, although mainly composed of agglomerate, features a vent intrusion of hawaiite on its north side that is similar in its geochemistry and petrography to the Jenny's Lum hawaiite (MacDonald and Whyte, 1981). It is thus possible that the latter could have been erupted from this vent and hence flowed to the south-east for a minimum distance of nearly 4 km from its point of eruption. The phonolitic trachyte flow that marks the base of the Fin Glen Lava Member has a present-day extent of about 10 km^2. If the source of this flow is the Fintry phonolite intrusion (Hall *et al.*, 1998) it could originally have had an aerial extent in excess of 20 km^2 and flowed south for at least 6 km from its source. The dominantly felspar-phyric basaltic Holehead lavas at the top of the succession were most probably erupted from a large central volcanic complex at Waterhead, some 3.5 km to the east of the area covered by Figure 2.28, which has been described by Craig (1980) and Forsyth *et al.* (1996).

Conclusions

The Campsie Fells GCR site exhibits the lower part of the volcanic succession in the Campsie Fells; it is typical in many respects of the northern outcrops of the Visean Clyde Plateau Volcanic Formation. The lava pile is bounded to the north-west by a line of deeply eroded volcanic vents, representing the roots of small volcanoes, and a continuous apron of fragmental rocks formed from the ash and cinders of the volcanic cones. The vents consist of coarse blocky material that collapsed back into the conduit of the volcano at the end of each eruption, and many are intruded by volcanic plugs, formed as fresh magma forced its way towards the surface.

The North Campsie Linear Vent System is the most concentrated example of multiple volcanic vents preserved in Dinantian times in the Midland Valley, and the lava sequence of the Campsie Fells is one of few for which the general source area and hence the type of eruption can be clearly identified. It has even been possible to tentatively suggest specific vents as the sources for some individual lavas. Some of the more distinctive lavas can be traced for considerable distances. The lavas and intrusions have been the subject of several geochemical investigations and could provide material for a variety of further studies into magmatism in the Midland Valley and the origin and evolution of magmas in general. The volcanic plugs in particular could provide fresh rocks suitable for radiometric dating, which would have wider significance for the timing of events in the Midland Valley.

DUMBARTON ROCK, WEST DUNBARTONSHIRE (NS 400 745)

J.G. MacDonald

Introduction

The prominent landmark of Dumbarton Rock, on the north bank of the River Clyde at its confluence with the River Leven, has been a fortified site since the 5th century AD or earlier. Its situation, visual impact and state of preservation make it particularly significant as an example of a volcanic plug. It is the westernmost of a series of basaltic plugs and necks, extending in a broad belt for more than 25 km in an ENE direction as far as the Campsie Fells, that define the Dumbarton–Fintry volcanotectonic line (Whyte and MacDonald, 1974; Craig and Hall, 1975; Figure 2.3; see **Campsie Fells** GCR site report). The plug cuts Tournaisian sedimentary rocks of the Inverclyde Group, and the nearest outcrops of possible associated lavas (the Visean Clyde Plateau Volcanic Formation) occur about 2.5 km to the north-east in the Kilpatrick Hills, and 1.5 km to the south, on the opposite bank of the River Clyde.

Despite its easy accessibility, the excellent exposures of fresh glacially smoothed rock and the well-exposed relationships of the intrusive basalt with adjacent tuffs, agglomerate and sandstone, very little was published on Dumbarton Rock prior to a detailed investigation by Whyte (1966). Its popularity as a geological excursion locality is reflected by descriptions in field guides, based largely upon Whyte's account (Whyte and Weedon in Lawson and Weedon, 1992). Further geochemical aspects were discussed by Whyte (1980) and a single K-Ar whole-rock age determination of 302 ± 8 Ma (c. 308 Ma using new constants) was reported by De Souza (1979).

Description

Dumbarton Rock rises to a height of 73 m above the reclaimed intertidal mudflats at the mouth of the River Leven (Figure 2.30). It is roughly oval in plan having an east–west elongation of 275 m and a north–south width of 200 m. A NW-trending gully divides the summit area. There is a distinctive pattern of columnar jointing. The columns, averaging about 60 cm in diameter, fan downwards and outwards at steep angles, with a tendency in some places for the inclination to become shallower near the base of the Rock (Figure 2.31).

The relationship between the intrusive basalt, adjacent pyroclastic rocks and associated sedimentary rocks is seen only on the north-west side of the plug (NS 399 746) where bedrock is exposed along about 80 m of shoreline. At the southern end of the section, sandstone, beds of fissile mudrock and carbonate rocks ('cementstones') of the (Tournaisian) Ballagan Formation dip steeply towards the contact. The sedimentary rocks are in the form of isolated blocks up to about 20 m in length, which are either faulted against tuffs and agglomerates or have fallen into them in the volcanic vent (Whyte, 1966).

Figure 2.30 Dumbarton Rock, a plug of olivine basalt, from the River Clyde. (Photo: J.G. MacDonald.)

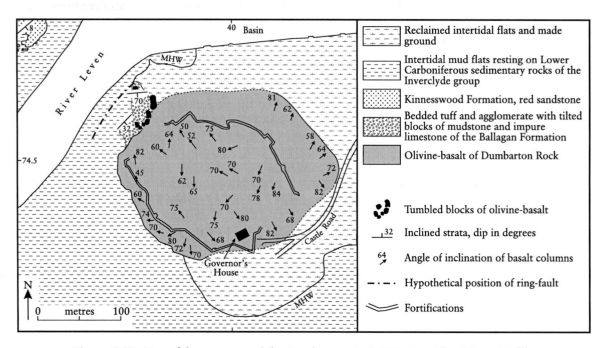

Figure 2.31 Map of the area around the Dumbarton Rock GCR site. After Whyte (1966).

There is a narrow zone of contact alteration, up to 15 cm wide, in the sandstones and 'cementstones' adjacent to the plug, and sandstone xenoliths up to about 30 cm in diameter have been incorporated in the basalt. In the xenoliths, quartz may have been altered to tridymite in reaction rims. The basalt close to the contact is chilled and highly altered. The groundmass olivine and augite are completely altered to chlorite and the feldspar to albite; abundant amygdales are also present, containing spherulitic green chlorite and in some cases a little calcite. Chemical analyses indicate the incorporation of a significant amount of water into the basalt at, or closely following, the time of intrusion. This effect decreases away from the

92

contact and is hardly discernible a metre or so into the plug. Within this 1 m zone, barium and strontium decrease in concentration towards the margin of the basalt and there is a corresponding increase in concentration of barium and, to a lesser extent, strontium in the immediately adjacent sedimentary rocks, especially in sandstone (Whyte, 1980).

Away from the contact zone the basalt of the plug is fine grained and has a uniform microporphyritic texture with microphenocrysts of labradoritic plagioclase and olivine (Fa_{31}) set in a fine-grained groundmass of plagioclase, generally granular augite and opaque iron oxides. Accessory minerals include chlorite, analcime and apatite. In addition to the xenoliths of country rock incorporated in the margins, a few dunitic xenoliths have been found. Although no mineral layering has been detected, flow texture of microphenocrysts and groundmass feldspar laths is common. There is an apparent increase in the ratio of plagioclase to augite from an average of 2.3:1 at the base of the rock to 4.2:1 at the summit. Such variations in mode are common within lavas and plugs of basaltic affinity in the Clyde Plateau Volcanic Formation.

Compositions of fresh basalts from Dumbarton Rock (Whyte, 1966, table 2) are similar in most respects to those found in lavas and plugs of Visean age in the nearby Kilpatrick Hills. The magnesium content, although unusually low, is within the range of variation found within the Clyde Plateau Volcanic Formation (MacDonald and Whyte, 1981). The fresh rock is nepheline-normative and De Souza (1979) suggested that it should therefore be regarded as basanitic. However, no modal nepheline and only accessory amounts of analcime have been identified. On these grounds the rock should be termed an alkali olivine basalt. It differs petrographically from many lavas of the Kilpatrick Hills and other parts of the Clyde Plateau Volcanic Formation only in the freshness of the olivine. The freshness is reflected by relatively high FeO/Fe_2O_3 ratios, a feature that it shares with other plugs associated with the formation. This contrasts with the lavas, in which late-stage alteration, attributable to autometasomatism, increases the proportion of ferric iron. In turn this affects the norm calculation in such a way that the lavas often appear to be more silica-saturated than the plugs.

Interpretation

It has commonly been assumed that Dumbarton Rock was emplaced as a vent intrusion at or near the top of the conduit of a volcano that was active during the time of eruption of the lavas of the Kilpatrick Hills (Whyte, 1966). However, whereas the northern outcrops of the Clyde Plateau Volcanic Formation appear to have been erupted between about 330 Ma and 320 Ma (*c.* 337–327 Ma with new constants), a single K-Ar determination of a sample of fresh basalt from Dumbarton Rock yielded a date of *c.* 308 Ma with new constants (De Souza, 1979). This, together with the perceived basanitic nature of the plug, led De Souza to suggest that the emplacement of the plug took place in Late Carboniferous time and hence that it was not related directly to the Visean volcanism. There is nothing particularly distinctive about Dumbarton Rock in its geographical setting that would set it apart from other vent intrusions in the northern Clyde Plateau and, given the apparent petrographical affinities with the adjacent lavas and plugs, it seems appropriate, for now, to regard the single Late Carboniferous K-Ar date as an anomaly. This fresh intrusion would, however, be a good subject for further dating by the Ar-Ar method, not only to clarify its own association but also to date the age of volcanism in this part of the Midland Valley more accurately.

The joint pattern of Dumbarton Rock is consistent with the base of the cooling body of intruded basalt liquid having the form of an inverted cone. Hence Whyte (1966) deduced that the form of the base of the intrusion could have been determined by the shape of the volcanic crater into which it was emplaced. The basalt of the plug contains abundant amygdales in the contact zone but these become much less common away from the contacts. The presence of amygdales is a clear indication that the basalt was emplaced at low pressure and most likely at a time when there was a connection with the surface. From this it can be inferred that the plug infilled the vent of an active volcano and might indeed represent the lower part of a lava lake that formed in the active crater. Lava lakes formed in such conditions can remain liquid for sufficient time to allow degassing to take place; hence the paucity of amygdales in all but the chilled margins of the plug. The degassing of the magma could account for the freshness of the olivine, which in Visean volcanic rocks is almost invariably replaced by secondary minerals. Mineralogical and geochemical evidence also suggests the subsequent outward migration of volatiles, resulting in chloritization, albitization and some leaching of trace elements from the basalt into the immediately adjacent country rock (Whyte, 1980).

The marginal ring of pyroclastic rocks contains tilted blocks of the Ballagan Formation that are at a structural level below its inferred base in this area. Hence the Ballagan Formation beds most likely collapsed into the open vent, along with parts of the cone, during an interval of decreased eruptive intensity, and are preserved in a subsided cylindrical block within an inferred ring-fault (Figures 2.31 and 2.32). From the above it appears highly probable that the plug was emplaced at a time when the crater of the volcano was open. The lava lake so formed could well have been overflowing to produce a lava flow, now removed by erosion. Similar historical monogenetic volcanoes commonly erupt continuously for periods of many weeks or months and so there would have been adequate time to supply the fluids, and maintain the temperatures needed to account for the observed contact phenomena.

Conclusions

The Dumbarton Rock GCR site combines historical significance as a fortified site with geological importance as the remnant of a mass of lava that solidified in the crater of an Early Carboniferous volcano. It is composed of alkali olivine basalt and has close petrographical and geochemical affinities with the Visean volcanic rocks of the Clyde Plateau Volcanic Formation in the adjacent Kilpatrick Hills. It has special significance as an example of a volcanic plug. Its isolated position, standing above the mudflats of the Clyde estuary, provides a three-dimensional view of the columnar joint pattern that is unrivalled in the west of Scotland. The level of erosion also exhibits the relationships between the basalt plug, remnants of the volcanic cone and country rocks that are seldom seen in the remains of Palaeozoic volcanoes. A single K-Ar radiometric date that suggests a Late Carboniferous age appears to be anomalous in the light of the other evidence and highlights the need for further dating using more accurate modern methods.

DUNROD HILL, INVERCLYDE (NS 236 741–NS 246 721)

D. Stephenson

Introduction

Dunrod Hill, 5 km south of Gourock, is part of the Renfrewshire Hills succession of the Clyde Plateau Volcanic Formation, of Dinantian age. The lavas are typical representatives of the Strathgryfe Lava Member, which comprises the thickest part of the formation and dominates the northern part of the Renfrewshire Hills. It has been selected for the GCR because of excellent exposures of composite lava flows of hawaiite composition, first described by W.Q. Kennedy in 1931. Such flows, comprising a markedly feldspar-phyric upper part overlying an aphyric base, are fairly common in the Strathgryfe Lava Member and have also been described else-

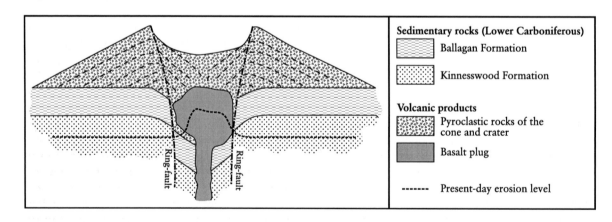

Figure 2.32 Diagrammatic cross-section illustrating possible structures associated with the Dumbarton Rock volcano. After Whyte (1966, fig. 4).

where in the Clyde Plateau Volcanic Formation. They also occur in the Paleocene lava sequence of the Isle of Skye, where they are represented by the Roineval GCR site in the *British Tertiary Volcanic Province* GCR Volume (Emeleus and Gyopari, 1992).

The Renfrewshire Hills succession is typical of the Clyde Plateau Volcanic Formation in that it comprises mainly lavas of a mildly alkaline to transitional, alkali-basalt series, dominated by olivine basalts, hawaiites and mugearites, but ranging locally through to trachyandesites, trachytes and rhyolites (Johnstone, 1965; Paterson *et al.*, 1990; Monro, 1999). The whole succession may be up to 1000 m thick in the north of the hills, of which up to 750 m are the Strathgryfe Lava Member. This member is characterized by feldspar-phyric flows ('Markle' type in the local classification), mostly of hawai-itic composition, and aphyric mugearites in approximately equal proportions; there are few basalts. The eruptions were entirely subaerial and the presence of reddened flow tops and lat-eritic beds are indicators of tropical weathering between eruptions. Pyroclastic rocks are rare in the main basalt–hawaiite–mugearite sequences and there are no features to suggest a central volcano. The lower parts of the lava pile are cut by numerous dykes with a predominant north-eastward trend, particularly along the projected continuation of the Dumbarton–Fintry Line (see 'Introduction' to this chapter), which may mark the site of fissure eruptions.

A general description of the volcanic succes-sion in the northern part of the Renfrewshire Hills is given in the British Geological Survey memoir (Paterson *et al.*, 1990), and many analyses from the district have been included in a geochemical and petrological study of Dinantian lavas of the Midland Valley by Smedley (1986a,b, 1988a). Subsequent to the descrip-tion by Kennedy (1931), the composite lavas were included in a general study of composite bodies by Boyd (1974), who included 18 analyses from this GCR site. The radiometric age of the Clyde Plateau Volcanic Formation as a whole has been suggested as 335 Ma to 325 Ma, based upon K-Ar whole-rock and mineral dates of the freshest lavas and associated intrusions (De Souza, 1982). This is broadly compatible with its lithostratigraphical position (within the Strathclyde Group), which, in the absence of any reliable biostratigraphical data, suggests a Visean age.

Description

The area between Dunrod Hill and Greenock is a fault-bound block of lavas, separated from the main outcrop of the Clyde Plateau Volcanic Formation in the northern Renfrew-shire Hills by the Largs Fault Zone. This struc-ture is a major NNE-trending splay off the Highland Boundary Fault and has a complex history of movement, mainly prior to the erup-tion of the lavas, but with some post-lava move-ment (Paterson *et al.*, 1990). To the north-west, the lava outcrop is cut by the Spango Valley along the line of the NE-trending Inverkip faults, which are also probably related to the Highland Boundary Fault. The south-western flank of Dunrod Hill is controlled by the Dunrod Fault, juxtaposing the lava sequence against the strati-graphically lower Clyde Sandstone Formation which forms slightly lower hills to the south-west.

The name 'Dunrod Hill' was formerly applied to the whole of the hill above and to the north-east of Shielhill Glen (cf. Kennedy, 1931), where-as on modern maps it is restricted to the 298 m hilltop with a triangulation pillar (NS 240 726). The GCR site is centred upon the hilltop now known as 'Cauldron Hill' (NS 236 729) and is bound to the south-west and north-west by the aqueduct that takes water from Loch Thom to Greenock (Figure 2.33).

Within this area the volcanic succession dips gently to the north or NNE and consists entirely of hawaiite and mugearite lavas. The former are notably feldspar-macrophyric with a dark-purple matrix. The central parts of flows are generally massive and these tend to form low crags and the more obvious topographical features of the area. The mugearites are pale grey, fine grained and aphyric. Their exposures are characterized by closely spaced jointing broadly parallel to the flow surfaces, and some weathered surfaces have lines etched in a similar orientation. In thin section these planar features are seen to reflect an orientation of the ground-mass feldspars, which is almost certainly due to flow foliation. Both types of lava have amyg-daloidal zones, most notably, but not exclusively, at the top and bottom of the flow, where they are commonly associated with autobrecciation and hydrothermal alteration. Such zones weather more easily than the more massive central parts of flows and are exposed mainly in stream sections.

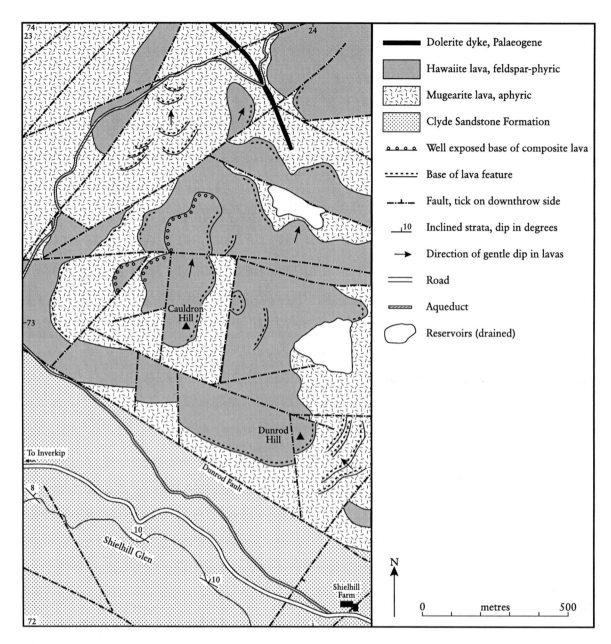

Figure 2.33 Map of the area around the Dunrod Hill GCR site. Based on British Geological Survey 1:10 000 Sheet NS 27 SW (1987).

The composite lavas that are the main feature of this site are best exposed high on the western flank of Cauldron Hill, where they form conspicuous crag features (Figure 2.34). Kennedy (1931) identified two such flows on Cauldron Hill and a further one around the headwaters of the Hole of Spango. The current 1:10 000 scale British Geological Survey map (NS 27 SW, 1987) shows far more faults than the original (Kennedy) mapping, so that the correlation of flows between fault blocks is less certain, but

there are certainly at least two composite flows in this area. Similar flows also occur a short distance to the north of the site.

The lower part of each composite flow is aphyric and usually exhibits the platy jointing and foliation that is characteristic of mugearite flows. This is overlain by macroporphyritic lava with abundant (15 to 22%) feldspar phenocrysts up to 15 mm in diameter and rare (less than 1%) microphenocrysts of clinopyroxene and titanomagnetite. The relative proportions of the two

96

Figure 2.34 View from the north-west flank of Cauldron Hill, towards Gourock and the River Clyde. The low crag is typical of the composite hawaiitic lavas in the Dunrod Hill GCR site. (Photo: D. Stephenson.)

facies vary, but the flows are always asymmetrical with typical thicknesses of about 1 m for the lower facies and 5 m for the upper. The junction between the facies is gradational in places, but more commonly it occurs abruptly over a distance of only a few centimeters. There is no sharp contact and neither facies is chilled. The fine-grained groundmass of the upper facies is indistinguishable from the lower facies and seems to be in continuity with it. In some places, rare macrophenocrysts of feldspar, similar to those of the porphyritic facies, are observed in the upper 80 cm of the aphyric facies. The junction occurs within the massive, central part of the flow and there is never any intervening amygdaloidal or slaggy, brecciated zone, such as is usually seen at flow margins. In most exposures the junction is planar and parallel to the flow surface, with only minor irregularities. However, Kennedy (1931) recorded interfingering in places and cites several instances where one or other of the facies is pinched out. In most cases, this absence of one facies is based on correlation of flows between exposures and is difficult to substantiate. However, at one place the aphyric lower facies is seen to cut up through the porphyritic upper facies, with platy jointing parallel to the junction and

clearly dipping at a higher angle than is usual (Kennedy, 1931, locality B; NS 2333 7316). Junctions with underlying and overlying flows, where seen, exhibit the slaggy, brecciated and amygdaloidal zones that are typical of the lava sequence and leave its extrusive nature in no doubt.

Almost all analyses from the composite flows (Kennedy, 1931; Boyd, 1974) fall within the field of hawaiite, whether in the classification based on normative composition (as used for Scottish Dinantian lavas by Macdonald, 1975; Smedley, 1986a; Paterson *et al.*, 1990; Monro, 1999), or in the TAS (total alkalis/silica) system based on oxide percentages (as favoured by Boyd, 1974, and the IUGS classification of Le Maitre, 2002). In the normative classification the more basic compositions could be classed as 'basaltic hawaiites'. Boyd (1974) analysed both whole-rock and groundmass from several samples, confirming field and petrographical observations that the groundmass of the porphyritic facies is very similar to analyses of aphyric rocks close to the junction of the facies. Slightly more fractionated aphyric rocks occur in the lowest parts of the flows, farthest from the junction; these fall just within the mugearite field in the TAS classification. In common with most lavas of the Clyde Plateau Volcanic Formation, the rocks are transitional alkaline and are mostly olivine-hypersthene-normative.

The petrography of the two facies has been described in detail by Kennedy (1931). Feldspar compositions are particularly instructive and have been studied by Boyd (1974). Despite the hawaiitic whole-rock compositions, the plagioclase macrophenocrysts in both facies are very calcic. In the porphyritic facies, complexly zoned cores of bytownite ranging from An_{78-68} are surrounded by normally zoned rims of labradorite, An_{70-58}. The rare macrophenocrysts in the top of the aphyric facies have compositions of An_{76-70}, identical to the cores in the porphyritic rock. Scattered microphenocrysts in the aphyric facies (An_{55-28}) are andesine, identical in composition to the groundmass feldspars of the porphyritic facies (An_{55-30}). Groundmass feldspars in the aphyric rocks are strongly zoned in the andesine range, An_{40-28}. Normative feldspar compositions suggest that significant alkali feldspar (?anorthoclase) may be present in the groundmass.

Interpretation

There can be little doubt that where the two rock-types at Dunrod Hill are juxtaposed as described above, they are parts of a single composite body. The massive, fresh exposures pass upwards and downwards into typically rubbly and amygdaloidal marginal zones, but the internal junction is near planar, undisturbed, unaltered and the aphyric facies seems to be continuous with the groundmass of the porphyritic facies. The two facies cannot have originated as separate flows. Although the transition from porphyritic to non-porphyritic is abrupt, there is no sign of a chill or any other manifestation of a sharp intrusive contact. Nor are any other sharp contacts observed within the bodies, so the possibility of either (or both) of the components having been intruded as sills into a pre-existing lava is unlikely.

The mechanisms whereby composite lava flows may be generated and preserved are more difficult to envisage than those responsible for composite intrusions, in which pulses of magma from either the same or from various sources are channelled up a common conduit. Kennedy (1931) discussed the possibility of some form of in-situ separation of crystals that were suspended in the magma on extrusion. He

dismissed gravitative differentiation on the grounds that plagioclase crystals should sink, rather than float, in a magma of hawaiitic composition. He also reasoned that complete separation would be unlikely in the short time between eruption and the cooling magma becoming too viscous to allow movement of crystals. Separation due to liquid or viscous flow also seems unlikely to have produced such clear and complete separation without any sign of turbulent flow patterns, however slight, or of intermingling at the junction of facies.

Kennedy (1931) concluded that the differentiation must have occurred prior to extrusion and that the eruption involved two types of magma from 'separate bodies within the magma basin'. Although near-simultaneous eruption and intermingling of two distinct magmas can be inferred at Craigmarloch Wood (NS 345 719), from another composite flow in the Renfrewshire Hills described by Kennedy (1933), it does not seem necessary to invoke such a complex and coincidental event for the Cauldron Hill flows. The detailed geochemical and mineralogical data of Boyd (1974) confirm the impression gained from field relationships and petrography that the two rock-types are not only close in whole-rock composition, but also show evidence of a close genetic inter-relationship. The distribution of trace elements, particularly Sr, Ba and Rb, strongly suggests plagioclase fractionation, and numerical modelling is able to predict the observed compositional range simply by fractionation of the observed phenocryst phases. In this respect the Cauldron Hill composite flows differ from others studied by Boyd, which require more complex processes.

So, it is likely that the flows were erupted from magma chambers in which the crystallization and settling of plagioclase and, to a much lesser extent, clinopyroxene and titanomagnetite had resulted in zoning in terms of both mineral proportions and bulk magma composition. The upper, phenocryst-free portion was erupted first, followed by phenocryst-bearing magma, possibly as the phenocryst-free magma became exhausted. The continuous nature of the groundmass at the junction between the two phases suggests that full crystallization of the first pulse had not occurred when it was over-ridden by the second, possibly within a few hours by analogy with modern flows. Kennedy (1931) cited localities where the later pulse completely over-ran the earlier pulse to rest directly on the underlying flow, and other localities where only the earlier pulse reached. Such occurrences are highly likely, but are difficult to recognize and substantiate on the ground.

Given the limited variation in whole-rock composition seen in the composite flows and the inferred rapid sequential changes during the eruptions, it is probable that the magma chambers were small local developments, quite close to the surface. Maybe they were similar in form to compositionally zoned dykes that are exposed elsewhere in the world (e.g. South Greenland; Bridgwater and Harry, 1968). These in turn were probably fed from deeper magma chambers where the hawaiitic magmas were produced by higher pressure fractionation of mantle-derived alkali olivine basalts; the bytownite cores to the macrophenocrysts may be relics of this early stage. The compositional range throughout most of the Strathgryfe Lava Member is not much greater than that seen in the composite flows, which may therefore provide a model for magmatic differentiation in the whole lava field and possibly even for similar fields worldwide.

Conclusions

The lava sequence exposed in the area around Dunrod Hill is typical of the Strathgryfe Lava Member, which comprises by far the greatest part of the Visean Clyde Plateau Volcanic Formation in the Renfrewshire Hills. The member is characterized by a restricted range of lavas which are almost all either hawaiites, with phenocrysts (large crystals) of plagioclase feldspar, or slightly more evolved mugearites, which have no crystals visible to the naked eye.

On Cauldron Hill both rock-types can be seen, one above the other, in the same 'composite' lava flows. The relatively sharp but uninterrupted transition between the two rock-types and the close geochemical and mineralogical relationships between them suggest that they were emplaced in rapid succession as pulses of the same eruption. It is likely that the pulses tapped different levels of a near-surface magma chamber that had become compositionally zoned as some of the earliest minerals to crystallize (mainly feldspars) settled out. The Cauldron Hill composite flows are some of the best in Britain and have potential international importance for further studies on the evolution of magmas in high-level magma chambers that feed surface eruptions.

MACHRIHANISH COAST AND SOUTH KINTYRE, ARGYLL AND BUTE (NR 625 201–NR 640 208, NR 629 192–NR 651 182 and NR 688 171–NR 707 155)

I.T. Williamson

Introduction

The Dinantian volcanic rocks that crop out in the south of the Kintyre peninsula belong to the Clyde Plateau Volcanic Formation (Strathclyde Group), the most extensive lava succession within the Carboniferous–Permian Igneous Province of northern Britain. The succession is typical of continental lava plateaux formed by the accumulation of overlapping lava sequences. However, unlike the other lava fields that make up the Clyde Plateau Volcanic Formation the Kintyre sequence lies entirely north of the Highland Boundary Fault and, like the nearby Visean volcanic rocks at Ballycastle in Northern Ireland, is therefore structurally outside the graben of the Midland Valley. The Kintyre sequence is also separated by a considerable distance from coeval lava fields in central Scotland and it is not known if these were ever in physical continuity.

The Machrihanish Coast and South Kintyre GCR site (Figure 2.35) contains some lithologies that are either absent or poorly represented elsewhere within the Clyde Plateau Volcanic Formation. Low-potassium tholeiitic basalt lavas are known only from the Kintyre succession, and benmoreites and trachytes are underrepresented elsewhere.

The earliest accounts of the igneous rocks of this district are rather sketchy and appear in the writings of John MacCulloch (1819); they were shown on his general geological map of Scotland in 1840 as a band extending from Campbeltown to the west coast. These igneous rocks figure briefly in papers by Nicol (1852) and Thomson (1865). Nicol divided them into 'Porphyries' and 'Augitic traps' and noted their association with the 'red sandstones and Carboniferous strata' of the district. However, it was Geikie (1897) who was the first to recognize that the Kintyre lava field forms an outlying portion of what he termed the Clyde Plateau.

The Kintyre area was first surveyed in detail by R.G. Symes and the map was published at the 1:63 360 scale by the Geological Survey

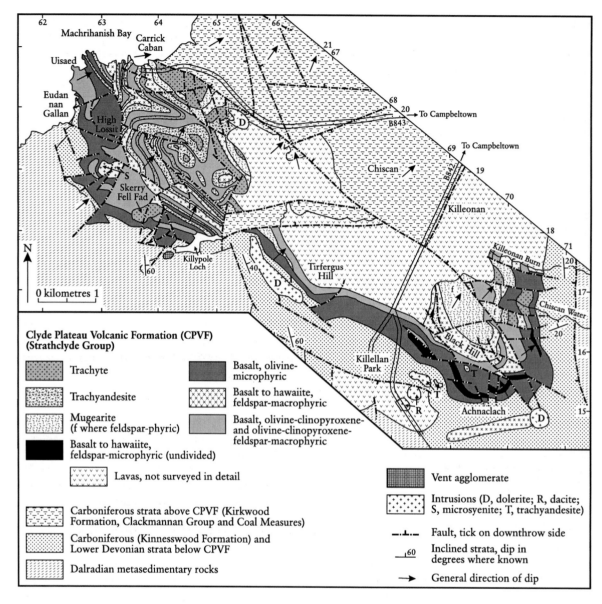

Figure 2.35 Map of the area around the Machrihanish Coast and South Kintyre GCR site. Based on British Geological Survey 1:50 000 Provisional Series Sheet 12, Campbeltown (1996).

in 1894. Details of the volcanic succession were not known until considerably later, when many of the area's pertinent features were described by McCallien (1927). The most recent mapping is by M.M. Avison and M.K. Carr in 1976, and H.M. Ayles and S.P. Duckworth in 1977, undergraduates at the University of Lancaster supervised by R. Macdonald. Their work has been incorporated in the 1:50 000 scale Provisional Series map of the British Geological Survey (Sheet 12, Campbeltown, 1996).

The Kintyre lavas have been featured in several wide-ranging studies of the geochemistry of Dinantian volcanism across the Scottish part of the Carboniferous–Permian Igneous Province of northern Britain by Macdonald (1975, 1980) and Smedley (1986a,b, 1988a) and consequently over 60 whole-rock analyses are available. They were also the main subject of a specific geochemical investigation by Smedley (1988b), highlighting differences in the mantle source of Dinantian magmas across the Highland Boundary Fault.

Machrihanish Coast and South Kintyre

Description

There are five outcrops of the Clyde Plateau Volcanic Formation in south Kintyre. They comprise a broad belt extending south-eastwards from Machrihanish on the west coast to Tirfergus Hill and Killellan (the 'Machrihanish Lavas' of McCallien, 1927), three relatively small outliers north of Campbeltown, and an outlier on the south-east coast, east of Southend (the 'Southend Lavas' of McCallien, 1927 and Smedley, 1986a). The Machrihanish Coast and South Kintyre GCR site is a composite site made up of three areas selected from the first, and largest, of these outcrops (Figure 2.35). These are the coast section west and north of Machrihanish village (NR 640 208–NR 625 201), the area around the hill of Skerry Fell Fad (NR 638 183) and the area around Black Hill (NR 692 162).

In all three areas of the GCR site the Kintyre lavas overlie an unconformity. Along the western margin of the Machrihanish coast section and in the Chiscan Water on the eastern flank of Black Hill, the volcanic sequence rests upon the Kinnesswood Formation of the Inverclyde Group. This comprises white and red cross-bedded sandstones, and red-brown siltstones with nodules and beds of pedogenic limestone ('cornstone'). At Skerry Fell Fad the Kinnesswood Formation is only present in a small area in the west. Elsewhere, the lavas rest directly upon the Stonefield Schists, a unit of the Neoproterozoic Dalradian Supergroup.

The top of the Clyde Plateau Volcanic Formation in Kintyre is marked by a non-sequence, above which there is, in places, a reddish bauxitic deposit. This, the Kirkwood Formation, mostly comprises a diachronous lateritized, coarse- to fine-grained detrital volcaniclastic deposit that is interpreted as having formed by the contemporaneous weathering of the volcanic rocks. Elsewhere, the overlying rocks belong to the Lower Limestone Formation and Limestone Coal Formation of the Machrihanish Coalfield (McCallien and Anderson, 1930).

The Clyde Plateau Volcanic Formation in southern Kintyre comprises up to 400 m of volcanic rocks, predominantly lavas, dipping to the south-east (Figure 2.35). At some stratigraphical levels the lavas are complexly interdigitated, especially in the lower parts of the Black Hill section. Differences in the mineralogical composition and internal structure of the

flows are exploited by weathering to produce a terraced landform ('trap topography') which is particularly well developed on Tirfergus Hill (NR 6645 1722), between the Skerry Fell Fad and Black Hill areas, and near Killellan. By contrast, the areas around Machrihanish and Skerry Fell Fad are characterized by much more rounded and lenticular landscape features, the difference resulting from variations in composition and morphology of the flows. The lava field is cut by a number of NW-trending faults.

The lower part of the lava succession is dominantly olivine basalt that is commonly macroporphyritic, along with some interbedded olivine-pyroxene-macrophyric (ankaramitic) basalt. The upper part contains most of the more evolved rock-types, including hawaiite, mugearite, benmoreite, trachyandesite and trachyte. Some of these lavas may be composite bodies. Several plugs, sills and dykes with compositions ranging from olivine-dolerite to microsyenite and dacite are also exposed (Macdonald, 1975).

Machrihanish coast

The coastal section from Machrihanish Bay westwards offers the most readily accessible part of the GCR site. Within it, a range of lithologies and structures typical of the Clyde Plateau Volcanic Formation may be examined.

A west to east traverse along the coast from Eudan nan Gallan (NR 6260 2027) to east of Carrick Caban (NR 6400 2085) passes up through the volcanic sequence of more than 20 lavas. The lower two-thirds of the sequence comprises basalt with various olivine, clinopyroxene and plagioclase phenocryst assemblages, interbedded with trachyandesites. The higher part of the sequence, east of Big Stone (NR 6350 2090), comprises up to seven flows of trachyte, mugearite and trachyandesite with a thin porphyritic basalt near the base. McCallien (1927) stated that 'tuffs and agglomerates are common associates of the lavas' in this section, but these lithologies are not shown on the latest British Geological Survey map.

Most of the lavas are tabular, sheet-like bodies. The wide range of characteristic lava-flow features exhibited include glassy (in places devitrified) flows, porphyritic variants including some with glomeroporphyritic textures, amygdaloidal and massive flow-units, blocky autobreccias, flow-base and flow-top breccias, ramp structures, and

101

a variety of flow-induced structures. Some flows are remarkably fresh, but most are severely weathered or intensely altered. Olivine is almost always seen as pseudomorphs.

Skerry Fell Fad

The lower part of the volcanic succession also crops out on the slopes of Skerry Fell Fad (NR 6375 1820). The sequence includes olivine-microphyric basalts ('Dalmeny' type), olivine-clinopyroxene-feldspar-macrophyric basalts ('Dunsapie' type) and an olivine-clinopyroxene-macrophyric (ankaramitic) basalt ('Craiglockhart' type), succeeded by inter-bedded basalt and trachyandesite. The ankaramitic basalt is the same flow that occurs close to the base of the Clyde Plateau Volcanic Formation sequence at Eudan nan Gallan on the coastal section. The more evolved rock-types seen in the upper part of the succession in the coastal section are not present. However, a pale-weathered trachyte forms the summit of Skerry Fell Fad (Figure 2.36).

Apart from supplementing the range of lithologies and volcanic structures observed in the Machrihanish coastal section, this area exhibits the following features:

- The disconformable nature of the base of the Clyde Plateau Volcanic Formation may be demonstrated.
- The trachyte that caps Skerry Fell Fad has an unusual form. The body has both steep-sided and gently inclined basal contacts with at least two different basaltic lavas.
- Close to the base of the succession, south-west of Skerry Fell Fad, a single lava of tholeiitic (hypersthene-normative) basalt is interbedded with aphyric or microporphyritic basaltic lavas (Macdonald, 1975; Smedley, 1986a, 1988b). This basalt has the lowest K_2O content of any analysed Dinantian basalt and also has distinctive trace-element, rare-earth-element and isotopic compositions.
- Locally, there are minor intrusions and pyroclastic breccias, the latter possibly representing the sites of volcanic vents (Figure 2.35). Minor intrusions, mostly thought to be contemporaneous with the Dinantian volcanism, are not particularly widespread in the southern Kintyre lava field. Of note is a sheet, possibly a sill, of albite-phyric microsyenite exposed in a disused quarry (NR 6308 1907), 400 m SSW of High Lossit, which appears to have been intruded along the unconformity below the lavas. South-west

Figure 2.36 Skerry Fell Fad, Macrihanish Coast and South Kintyre GCR site. The summit rocks are trachyte, either infilling an earlier valley feature or possibly forming a lava dome. Note the terracettes due to soil creep on the steep slopes below the summit. (Photo: C. Bond.)

Machrihanish Coast and South Kintyre

of Killypole Loch (NR 6415 1757), a small outcrop of igneous breccia, containing mostly basaltic clasts and mapped as 'vent' agglomerate, is associated with a small plug of olivine-dolerite. Its exact relationship to the rest of the lavas is unclear.

Black Hill

Black Hill, SSW of Campbeltown, is separated from the Skerry Fell Fad area by an extensive tract of relatively poorly exposed ground. The Clyde Plateau Volcanic Formation sequence around Black Hill is broadly similar to that in the other areas, with the proportion of lavas of more evolved composition generally increasing stratigraphically upwards. However, in contrast to the other areas, the lower part of the succession also includes some evolved flows. Trachyte near the base of the formation in the Chiscan Water (NR 7025 1680) about 1.25 km north-east of Black Hill, and benmoreite south of Black Hill (NR 691 163) may in fact be parts of the same flow (Smedley, 1986a). Also, within the higher units on Black Hill, there are aphyric and feldspar-phyric mugearite lavas.

Between Killellan Park (NR 6815 1640) and Killeonan Burn (NR 6970 1770–NR 7055 1740), there are lateral stratigraphical variations and other complex relationships between the lavas. The outcrop is much faulted and some lavas appear to be restricted to certain fault blocks. This is especially true of the sequences either side of the major NW-trending fault that runs from Carrick Caban on Machrihanish Bay (NR 6390 2080) to a point (NR 7045 1525) about 1 km east of Achnaclach (Figure 2.35).

Interpretation

The Kintyre sequence of the Clyde Plateau Volcanic Formation shows a broad, two-fold subdivision, with basic lithologies more common in the lower part and more evolved rocks dominating the upper part. Smaller scale variations in lithostratigraphy, such as those suggested by the different fault-block successions in the Black Hill area, may be explained in part by pre-existing topography. Lavas may have been channelled through low-lying areas between older flows and in graben-like structures between contemporaneous volcanic fault scarps. Some of the faults may be re-activations of older, deep-seated (?Caledonian) structures. Similar abrupt varia-

tions in local successions are also characteristic of the Lower Dinantian Birrenswark Volcanic Formation in the Anglo-Scottish Borders Region (see **Langholm–Newcastleton Hills** GCR site report). Small-scale fault-control of this type within the lava field may be common throughout the Clyde Plateau Volcanic Formation in the Midland Valley of Scotland.

The basal contact relationships of the trachytic body capping Skerry Fell Fad suggest that it is either a shallow intrusive body or that the underlying lavas had been eroded prior to its emplacement. Trachytic lavas are normally highly viscous and typically do not travel any great distance from their source. Hence, the trachyte could be interpreted as a lava dome capping its feeder pipe.

The south Kintyre lavas are typical of the transitional tholeiitic to mildly alkaline suite of Dinantian age in northern Britain. The sequence in the Macrihanish Coast and South Kintyre GCR site preserves some of the most basic (olivine-pyroxene-phyric basalt) and the most evolved rocks in the formation. Overall, this is a mildly silica-undersaturated and mildly sodic suite, which includes low Fe-variants and exhibits strong P_2O_5 and TiO_2 enrichment. Macdonald (1975) drew an important petrographical distinction between flows from the Kintyre and Campsie sequences of the Clyde Plateau Volcanic Formation, stating that, while in the Kintyre rocks clinopyroxene persisted as a phenocryst phase into the hawaiites, it is completely absent as phenocrysts from even the most basic Campsie lavas. Further sampling and analytical work by Macdonald (1980) and Smedley (1986a, 1988b) established that the Kintyre lavas may also be discriminated from many other Dinantian suites by geochemical parameters such as incompatible trace elements, rare-earth elements and isotopes. The additional data reported by Smedley (1988b) showed that the basaltic lavas from Kintyre are isotopically distinct from their counterparts in the Midland Valley and southern Scotland, having, in particular, lower Nd and higher Sr values. This correlates well with differences seen in the Siluro–Devonian calc-alkaline igneous rocks over the same terranes (e.g. Thirlwall, 1986) and implies long-term differences in the mantle source regions, which were more enriched in incompatible elements north-west of the Highland Boundary Fault.

103

Xenocrysts of quartz, surrounded by complex reaction rims of clinopyroxene, are a feature of some Kintyre basalts, and according to Smedley (1986a) represent tangible evidence that a degree of crustal assimilation may have occurred. However, isotopic evidence for crustal contamination has been detected in only one trachyte sample.

The low-potassium tholeiitic basalt flow within the lowest part of the Kintyre sequence is unique in the Clyde Plateau Volcanic Formation and its presence is fundamental to the overall understanding of the development of the Carboniferous magma types of the Carboniferous–Permian Igneous Province of northern Britain. Macdonald (1975) and Smedley (1986a) have both shown that it is relatively depleted of incompatible elements. This suggests that it was derived from a depleted mantle source, probably from the same type of spinel lherzolite as the other Clyde Plateau Volcanic Formation basalts, but by substantially greater degrees of partial melting. Contamination by crustal material is not thought to have been significant in this case.

Conclusions

Visean lavas in the Kintyre peninsula, represented by the Machrihanish Coast and South Kintyre GCR site, are the only significant occurrence of the widespread Clyde Plateau Volcanic Formation north of the Highland Boundary Fault. The 400 m-thick succession comprises at least 20 lavas mainly of olivine basalt, but more evolved rock compositions, including mugearite, benmoreite and trachyte, are more common in the upper part. Most of the lavas are extensive sheet-like bodies, but some are lenticular. Some appear to have flowed into contemporaneous topographical hollows, possibly small fault-bound grabens. A trachyte forming the summit of Skerry Fell Fad is a splendid example of a lava dome.

Geochemically, the Kintyre lavas are broadly similar to the transitional to mildly alkaline rocks that constitute the Clyde Plateau Volcanic Formation in the Midland Valley of Scotland, though with some subtle differences. In particular, a single lava of tholeiitic basalt with unusually low potassium content, near the base of the sequence on Skerry Fell Fad, is unique within the formation.

HEADS OF AYR, SOUTH AYRSHIRE (NS 279 183–NS 296 186)

I.T. Williamson and A.A. Monaghan (nee Sowerbutts)

Introduction

The Heads of Ayr, a prominent headland and coastal cliffs, is situated on the Ayrshire coast 5 km south-west of the town of Ayr (Figures 2.37a and 2.38). It is formed of a succession of volcaniclastic rocks and minor basalt intrusions, interpreted as a volcanic neck and believed to be related to the growth of a moderately sized volcano in Dinantian times. The rocks exposed at the GCR site allow the internal structure of the neck and its lithologies to be investigated in some detail. Some of the included rock fragments are probably derived from the mantle and hence provide an insight into the source region of the magma responsible for the volcanism.

Early, brief accounts of the geology of the area were by Geikie *et al*. (1869) and Geikie (1897). However, the first detailed observations were made by Tyrrell (1920) and these were added to by Eyles *et al*. (1929). Many of their observations were confirmed by Whyte (1963b) in his comprehensive study of the neck. The area has been re-described recently by Sowerbutts (1999) as part of a re-survey of the area by the British Geological Survey. The Heads of Ayr GCR site is frequently used for educational purposes and features in field guides to the region (e.g. Whyte in Lawson and Weedon, 1992).

Description

The volcaniclastic rocks at the Heads of Ayr are well exposed along 850 m of foreshore (NS 284 187–NS 295 188), on a wavecut platform and in the adjacent sea cliffs. The cliffs reach a maximum height of 75 m and form a double headland separated by a central embayment (Figures 2.37b and 2.38). The volcaniclastic rocks are juxtaposed against sedimentary rocks of the Dinantian Ballagan Formation (Inverclyde Group) (Sowerbutts, 1999). These generally gently dipping strata comprise interbedded micaceous sandstone, calcareous siltstone and dolomitic limestone ('cement-

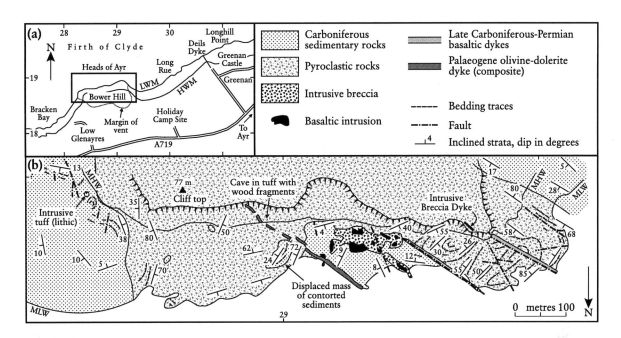

Figure 2.37 Geological map of the area around the Heads of Ayr GCR site. After Whyte (1964); and Lawson and Weedon (1992). Note the unconventional orientation of 2.37b (north at bottom) for easy comparison with Figure 2.38.

Figure 2.38 The West Cliff, at Heads of Ayr. Note the folded bedded tuffs within the Heads of Ayr Neck and the straight dykes on the wave-cut platform (compare with Figure 2.37b). (Photo: P. Macdonald.)

stone'). The contact between the volcaniclastic and sedimentary rocks appears to be nearly vertical, though there are small-scale irregularities where the contact becomes sub-parallel to bedding in the sedimentary rocks. Close to the contact with the volcaniclastic rocks, the sedimentary rocks have been deformed; on the west side of the Heads of Ayr, there is a noticeable increase in dip from about 5° to 28° towards the margin, and rocks on the east side are folded and faulted. Faults are both parallel and radial to the contact, the throws of the latter decreasing abruptly away from it. Sedimentary rocks on the foreshore beyond the eastern margins of the vent are folded into small basin-like structures a few tens of metres across and are intruded by a small boss-shaped mass of lithic tuff (Figure 2.37b).

The volcaniclastic rocks are interpreted to be pyroclastic, and comprise mainly coarse-tuff, lapilli-tuff, and tuff-breccia, with thin beds of fine-tuff. They vary in colour from green to blue-grey to purplish, generally reflecting the colour of the dominant basaltic clast-type and the degree of alteration of the finer-grained constituents. Most pyroclasts are igneous in origin, but there is also a proportion of sedimentary rock. According to Whyte (1963b), bedded tuff in the western part of the outcrop comprises 96.1% volcanic fragments, commonly cemented by carbonate, whereas rocks in the eastern part contain 97.6% volcanic clasts in a matrix of fine-tuff and crystals. There is a small population of dark-green clasts of serpentinized lherzolite up to 30 cm across. Other clasts include baked 'cementstone', 'cementstone' conglomerate and calcareous sandstone derived from the Ballagan Formation, Devonian pebbly and siliceous sandstones, and Lower Palaeozoic chert and siltstone. Also found are carbonized fragments of wood.

Sowerbutts (1999) identified several volcaniclastic lithofacies within the Heads of Ayr GCR site:

- *Coarse lithic lapilli-tuff and tuff-breccia* is most common and comprises massive and crudely bedded, poorly sorted rocks. On the western side of the Heads of Ayr are metre-thick massive beds of this lithofacies. On the eastern side, some larger slabs of disrupted Ballagan Formation rocks also occur, including one up to 20 m across (Whyte, 1963b).

Clasts in this lithofacies are dominantly of vesicular basalt, rounded to sub-angular and commonly up to 40 cm across. Under the microscope, some very irregular basalt clasts have altered haloes, indicative perhaps of their emplacement as hot pyroclasts. The matrix is poorly sorted fine-tuff.

- *Fine lithic lapilli-tuff* is found on the westernmost side of the neck, consisting of poorly sorted lapilli-tuff in which clasts are generally less than 2 cm across. These rocks are bedded, and normal and reverse grading are common. Some poorly defined, low-angle erosional trough- and cross-bedded structures are present. Locally, strings of larger volcanic clasts also define bedding and some rare, large, almost spherical volcanic blocks of cobble size have sags in the bedding beneath them. The finer fraction comprises lithic volcaniclastic debris and quartz grains.

- *Laminated tuff* is intimately and discontinuously interbedded with the fine lithic lapilli-tuff. In places these beds contain weakly developed troughs and erosion surfaces.

Between the high- and low-tide mark in the central embayment at Heads of Ayr, Whyte (1963b) described mudstone and 'cementstone' country rocks that are cut by an irregular mass of intrusive breccia, and irregular small intrusions of basalt (Figure 2.37b). The outcrop of sedimentary strata and its intrusive mass is constrained between two NW-trending faults along which dykes have been emplaced *en échelon*. The western marginal dyke is an analcime-basalt considered to be Carboniferous in age, whereas the larger eastern dyke is a composite body with a marginal facies of tholeiitic basalt intruded by olivine-dolerite and probably of Palaeogene age.

Whyte (1963b) described the intrusive breccia as consisting mainly of angular clasts of igneous and much sedimentary rock in a highly chloritized groundmass. Cutting these rocks are small, irregular masses of olivine-augite-phyric 'monchiquitic basalt' (probably a basanite) with fresh nepheline in some samples; clusters of olivine and augite crystals may be derived from ultramafic xenoliths. The margins of these masses are fragmented and grade into the breccia, forming an igneous matrix to the clasts.

Heads of Ayr

Interpretation

Volcaniclastic lithofacies such as those at the Heads of Ayr are difficult to interpret because many of the bedforms, and lithological and sorting characteristics are compatible with deposition in both sedimentary and volcanic regimes. Nevertheless, a volcanic origin has been favoured by all researchers to date. Tyrrell (1920) considered that the two main parts of the Heads of Ayr outcrop formed independently as two necks beneath vents that later coalesced. However, Whyte (1963b, 1968) demonstrated that the two units represent different facies of the same volcanic structure and emphasized the role of subsidence and collapse along ring-fractures in the later stages of the vent's formation. The steep dips in the country rock near the neck, the inward dip of the bedded pyroclastic facies and the orientation of the faults indicated to Whyte (1963b) that subsidence occurred along ring-fractures when magma was withdrawn from beneath the vent. He suggested that the layering in the tuffs could be interpreted as being due to either normal sedimentary processes or fluidization, especially at the neck margins and close to minor intrusions. He also indicated that a fluidization model could explain the emplacement of the intrusive lithic tuff east of the neck.

According to Whyte (1963b), the Heads of Ayr volcano may have reached a height of 600–900 m with a diameter at its base of about 3 km. He proposed the following five-stage model for its development:

1. Neck emplacement and deformation of adjacent sediments (brecciation and upturning) beneath a volcanic vent. A tephra cone was constructed, but was rapidly degraded and re-deposited in a subsiding marginal basin.
2. A larger volcanic cone grew, but subsidence in the basin continued.
3. Subsidence continued with the lateral spread of the volcanic cone and subaerial deposits. There was some deformation of bedded tuffs due to subsidence.
4. Vent collapse and further deformation of the bedded tuffs.
5. Further faulting and intrusion of basaltic magma, with marginal brecciation to produce intrusive breccias and tuffs; followed by regional tilting.

Sowerbutts (1999) concurred that volcanic processes were dominant at the Heads of Ayr. The massive and weak bedforms present with low-angle cross-bedding and abrupt bed-by-bed changes in grain size are typical of phreatomagmatic eruptions involving the interplay between pyroclastic surge and ash-fall mechanisms; the large blocks with bedding sags beneath are typical of ballistic fallout. Eruptive processes of this type would have been readily able to gather sedimentary and ultramafic rock clasts and quartz grains from various depths beneath the volcano. The coherent form of the fragments of Ballagan Formation rocks indicates that at the time of eruption they were sufficiently well lithified to resist disaggregation, but were still plastic enough to deform. It is not unusual to find carbonized wood fragments preserved in modern deposits of this type and they are probably the remains of vegetation growing on the slopes of the volcano.

However, it is unlikely that the volcanic rocks at the Heads of Ayr are the relics of a tephra cone. Such structures have very low potential for preservation within the geological record. The steep, cross-cutting contacts seen at the Heads of Ayr suggest that these rocks represent levels beneath the substrate, probably within the volcanic neck of a tuff-ring. In such a dynamic volcanic environment, collapse of the vent rim along faults and slumping of blocks of strata into the crater are typical features, and localized erosion, mixing with newly fragmented magma and re-deposition of the pyroclastic sediment is commonplace (cf. Kokelaar, 1983). The diameter of modern maar craters, which are regarded as having similar dimensions to tuff-rings, varies up to 3 km with the mode around 800 m (Cas and Wright, 1987). At about 850 m the diameter of the Heads of Ayr structure is consistent with this. Thus, based on both lithofacies and size, the Heads of Ayr Neck may be considered as the concealed part of a substantial tuff-ring. Similar structures have also been deduced from necks in the eastern Midland Valley (see **East Fife Coast** and **North Berwick Coast** GCR site reports).

Though a Dinantian age has long been assumed for the volcanic rocks, the strong affinities between the 'monchiquitic basalt' intrusions that cut them and Permian volcanism nearby have confused discussions on the age of the neck from the earliest investigations in this area.

Recent palynological studies on the sedimentary rocks of the Ballagan and Lawmuir formations exposed a short distance east of the Heads of Ayr have thrown new light on this debate (M.H. Stephenson, 2000). Separating these two formations are volcaniclastic rocks, named the 'Greenan Castle Member', which are considered to be associated with the Heads of Ayr Neck. Evidence for the correlation of these two volcanic outcrops includes the lithofacies similarity between the Greenan Castle Member and the lowest tuffs in the western part of the Heads of Ayr, cited by Whyte (1963b). Moreover, the most common clast in the member is a greenish basalt that is distinctly different to basalts in the underlying Devonian strata, and therefore unlikely to have been derived from those earlier volcanic beds. Beds below and above the Greenan Castle Member contain a palynological assemblage indicative of a latest Tournasian and early Asbian age respectively. If the Greenan Castle Member is coeval with the volcanism at the Heads of Ayr, this gives a constrained age for the volcanism within the mid-Dinantian, and for the first time confirms correlation with the Clyde Plateau Volcanic Formation.

Thus, a scenario can be envisaged where, early in the development of the Dinantian lava fields in the Midland Valley of Scotland, magmas rising through the near-surface crust would probably have encountered groundwater, wet, unconsolidated sediments and standing bodies of water. Interaction between these and magma would have resulted in intense phreato-magmatic activity, building cones along the line of the controlling fissures. Apart from the Greenan Castle Member there are no other tuffs, lavas nor volcaniclastic sedimentary rocks in the area known to have been derived from the Heads of Ayr vent, supporting the view that such volcanoes in Dinantian times were generally short-lived structures.

Megacryst and ultramafic xenolith assemblages within fragmental deposits, lavas and intrusions are a common feature of alkali basalts across the Midland Valley of Scotland (see **East Fife Coast**, **North Berwick Coast** and **Dubh Loch** GCR site reports). Such assemblages provide valuable clues to magmatic processes and the nature of the crust and mantle beneath the Carboniferous–Permian Igneous Province of northern Britain. The discovery of some ultramafic xenoliths in the Heads of Ayr Neck, and megacrysts in the associated basaltic intrusions, lends added importance to the site (see Chapter 1).

Conclusions

The superb coastal exposures in the Heads of Ayr GCR site beautifully demonstrate the rock-types and internal three-dimensional structure of a major volcanic neck of latest Tournaisian to Visean age and its relationships with the surrounding strata. This neck was emplaced through sedimentary rocks of the Ballagan Formation (Inverclyde Group) and is believed to correlate with volcaniclastic rocks that occur between the Ballagan and Lawmuir formations a little to the east of the GCR site. It is therefore thought to be contemporaneous with the western part of the extensive Clyde Plateau lava field.

The poor size-sorting of fragments, the presence of volcanic bombs (ejected in a molten or plastic state) and the general characteristics of bedding within the neck are indicators of the type of eruption. Together they suggest an explosive (phreatomagmatic) eruption due to the interaction of basaltic magma with water-saturated sediment and/or bodies of water, giving rise to a mixture of pyroclastic surge deposits from the lateral blast and ash-fall deposits that settled out of the ash-cloud. At the time of the eruptions the Ballagan Formation substrate was sufficiently lithified to be fragmented and incorporated in the ejected material and yet still plastic enough to deform around the margin of the neck. Large slumped blocks within the neck testify to the collapse of an overlying vent structure. The Heads of Ayr Neck is thought to have underlain a tuff-ring of substantial size, but there is no evidence to suggest that large volumes of lava were erupted.

Some of the rocks in the neck contain sparse inclusions of rocks and individual crystals that are thought to have been transported from deep within the Earth's crust or from the source region of the magma in the underlying mantle.

Chapter 3

Dinantian volcanic rocks of the Northumberland, Solway and Tweed basins

Introduction

INTRODUCTION

D. Millward and I.T. Williamson

Tournaisian to early Visean basaltic volcanism occurred locally along the margins of the Northumberland, Solway and Tweed basins during the initial phase of rapid, fault-controlled back-arc extension of the crust to the north of the Variscan Front. The E–W-orientated basins are markedly asymmetrical and lie between 'blocks'

of deformed and weakly metamorphosed Lower Palaeozoic basement rocks. To the north lies the Southern Uplands, to the south are the Lake District and Alston blocks, and separating the Tweed and Northumberland basins is the Cheviot Block, which also comprises a succession of Early Devonian lavas (Figure 3.1; Kimbell *et al.*, 1989; Leeder *et al.*, 1989; Chadwick *et al.*, 1995). Ordovician to Early Devonian granitic plutons are major intrusions within the Cheviot, Lake District and Alston blocks.

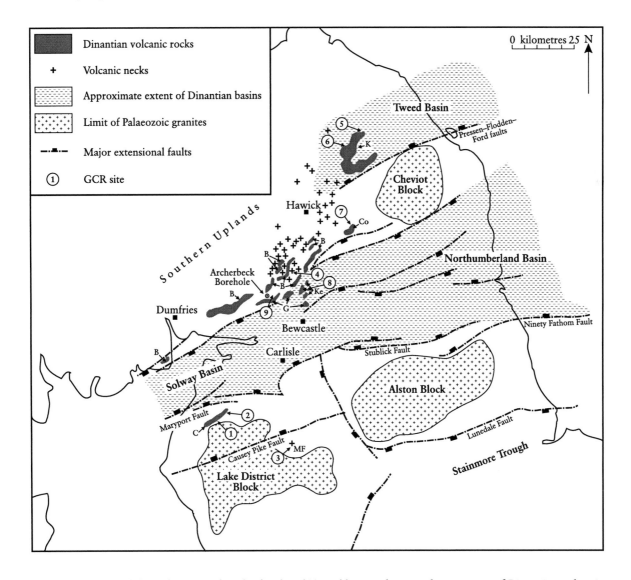

Figure 3.1 Map of the Solway, Northumberland and Tweed basins showing the outcrops of Dinantian volcanic rocks and the major structural components. GCR sites: 1 = Gill Beck; 2 = Bothel Craggs Quarry; 3 = Little Mell Fell Quarry; 4 = Langholm–Newcastleton Hills; 5 = Lintmill Railway Cutting; 6 = Hareheugh Craigs; 7 = Cottonshope Head Quarry; 8 = Kershope Bridge; 9 = River Esk, Glencartholm. (Volcanic units are as follows: B = Birrenswark Volcanic Formation; C = Cockermouth Lavas; Co = Cottonshope Basalts; G = Glencartholm Volcanic Beds; K = Kelso Lavas; Ke = Kershopefoot Lavas; MF = Mell Fell Vent.) Information from published sources including Chadwick and Holliday (1991); Chadwick *et al.* (1995); Leeder (1974); and British Geological Survey (Tectonic map of Britain, Ireland and adjacent areas, 1996).

The Northumberland and Solway basins lie above the inferred line of the Iapetus Suture, marking the junction of the former continents of Laurentia and Avalonia, which were finally locked together during the latest phase of the Caledonian Orogeny (see Chapter 1). Leeder (1971, 1974) was the first to propose that Dinantian magmatism preceded the structural development of the basins, invoking Bott's (1964) model of mantle flow. Since then, studies of subsidence history (e.g. Leeder and McMahon, 1988; Kimbell *et al.*, 1989) have shown that the development of these basins fits well with the uniform lithospheric extension model proposed by McKenzie (1978). In this model, magmatism resulting from partial melting of the upper mantle is a common feature of the early phase of rapid extension. Fracturing along the main hinge lines during this initial stage not only controlled basin development, but is also thought to have allowed the magmas to reach the surface (e.g. Leeder, 1971, 1974; Macdonald and Walker, 1985; Chadwick *et al.*, 1995).

Growth faults controlling the Carboniferous basins of northern Britain were formed by re-activation of earlier faults and thrusts with general ENE Caledonian orientations. The southern margin of the Solway and Northumberland basins is taken at the *en échelon* set of normal faults that includes the Maryport Fault in Cumbria and the Stublick and Ninety Fathom faults in Northumberland. The thickest Lower Carboniferous strata in these basins occur adjacent to these faults and the maximum fault displacement, measured from the top of the Lower Palaeozoic basement, is 5000 m down to the north. The Lower Carboniferous sedimentary succession thins markedly towards the northern, hinge-like margin, and the faults there are interpreted to be antithetic structures to the southern faults; syn-extensional displacement locally exceeds 1000 m down to the south (Figure 3.1; Lumsden *et al.*, 1967; Chadwick *et al.*, 1995). The southern margin of the Tweed Basin is taken at the Pressen–Flodden–Ford faults, but its northern margin does not appear to be fault-controlled (Chadwick and Holliday, 1991). The geometry of the basins controlled both facies development and sediment accumulation (Leeder *et al.*, 1989).

The dominantly effusive basaltic volcanism occurred in two broad sets of events, first during Tournaisian time as subaerial outpourings in an essentially fluvial setting at the onset of subsidence, and secondly during Visean time as intercalations within the dominantly marine basin succession (Figure 3.2). The initial phase is represented along the southern margin of the

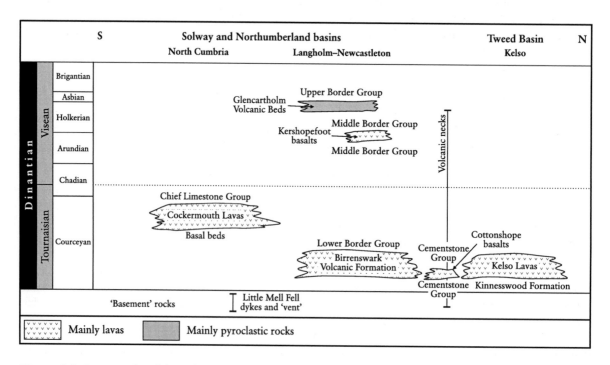

Figure 3.2 Stratigraphy of the volcanic rocks of the Solway, Northumberland and Tweed basins. The range of strata cut by intrusions and volcanic rocks is also shown. After Gawthorpe *et al.* (1989).

basins only by the Cockermouth Lavas, whereas on the northern margin, adjacent to the Southern Uplands, there are the Birrenswark Volcanic Formation and the Kelso Lavas. The Cottonshope basalts, located on the south-western flanks of the Cheviot Block, also belong to this episode. The later phase is known only from the northern margins and comprises the Kershopefoot basalts and the Glencartholm Volcanic Beds. In the Isle of Man, basalt and basaltic pyroclastic rocks of the Brigantian Scarlett Volcanic Formation (Dickson *et al.*, 1987) may also be part of this phase. A substantial number of intrusive bodies, commonly referred to in the literature as 'volcanic necks', form a broad arc linking the outcrops of the Birrenswark Volcanic Formation and the Kelso Lavas, and are probably associated with both volcanic episodes (Figure 3.1). Vent structures are not known from the Cockermouth Lavas, though pyroclastic rocks and basalt dykes within the Lake District Block, some 27 km to the ESE of the lavas, may have been part of such features.

Isopachytes on the Birrenswark Volcanic Formation show that these rocks form an elongated, localized structure parallel to the basin margin (Leeder, 1974). It seems likely that the other volcanic formations have similar distributions. It is not known whether volcanic rocks are present in the axial part of the Solway and Northumberland basins because the base of the Dinantian succession in this area is not seen. Kimbell *et al.* (1989) interpreted strong reflectors in the basal part of the succession in Northumberland as possibly from a basaltic unit, though there could be other causes.

The Lower Carboniferous volcanic units and the GCR sites are introduced briefly below in relation to their regional context; the GCR sites are located on Figure 3.1.

Cockermouth Lavas

In north Cumbria, the Cockermouth Lavas are the only exposed remnants of Early Carboniferous volcanism that occurred on the southern margin of the Northumberland and Solway basins. The sequence of tholeiitic, olivine-phyric basalt and subordinate andesite, up to 105 m thick, crops out for about 12 km north-eastwards from Cockermouth. These rocks form a southerly facing escarpment on the northern side of the River Derwent, only a few kilometres to the south of the Gilcrux and Maryport faults

that mark the basin margin (Figure 3.1). The subcrop extent of the Cockermouth Lavas is unknown; a prominent magnetic anomaly in this area is more likely to be attributable to the concealed westward extent of the Ordovician Eycott Volcanic Group, than to the weakly magnetic Cockermouth Lavas (Millward *et al.*, 1999).

The volcanic rocks are within the basal part of the Dinantian succession in Cumbria, resting conformably on conglomerate and sandstone of the Basal Beds, and overlain by the lowest strata of the Chief Limestone Group. The sedimentary rocks above and below the lavas have been identified as Courceyan (C.E. Butcher, pers. comm. in Mitchell *et al.*, 1978). This tightly constrains the age of the volcanic episode.

The Cockermouth Lavas are not well exposed, but probably comprise between four and six flows, based on the trap-like topography and the patchy distribution of clinkery, scoriaceous zones (Eastwood *et al.*, 1968; Macdonald and Walker, 1985). No pyroclastic rocks are preserved within the sequence. The formation thins north-eastwards from its maximum of about 105 m in the Cockermouth area to 30 m near Sunderland (NY 170 352) and 40 m near Bothel Craggs (NY 149 342) (Macdonald and Walker, 1985). A little to the north of Bothel Craggs the lavas are overstepped by the basal beds of the Chief Limestone Group. The **Gill Beck** GCR site provides a representative section through most of the succession.

Macdonald and Walker (1985) identified tholeiitic andesite in the Cockermouth Lavas, indicating limited fractionation of the tholeiitic magmas. Compared with other Early Carboniferous volcanic sequences of northern Britain, these rocks therefore represent a transitional state of evolution between sequences of the Midland Valley of Scotland, where intermediate and felsic compositions are common, and those of Derbyshire, where such compositions are apparently absent. The tholeiitic andesite in the **Bothel Craggs Quarry** GCR site highlights this significance.

Basalt dykes cropping out on Little Mell Fell, 27 km to the ESE of the Cockermouth Lavas, were first described by Capewell (1954). He suggested that these rocks were associated with the early Dinantian volcanic activity. Macdonald and Walker (1985) later recognized geochemical similarities between the dykes and the Cockermouth Lavas, which supported this theory. The basalt dykes are represented by the **Little Mell Fell Quarry** GCR site, which also includes exposures of unbedded lapilli-tuff. These are the only recorded occurrence of pyroclastic rocks associated with Early Carboniferous volcanism on the southern side of the basin.

Birrenswark Volcanic Formation and Kelso Lavas

The earliest volcanic eruptions on the northern margin of the basin are represented by the Birrenswark Volcanic Formation and the Kelso Lavas. Both sequences consist predominantly of subaerial basaltic lavas, with rare hawaiite or mugearite. Individual flows have massive central portions, scoriaceous upper parts and lobate or rubbly bases. Some lava surfaces are reddened and locally they are overlain by thin palaeosols (boles). The lavas are intercalated with thin beds of sedimentary or pyroclastic rock. For example, the Birrenswark Volcanic Formation includes thin beds of red sandstone and siltstone (Pallister, 1952; Elliott, 1960; Lumsden *et al.*, 1967), and interbedded volcaniclastic rocks are reported from parts of the Kelso Lavas (Eckford and Ritchie, 1939; Tomkeieff, 1945, 1953).

The Birrenswark Volcanic Formation comprises a series of unconnected NE-trending outcrops, extending for a distance of over 70 km from Kirkbean, south of Dumfries, to near Saughtree south-east of Hawick (Figure 3.1). These rocks overlie either Lower Palaeozoic basement or Lower Carboniferous rocks of Upper Old Red Sandstone facies, and are overlain conformably by Tournaisian sedimentary rocks of the Lower Border Group (Lumsden *et al.*, 1967). The succession of olivine basalt, basaltic hawaiite and hawaiite lavas is intercalated with some reddened siltstone and sandstone beds up to 10 m thick. A whole-rock K-Ar radiometric age of 361 ± 7 Ma for the Birrenswark Volcanic Formation was obtained by De Souza (1982). The **Langholm–Newcastleton Hills** GCR site is representative of the Birrenswark Volcanic Formation and contains several excellent stream sections through this otherwise poorly exposed formation.

The maximum thickness of the formation, *c.* 90 m, is recorded around Birrenswark Hill, south-west of Langholm. Leeder (1974) showed that the thickness of the lavas varies systematically across the area, and that the lavas originally extended over an area of approximately 1830 km². This inferred distribution coincides broadly with the south-west part of the Upper Old Red Sandstone fluvial basin (Leeder, 1974). However, the isopachytes also show that the lavas occur in two distinct areas, south-west and north-east of Langholm, separated by a narrow zone just west of the town where Tournaisian sedimentary rocks rest directly on Silurian basement (Nairn, 1956). Leeder (1974) attributed this either to the persistence of a topographical high, implying two separate basins, or to uplift and erosion after the volcanism.

The Kelso Lavas form a roughly horseshoe-shaped outcrop between the Blackadder Water near Duns and Carham-on-Tweed, north-west of the Cheviot massif in the Tweed Basin. The lavas overlie Upper Old Red Sandstone sedimentary rocks and are thought to be of Tournaisian age (Figure 3.2). A succession of up to 12 basalt, basaltic hawaiite and hawaiite lavas are intercalated with thin tuffs and sedimentary rocks (Smedley, 1986a). The sequence is generally poorly exposed, though in some parts a terraced or 'trap' topography is well developed locally. According to Eckford and Ritchie (1939), the succession is about 120 m thick. Tomkeieff (1953) showed that the lower flows are mostly feldspar phyric in contrast to the upper ones, which contain olivine and clinopyroxene phenocrysts. The rocks are pervasively altered. The Kelso Lavas are represented by the **Lintmill Railway Cutting** GCR site, which is situated alongside the Blackadder Water.

The Birrenswark Volcanic Formation and the Kelso Lavas clearly accumulated at separate centres (Leeder, 1974), though they were probably erupted penecontemporaneously. The presence of palaeosols and interbedded sedimentary rocks is taken to indicate a subaerial environment with periods of relative quiescence between eruptions. Most of the volcanic activity is inferred to have been quietly effusive.

Cottonshope basalts

On the south-western flanks of the Cheviot massif, relatively small outcrops of amygdaloidal tholeiitic, olivine-phyric basalt are present in Cottonshope Burn, Spithope Burn, at Hungry Law and between the Bareinghope Burn and the Chattlehope Burn. These are the Cottonshope basalts, which comprise three lavas with a total thickness of 24 m. These volcanic rocks are

Introduction

represented by the **Cottonshope Head Quarry** GCR site. They are interbedded with fluvial and lagoonal sedimentary rocks of the Cementstone Group of Northumberland (Miller, 1887; Taylor *et al.*, 1971), which is probably equivalent to the Lower Border Group farther west. Some uncertainty has surrounded the age of the Cottonshope basalts. They lie only about 100 m beneath the top of the Cementstone Group in this area and this datum probably corresponds approximately with the top of the Tournaisian Series. However, evidence first recorded here in the GCR site report suggests that the basalts may be early Tournaisian in age and therefore probably part of the Birrenswark–Kelso event.

Kershopefoot basalts

The Kershopefoot basalts crop out in the area between Langholm and Kershope Burn on the Anglo–Scottish border. The volcanic rocks are interbedded with the uppermost strata of the Visean Middle Border Group and represent a resurgence of volcanic activity following the widespread marine sedimentation that inundated the earlier Birrenswark Volcanic Formation. Numerous flows of either basalt, basaltic hawaiite or hawaiite composition (Smedley, 1986a) comprise a succession that is generally 30–36 m thick (Lumsden *et al.*, 1967; Day, 1970). These rocks have generally been assumed to be extrusive, though some doubt was expressed by Lumsden *et al.* (1967) because contacts are not exposed. These rocks are particularly well exposed at the **Kershope Bridge** GCR site.

Glencartholm Volcanic Beds

At the base of the Upper Border Group in the Langholm district, the Glencartholm Volcanic Beds are the youngest known products of syn-extensional volcanism associated with the Solway, Northumberland and Tweed basins. In contrast to the earlier phases of Dinantian volcanism, the formation almost entirely comprises interbedded basaltic and trachytic pyroclastic rocks, along with other volcaniclastic and sedimentary units (Lumsden *et al.*, 1967). There are a few local occurrences of basaltic lavas, up to 15 m thick. The thickness of the Glencartholm Volcanic Beds locally reaches about 180 m. Bedded volcaniclastic rocks in a similar stratigraphical position have been proved in the Archerbeck borehole about 8 km south of

Langholm (Lumsden and Wilson, 1961), and are represented in the Bewcastle area, by the Oakshaw Tuff (Day, 1970), suggesting that these volcanic deposits are widespread. The volcanism occurred within a mainly marine environment, though periodic emergence is shown by the presence of seatearths and coals (Lumsden *et al.*, 1967).

The Glencartholm Volcanic Beds are of Visean age, though the ages determined by different palaeontological methods are not consistent. Dineley and Metcalf (1999) suggested an early Visean age based on the faunal macropalaeontology, whereas according to Cleal and Thomas (1995), a late Visean age is more consistent with palaeobotanical data; foraminiferans from the sequence suggest a position near the Holkerian–Asbian boundary (George *et al.*, 1976).

The fragmental volcanic rocks are readily weathered and thus poorly exposed, except in stream sections. The **River Esk, Glencartholm** GCR site is representative of the Glencartholm Volcanic Beds. This site is also highly significant because of the unusual fish and arthropod fauna from shallow marine or lagoonal mudstone interbeds; these were first reported by Peach and Horne (1903) (see Dineley and Metcalf, 1999).

Volcanic necks

More than 50 pipe-like bodies of pyroclastic rocks lie within an arc that broadly connects the outcrops of the Birrenswark Volcanic Formation and the Kelso Lavas (Figure 3.1; Leeder, 1974). Some of the pipes are cut by plugs of basalt and some of the intrusions are composite. They occur within Dinantian or adjacent Silurian rocks, though none cut strata younger than the Glencartholm Volcanic Beds and they are not known from Dinantian rocks in the centre and south of the basin (Lumsden *et al.*, 1967). These masses have long been interpreted as marking the site of volcanic conduits, and this remarkable development was referred to as the 'Border Puy-country' by Geikie (1897), because of the perceived similarity with the spectacular Puy landscape in central France.

Plugs of basaltic rocks are numerous and some of these, particularly in the Kelso area, are composite intrusions of basalt, hawaiite and/or mugearite (Macdonald, 1975). However, in contrast to the entirely basic lava successions, the intrusions also include a number of alkaline and peralkaline felsic rocks. For example, the well-known laccolith complex of the Eildon Hills, near Melrose, comprises basaltic, trachytic and riebeckite-microgranitic components (McRobert, 1914) and other alkaline felsic intrusions occur south-west of Duns (Irving, 1930). About 10 km SSW of Hawick, the Skelfhill Pen intrusion is significant because of the association there of quartz-trachyte, aegirine trachyte and riebeckite-aegirine phonolite (McRobert, 1920). Many of the felsic intrusions are aligned about major NE-trending faults and some dykes define a diffuse swarm with a similar trend, suggesting structural control on their emplacement, as in the Campsie Fells and Garleton Hills (Upton, 1982).

The igneous clasts in the breccia-filled pipes include vesicular basaltic glass and crystalline olivine basalt, most of which is thoroughly decomposed. A single block of altered peridotite is recorded from the Black Burn–Rough Gill Vent (Lumsden *et al.*, 1967). There are also variable quantities of sedimentary rock fragments, including sandstone, mudstone, limestone and chert.

The basaltic to mugearitic volcanic necks in the Scottish Borders region have long been considered the most likely sources of the lavas and pyroclastic rocks of the Tournaisian Birrenswark Volcanic Formation and Kelso Lavas (e.g. McRobert, 1920). It is also possible that the

felsic intrusions may be associated with this early volcanism, since an Ar-Ar date of 352.5 ± 1.4 Ma has been obtained recently from sanidine in a trachyte from the Eildon Hills (A.A. Monaghan and M.S. Pringle, pers. comm., 2002). However, many of the pyroclastic breccia-filled bodies north-east of Langholm cut upper Tournaisian sedimentary rocks and hence these may represent the sub-volcanic sources of the Glencartholm Volcanic Beds and perhaps the Kershopefoot basalts (McRobert, 1920).

Volcanic necks cutting the Birrenswark Volcanic Formation are described in the **Langholm–Newcastleton Hills** GCR site. The **Hareheugh Craigs** GCR site is a particularly good example of a composite intrusion, possibly associated with emplacement of the Kelso Lavas.

GILL BECK, CUMBRIA (NY 149 342)

D. Millward

Introduction

The Lower Carboniferous (Dinantian) Cockermouth Lavas are probably best displayed in the Gill Beck GCR site, south of Blindcrake and about 4.5 km north-east of Cockermouth (Figure 3.3). There, a sequence of basalt lavas,

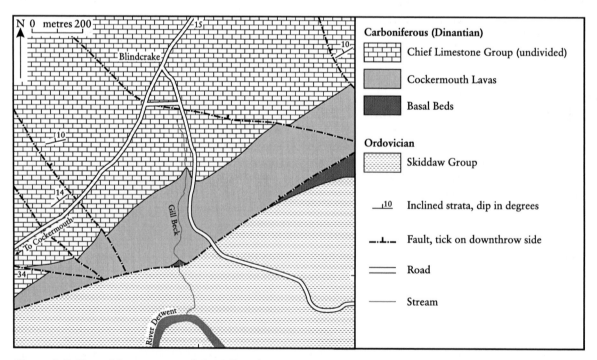

Figure 3.3 Map of the area around the Gill Beck GCR site. Based on British Geological Survey 1:10 000 sheets NY 13 SE; and NY 13 SW (both 1991).

approximately 67 m thick, overlies basal Carboniferous conglomerates referred to formally as the Basal Beds. Above the lavas are bedded mudstone, limestone and sandstone at the base of the Chief Limestone Group. The Cockermouth Lavas are the only known example of effusive basaltic volcanism focused upon the southern hinge-zone margin of the Solway Basin. In general, the volcanic rocks are poorly exposed and this GCR site is especially valuable in providing good stream exposure.

The presence of amygdaloidal 'greenstones' in Gill Beck was recorded by the primary geological survey of the area during the 19th century, and the stream exposures are mentioned in accounts of the Cockermouth Lavas by Eastwood (1928), Eastwood *et al.* (1968), and Macdonald and Walker (1985). The GCR site is included within the British Geological Survey's 1:50 000 Sheet 23, Cockermouth (1997). The age of the Cockermouth Lavas is tightly constrained to the Courceyan (C.E. Butcher, pers. comm. in Mitchell *et al.*, 1978). This is indicated by the presence of CM Zone miospore assemblages in sedimentary rocks from the Chief Limestone Group overlying

the lavas at Gill Beck. Nearby, exposures of the Basal Beds underlying the lavas have also yielded spores of the same zone.

The geochemistry of the Cockermouth Lavas has been described and interpreted by Macdonald and Walker (1985); a single whole-rock analysis from Gill Beck is cited by these authors. Tholeiitic andesite has been recognized within the sequence at Gill Beck and this has implications for the petrogenesis of the Cockermouth Lavas (Macdonald and Walker, 1985) (see **Bothel Craggs Quarry** GCR site report).

Description

The following description is based on the published accounts listed above. The lithostratigraphical nomenclature follows that used on the British Geological Survey's Sheet 23, Cockermouth (1997). The site consists of a stream section, within which the Carboniferous rocks dip gently to the NNW (Figure 3.3). The base of the lava succession is not exposed, though a small exposure of conglomerate is seen beneath its inferred position (Figure 3.4). The

Figure 3.4 An exposure of conglomerate, belonging to the Lower Carboniferous Basal Beds, below the base of the Cockermouth Lavas in Gill Beck. The hammer shaft is 40 cm long. (Photo: D. Stephenson.)

top of the succession is also not exposed, though mudstones and thin limestones near the base of the Chief Limestone Group are seen along the stream close to the highest exposure of the lavas (Eastwood, 1928). Here the Cockermouth Lavas are about 67 m thick.

On field maps in the British Geological Survey archive, T. Eastwood recorded the basalts as variably massive to highly scoriaceous. He described most of the rocks as compact to slightly amygdaloidal, but especially amygdaloidal and scoriaceous rocks are characteristic of the top and base of the flows; in some places he described the distribution of scoriaceous rock as 'haphazard' (Eastwood, 1928). Though vesicles are commonly distorted, there is little evidence for linear structures indicating directions of flow. The vesicles are mainly filled with carbonate or various forms of silica. The more massive rocks in the centres of the lavas are dark blue or grey and finely granular. Intercalations of pyroclastic or sedimentary rocks have not been recorded from the sequence, but the presence of at least four lavas may be inferred from the distribution of scoriaceous basalt within the section.

The petrography of the Cockermouth Lavas was first outlined by H.H. Thomas (in Eastwood, 1928; Eastwood *et al.*, 1968). The microcrystalline basalts typically comprise plagioclase, augite and iron oxide with variable amounts of olivine microphenocrysts; some rocks contain plagioclase and/or augite phenocrysts. Most of the rocks have ophitic or sub-ophitic texture, and in some of these the tabular plagioclase laths form a sub-parallel fabric; intergranular texture is seen sporadically. Geochemical analyses reported by Macdonald and Walker (1985) show that both basalt and andesite are present in the Gill Beck succession. They described the andesite from Gill Beck as aphyric and fine grained, comprising plagioclase laths, granular, partially serpentinized augite and abundant iron oxide; interstitial quartz, alkali feldspar and chlorite are also present. The plagioclase defines a marked flow texture in the andesite.

The basalts are noted for their pervasive secondary alteration. Olivine is entirely replaced by an aggregate of 'serpentine', chlorite, green mica, quartz, opaques and carbonate. The pyroxene is partially fresh in places, though it is normally altered to 'serpentine' and, in some cases, carbonate. The plagioclase is generally much fresher though it

may be albitized or replaced by carbonate. Loveland and Bendelow (1984) reported celadonite-like grains in highly altered basalt nearby at Bridekirk; this was the first recorded occurrence of the mineral in England. Macdonald and Walker (1985) also noted that, as a result of the alteration, Ca-poor pyroxene has not been identified in these rocks even though its presence may be suspected by analogy with compositionally similar rocks in the Dinantian lavas of Derbyshire.

Despite the intense mineralogical alteration of the basalts, magmatic characteristics are retained, particularly with respect to the incompatible minor- and trace-element abundances (Ti, P, Zr, Nb, Ce, Y) (Macdonald and Walker, 1985). The Cockermouth Lavas have a relatively small range in silica saturation, attributable to magmatic processes rather than alteration. This is indicated by the negative correlation of the ratios Zr/Y and Nb/Y, and positive correlation of Zr/Nb with increasing silica saturation, which is typical of basalts as a whole. The basalts are quartz- and hypersthene-normative and may be described as quartz tholeiitic. Plots of incompatible elements show that the Cockermouth Lavas form a very coherent suite of genetically related rocks. However, the range of variation for some elements is very wide (e.g. Nb 9–32 ppm and Zr 70–258 ppm) (Macdonald and Walker, 1985).

Interpretation

The Cockermouth Lavas were considered to be of Ordovician age by J.C. Ward and J.G. Goodchild who made the primary geological survey of the Cockermouth area, late in the 19th century. These basalts were thought to be part of the same volcanic episode that produced the widespread Eycott and Borrowdale volcanic groups (at this time these two groups were included under the latter name). By contrast, a Carboniferous age was assigned to the more extensive conglomerate, now formally the Basal Beds. Exposures of the conglomerate, for example in Gill Beck, which are apparently located below the basalts, were considered to be faulted against the base of the basalts.

In re-surveying the area, Eastwood (1928) found that, although the junction is not exposed, the basalts undoubtedly overlie the conglomerates conformably. He then contemplated that if the lavas were Ordovician in age, the conglomerate must be of 'early Borrowdale age' and thus also Ordovician. However, the petrographical descriptions by H.H. Thomas (in Eastwood, 1928) showed that the basalts contain phenocrysts of olivine and thus differ markedly from the Eycott and Borrowdale volcanic group rocks. Eastwood noted that there are also other lithological differences between the volcanic rocks, but that the conglomerate has some similarity with the Mell Fell Conglomerate farther east in Cumbria. Considering these observations, Eastwood (1928) then proposed that the basalts are probably Carboniferous in age and should be designated as the Cockermouth Lavas. A Dinantian (Courceyan) age has since been confirmed from spore assemblages obtained from the sedimentary rocks, both beneath and above the basalts (C.E. Butcher, pers. comm. in Mitchell *et al.*, 1978).

The variably clinkery and scoriaceous character of the basalt sheets supports the widely held interpretation of these rocks as lavas. Furthermore, the occurrence in a stream (NY 128 327) to the north-east of Wood Hall of 'a roughly lenticular mass of red and green marl...interspersed with lumps of very rotten amygdaloidal rock' was interpreted by Eastwood (1928) to be bole-like, indicating subaerial weathering of the basalt. No evidence has come to light that contradicts this interpretation. However, in the absence of unequivocal evidence for the nature of the uppermost contacts of the sheets, it is possible that some sills may be present. One piece of evidence that may be pertinent to the method of emplacement of the sheets is described by Eastwood *et al.* (1968). Near Redmain, south-west of the GCR site, they reported that the upper zone of a basalt sheet is cut by narrow veins and irregular patches of dark-purple flinty material that die out downwards, while some appear to pass upwards into 'bole'. Eastwood *et al.* offered no explanation, but it is possible that these are sedimentary enclaves.

The apparent absence of volcaniclastic rocks from the sequence suggested to Eastwood (1928) and Macdonald and Walker (1985) that Carboniferous volcanism in the area was mildly effusive and perhaps from fissure-type vents. Possible eruption sites have not been identified in the field, though Eastwood *et al.* (1968) suggested that they lay to the west of the outcrop, and Macdonald and Walker (1985) inferred

a fissure or series of vents along the outcrop. However, if the volcanism is associated with crustal extension and basin formation, then the hinge-line faults such as the Maryport and Gilcrux faults located to the north of the Cockermouth Lavas outcrop (Figure 3.1) must be considered as potential magma channels. Effusive to mildly explosive volcanism with extensive lavas is typical in extensional tectonic regimes such as in the Solway and Northumberland basins. The apparent absence of pyroclastic rocks from the subaerial Cockermouth Lavas does not necessarily indicate that none were erupted; any accumulated tephra deposits would have been localized as small cones, and would have been subjected to rapid erosion and possibly complete removal. Further, if the vents were located along the basin hinge-line fault system, then the present outcrop of the Cockermouth Lavas is at least 2 km from these, mostly well outside the depositional range for mildly explosive eruptions.

The Cockermouth Lavas are unlikely to represent primary basalts because of their characteristically low Mg numbers ($100 \times Mg/(Mg + Fe)$ 60). Furthermore, on the diopside–olivine–hypersthene–nepheline–quartz phase diagram, representing the crystallization of basaltic liquids, the normative compositions of the Cumbrian rocks plot close to the cotectic at 1 atmosphere. However, Macdonald and Walker (1985) argued that the basalts cannot represent a simple low-pressure fractionation series, because the levels of incompatible elements, such as Zr, Nb, P, Ce and Y, do not decrease systematically with MgO, which is used as an index of fractionation. On the contrary, the most magnesian rocks contain the highest levels of K, Ti, P and incompatible trace elements. Thus, in addition to low-pressure fractionation, the chemical variation in the Cockermouth Lavas must have resulted from variable amounts of partial melting, or from fractionation at higher pressures.

Macdonald and Walker (1985) concluded that the Cockermouth Lavas were probably generated from upper-mantle sources; immobile trace-element ratios such as Zr/Nb, Zr/Y and Ce/P_2O_5 do not suggest that the source region was heterogeneous. Macdonald and Walker (1985) also suggested that, like the Dinantian lavas of Derbyshire, compositional variations in the Cockermouth Lavas resulted from a two-stage process involving variable degrees of

Dinantian volcanic rocks of the Scotland–England borders

partial melting to produce parent liquids with a range of silica saturation, followed by low-pressure fractional crystallization, probably in the upper crust.

Conclusions

The Gill Beck GCR site is representative of the Tournaisian Cockermouth Lavas, the only exposed example of volcanic rocks of this age along the southern margin of the Solway Basin. The formation comprises tholeiitic olivine-phyric basalt and aphyric andesite, and is approximately 67 m thick. At least four lavas are present, but no pyroclastic rocks are preserved. The volcanic rocks conformably overlie conglomerates at the base of the Carboniferous succession in Cumbria (the Basal Beds), and are overlain by sedimentary rocks of the Chief Limestone Group. The basalt magmas are thought to have evolved through variable degrees of partial melting of upper-mantle source rocks, followed by moderate- to low-pressure crystal fractionation.

BOTHEL CRAGGS QUARRY, CUMBRIA (NY 186 371)

D. Millward

Introduction

Tholeiitic andesite in the Lower Carboniferous (Dinantian) Cockermouth Lavas is exposed in the small quarry on the west side of the A591 road, near Bothel Craggs, about 1.5 km SSE of the village of Bothel in Cumbria (Figure 3.5). The Bothel Craggs Quarry GCR site is at the eastern extent of the Cockermouth Lavas, the only exposed example of effusive volcanism localized along the southern hinge-zone margin of the Solway Basin.

The Cockermouth Lavas were first described by Eastwood (1928) and by Eastwood *et al.* (1968), and the Bothel Craggs Quarry GCR site is included within the British Geological Survey's 1:50 000 Sheet 23, Cockermouth (1997). Geochemical analysis of the lava from this quarry by Macdonald and Walker (1985) showed that it is a tholeiitic andesite, which has implications for the petrogenesis of the Cockermouth Lavas in the wider context of Early Carboniferous magmatism in Great Britain.

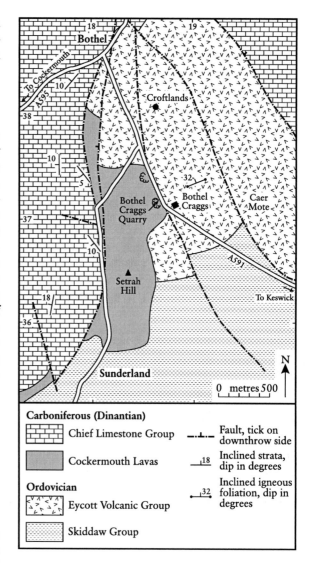

Figure 3.5 Map of the area around the Bothel Craggs Quarry GCR site. Based on British Geological Survey 1:50 000 Sheet 23, Cockermouth (1997).

Description

The description of the Bothel Craggs Quarry GCR site is based on the published accounts by Eastwood (1928) and Eastwood *et al.* (1968), and on field maps in the archives of the British Geological Survey. Approximately 4 m of blue-black, sparsely amygdaloidal, fine-grained tholeiitic andesite are exposed in the quarry (Figure 3.6). Pseudo-columnar joints are very poorly developed and there are weak sub-horizontal joints and perhaps a faint sub-horizontal lamination. There is no evidence that more than one lava is present. Neither the top nor the base of

Figure 3.6 Bothel Craggs Quarry, excavated in fresh tholeiitic andesite of the Cockermouth Lavas; view south towards the western fells of the Lake District. (Photo: D. Stephenson.)

the Cockermouth Lavas is exposed hereabouts. The andesite is similar to that described in the **Gill Beck** GCR site report, though mineralogical alteration is ubiquitous, with albitization, carbonation and sericitization of the plagioclase, and replacement of the clinopyroxene by aggregates of carbonate and 'serpentine' (Macdonald and Walker, 1985).

Interpretation

The rock from the Bothel Craggs Quarry was described as basalt on field maps by T. Eastwood. However, despite strong alteration, an intermediate composition was determined for this rock by Macdonald and Walker (1985), who classified it as tholeiitic andesite. They also recorded tholeiitic andesite in **Gill Beck** (see GCR site report), and possibly from Ullerance Gill (NY 170 351) as an altered xenolith in basalt lava. Their paper contained the first use of the term tholeiitic andesite for any British Carboniferous lava.

The magmatic evolution of the Cockermouth Lavas, as outlined in the **Gill Beck** GCR site report, probably involved low- to medium-pressure fractional crystallization. The presence of tholeiitic andesite within the Cockermouth Lavas further suggests that high-level magma chambers were established, at least locally, enabling crystal fractionation of the parental basaltic magma to take place.

The hypersthene-normative, transitional to alkaline Dinantian volcanic rocks of the Midland Valley of Scotland, to the north, include relatively common intermediate and silicic rocks (Macdonald, 1975). In contrast, the tholeiitic lavas in Derbyshire to the south, in many respects compositionally similar to the Cockermouth Lavas, are entirely basaltic (Macdonald *et al.*, 1984). The Cockermouth Lavas are thus transitional in terms of their most evolved composition between the suites of the Midland Valley and Derbyshire.

Conclusions

Approximately 4 m of sparsely amygdaloidal, tholeiitic andesite are exposed in the Bothel Craggs Quarry GCR site. The andesite in the quarry is probably part of a single lava flow and occurs at the eastern extent of the outcrop of the Tournaisian Cockermouth Lavas. This was the first tholeiitic andesite to be recognized in a British Carboniferous lava succession and its presence suggests that high-level magma chambers were established, enabling some crystal fractionation of the basaltic parental magmas to take place. Its presence is also regionally significant among similar Dinantian rocks in Great Britain, because it shows that the Cockermouth Lavas reached a state of magmatic evolution between that seen in the Midland Valley of Scotland, where intermediate and felsic compositions are common, and that of Derbyshire, where only basic rocks occur.

LITTLE MELL FELL QUARRY, CUMBRIA (NY 429 239)

D. Millward

Introduction

A number of small, basalt intrusions and a single exposure of probable pyroclastic rocks crop out on the eastern flanks of Little Mell Fell, up to about 400 m west and north of Mellfell House (Figure 3.7). Published evidence suggests that they are related to the Dinantian Cockermouth Lavas of the north-west Lake District (Capewell, 1954; Macdonald and Walker, 1985). The igneous rocks were emplaced into cobble conglomerates of the Mell Fell Conglomerate, an alluvial-fan deposit of probable Mid- or Late Devonian age (Capewell, 1955; Wadge, 1978; Cooper *et al.*, 1993). The basalts are compositionally similar to, but are fresher than, rocks of the main outcrop of Cockermouth Lavas (see **Gill Beck** and **Bothel Craggs Quarry** GCR site reports). Thus, the intrusions represent the easternmost manifestation of this volcanic episode along the northern margin of the Lake District. Furthermore, the nearby exposure of pyroclastic rocks is the only known example of tephra deposits associated with Dinantian volcanism at the southern margin of the Solway Basin.

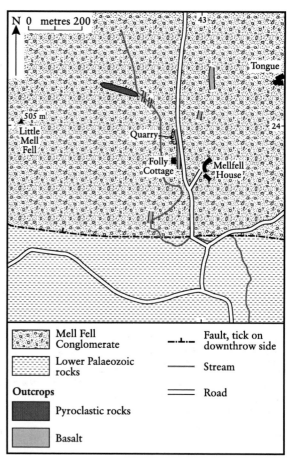

Figure 3.7 Map of the area around the Little Mell Fell Quarry GCR site. Based on British Geological Survey 1:10 000 Sheet NY 42 SW (2000).

The igneous rocks were located during the primary geological survey and described briefly in the memoir for the area (Dakyns *et al.*, 1897). Dykes near this location were mapped by Green (1918). Capewell (1954) described the Mell Fell rocks in detail, and geochemical analyses of these rocks have been interpreted by Macdonald and Walker (1985). The Little Mell Fell Quarry GCR site is included within the British Geological Survey's 1:50 000 Sheet 30, Appleby (in press).

Description

Description of these rocks is based on the accounts by Capewell (1954), and Macdonald and Walker (1985). The Little Mell Fell Quarry GCR site is the small abandoned quarry (NY 4291 2397) adjacent to the road, approximately 100 m north of Folly Cottage (Figure 3.7). Within the quarry a northerly trending basalt dyke cuts the Mell Fell Conglomerate, here composed of greywacke cobbles. The dyke forms a steep bank for about 180 m to the north of the quarry and it is further exposed immediately below the cottage; however, the dyke is not exposed in the stream 100 m south of the cottage. The width of the dyke was not recorded by Capewell (1954), but during a recent re-survey of the area the dyke width was recorded as approximately 10 m (M. McCormac, pers. comm., 1999). Capewell recorded that the western contact of the dyke dips at about 60° to the west, but that the eastern contact is irregular and nearly vertical. Trails of mainly quartz-filled vesicles are present parallel to, and 0.3–0.6 m from, the contacts. Adjacent to the dyke contacts the conglomerate matrix is slightly hardened and bleached. Towards the north end of the quarry, bleached conglomeratic rock probably represents screens of the host rock within the dyke.

Three further exposures of basalt between the road and Tongue Farm (Figure 3.7) were recorded by Capewell (1954). These may be *en échelon* segments of the dyke in the quarry or may represent at least one other separate, northerly trending dyke. At one of these exposures Capewell recorded similar contact relationships to those seen in the quarry. Other small occurrences of basalt are found in the water course approximately 300 m north-west of Mellfell House. An isolated crag of basalt 300 m south-west of Mellfell House is close to the mapped contact of the Mell Fell Conglomerate with the underlying Skiddaw Group. The geometry and contact relationships of these occurrences are not known. A NNE-trending dyke WSW of Little Mell Fell illustrated by Green (1918) could not be located by Capewell (1954), nor was it recorded during the primary geological survey.

Basalt in the Little Mell Fell Quarry is microporphyritic, with euhedral olivine and subordinate plagioclase phenocrysts. The fine-grained groundmass comprises plagioclase, augite and iron oxide. These rocks are altered, but considerably less so than the Cockermouth Lavas; olivine in particular is replaced by a chlorite-like mineral ('serpentine' according to W.W. Watts in Dakyns *et al.*, 1897; 'chlorophaeite' according to Capewell, 1954). Amygdales are of chlorite, carbonate and chalcedony. The rock exposed in the water course north-west of the quarry is a fresh sub-ophitic dolerite, in which the olivine is remarkably fresh and only serpentinized at the crystal margins.

Geochemical analyses of two rocks from this area were presented by Macdonald and Walker (1985). In common with the Cockermouth Lavas, the basalts at Little Mell Fell are tholeiitic; one of the samples is quartz-normative, the other is just olivine-normative. The Mell Fell basalts have incompatible element concentrations that are at the higher end of the compositional range encountered in the Cockermouth Lavas, suggesting that they represent some of the more enriched rocks in this formation. Macdonald and Walker (1985) expressed little doubt that the Mell Fell rocks are similar to the Cockermouth Lavas and considered them to be part of this volcanic episode.

An exposure of highly porous, greenish, unbedded lapilli-tuff, identified first by Capewell (1954), is located on the eastern slopes of Little Mell Fell approximately on the 400 m contour and 140 m ENE of the summit. The marked colour difference with the Mell Fell Conglomerate is readily noticeable. However, the contact relationship between the lapilli-tuff and the conglomerate is seen nowhere. Sub-horizontally bedded conglomerate is exposed nearby, and Capewell (1954) interpreted a steep margin to the pyroclastic rock. He also noted seepages at the base of the crags and inferred that the lapilli-tuff is underlain by impermeable basalt, either a plug or one of the north–south dykes at the base of the slope.

The lapilli-tuff comprises sub-angular clasts, mainly cobbles and pebbles of country rock, but also with glassy basaltic lapilli and blocks (Figure 3.8). Some clasts of the probable juvenile material appear to have been fused together while they were still plastic. In thin section the smaller clasts and sand-grade grains also include greywacke, siltstone and slaty mudstone. Capewell (1954) noted that parts of the rock are apparently cemented by palagonite.

Interpretation

The basalt in the quarry at Little Mell Fell was interpreted as an intrusion during the primary survey of the area (Dakyns *et al.*, 1897). The pyroclastic rocks were described first by Capewell (1954), who suggested that, because of their close proximity to the dyke-like masses of basalt, they belong to a single volcanic episode. It is also possible that these are the sub-surface remains of a single volcano. Capewell considered that, although a pipe-like

Figure 3.8 Lapilli-tuff from an inferred volcanic vent, possibly related to the Cockermouth Lavas, exposed on the hillside above the Little Mell Fell Quarry GCR site. (Photo: British Geological Survey, No. P505644, reproduced with the permission of the director, British Geological Survey, © NERC.)

geometry for the lapilli-tuff was far from certain from the field evidence, the pyroclastic rocks are likely to infill a vent conduit. The substantial amounts of country-rock pyroclasts and the presence of plastic, juvenile tephra in the lapilli-tuff clearly suggest a phreatomagmatic mode of emplacement. No other occurrences are known of pyroclastic rocks associated with the Early Carboniferous volcanism on the southern side of the Solway Basin.

Some uncertainty surrounds the age of the volcanic rocks at Little Mell Fell because there is no biostratigraphical control and no radiometric ages of these rocks have been determined. Intrusion into the probable Middle or Upper Devonian Mell Fell Conglomerate gives a maximum age, but a minimum age is not discernible from the geological relationships. Ward (in Dakyns *et al.*, 1897) considered

these and other basalts in the area to be associated with the Late Carboniferous Whin Sill magmatism. Wadge *et al.* (1972) proposed a similar correlation for some olivine-dolerite dykes cutting the Eycott Volcanic Group near Melmerby in the northern part of the Cross Fell inlier. However, Capewell (1954) thought the association of olivine basalt with the quartz-dolerite sills unlikely on petrological grounds. He considered the few other occurrences of olivine-bearing basalt in the north-west of England and concluded that the best association for the Little Mell Fell rocks was with the Cockermouth Lavas. Thus, he concluded that the dykes and pyroclastic rocks were Early Carboniferous in age and that these occurrences can be regarded as an outlier of the southern Scottish Early Carboniferous volcanism. This conclusion gained further support from Macdonald and Walker (1985), who demonstrated the geochemical similarity of the Little Mell Fell Quarry rocks with the Cockermouth Lavas.

The nearest outcrop of the Cockermouth Lavas lies some 27 km to the WNW of Little Mell Fell Quarry. No similar rocks have been encountered in the intervening ground, though the base of the Carboniferous strata is well exposed. Furthermore, no dykes of similar affinity have been reported within the Lower Palaeozoic strata, an observation commented on long ago by Green (1918). However, the geochemical analyses of the dykes at Little Mell Fell confirm the earlier suggestion by Capewell (1954) that Dinantian volcanism did occur on the Lake District Block, some distance from the defined margin of the Solway Basin. Just to the north of Little Mell Fell lies the ENE-trending Causey Pike Fault (Chadwick *et al.*, 1995, fig. 3). This structure is of major importance in the development of the Lower Palaeozoic rocks of the Lake District Block (Cooper *et al.*, 1988) and is probably linked at depth to the major crustal shear zone that was re-activated during Carboniferous extension to form the Solway Basin (Chadwick *et al.*, 1995). Re-activation of the Causey Pike Fault may have provided the necessary channel for magma to reach the surface.

Conclusions

Northerly trending, near-vertical dykes of tholeiitic olivine-microphyric basalt and dolerite intrude the Devonian (Old Red Sandstone) Mell Fell Conglomerate in a quarry on the eastern flanks of Little Mell Fell and nearby. Though the dykes occur some 27 km ESE of the Cockermouth Lavas they are considered to be the easternmost manifestation of this volcanism, and thus of Tournaisian age. Some of the mafic rocks on Little Mell Fell are fresh compared with the Cockermouth Lavas. A small outcrop of unbedded lapilli-tuff, comprising pyroclasts of basalt and country rock, is considered to be the remains of an infilled vent conduit and is the only recorded occurrence of pyroclastic rocks within the Lower Carboniferous rocks of the southern margin of the Solway Basin. The volcanic rocks at Little Mell Fell are located within the Lake District Block, and the nearby Causey Pike Fault may have acted as a channel.

LANGHOLM–NEWCASTLETON HILLS, DUMFRIES AND GALLOWAY and SCOTTISH BORDERS (NY 423 901–NY 452 940)

I.T. Williamson

Introduction

The earliest phase of volcanic activity in the Northumberland, Solway and Tweed basins is probably Courceyan (early Tournaisian) in age and occurs stratigraphically at the base of the Lower Border Group, where it is represented by both the Birrenswark Volcanic Formation and the Kelso Lavas (see **Lintmill Railway Cutting** GCR site report) (Figure 3.2). Other than a minor occurrence of basaltic lava and tuff at Craiglockhart Hill in Edinburgh, these are also the earliest known examples of Dinantian volcanism within the Carboniferous–Permian Igneous Province of northern Britain.

The Langholm–Newcastleton Hills GCR site is located approximately 7 km north-east and 5 km north-west of the towns of Langholm and Newcastleton respectively. It exposes a representative section through the Birrenswark Volcanic Formation, consisting of up to 90 m of basaltic lavas with thin intercalations of reddened siltstone and sandstone. The formation extends from Annandale eastward for about 22.5 km, to the north of Newcastleton, and takes its name from exposures on Birrenswark Hill (NY 185 787), several kilometres to the west of the GCR site. However, as the level of exposure and range of lithologies and structures there are comparatively poor, this site has been selected in preference (Figure 3.9).

Though these volcanic rocks received passing mention in Teall (1888) and Geikie (1897), they were referred to as contemporaneous 'porphyrites' of Early Carboniferous age on the one-inch scale primary geological map of the area (Langholm, Sheet 11, 1883), and described as the 'volcanic rocks of Tarras Water and Birrenswark' by Peach and Horne (1903). McRobert (1920) outlined the distribution and nature of these rocks, and fuller accounts, particularly of the petrography, were given by Pallister (1952) and Elliott (1960). Details of the Birrenswark Volcanic Formation were included in the Geological Survey memoir (Lumsden *et al.*, 1967). Leeder (1974) discussed the lavas in some detail in relation to

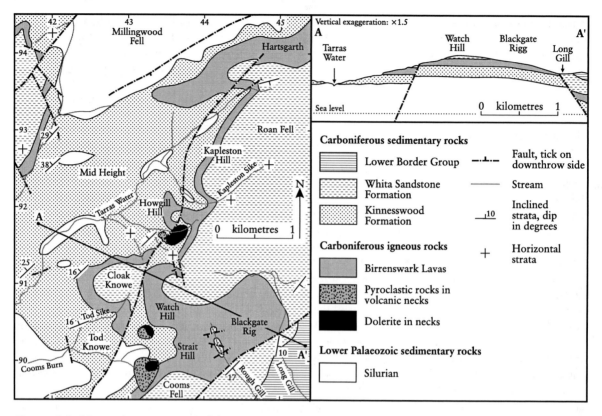

Figure 3.9 Map and cross-section of the area around the Langholm–Newcastleton Hills GCR site. Based on Geological Survey 1:63 360 Sheet 11, Langholm (1968).

Description

The Langholm–Newcastleton Hills is a poorly defined area of upland situated between Eskdale and Liddesdale in the foothills of the Southern Uplands. The area covered by the GCR site contains peaty moorland and rough hill grazing with incised river valleys and erosional gullies on the principal escarpment. The Birrenswark Volcanic Formation forms a persistent bench-like feature along the scarp slopes on the eastern side of the valley of the Tarras Water (Figure 3.10).

In the GCR site, the Birrenswark Volcanic Formation overlies Upper Old Red Sandstone (ORS) facies rocks unconformably, though elsewhere the volcanic rocks rest directly on base-

the origin and overall development of the Early Carboniferous sedimentary basins. More recently, the petrology and geochemistry of these rocks have contributed to wider-ranging studies of the genesis of magmas in this tectonic setting by Macdonald (1975) and Smedley (1986a,b, 1988a).

ment rocks of Silurian (Wenlock) greywackes, siltstones and mudstones. The ORS facies sequence, now designated the Kinnesswood Formation, is dominated by red, cross-bedded sandstones, but a distinctive compact, light-grey-brown, calcareous sandstone overlain by 1.2 m of red calcareous mudstones, immediately underlies the lavas in Kapleston Sike (NY 4409 9203). Similar sandstone beds are also present below the base of the lavas in the Tod Sike section at NY 4284 9061. These rocks are believed to have been deposited as fluvial sediments in a hot and semi-arid environment (Leeder, 1971, 1974). The basalts are succeeded by a sequence of predominantly fine- to medium-grained arenaceous strata that is over 300 m thick in the Langholm district, where it is known as the 'Whita Sandstone Formation' (Nairn, 1956, 1958; Lumsden *et al.*, 1967). Conglomerates within the lower parts of this sequence contain basalt clasts.

In the Langholm–Newcastleton Hills the Birrenswark Volcanic Formation comprises a sequence of olivine basalts and hawaiites, with a maximum composite thickness of just over 61 m

126

Langholm–Newcastleton Hills

Figure 3.10 View from the bank of the Tarras Water, towards the slopes of Cloak Knowe in the Langholm–Newcastleton Hills GCR site. Lavas of the Birrenswark Volcanic Formation form the distinct feature with scattered exposures midway up the slope; the lower slopes are till covered, and river terraces occupy the foreground. (Photo: K.M. Goodenough.)

(Lumsden *et al.*, 1967). However, Leeder (1974) has demonstrated considerable variation over the whole outcrop: the basalts may be up to 90 m thick but are absent locally west of Langholm. Individual basalt sheets, interpreted as lava, are generally less than 30 m thick and may be massive, amygdaloidal or glassy. Many parts are vesicular and vein breccias are a characteristic feature of some flows. Thin reddened carapaces occur on some lavas and, rarely, lateritic palaeosols are developed on the upper surfaces. Sedimentary intercalations of reddened siltstone and sandstone are present locally. Most exposures are extremely weathered, and spheroidal weathering is common.

The better sections through the formation were described by Lumsden *et al.* (1967). Three of these, at Tod Sike (NY 4294 9070), Howgill Hill (NY 4365 9190) and Hartsgarth Fell (NY 4470 9350), fall within the GCR site (Figure 3.9).

Tod Sike

In Tod Sike, on the south side of Cloak Knowe, there is intermittent exposure of 24.4 m of highly weathered basaltic lavas. There are probably several lavas or lava-flow units present,

perhaps up to seven, though the tops and bases of these are often difficult to distinguish. Only two flows can be identified with any confidence. These are an olivine-microphyric basalt with a few scattered feldspar phenocrysts ('Dalmeny' type of MacGregor, 1928) that occurs at the base, and a glassy, macroporphyritic olivine basalt with phenocrysts of both feldspar and olivine ('Markle' type) that occurs higher in the sequence. Lumsden *et al.* (1967) recorded the presence of a single thin sedimentary intercalation some 18.3 m above the base of the section, but did not give further lithological details.

Howgill Hill and Kapleston Sike

A 22 m-thick complete section through the Birrenswark Volcanic Formation is exposed in the stream section of Kapleston Sike on the north-eastern side of Howgill Hill (Figure 3.9). Four lavas are present, ranging in thickness from 3.66 m to 7.32 m. All are deeply weathered and red-stained, amygdaloidal olivine-microphyric basalts ('Dalmeny' type), but the middle two flows may be distinguished by their glassy and compact nature. A thin sedimentary unit comprising 1.5 m of red silty sandstone separates the top two lavas.

Around Howgill Hill the basal lava forms a strong, readily mapped feature. The flow forming this feature is a highly weathered olivine- and feldspar-microphyric basalt ('Jedburgh' type) which does not appear to be represented in the Kapleston Sike section.

Hartsgarth Fell

North of Kapleston Sike the lavas crop out along Kapleston Hill and extend into the deep valley at the head of the Tarras Water under Hartsgarth Fell. There are several excellent sections here and the formation is about 29 m thick. The basal flow is a 7.6 m-thick, coarse-grained, olivine-clinopyroxene-plagioclase-macrophyric basalt ('Dunsapie' type). As elsewhere, the rest of the succession is dominated by olivine-microphyric basalts ('Dalmeny' type), some of them glassy, and at least three flows have been identified. A thin sandstone unit up to 0.6 m thick, overlies the lowest 'Dalmeny'-type flow.

Although the sections described above are relatively close to one another, exact correlation between them is difficult. For example, the different types of lava at the base of each section clearly demonstrate a considerable degree of overstep of various early flows by later olivine-microporphyritic types. Sections around Watch Hill (NY 436 908) also show this contrast in basal flow types.

Numerous volcanic necks and attendant intrusions are associated geographically with the more easterly outcrops of the Birrenswark Volcanic Formation. They cut Lower Carboniferous strata up to the level of the Glencartholm Volcanic Beds (see **River Esk, Glencartholm** GCR site report) and so it is clear that many have no possible connection with the Birrenswark Volcanic Formation. However, it has been suggested that the large Strait Hill–Cooms Fell Neck (NY 433 899) may have been one of several in the near vicinity that erupted the basalts of the Birrenswark Volcanic Formation (McRobert, 1920; Elliott, 1960; Lumsden *et al.*, 1967; Figure 3.9). Here, pyroclastic breccia, in an outcrop approximately 350 m by 400 m, is intruded by a small plug of olivine-augite-microphyric basalt that does not match any of the lavas within the GCR site. Other examples within the GCR site occur on the south-west flank of Watch Hill (NY 433 904) and to the south of Howgill Hill (NY 436 916). The necks mainly comprise unbedded basaltic tuff and pyroclastic breccia

containing clasts of igneous rock, especially much decomposed basaltic glass and olivine basalt; there is also a variable proportion of sedimentary rock debris. The intrusions are usually plug-like bodies of basalt or dolerite that are compositionally similar to the lavas. The Howgill Sike Plug, which intrudes the Howgill Hill Neck, is larger than that of Strait Hill. It is a porphyritic basalt with zoned, partially resorbed phenocrysts of plagioclase and corroded phenocrysts of augite and olivine. Orthopyroxene and spinel are rare components of both the Strait Hill and Howgill Sike plugs, though it is unclear whether these are partially resorbed high-pressure phenocrysts, or xenocrysts, derived from disaggregating lherzolite inclusions carried in the magma from deep crustal levels (Upton, 1982).

The basalts of the Birrenswark Volcanic Formation provide some of the best data on the earliest Dinantian phase of volcanic activity in northern Britain. Earlier field-orientated studies suggested that they are entirely basaltic. However, Smedley (1986a) referred to the lavas of the Birrenswark Volcanic Formation collectively as transitional basalt and hawaiite, and the sequence on Kirk Hill (NY 462 864) some 6 km to the south-east of the GCR site comprises mainly basaltic hawaiites and hawaiites. More evolved compositions have not been reported from the GCR site, but mugearite occurs elsewhere, for example at Middlebie Burn (NY 216 767) near Birrenswark. Both Macdonald (1975) and Smedley (1986a) have shown that the basalts of the Birrenswark Volcanic Formation, being relatively low in alkalis and predominantly hypersthene ± quartz-normative, are among the most transitional to tholeiitic of all the Dinantian volcanic sequences in northern Britain; only the Cockermouth Lavas are more tholeiitic. However, Smedley (1986a) also found that some of the basalts of the Birrenswark Volcanic Formation are nepheline-normative.

Interpretation

Eruption of the Birrenswark Volcanic Formation probably occurred during Tournaisian times, though the biostratigraphical evidence for this is far from certain (e.g. Elliott, 1960; Lumsden *et al.*, 1967; Chadwick *et al.*, 1995). A contrary view was put forward by Nairn (1956) who, in his study of the Lower Carboniferous rocks west of the River Esk, considered that the base of the

Carboniferous System should be placed at the base of the sedimentary rocks overlying the Birrenswark Volcanic Formation. The Upper Old Red Sandstone facies rocks conformably underlying the volcanic rocks were formerly regarded as Late Devonian, but are now considered to be of Tournaisian age (Lumsden *et al.*, 1967; Day, 1970; Leeder, 1971). The succeeding sedimentary rocks are known to be younger than earliest Tournaisian age.

All of the lavas appear to have been erupted in a subaerial environment and there is no record of either pillow lavas or the development of hyaloclastites. Pahoehoe structures have not been seen and most lavas are probably aa type; some show reddened oxidized tops and possible lateritic palaeosols (boles). Sedimentary interbeds up to 10 m thick show that the volcanism was often punctuated by long periods of quiescence that allowed the establishment of localized fluvial and lacustrine systems. The number, thickness and composition of the lavas in any one section vary over comparatively short distances. This probably indicates that most of the lavas were small in volume, originating from a series of small volcanoes or fissures rather than from one large composite fissure system, in contrast to the extensive flood-basalts of the Clyde Plateau Volcanic Formation, for example (see Chapter 2). The overall form of the lava field appears therefore to be one of a shallow-dipping plateau that was constructed as a series of overlapping flows of restricted lateral extent.

The basalts of the Birrenswark Volcanic Formation are considered to be penecontemporaneous with the Kelso Lavas that crop out farther to the north-east (e.g. Eckford and Ritchie, 1939), but were almost certainly erupted as a geographically separate lava field. Nairn (1956) noted thinning to both the east and west from the type locality at Birrenswark. The conclusion of Lumsden *et al.* (1967) that the volcanic formation in the area east of Tarras Water, which includes the Langholm–Newcastleton Hills GCR site, does not thin significantly in any direction, has subsequently been shown to be incorrect. The most significant advance in our understanding of the palaeogeography of these times was made by Leeder (1971, 1974). He demonstrated, using isopachytes, that the volcanic formation thins overall to the north and north-east (Leeder, 1974). He also concluded that the succession thins south-west, but evidence for this is indirect and is based on thinning south-

westwards of the later Glencartholm Volcanic Beds into the Bewcastle anticline.

Leeder (1974) considered three hypotheses to explain the pattern of isopachytes. First, the current distribution could be the erosional remnants of a larger volcanic field of unknown extent. He thought this unlikely because of the conformable relationship between the lavas and overlying sedimentary rocks, and because basalt pebbles in the basal sedimentary rocks above the lavas are only present locally. His second hypothesis involved eruption from a line of fissures orientated along the line of maximum thickness. Though he considered this to be attractive, there is little support from the distribution of the volcanic necks, many of which are some distance from the maximum lava thickness. The third, and most likely, hypothesis is a relationship between the geometry of the lava pile and the pre-existing Upper Old Red Sandstone facies sedimentary basin, which is known to have had a south-west–north-east orientation (Leeder, 1974, fig. 4). Locally, within the basin, the lavas are absent and this may have been due to the presence of a palaeohigh. Leeder (1971) also concluded that emplacement of the lava field had a profound effect on sediment distribution in the area: prior to the eruptions the mean sediment transport direction was north-eastwards, but subsequently this changed to south-east-wards. However, such a change may be related more to the initiation of the Northumberland, Solway and Tweed basins and thus a change in basin geometry.

On a regional scale, the Birrenswark Volcanic Formation lavas are quite localized along the northern margins of the Northumberland and Solway basins, and are an integral part of the early basin development. According to some (e.g. Leeder, 1974), they probably do not extend far into the sub-surface beneath the basins, and Chadwick *et al.* (1995), in considering the seismic reflection data of Kimbell *et al.* (1989), pointed out that although there may be lavas at the base of the sequence elsewhere in the basins, there is no proof of this. A time interval of unknown duration is implied between emplacement of the last lava of the Birrenswark Volcanic Formation and deposition of the fluvio-deltaic sandstones of the Whita Sandstone Formation. As deposition of such thick sequences of strata requires the creation of considerable 'accommodation space', a significant degree of basin subsidence is implied, following the volcanism.

Dinantian volcanic rocks of the Scotland–England borders

Conclusions

The Langholm–Newcastleton Hills GCR site is representative of the Tournaisian Birrenswark Volcanic Formation, a lava succession consisting of up to 90 m of basalt, basaltic hawaiite, hawaiite and rare mugearite. The GCR site neatly demonstrates many of the key features of the formation, including evidence for the structure of the lava field, form of flows, details of the rock-types present and the variations in local successions. Associated volcanic necks of tuff and pyroclastic breccia, intruded by basalt plugs, may have been the sites of eruption for some of the lavas. The conformable stratigraphical relationships with sedimentary strata above and below the lavas are particularly clear.

The lavas of the Birrenswark Volcanic Formation are an important feature of the Early Carboniferous development of the Northumberland and Solway basins and are among the earliest manifestations of volcanic activity within the Carboniferous–Permian Igneous Province of northern Britain. Their position in space and time clearly illustrates the close association of basic volcanism with the early phases of development of sedimentary basins. They have formed an integral part of petrological and geochemical studies of the igneous province and will continue to provide an important source of material for any such studies in the future.

LINTMILL RAILWAY CUTTING, SCOTTISH BORDERS (NT 727 463– NT 736 466)

I.T. Williamson

Introduction

The Lintmill Railway Cutting GCR site has been selected to represent the basaltic to hawaiitic Kelso Lavas of the Tweed Basin. These early Dinantian volcanic rocks, along with the broadly coeval, but geographically separated, Birrenswark Volcanic Formation and Cockermouth Lavas in the Solway Basin to the south-west, are important to the understanding of crustal development during the early phase of the tectonic and sedimentary evolution of the Northumberland, Solway and Tweed basins (see also **Langholm–Newcastleton Hills**, **Gill Beck** and **Bothel Craggs Quarry** GCR site reports).

The Lintmill Railway Cutting GCR site is located some 3 km east of the small town of Greenlaw, at the northern end of the arcuate outcrop of the Kelso Lavas (Figure 3.1). Here, the volcanic rocks are exposed over a distance of about 600 m within the old railway cutting and along the banks of the Blackadder Water, west of Lintmill Bridge (Figures 3.11 and 3.12); elsewhere, exposure of the Kelso Lavas is only sporadic.

The Kelso Lavas attracted some interest during the early days of Scottish geology. The well-exposed parts of these igneous rocks were first mapped by Milne (1837) and the synclinal form of the outcrop was traced by Nicol (1847). The Geological Survey six-inch to one-mile map of the Kelso area was made by J. Geikie and published on the scale of one-inch to one-mile in 1879 (Sheet 25). No memoir for the area has been published, and as yet there has been no published re-survey. Brief references to the Kelso Lavas have subsequently been made by

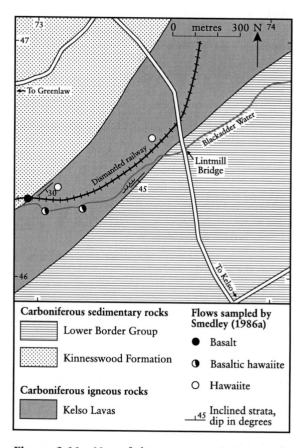

Figure 3.11 Map of the area around the Lintmill Railway Cutting GCR site. Based on Geological Survey Old Series 1:63 360 Sheet 25, Galashiels (1879); geochemical sample points from Smedley (1986a).

130

Figure 3.12 View east along the Lintmill Railway Cutting, with the Kelso Lavas exposed in the cutting on the left. (Photo: I.T. Williamson.)

J. Geikie (1893), A. Geikie (1897) and Goodchild (1904), but the main descriptions of the rocks are by Eckford and Ritchie (1939) and Tomkeieff (1945, 1953). More recently, the geochemistry of the Kelso Lavas has formed part of major petrogenetic studies of the Dinantian volcanic rocks of northern Britain by Macdonald (1975) and Smedley (1986a,b, 1988a).

Description

The Kelso Lavas comprise up to 12 basic and intermediate flows in their maximum development to the south of the Lintmill area (Tomkeieff, 1953), but there is little information on thickness variations over their outcrop. In the Lintmill Railway Cutting GCR site a 120 m-thick sequence of volcanic rocks rests unconformably upon sandstones of Upper Old Red Sandstone facies, and comprises perhaps six or seven lavas, interbedded with breccias, sparse thin volcaniclastic sedimentary units and possibly some thin palaeosols (see stratigraphical section below). The volcanic sequence within the site dips towards the south-east, with dips of individual units varying from 15° up to about 40°, but averaging about 25°. The top part of the sequence is not seen within the site, though nearby to the east in the Blackadder Water there are exposures of younger sedimentary rocks, dipping to the south-east at 4°–7°. The composite stratigraphical section, described from top to bottom, is described below.

	Thickness (m)
Sandstone and pebbly coarse sandstone seen 3–4 m above uppermost lava; contact not seen	
Basalt, feldspar-phyric, deeply weathered	*c.* 4
Basalt, feldspar-phyric, greenish-grey, amygdaloidal, weathered	*c.* 5
Hawaiite or basaltic hawaiite, showing crude columnar jointing and platy joints inclined at 45°–50° to the south-east, weathered; exposed in crags along the river, but not exposed in the cutting	*c.* 20
Basalts, olivine- and olivine-feldspar-phyric, inter-bedded massive, scoriaceous and amygdaloidal facies; localized thin, reddish-brown tuffs and/ or volcaniclastic siltstone, some beds with palaeosol development; dip in cutting is 30°–40°; some calcite mineralization	*c.* 33
Basalt, predominantly massive, sporadic and irregularly developed amygdaloidal facies; feldspar phenocrysts rare and widely scattered	*c.* 12
No exposure	*c.* 12
Basalt or basaltic hawaiite, massive, fine grained, rare feldspar phenocrysts; thin amygdaloidal basal facies; crude prismatic jointing inclined to the north-west at 70°–80°	*c.* 8
Basalt or dolerite, massive; may represent a thin sill intruded along base of overlying flow	*c.* 5
Sandstone, tuffaceous, fine grained to medium grained, reddish-brown; thin lenticular unit	*c.* 1
Basalt and locally basaltic hawaiite, olivine-phyric; flow jointed in part; undulating sharp base	
Sandstones, medium grained, red and reddish-brown with some red-grey to pale-buff mottling, cross-bedded; dip about 30° to the south-east or ESE (Upper Old Red Sandstone facies)	?

Some of the lavas are probably aa flows, in which massive and rubbly or scoriaceous facies are well developed. However, the middle parts of the sequence comprise a number of individual flow units, a characteristic of pahoehoe lavas. Most of the rocks are altered and weathered with mafic phenocrysts typically replaced by iddingsite, chlorite and calcite. Brecciation and calcite veining is conspicuous locally. Tomkeieff (1953) recognized a two-fold petrographical division within the Kelso Lavas: a lower group of dominantly feldspar-phyric rocks and an upper group with clinopyroxene and/or olivine phenocrysts. The Kelso Lavas include basalt, basaltic hawaiite and hawaiite; all are hypersthene-normative and a few also have quartz in the norm, and hence they are tholeiitic (Smedley, 1986a). These rocks have remarkably similar geochemistry to the Birrenswark Volcanic Formation, but are enriched in most elements relative to the Cockermouth Lavas (Smedley, 1988a).

Interpretation

The Kelso Lavas overlie Upper Old Red Sandstone facies rocks (Kinnesswood Formation) that are thought to have been deposited on a hot semi-arid alluvial floodplain by a system of interior drainage (Leeder, 1974). The sedimentary rocks are very early Carboniferous in age and the lavas are thought to be Tournaisian, probably Courceyan (Lumsden *et al.*, 1967; George *et al.*, 1976; House *et al.*, 1977). The lavas are therefore thought to be contemporaneous with the Birrenswark Volcanic Formation and the Cockermouth Lavas.

There is no major linear dyke-swarm associated with the volcanism though small dykes and sills occur locally. The lavas are therefore presumed to have been erupted from a series of small volcanic vents (Eckford and Ritchie, 1939). More than 50 such centres are scattered over a distance of about 16 km from Langholm to Duns. They are exposed at various levels of erosion so that some appear wholly or partially filled by plugs (see **Hareheugh Craigs** and **Langholm–Newcastleton Hills** GCR site reports), or by tuff and pyroclastic breccia.

The similarity in rock-types of the Kelso Lavas and Birrenswark Volcanic Formation and the abundance of volcanic necks between the outcrops led Francis (1967) to suggest that the outcrops were once continuous. However,

by constructing isopachytes for the Birrenswark lava field, Leeder (1974) demonstrated convincingly that the two most likely developed as separate though coeval fields. He also suggested that their original extent was little more than that occupied by the lavas today.

Macdonald (1975) and Smedley (1986a) demonstrated the overall similarity in geochemistry between the Kelso Lavas, the Birrenswark Volcanic Formation and the Cockermouth Lavas. However, the volcanic rocks from the Scottish Borders are considerably more enriched in minor and trace elements than those from the southern margin of the basins (Smedley, 1988a). The tholeiitic Kelso Lavas were shown clearly to be part of the mildly alkaline to tholeiitic suite that is characteristic of the Early Carboniferous volcanism in southern Scotland and northern England.

Conclusions

The Lintmill Railway Cutting GCR site is representative of the Kelso Lavas (see also **Hareheugh Craigs** GCR site report), a localized basaltic to hawaiitic lava field up to 120 m thick that was emplaced on the northern flank of the Tweed Basin during Early Carboniferous (Tournaisian, possibly Courceyan) times. The site provides a good section through six or seven basalt, basaltic hawaiite and hawaiite lavas with sparse intercalated volcaniclastic sedimentary rocks. The volcanic rocks are tholeiitic and are the products of magmatic events induced by crustal extension associated with the early evolution of the Tweed Basin. They provide vital information for the understanding of this development and also enable comparative studies with other Dinantian volcanic rocks from elsewhere within the Carboniferous–Permian Igneous Province of northern Britain.

HAREHEUGH CRAIGS, SCOTTISH BORDERS (NT 688 401)

I.T. Williamson

Introduction

The Hareheugh Craigs GCR site has been selected because it contains a particularly good example of a plug-like composite intrusion of basaltic hawaiite to hawaiite composition, associated with the early Dinantian Kelso Lavas in the Tweed Basin, which are represented by the **Lintmill Railway Cutting** GCR site.

Hareheugh Craigs is a craggy hilltop about 2.5 km north-west of the village of Stichill and close to the town of Kelso (Figures 3.13 and 3.14). The 1879 Geological Survey one-inch map shows an intrusive body of 'felstone' within the Kelso Lavas and the underlying Upper Old Red Sandstone strata. The revision survey concluded that this intrusion is probably a plug (Fowler and MacGregor, 1938). The petrography of the intrusion has been described in several papers on the igneous rocks of the Kelso area (Eckford and Ritchie, 1939; Tomkeieff, 1945, 1953) and it has been included in geochemical studies of Dinantian magmatism in northern Britain by Macdonald (1975) and Smedley (1986a).

Description

The Hareheugh Craigs intrusion cuts the Kelso Lavas, which are exposed intermittently in the immediately surrounding area and are represented by the nearby **Lintmill Railway Cutting** GCR site. The intrusion has a diameter of up to about 600 m and comprises two lithologically contrasting facies, one above the other. The best section through the lower part of the intrusion is seen in a former road-metal quarry (NT 6880 3990). Though partially obscured by waste tipping and natural degradation, the lower parts of the 20 m-high, main face of the quarry expose a beautifully fresh, feldspar-macrophyric basaltic hawaiite or hawaiite, with dark, lustrous feldspars having a tendency to weather-out on rock faces. The feldspars are irregularly distributed giving a diffusely banded or layered appearance of alternating porphyritic and aphyric zones. The upper parts of the face show a coarser-grained, though less porphyritic, or aphyric basaltic hawaiite or hawaiite. The highest exposures in the quarry and those on adjacent hillsides are of the upper facies. This comprises large phenocrysts of olivine, clinopyroxene and spinel in addition to plagioclase in a fine-grained groundmass. The junction between the two types is poorly exposed, but appears to be regular with only a thin zone of transition and no obvious cooling of one facies against the other.

Columnar cooling joints are up to 1.75 m across and are inclined radially outwards at up to 70°. A number of calcite-filled vugs occur, and thin, irregular veins cut the intrusion. The presence of shear zones with some slickensides and veining probably indicates faulting.

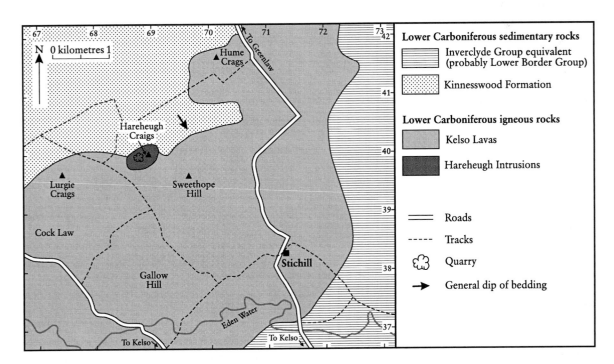

Figure 3.13 Map of the area around the Hareheugh Craigs GCR site. Based on Geological Survey Old Series 1:63 360 Sheet 25, Galashiels (1879).

133

Figure 3.14 View from the south-west of Hareheugh Craigs; a plug-like intrusion of hawaiitic rocks within the Kelso Lavas. (Photo: C. MacFadyen.)

Eckford and Ritchie (1939) described the intrusion as a 'Markle' (or related) basalt in the local classification scheme of MacGregor (1928); that is, an olivine basalt with feldspar phenocrysts, and ophitic augite forming part of a coarse-grained groundmass. Tomkeieff (1945) described the quarry exposures as olivine dolerite with patches and bands of 'Markle'-type basalt, and classed the exposures on the upper part of the hill as 'Dunsapie'-type basalt. In his later paper he referred to the intrusion as a composite plug of 'Markle' type (Tomkeieff, 1953). However, both Macdonald (1975) and Smedley (1986a) demonstrated that both facies of the Hareheugh Craigs intrusion are of hawaiite or basaltic hawaiite composition. Both are hypersthene-normative and are typical members of the mildly alkaline to transitional Carboniferous–Permian Igneous Province of northern Britain.

Interpretation

The Hareheugh Craigs intrusion is one of more than 50 intrusions and volcanic necks scattered across the area between Duns and Langholm (Tomkeieff, 1953). They occur on the margins of the Tweed and Solway basins and span the intervening Cheviot Block. These intrusions do not cut later Carboniferous sedimentary rocks and the likelihood is that they represent the subsurface expressions of the sites from which most of the Dinantian volcanic rocks (Birrenswark Volcanic Formation, Kershopefoot basalts and Kelso Lavas) of the district were erupted. Some may have fed younger flows that have been subsequently lost through erosion. There is no evidence, in the form of linear dyke-swarms for

example, for major fissure eruption, though some of these volcanic 'centres' define crude lineaments. The Hareheugh Craigs intrusion is one of several forming a NE-trending lineament from Hume (NT 710 420) towards Smailholm (NT 640 350) (Tomkeieff, 1953, fig. 1).

At Hareheugh Craigs, basaltic hawaiites and hawaiites are intruded into the generally more basic Kelso Lavas. Contact relationships are not entirely clear. There is some suggestion of systematic variations in grain size across the margins of the intrusion and some evidence for the presence of steeply inclined contacts. These features suggest that the body does indeed have an irregular plug-like geometry, as deduced by previous surveyors.

The differentiation of the intrusion into two separate but closely related, and possibly intergradational, lithologies suggests that the body is composite. The less porphyritic facies is the lower of the two. This arrangement is similar to that shown by composite Dinantian lavas from the Clyde Plateau Volcanic Formation near Greenock (Kennedy, 1931; Boyd, 1974) (see **Dunrod Hill** GCR site report) and in the Stirling area (MacDonald, 1967; Francis *et al.*, 1970) (see **Campsie Fells** GCR site report). Several other composite bodies from the province are listed by Macdonald (1975), the closest to Hareheugh Craigs being the hawaiite–basalt association exposed on Lurgie Craigs some 1.3 km to the west.

The compositions of the two facies indicate a degree of differentiation of the original magma from alkali olivine basalt to hawaiite, probably through the mechanism of crystal fractionation at relatively high pressures (Macdonald, 1975).

It is unlikely that such differentiation occurred *in situ* at the levels seen today in the Hareheugh Craigs intrusion. Rather, the emplacement may have resulted from a series of closely spaced, pulsed evacuations of a deeper level, internally stratified or zoned magma chamber, in which there was a downward gradation from more to less differentiated material. Another possibility is that fractionation took place during slow ascent of the magma and that this led to the postulated vertical zonation. Both mechanisms could lead to the internal intrusive arrangements seen today.

In general, where relative ages of emplacement can be deduced in such composite bodies, the more evolved aphyric or microporphyritic component is intruded before the less evolved macroporphyritic one. This is probably because, due to crystal-settling mechanisms, most phenocrysts are concentrated in the lower parts of the underlying magma chamber, and this crystal-charged batch of magma is usually the last to be either erupted or intruded at shallower crustal levels. It is significant that the porphyritic facies includes plagioclase in addition to mafic phenocrysts, suggesting that the magma at this level was already somewhat fractionated and hence of lower density that a basaltic magma, allowing the plagioclase to sink. At Hareheugh Craigs, the relative ages of the two facies are not known and the few available analyses suggest little correlation between the phenocryst content and whole-rock composition. Hence the exact sequence of fractionation and emplacement remains somewhat enigmatic.

Conclusions

The intrusion at the Hareheugh Craigs GCR site is representative of the many small plug-like intrusions that cut the Tournaisian Kelso Lavas and forms part of a swarm of over 50 sub-volcanic necks extending south-westwards into the Birrenswark Volcanic Formation. These may have been the sites of eruption of the lavas. It is one of few intrusions in the swarm that are composite. The two components present are basaltic hawaiite or hawaiite in composition; the lower one is generally aphyric to sparsely porphyritic, but the upper component contains large phenocrysts of feldspar, olivine, clinopyroxene and spinel.

The components of the composite intrusion are considered to have been emplaced as two

magmas of differing composition that formed within a single, vertically zoned magma column at deeper levels in the Earth's crust. Such composite bodies, whether in the form of lava flows or intrusions, provide a valuable insight into the crystallization and chemical evolution of magmas as they rise through the crust (see **Dunrod Hill** GCR site report). The fresh rocks of this intrusion have contributed to several important petrographical and geochemical studies of the igneous rocks associated with the early development of the Tweed, Northumberland and Solway basins.

COTTONSHOPE HEAD QUARRY, NORTHUMBERLAND (NT 803 058)

D. Millward

Introduction

A thin succession of tholeiitic, olivine-phyric basalts, referred to as the 'Cottonshope lavas' or 'Cottonshope basalts', is the only exposed record of effusive volcanic activity associated with development of the Northumberland Basin in Early Carboniferous times. The lavas crop out in a handful of localities south-west of the Cheviot Block, including Spithope Burn (NT 760 050), Hungry Law (NT 747 062), and between the Baseinghope Burn (NT 700 045) and the Chattlehope Burn (NT 730 028). They are thickest and best exposed in the valley of the Cottonshope Burn, in Upper Redesdale. The Cottonshope Head Quarry GCR site is located on the north-facing side of an unnamed tributary, due south of Cottonshope Head, where these rocks are seen particularly well (Figure 3.15). The basalts occur within a probable Tournaisian succession of sedimentary rocks that are currently included in the Cementstone Group of Northumberland (Miller, 1887; Taylor *et al.*, 1971).

The few published descriptions of the Cottonshope basalts are brief. C.T. Clough carried out the original geological survey of the area and his description of these rocks was incorporated in the Otterburn and Elsdon memoir (Miller, 1887). The succession and petrography were described later by Tomkeieff (1931). The area including the GCR site was re-mapped in 1932 by W. Anderson and is included in the Geological Survey Sheet 8 (1951). Previous work was summarized by Randall (1995a).

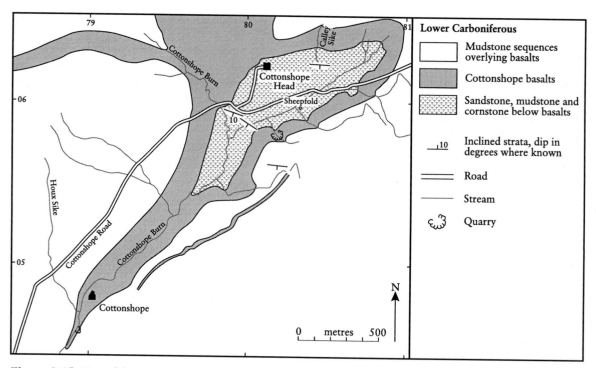

Figure 3.15 Map of the area around the Cottonshope Head Quarry GCR site. Based on geological mapping by W. Anderson (1932, Geological Survey Archives).

Description

The description of the Cottonshope Head Quarry GCR site is based on the published accounts and on field maps and manuscript notes in the British Geological Survey archives; this is supplemented by recent observations.

The upper part of the Cottonshope valley provides a complete section through the relatively poorly exposed Cottonshope basalts (Figure 3.15). Lower Carboniferous strata there dip at about 10° to the SSW or south. The succession underlying the basalts is dominated by red or grey flaggy sandstones with brown ochreous spotting, along with interbedded purple, red, lilac and green mudstones containing ochreous concretions. Thin beds of concretionary carbonate ('cornstone') were noted during a visit to the site in 2000. These strata were called the 'Lower Freestone Beds' by Miller (1887) and Taylor *et al*. (1971), but the presence of the 'cornstones' is a diagnostic feature of the Kinnesswood Formation of central Scotland. In places, grey mudstone is exposed just beneath the basalts and a prominent spring line occurs along the junction. The volcanic rocks are overlain by dark-grey and greenish mudstones with sandstones and thin 'cementstones'.

The volcanic succession comprises three sheets of basalt. The lowest one is 12 m thick and has an undulating pillow-like to slaggy, scoriaceous top in which there are sedimentary infills. This is overlain directly by vesicular basalt, 6 m thick. The uppermost basalt is also 6 m thick, but is separated from the underlying ones by 6 m of bedded mudstones, flaggy sandstones and 'cementstones'. In the Spithope Burn (NT 767 057), 3 km west of the GCR site, these beds contain fragments of basalt. The lowest two basalt sheets are exposed in a small road-metal quarry within the GCR site (Figure 3.15). The section exposed there in 1946 is recorded in manuscript notes in the British Geological Survey archives as follows:

'Upper lava: lava, dark grey with a few small vesicles 10 feet [3 m].
Vesicular lava with inclusions of shale and cementstones up to 2 × 1 feet in size, 1 to 10 feet [0.3–3 m].
Junction between lavas slightly undulating.
Lower lava: vesicular lava, coloured. The amygdales are filled with quartz and calcite, lined with green earth (chlorite) 3 feet [0.9 m].
Grey lava, apparently similar to top lava 8 feet [2.4 m].'

Miller (1887) described the inclusions of sedimentary rock recorded from the upper unit as having been bleached and altered by heat. The base of the upper unit was poorly exposed at the rear of the quarry in the summer of 2000, adjacent to a small stream. There, unbedded carbonate rock appeared to contain scattered angular fragments of basalt.

Though the volcanic rocks are generally conformable with the sedimentary rocks, Miller (1887) noted possible irregularity at the base of the lowest basalt in a stream about 800 m south of Cottonshope Head, probably at about NT 799 054. There, the base of the basalt cuts down at least 20 cm into the underlying 'cementstone' bed.

Generally, the basalt is closely fractured and considerably altered, though fresher material is noted from Calley Sike (NT 804 064), 600 m NNE of the quarry. The rock has been described by Tomkeieff (1931), as a typical 'Dalmeny'-type basalt, according to the classification of MacGregor (1928). It is a grey microporphyritic basalt containing phenocrysts of olivine, plagioclase and augite. There are numerous subhedral pseudomorphs of 'serpentine', iddingsite, chlorite and calcite after olivine phenocrysts. The groundmass comprises altered feldspar laths with intergranular chloritized augite and iron oxide. The major element composition of the lowest basalt in the succession, collected a little downstream from the GCR site at NT 7959 0537, is given by Tomkeieff (1931). Recalculation of this analysis shows the rock to be hypersthene- and very slightly quartz-normative.

The manuscript notes also record that the southern face of the quarry is formed by an easterly trending vein of quartz and galena about 80 mm wide. This is one of two similarly orientated veins, the second of which is exposed in Cottonshope Burn, 250 m downstream from Cottonshope (NT 7891 0456).

Interpretation

The Cottonshope basalts were interpreted as subaqueous by Miller (1887) and as submarine by Taylor *et al.* (1971). However, the presence of 'cornstones' in the sequence below the lavas suggests a subaerial environment. 'Cornstones' form as a result of a fluctuating water table through the soils of semi-arid floodplains. The 'cementstone' succession interbedded with, and overlying, the lavas is also thought to have been deposited on a fluvial coastal plain with lagoons (Taylor *et al.*, 1971).

Miller (1887) considered that the inclusions of sedimentary rock seen in the basalts were caught up in the moving flow and that some of the larger masses of sandstone represent the filling of an irregular topography during the intervals between eruptions. However, the undulating and pillow-like form to the top of each basalt was thought by Tomkeieff (1931) to resemble the hummocky and ropy surface of subaerial pahoehoe lava, though similar surface features are now known to be characteristic of submarine sheet-flows. He also concluded that fragments of sediment within the lava, and clasts of basalt within the sedimentary rocks overlying the second unit at Spithope, indicate that the basalts and sediments were contemporaneous, and hence imply an extrusive origin.

The three basalt lavas preserved in the Cottonshope Burn outcrop make this the thickest and best development of the Cottonshope basalts. Elsewhere, only one lava is thought to be present. Tomkeieff (1931) speculated on the source of the lavas. On Carter Fell (NT 680 060), a basalt plug and associated mushroom-like sill cut through a lenticular bed of agglomerate, rising into the lower part of the Fell Sandstone Group above the Cementstone Group. Though this basalt is clearly later than the Cottonshope basalts, Tomkeieff thought it possible that, as the agglomerate rests directly on the Lower Freestones, it could have been the site of an active volcano at the earlier time.

The Cottonshope basalts, which lie only about 100 m beneath the top of the Cementstone Group in Redesdale, have been tentatively assigned an early Tournaisian age. This is not well constrained because of the restricted nature of the fossils in the enclosing sedimentary rocks (Taylor *et al.*, 1971). The Cementstone Group of Northumberland probably correlates with the Lower Border Group farther west, and the top of the latter corresponds approximately to the Tournaisian–Visean boundary.

The recent discovery of 'cornstones' within the Lower Freestone Beds provides significant new evidence for eruption of the Cottonshope basalts during early Tournaisian times. M.A.E. Browne (pers. comm., 2000) examined the succession in Cottonshope Burn and concluded that the lithofacies present are typical of the Kinnesswood Formation of central Scotland. In the New Cumnock area (NS 6670 2158) this formation has been found to contain miospores of earliest Tournaisian age (LN–PC biozones) (Turner, 1994). This would place the volcanism at approximately the same time as the Birrenswark Volcanic Formation and the Kelso Lavas. Though the geochemical composition of the Cottonshope basalts is known only from a single major-element analysis, this suggests that these rocks are probably little different from the transitional, tholeiitic to mildly alkaline rocks that constitute the other early Dinantian volcanic rocks of northern England.

Conclusions

The Cottonshope Head Quarry GCR site is representative of the Cottonshope basalts, the only exposed sequence of Early Carboniferous volcanic rocks within the Northumberland Basin. The volcanic succession crops out southwest of the Cheviot Block and comprises up to three intensely altered, massive to highly amygdaloidal and scoriaceous, basalt lavas. The lavas are intercalated with sedimentary rocks of the Cementstone Group of Northumberland and overlie a sequence of sandstone, mudstone and concretionary carbonate ('cornstone') that was deposited on a semi-arid floodplain. The sedimentary rocks below the lavas were formerly assigned to the Lower Freestone Beds, a local formation, but they may be correlated with the Kinnesswood Formation of central Scotland. The age of the latter suggests that the Cottonshope basalts are early Tournaisian in age and hence they are part of the Birrenswark–Kelso volcanic episode.

KERSHOPE BRIDGE, SCOTTISH BORDERS (NY 496 833–NY 501 835)

I.T. Williamson

Introduction

The Kershope Bridge GCR site has been selected to represent the Kershopefoot basalts, a sequence of basaltic rocks that occurs within the upper part of the (Holkerian) Middle Border Group in a number of places south and southeast of Langholm. The site includes the disused road-metal quarry at Kershope Bridge and a section in the nearby Kershope Burn that here forms the border between Scotland and England (Figure 3.16). There are several other small,

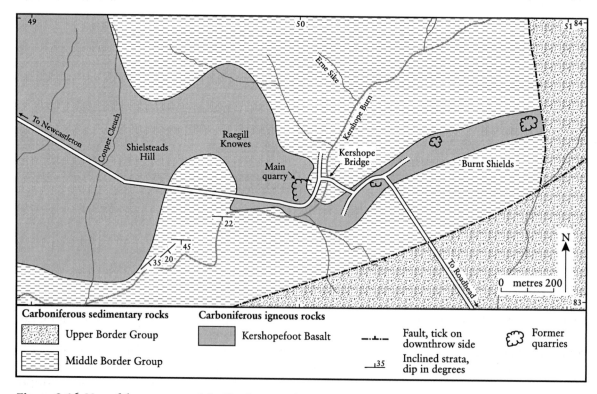

Carboniferous sedimentary rocks	Carboniferous igneous rocks			
Upper Border Group	Kershopefoot Basalt	Fault, tick on downthrow side	Former quarries	
Middle Border Group		Inclined strata, dip in degrees		

Figure 3.16 Map of the area around the Kershope Bridge GCR site. Based on Geological Survey 1:63 360 Sheet 11, Langholm (1968).

disconnected outcrops in the area, mostly on the Scottish side of the border to the west and north-east. These rocks represent a phase of tholeiitic to mildly alkaline volcanic activity younger than that of the Kelso Lavas, the Birrenswark Volcanic Formation and the Cockermouth basalts but older than the Glencartholm Volcanic Beds. All of these are associated with the early tectonic and sedimentary evolution of the Northumberland, Solway and Tweed basins.

The various exposures of the Kershopefoot basalts occupy more-or-less the same stratigraphical position throughout their outcrop. They attain a maximum thickness of about 36.5 m and probably represent several lava flows. Doubt has been expressed about their extrusive origin. Peach and Horne (1903) believed that some of the outcrops of the Kershopefoot basalts are lavas whereas others are intrusions. Garwood (1931), Lumsden *et al.* (1967) and Day (1970) referred to these rocks non-committally as the 'Kershopefoot Basalt'. Detailed descriptions of the rocks are to be found in Geological Survey memoirs (Lumsden *et al.*, 1967; Day, 1970) and the basalts were included in a widespread geochemical study of Dinantian magmatism in northern Britain by Smedley (1986a).

Description

The Kershopefoot basalts occur within the Middle Border Group, part of the Carboniferous Limestone Series. Possibly up to 490 m thick, the group shows an overall upward transition from mudstones and limestones with marine faunas and algal bands, through alternating, thinly bedded siltstones, sandstones, calcareous siltstones and limestones, to a massive, current-bedded sandstone unit known as the Larriston Sandstone. However, according to Lumsden *et al.* (1967), this sandstone facies cannot be traced confidently south of Newcastleton into the region occupied by the Kershopefoot basalts. Here, the sequence in the Kershope Burn shows sandstones with many more interbeds of argillaceous and calcareous units (Day, 1970). Beds below the basalts, exposed on neighbouring hillsides, comprise yellow, cross-bedded, fine-grained sandstone.

Basaltic lava is well exposed in the quarry by Kershope Bridge (NY 5005 8339). Neither the top nor the bottom contact of the basalt is seen in the area, but Lumsden *et al.* (1967) reported

sedimentary rocks in the floor of the quarry. The quarry faces reveal a bluish- to greenish-grey fine- to medium-grained basalt with unevenly distributed, large feldspar phenocrysts (typically 5–6 mm). These are rare to absent towards the base and top of the section. The main mass of the rock is neither vesicular nor amygdaloidal, though there are scattered large drusy cavities with infillings and coatings of carbonate, quartz in various forms, and baryte. The higher parts of the exposed section are much more vesicular and brecciated with some scoriaceous fragments. Long-exposed surfaces show the development of spheroidal weathering. The worked faces are cut by jointing with well-developed near-vertical to steeply inclined NE- (prominent) and SW-directed sets.

In the Kershope Burn, downstream (south-westwards) from the bridge, there are exposures of basalt and associated sedimentary rocks. The burn crosses the axes of two synclines with the result that beds are repeated. The amygdaloidal basalt is weathered greenish-brown, and shows some signs of brecciation. In the more north-eastern exposures (NY 4973 8332), it is overlain by massive sandstone and limestone dipping to the south-west though the contact is not seen. The upper parts of the basalt are also seen a little farther to the south-west at NY 4941 8310. Here amygdales are filled with red and green clay and may be flattened and streaked out, parallel to a faint flow-induced igneous lamination. The basalt is overlain by limestones, cherty sandstone breccia and sandstones dipping to the south-east, but here also, the contact relationships are not seen. Dips are typically in the range 20° to 45°.

Comprehensive descriptions of the petrography of the Kershopefoot basalts were given by R.W. Elliot (in Lumsden *et al.*, 1967) and R.K. Harrison (in Day, 1970). In thin section they show some lateral variation. At Kershope Bridge the rock is a porphyritic olivine basalt with phenocrysts of abundant labradorite, and subordinate olivine and clinopyroxene. The groundmass consists of labradorite laths, commonly strongly flow-banded and ophitically enveloped by anhedral to subhedral, purplish titaniferous augite. At other localities the groundmass clinopyroxene of the basalt may be colourless and either microlitic or skeletal. Minor constituents include titaniferous magnetite, ilmenite, orthopyroxene and apatite. There is also a little interstitial analcime. Vesicles are infilled by chlorite, calcite, baryte, quartz, chalcedony and agate; amethystine quartz has been reported from low levels within the mass.

Whole-rock analyses show that the rocks range from basalt to hawaiite, with a range of silica saturation from hypersthene-normative to slightly nepheline-normative (Smedley, 1986a). As such they are typical of the transitional tholeiitic to mildly alkaline Dinantian lavas of northern Britain.

A yellow-weathered silty dolostone in the Kershope Burn (NY 4974 8332), about 0.6 m above the top of the basalt, is intensely brecciated, with veins of ankerite and joint surfaces coated with bitumen. There are also patches of chlorite, scattered grains of pyrite and the rock has been partially recrystallized. These features have been explained as a diagenetic rather than a contact metamorphic phenomena (Day, 1970).

Interpretation

On the first edition of the one-inch Geological Survey map (Sheet 11, Scotland; 1883), the western outcrops of the Kershopefoot basalts were shown as intrusive, whereas the others, including the outcrop of which the Kershope Bridge GCR site is part, were regarded as lava. Peach and Horne (1903) included the Kershope Bridge to Carby Hill outcrop as lavas within the Glencartholm Volcanic Beds. Elliott (1960) also considered some of the western outcrops of the Kershopefoot basalts to be intrusive, though the outcrop at Kershope Bridge was outside his area of study. Uncertainties over the mode of emplacement of these rocks were also expressed by Lumsden *et al.* (1967) and Day (1970), though eruption as lavas was suggested because of the slaggy vesicular upper part of the sequence. However, these authors agreed that the various outcrops are part of the same mass at a single stratigraphical level, and are at least 60 m (Day, 1970) or 120 m (Lumsden *et al.*, 1967) beneath the Glencartholm Volcanic Beds.

The doubt as to whether the Kershopefoot basalts are extrusive or intrusive arises because no contacts are exposed. There is a general lack of post-depositional recrystallization of the adjacent strata, but there are some thermal effects. At the base of the basalt in the Kershope Burn there is a general induration and some

subtle bleaching of the more argillaceous beds. This is typical of both lavas and shallow intrusions but is not diagnostic. The upper contact is potentially more informative and, in Kershope Quarry, the uppermost parts of the basalt show well-developed vesiculation and brecciation, both phenomena more typical of, but not exclusive to, extrusive rocks. The basalt here is considered to be most probably a lava and, though inconclusive, the weight of evidence suggests that the basalts in general are extrusive rather than intrusive, and hence are contemporaneous with sedimentation in the Middle Border Group. Although no interflow junctions are known, the overall thickness of the basalts (over 36 m) and the variation in petrography and geochemistry between the various outcrops suggest the presence of more than one flow.

In terms of major-and trace-element compositions the Kershopefoot basalts are similar to the older lavas of the Birrenswark Volcanic Formation, which crop out in the same area (Smedley, 1986a, 1988a). However, there are notable differences in some incompatible trace-element ratios that have been attributed to the derivation of magmas from a different portion of the mantle, despite the close geographical proximity and the relatively short time interval between the two volcanic episodes.

Conclusions

The Kershope Bridge GCR site is representative of the Kershopefoot basalts, a localized extrusive event during the deposition of the Visean Middle Border Group. Olivine-clinopyroxene-plagioclase-phyric basalt, basaltic hawaiite and hawaiite comprise a succession up to 36.5 m thick. Though commonly interpreted as lava, there is some doubt about this and an intrusive emplacement is possible. Like the younger Glencartholm Volcanic Beds and the older Kelso Lavas and Birrenswark Volcanic Formation, the activity that produced the basalts seen at Kershope Bridge is thought to relate to tensional fracturing along the northern margin of the actively subsiding Northumberland and Solway basins. This site provides important evidence within this framework for continued stretching and crustal thinning, allowing intermittent eruption of basaltic magmas during the development of Early Carboniferous basins.

River Esk, Glencartholm

RIVER ESK, GLENCARTHOLM, DUMFRIES AND GALLOWAY (NY 377 792–NY 376 799)

I.T. Williamson

Introduction

The River Esk at Glencartholm, some 5 km south of Langholm, is the type locality of the Glencartholm Volcanic Beds (Figure 3.17). These are the only preserved record of significant pyroclastic activity associated with development of the Northumberland, Solway and Tweed basins. Also, these beds are the youngest of three chronologically distinct volcanic episodes within the Dinantian succession of the Langholm area (Figure 3.2; the other two are the Birrenswark Volcanic Formation and the Kershopefoot basalts; see **Langholm–Newcastleton Hills** and **Kershope Bridge** GCR site reports). All of these volcanic successions are critical to our understanding of Late Palaeozoic crustal and mantle processes, during the development of the Northumberland, Solway and Tweed basins.

The Glencartholm Volcanic Beds were formed during the later part of the syn-extensional phase (Chadwick *et al.*, 1995).

The Glencartholm Volcanic Beds comprise a 150–180 m-thick sequence of tuffs, localized lavas and interbedded mudstone and sandstone (many of which are volcaniclastic) and thin limestones, that occurs at the base of the (Visean) Upper Border Group. Palaeontological data from the interbedded lithologies suggest an age close to the Holkerian–Asbian boundary (George *et al.*, 1976).

Brief accounts of the volcanic beds were included in publications by Peach and Horne (1903), Barrett and Richey (1945), Elliott (1960), Lumsden and Wilson (1961) and Leeder (1974); the most comprehensive description, including the type locality, is that of Lumsden *et al.* (1967).

Glencartholm has been credited as being the richest fossil fish site within the Carboniferous rocks of the British Isles, and in an international context is one of the most important Palaeozoic vertebrate sites in the world (see Dineley and Metcalf, 1999). It is also an important palaeobotanical site (see Cleal and Thomas, 1995).

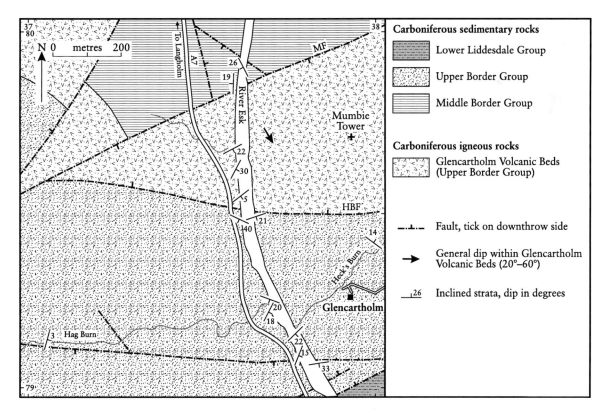

Figure 3.18 Map of the area around the River Esk, Glencartholm GCR site. (HBF = Heck's Burn Fault; MF = Mumbie Fault.) Based on Geological Survey 1:10 560 Sheet NY 37 NE (1967).

141

Dinantian volcanic rocks of the Scotland–England borders

Description

The Glencartholm Volcanic Beds are the basal unit of the Upper Border Group, a succession mainly composed of sedimentary rocks and in total probably up to 800 m thick. The group may be divided into a lower unit comprising the volcanic rocks, marine mudstones, limestones and subordinate sandstones and coals, and an overlying upper unit dominated by arenaceous rocks with only subordinate argillaceous strata and thin limestones. These, and equivalent strata of early Asbian age, are known to crop out widely in the western and central parts of the Northumberland Basin, and along the northern margins of the Solway Basin.

The Glencartholm Volcanic Beds form a disconnected series of narrow outcrops extending over a distance of about 10 km from the Irvine Burn north-eastwards to the Muir Burn. Owing to the relatively soft and easily weathered nature of these fragmental volcanic rocks, there are few exposures other than in stream sections. The most extensive sections are found in Haw Gill, Pow Gill and Rae Gill, all streams at the head of the Muir Burn, but the best known, and the designated type locality, is between the Heck's Burn and Mumbie faults in the River Esk at Glencartholm (Figure 3.17).

The best section is seen on the east bank of the River Esk. Here, the strata dip mainly towards the south or SSE at 5° to 60°, but the section is complicated by numerous small faults and folds. The lowest beds, at least 21 m thick, are poorly bedded blue-grey tuffs with thin beds of fine- to coarse-grained volcaniclastic sandstone. Both contain altered fragments of igneous and sedimentary rock. The larger fragments in the tuffs, up to 7.5 cm across, are mostly of sandstone, quartz, chert and 'cementstone'; the igneous clasts are considerably smaller. These are succeeded by interbedded tuffs, tuffaceous sandstones and siltstones, and 'cementstones'. There are numerous thin beds of chert, cherty sandstone and limestone.

The richly fossiliferous beds that have yielded internationally important arthropods and fish, first noted by Peach and Horne (1903), are exposed over a distance of 46 m about 460 m upstream from the mouth of Heck's Burn (NY 3764 7960). They are a gently dipping sequence of fissile calcareous sandstones with thin 'cementstones', and fine-grained sandy limestone up to 15 cm thick. Beyond these beds, and across a couple of faults, there is a gently folded sequence of soft sandstones, tuffaceous sandstones and thin tuffs. Some of the tuffaceous beds display upward-fining graded bedding. The highest beds in the section are exposed upstream from the Heck's Burn Fault. These comprise thinly bedded, multicoloured, tuffaceous siltstones and silty sandstones with numerous thin 'cementstones', limestones and rare coal.

The petrography of the volcaniclastic rocks in the River Esk section has been described by R.W. Elliot (in Lumsden et al., 1967). Descriptions of similar rocks in the Archerbeck Borehole (NY 4157 7815) were described by D.C. Knill (in Lumsden and Wilson, 1961). The igneous clasts in the tuffs provide clues to contemporary volcanism in the region. They include basalt, spilitic basalt, andesite, mugearite, trachyte and scoria. Other clasts include sandstone, quartz, chert and 'cementstone'. Small crystals of cassiterite have been found in samples from the borehole.

Effusive volcanic activity was not a major feature of this volcanic episode as there are few occurrences of lavas within the Glencartholm Volcanic Beds. None are noted from the River Esk section, but there are subordinate basalt occurrences up to 15 m thick elsewhere in the area. These include olivine-clinopyroxene-plagioclase-phyric basalt in Palling Burn (c. NT 305 788), some distance west of Glencartholm and, to the east, some very altered olivine-clinopyroxene-phyric basalts at Rae Gill (NT 4493 8240) and hawaiite or mugearite at Pow Gill (NT 4493 8289). All occur at or near the base of the volcanic sequence and, upon brecciation or erosion, may have supplied some of the clasts in the tuffs at higher levels.

Interpretation

The Glencartholm Volcanic Beds have a wide, but variable, distribution across the Northumberland and Solway basins and were proved at depth in the Archerbeck Borehole near Canonbie (Lumsden and Wilson, 1961). The Oakshawford Tuff of the Bewcastle Anticline (Day, 1970) is probably its lateral equivalent. The sequence in the Archerbeck Borehole is greater than 152 m thick, whereas only a metre of tuff at Oakshawford suggests an abrupt thinning to the south (Leeder, 1974). None of the natural sections is complete, being either faulted or poorly exposed.

River Esk, Glencartholm

The volcanic beds are predominantly of pyroclastic and volcaniclastic sedimentary origin; fine-grained crystal- and lapilli-tuffs in beds a few centimetres to over 20 m thick are typical. The thinner beds, often with upward-fining profiles, are dominated by volcanic material whereas many of the thicker units include a high proportion of non-volcanic detritus. The interbedded, commonly spectacularly fossiliferous, sedimentary rocks were interpreted by Lumsden *et al.* (1967) as lagoonal to shallow marine sequences that were buried periodically by volcanic, predominantly ash-fall, deposits. The volcanic eruptions effectively contaminated these sedimentary environments, killing off any biota for significant periods until re-colonization could take place.

Volcanic necks and associated minor intrusions in the region appear not to cut strata younger than the Glencartholm Volcanic Beds and have consequently been suggested as possible sources for the volcanic rocks (McRobert, 1920; Lumsden *et al.*, 1967). As much of the igneous detritus is compositionally distinct from the associated lavas, D.C. Knill (in Lumsden and Wilson, 1961) suggested that it may have been derived from the erosion of pre-existing volcanic rocks. However, this scenario was dismissed by Lumsden *et al.* (1967) on the grounds that similar detritus is not present in the interbedded sedimentary rocks and such rapid and repeated changes in provenance were unlikely to have occurred.

Conclusions

The section in the River Esk at Glencartholm is the type locality for the Visean Glencartholm Volcanic Beds. These predominantly bedded tuffs and volcaniclastic sedimentary rocks, in a succession 150–180 m thick, represent the latest and only significant volcaniclastic event during Dinantian volcanism associated with the early evolution of the Northumberland, Solway and Tweed basins. Fossil plant, arthropod and fish remains within the marine and lagoonal strata interbedded with these rocks are of international importance.

Chapter 4

Silesian and Early Permian volcanic rocks of Scotland

Introduction

INTRODUCTION

D. Stephenson

Volcanism continued intermittently throughout Dinantian time in the Midland Valley of Scotland, but as the sedimentary basins developed and the palaeogeography changed from fluvial plains with lakes to deltas, estuaries and shallow seas, so the nature of the volcanism changed. The vast subaerial lava plateaux and linear eruptive centres that dominated earlier Dinantian times were replaced in later Dinantian and Namurian times by more localized, short-lived, central vent complexes, characterized by more explosive, phreato-magmatic eruptions. Pyroclastic deposits are a major product of these eruptions and the lavas are almost exclusively basaltic (of micro-porphyritic 'Dalmeny' and 'Hillhouse' types); many are silica-undersaturated alkali olivine basalts and basanites. Basaltic hawaiites are rare, and the more fractionated rocks that are a feature of many early Dinantian successions, are absent.

These volcanic conditions were already widely established by the beginning of Namurian time and continued intermittently until at least mid-Westphalian times in the eastern Midland Valley, though at an overall less productive level than in Dinantian times. In the western Midland Valley, volcanism ceased following a major outpouring of lavas in late Namurian to earliest Westphalian times. Since there are no strata of Stephanian age preserved in Scotland we cannot be certain if there was any volcanism at this time. Large volumes of tholeiitic magma were intruded as dykes and sill-complexes during early Stephanian times (see Chapter 6) but, according to the model of Francis (1982), the magma was under insufficient pressure to reach the surface and there is no evidence of it having done so. Volcanism did resume in latest Stephanian or very early Permian times, when conditions had once again become continental, with localized outpourings of alkali basalt and basanite lavas in western and south-western areas and possibly also in the eastern Midland Valley where some sub-volcanic plugs and necks have late Stephanian to Early Permian radiometric ages.

Most of the Silesian volcanic rocks are interbedded with well-established, commonly fossiliferous, shallow-water sedimentary successions, and it is relatively easy to trace their stratigraphical development (Figure 4.1).

Lavas dominate volcanic successions in the early Namurian rocks of the Bathgate Hills, the late Namurian rocks of north Ayrshire and the Early Permian rocks of south-west Scotland (Figure 4.2). Other eruptions were predominantly of pyroclastic rocks and these are

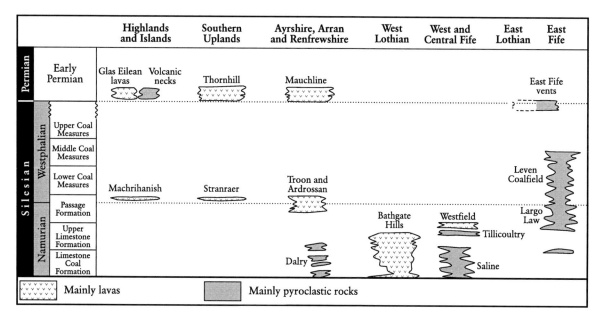

Figure 4.1 Range and distribution of the Silesian and Early Permian volcanic rocks of Scotland. After, in part, Cameron and Stephenson (1985).

147

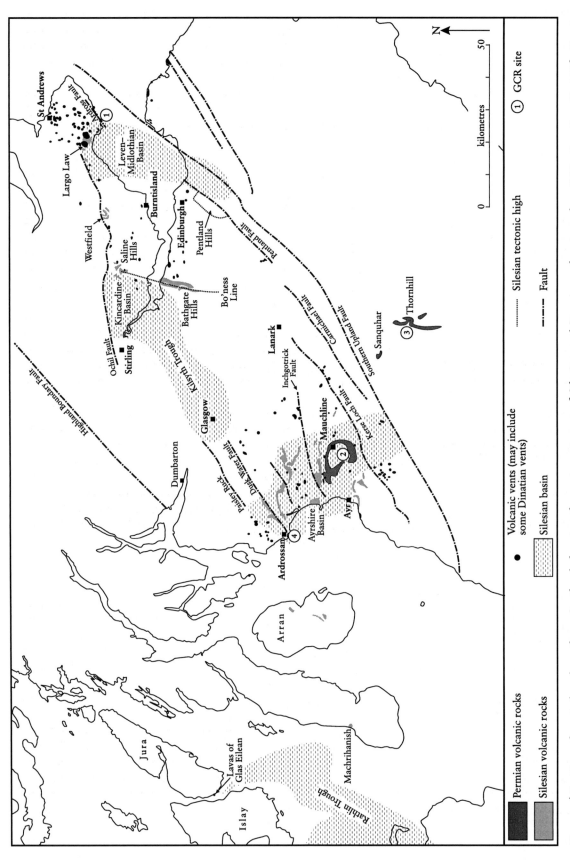

Figure 4.2 Map of central and southern Scotland showing the main outcrops of Silesian and Permian volcanic rocks. GCR sites: 1 = East Fife Coast; 2 = Howford Bridge; 3 = Carron Water; 4 = Ardrossan to Saltcoats Coast. Information from published sources, including Cameron and Stephenson (1985); Francis (1991); Read (1988); and Rippon *et al.* (1996).

represented only by sub-volcanic necks and beds of ash-fall tuff. However, throughout Silesian times, large volumes of magma solidified at depth as sill-complexes (see Chapter 5). It is likely that the increasing thickness of geotechnically weak sediments in the rapidly developing Silesian basins would be of too low density to support columns of magma, which spread laterally as sills (Francis, 1991). Magma that did have sufficient energy to rise to shallower levels reacted with groundwater and wet sediment to produce violent, phreatomagmatic eruptions. Such eruptions took place largely in areas of shallow water close to low-lying coastal plains. Here, accumulations of sediment and volcanic rocks broadly kept pace with subsidence, but periodically the volcanic rocks would build up above sea level where they were subjected to subaerial weathering, lateritization, erosion and re-deposition as volcaniclastic sediments. As the balance between rates of eruption, erosion and subsidence changed, so the relationships between the volcanic rocks and sediments within the preserved successions varied (Francis, 1961a,b, 1991). Since many of these successions include coal-bearing strata, studies of the volcanic rocks have had vital economic implications. Accumulations of volcanic rocks are commonly surrounded by shoals of volcaniclastic sand, and together these locally 'interrupt' the continuity of otherwise widespread contemporaneous coal seams. They also continued to influence the subsequent development of coal seams due to differential compaction, which led to marked attenuation above the relatively incompressible volcanic piles.

Bathgate Hills, Saline Hills and Kincardine Basin (late Visean to mid Namurian)

The most continuous volcanic activity from late Dinantian through to mid Namurian times occurred in the area around the Bathgate Hills (Peach *et al.*, 1910; Cadell, 1925; Macgregor and Haldane, 1933; Smith *et al.*, 1994; Stephenson in Cameron *et al.*, 1998). Here, a 600 m-thick succession of basaltic pyroclastic rocks and lavas, the Bathgate Hills Volcanic Formation, extends from the upper part of the Hopetoun Member, West Lothian Oil-shale Formation, to just above the Castlecary Limestone at the base of the Passage Formation. Unfortunately, there are no reliable radiometric dates for this prolonged

sequence, which spans the Dinantian–Silesian boundary; some precise Ar-Ar determinations would have clear international value. This important and extensive sequence is not represented at present by a GCR site.

Borehole and mining information to the west of the outcrop suggests that the volcanic deposits are restricted to a sub-circular area, 20–25 km in diameter, that coincides with spectacular positive gravity and magnetic anomalies. The source of these anomalies has been the subject of much debate, as the combined thickness of volcanic rocks (Bathgate Hills and earlier volcanic formations) is insufficient to generate the observed anomalies. Current interpretations favour up to 1 km of volcanic rocks, intruded in their lower part by a large basic mass extending to a depth of about 8 km, and all sited upon a WNW-trending structural high that may have acted as a focus for the igneous activity (Rollin in Cameron *et al.*, 1998). Several necks and plugs that cut older strata to the east of the main outcrop of volcanic rocks give some idea of the former eastward extent of the volcanic field, prior to erosion.

The basal part of the volcanic sequence, up to the base of the Lower Limestone Formation, is predominantly of pyroclastic rocks, except for some more persistent lavas in the Riccarton–Longmuir area. Sporadic graded bedding and load casts suggest subaqueous deposition in places, but numerous seatclays indicate frequent emergence. Layers of chert and spherulitic carbonate within the freshwater East Kirkton Limestone, famous for its terrestrial vertebrate, arthropod and plant fossils (Rolfe *et al.*, 1994; Dineley and Metcalfe, 1999), have been interpreted as evidence of hot spring activity associated with the volcanism (McGill *et al.*, 1990, 1994). From the top of the Lower Limestone Formation upwards, lavas become dominant at outcrop, although in boreholes to the west, thick, proximal pyroclastic deposits suggest the presence of a long-lived volcanic centre or centres in this area. The petrography of the lavas has been described by Falconer (1906) and Flett (in Peach *et al.*, 1910). They are all alkali olivine basalts or basanites, and are microporphyritic with phenocrysts of olivine and variable amounts of augite ('Dalmeny' and 'Hillhouse' type). Kaolinized or reddened flow tops indicate subaerial eruption.

The overall picture of the Bathgate Hills area is of a low-lying, heavily vegetated coastal plain in late Dinantian times, giving way periodically to shallow marine conditions in Lower Limestone and Upper Limestone formation times. Volcanoes accumulated above sea level to form islands surrounded by coastal plains, restricted lagoons and a variety of carbonate reefs, all neatly modelled by Jameson (1987) (see Petershill Quarry GCR site report in the *British Lower Carboniferous Stratigraphy* GCR volume – Cossey *et al.*, in prep). Carbonaceous mudstones and argillaceous limestones, interpreted as having formed in back-reef lagoons, contain synsedimentary Pb-Zn mineralization related to the volcanism (Stephenson, 1983).

The Saline Hills of western Fife are broadly along strike to the NNE of the Bathgate Hills along the Bo'ness High, a zone of relatively low subsidence that forms the eastern margin of the Silesian Kincardine Basin (Read, 1988). Here, thick tuffs, volcaniclastic sedimentary rocks and rare thin basalt flows occur in the Limestone Coal Formation and parts of the Upper Limestone Formation (Francis, 1961a). The succession is cut by several necks and plugs. Within the Kincardine Basin, boreholes and mine workings have revealed distal tuffs at various levels in the Limestone Coal Formation and Upper Limestone Formation that may correlate with the volcanism in the Bathgate Hills to the south (Francis *et al.*, 1961). These are mostly on the eastern side of the basin, on the flank of the Bo'ness High, where several necks have also been recognized (Francis, 1957, 1959; Barnett, 1985). However, a borehole at Tillicoultry in the centre of the basin revealed proximal agglomerates and some lavas in the top part of the Upper Limestone Formation. Rippon *et al.* (1996) have suggested that these were related to the NNE-trending Coalsnaughton Fault which may have been an active extensional fault parallel to the Bo'ness Line.

South-west Scotland (Namurian)

In the west of the Midland Valley, basic pyroclastic rocks are interbedded with sedimentary strata throughout the Limestone Coal Formation and to a lesser extent the Upper Limestone Formation to the west of Dalry; they are known mainly from borehole records (Richey *et al.*, 1930). All may have been derived from necks that cut older strata to the west.

A major episode of volcanism is represented in the upper part of the Passage Formation by the Troon Volcanic Member. This is recognizable over an area that extends from Ayrshire south to Stranraer and west to Arran, Kintyre and possibly to Northern Ireland (Richey *et al.*, 1930, fig. 25), but the main development occurs beneath the Coal Measures of the Ayrshire Basin (Monro, 1999). Outcrops of lava occur on the northern and southern flanks of the basin and the thickest development of over 160 m is just to the north of the town of Troon (Figure 4.3). Isopachs suggest contemporaneous movements along the Inchgotrick and Dusk Water faults. Specific volcanic centres have not been identified and may lie offshore. Miospores from interbedded sedimentary rocks constrain the biostratigraphical age to the KV zone (Kinderscoutian to early Marsdenian) and a minimum K-Ar radiometric age of 305 ± 6 Ma has been estimated by De Souza (1982). More precise Ar-Ar determinations would clearly be very useful at this well-defined point in time, just prior to the development of the major coalfield basins. The volcanic member is represented by the **Ardrossan to Saltcoats Coast** GCR site (see GCR site report).

The Troon Volcanic Member is composed almost entirely of subaerial basaltic lavas (olivine-microphyric, 'Dalmeny' type) with some interbedded sedimentary rocks. Petrographical details were given by MacGregor (in Richey *et al.*, 1930; in Eyles *et al.*, 1949). Like the earlier, Dinantian lavas, these are transitional in nature and range from hypersthene- to nepheline-normative; a few are basanites (Macdonald *et al.*, 1977; Wallis, 1989).

The lavas are generally decomposed, commonly with a characteristic red speckled appearance due to sideritic alteration. More advanced decomposition produces pseudostratified greenish-blue clays, thought to be the result of penecontemporaneous subaerial weathering. This weathering is particularly well developed at the top of the member, and on the northern side of the Ayrshire Basin it grades upwards into aluminous clayrocks interbedded with laminated mudstones, seatclays and coals that together comprise the Ayrshire Bauxitic Clay Member (Wilson, 1922; Eyles *et al.*, 1949; Monro, 1999) (see High Smithstone Quarry GCR site report in the *British Upper Carboniferous Stratigraphy* GCR volume – Cleal and Thomas,

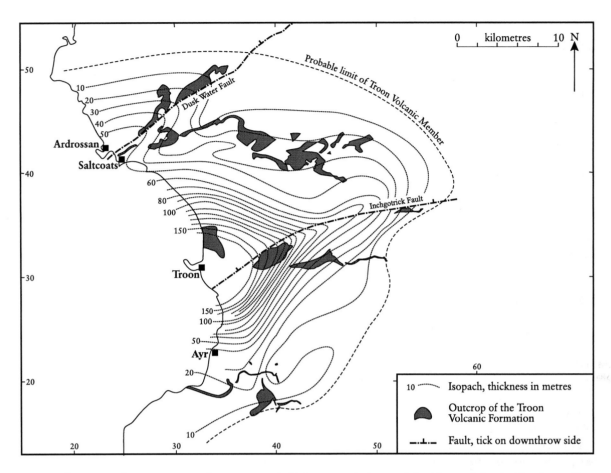

Figure 4.3 Map showing areas of outcrop, and thickness variations, of the Troon Volcanic Member. After Monro (1999); Geological Survey 1:50 000 sheets 14W, Ayr (1978); 14E, Cumnock (1976); and British Geological Survey 1:50 000 Sheet 22E, Kilmarnock (1999).

1996). This complex member is up to 20 m thick in places, but is more typically 2–4 m thick and has been extracted as a source of alum and specialist refractory clay. It contains some of the highest quality fireclay in Britain, with up to 42% Al_2O_3. Whilst the basal parts were undoubtedly formed by the weathering of basalt *in situ*, there has been much debate about additional sedimentary and diagenetic processes that may have operated (Monro *et al.*, 1983). Bauxitic laterites only form in tropical climates and require a significant time to build up any thickness. A variety of clastic clayrocks demonstrate the local reworking of the weathered crust and, in the absence of any other sediment input, we can deduce that the topography of the underlying lava surface was low. Coals, seatrocks and plant remains, including tree trunks, are abundant and, together with the presence of at least one marine band, suggest that the area was reduced to a heavily vegetated, flat, low-lying

coastal plain when the volcanism ended at the close of Namurian time.

To the west of the main outcrop, on the Isle of Arran, a thin succession of red tuff and basaltic lava overlain by bauxitic clays and Middle Coal Measures occurs in the Merkland Burn, near Brodick Castle. Tuffs with thin lavas occur in two outcrops to the west and WSW of Lamlash: in the Benlister Burn, bauxitic clays are found and in the larger outcrop at the head of the Sliddery Water, tuffs are overlain by red mudstones with mussels of Middle Coal Measures type (Leitch, 1942). Both occurrences have been assigned to the Passage Formation. Farther west, in Kintyre, about 100 m of thick basaltic lavas with thin tuffs and red lateritic mudstones are known only from boreholes at Machrihanish. The highest lavas have been weathered to bauxitic clay and there is a marked non-sequence beneath the overlying Lower Coal Measures. In Galloway, a single thin flow of basaltic lava near Kirkcolm, on the west side of Loch Ryan, occurs within a sequence of mottled sandstones, mudstones and seatclays that is overlain unconformably by Permian breccias.

Fife (mid Namurian to Early Permian)

Evidence of volcanicity in the form of inter-bedded tuffs and tuffaceous sedimentary rocks is widespread in the Silesian successions of Fife, south of the East Ochil Fault. Basaltic lavas are rare. Much of the information comes from underground coal mining and boreholes, both onshore and offshore, though there are some good exposures, particularly in coast sections. The area is renowned for its numerous, mainly small necks, many with plugs of alkali olivine basalt or basanite. These are particularly abundant in East Fife where over 100 are recorded, and are represented by the **East Fife Coast** GCR site. Here, the continuing influence of deep-seated Caledonian structures is well illustrated by the NE-trending Ardross Fault, along which ten or more necks are sited over a distance of 4 km (Francis and Hopgood, 1970). On the opposite side of the Firth of Forth, Howells (1969) recorded high-level vent structures near Longniddry that cut Namurian strata and lie directly on the projected north-eastwards continuation of the Southern Upland Fault, which may have controlled the rise of magma during Visean time (see Chapter 2). The East Fife necks are also renowned as some of the most productive sources in Scotland of megacrysts and/or rock clasts of deep-seated igneous material or metamorphic basement (e.g. Colvine, 1968; Chapman, 1974, 1976; Macintyre *et al.*, 1981; Donaldson, 1984) (see Chapter 1).

Onshore outcrops of interbedded volcanic rocks are concentrated mainly in two areas. Around the former Westfield opencast coal site in central Fife, there are five flows of basaltic pillow lava with associated tuffs and hyaloclastites in the top of the Upper Limestone Formation and the basal Passage Formation. The large complex necks of Largo Law and Rires in East Fife are surrounded by bedded tuffs and a few lavas that seem to be interbedded with the Upper Limestone Formation and Passage Formation, though in many places it is difficult to separate them from pyroclastic rocks within

the necks (Forsyth and Chisholm, 1977). Offshore, boreholes in the Firth of Forth have proved pyroclastic rocks and rare basalt lavas, ranging from the topmost Passage Formation up into the Middle Coal Measures.

The necks cut almost the full local age range of Dinantian and Namurian strata and it is likely that some are the source of the Namurian bedded tuffs. A few necks cut Coal Measures strata. The Viewforth Neck contains foundered blocks of tuffaceous sedimentary rocks that have yielded Langsettian spores, and the Lundin Links Neck cuts (Duckmantian) Middle Coal Measures. Some necks are thus of Duckmantian age or younger and it has been suggested that blocks of quartz-bearing dolerite in several necks (e.g. Ardross, St Monance, Viewforth, Lundin Links) are derived from the early Stephanian tholeiitic intrusive suite, though this has not been proved. The most reliable K-Ar radiometric dates from four of the necks are within a range of 295–288 Ma, which dates their time of emplacement as close to the Stephanian–Permian boundary (Wallis, 1989). The highly silica-undersaturated nature of plugs and other minor intrusions (basanites, olivine nephelinites and olivine analcimites) within many of the vents is characteristic of the latest magmatism elsewhere in the Carboniferous–Permian Igneous Province of northern Britain, especially the undoubted Early Permian lavas and associated necks of south Ayrshire (see below), and hence is compatible with the age estimates.

The morphology and physical volcanology of the Fife volcanoes and their relationships to surrounding contemporaneous sedimentation have been studied more intensively than in any other part of the Carboniferous–Permian Igneous Province of northern Britain. Much of this work has been by E.H. Francis, building upon earlier Geological Survey work and making extensive use of boreholes and mine sections (Francis, 1960, 1961b,c, 1968a,b, 1970b; Francis *et al.*, 1961; Francis and Ewing, 1961; Francis and Hopgood, 1970; Francis in Forsyth and Chisholm, 1977).

The bedded tuffs consist of a mixture of basaltic and comminuted sedimentary debris and are often well graded, indicative of ash fall into shallow water. Thin distal representatives have been traced for up to 30 km from their implied vents and have correlation value as effective time-planes (Francis, 1961c, 1968a).

Many of these thin tuffs have been altered diagenetically to kaolin, especially in, or near to, coal seams, and have been likened to the 'tonsteins' of north-west European coalfields (Francis *et al.*, 1961; Francis, 1969, 1985). Most of the necks appear to be funnel-shaped tuff-pipes filled by varying proportions of basaltic material and country rock. Initial updoming, with associated radial and concentric fracturing, was probably followed by gas-fluxioning and wall-rock stoping, prior to the rise of basaltic magma that interacted with groundwater and surface water in explosive, phreatomagmatic eruptions. Many of the larger necks contain inward-dipping bedded pyroclastic rocks and sediments, with fragments of fossil wood that show that they accumulated at the surface. The inward dips were generated by inward collapse of the areas surrounding the initial vent during the eruption, possibly along ring-fractures, and by immediate post eruptive subsidence (Francis, 1970b). Such features, together with the inter-pretation of cross-bedding and large-scale slumping as the results of base-surge eruptions, led Francis (in Forsyth and Chisholm, 1977) to compare the volcanoes with modern Surtseyan ash-rings of wide diameter and low height, which are typical of basaltic eruptions into shallow water. Magmas failing to reach the surface were emplaced as a variety of minor intrusions. Details, as illustrated by individual necks, are given in the **East Fife Coast** GCR site report.

East Lothian (?late Stephanian to Early Permian)

The volcanic rocks interbedded with the sedimentary succession of East Lothian are undoubtedly of Dinantian age, as are most of the closely related vents (see **North Berwick Coast** GCR site report). However, some of the associated intrusions are basanitic or foiditic and it seems reasonable to suggest that these may represent a south-eastern continuation of the East Fife late Stephanian to Early Permian volcanic field, from which they are separated by only 15 km. Available K-Ar whole-rock dates are equivocal, but suggest minimum ages in the range 295–229 Ma (Snelling and Chan in McAdam and Tulloch, 1985, recalculated; Wallis, 1989). Notable examples of these intrusions occur at Oldhamstocks, Kidlaw, Limplum, Gin

Head, Yellow Man, Yellow Craig Plantation and North Berwick Abbey, and it is probable that some of the breccia-filled necks in the area belong to this late phase of activity.

A large plug of nepheline basanite at Southdean, south of Jedburgh, is anomalous among the Dinantian plugs of south-east Scotland (see Chapter 3) and may be an isolated Early Permian occurrence.

Mauchline, Sanquar and Thornhill basins (Early Permian)

Bedded volcanic rocks of Early Permian age crop out in south Ayrshire, in an elliptical outcrop around the overlying aeolian sandstones of the Mauchline Basin, and in the NNW- to NW-trending, fault-controlled Sanquhar and Thorn-hill basins, within the Southern Uplands. Together these mid-Carboniferous–Permian basins define a broad NW-trending lineament that continues to the south-east through the Permian sedimentary basins at Dumfries, Lochmaben and the Vale of Eden. Contempora-neous necks and sub-volcanic intrusions within and around the Mauchline lavas and in the Sanquhar Basin extend the known limits of the volcanic fields, but it is not known if they were ever interconnected.

The Mauchline Volcanic Formation, repre-sented by the **Howford Bridge** GCR site, is up to 238 m thick and rests unconformably but with no marked discordance upon the 'Barren Red Beds' of the Upper Coal Measures. Plant debris found near the base of the volcanic sequence suggests an earliest Permian age (Wagner, 1983) and K-Ar whole-rock dates around 286 ± 7 Ma are Early Permian (De Souza, 1982). Palaeo-magnetic measurements have also indicated pole positions close to those of Carboniferous–Permian boundary time (Du Bois, 1957; Harcombe-Smee *et al.*, 1996). The lavas are pre-dominantly microporphyritic olivine basalts ('Dalmeny' type), but basanites are common and some strongly silica-undersaturated olivine nephelinites are present. However, analyses include some hypersthene-normative transi-tional basalts (Macdonald *et al.*, 1977; Wallis, 1989). Pyroclastic rocks comprise a large part of the succession, becoming more abundant in the thicker, eastern parts. Sedimentary rocks within the volcanic sequence contain wind-rounded sand grains, indicating that the lavas were erupted in predominantly desert conditions, but fluvial sandstones and mudstones imply spasmodic sheet-floods and ephemeral lakes.

Over 60 necks are known, mostly within a 20–30 km radius of the centre of the Mauchline Basin, but also extending to West Kilbride in the north (Alexander *et al.*, 1986), Muirkirk in the east and Dalmellington in the south (Figure 4.2). Numerous lines of evidence suggest that these necks are contemporaneous with the lavas and hence delimit the former extent of the volcanic field. Necks are known to cut the Coal Measures succession, post-Coal Measures alkali dolerite sills and the Mauchline Volcanic Formation, but not the overlying Mauchline Sandstone Formation. Many of the necks contain wind-rounded sand grains and some include large subsided blocks of aeolian and fluvial sandstones. Plugs and other vent intrusions are predominantly of highly silica-undersaturated olivine analcimite or monchiquite, but camptonite, basanite and alkali dolerite are also known. Monchiquite dykes, common in the Irvine Valley and the Patna area, are assumed to be related. Xenolithic megacrysts and ultramafic nodules in many of the vent intrusions yield valuable information on the upper mantle source area of the magmas.

In the Thornhill Basin, the Carron Basalt Formation, represented by the **Carron Water** GCR site, is up to 50 m thick and rests unconformably on reddened Coal Measures and Lower Palaeozoic rocks. It comprises subaerial olivine-microphyric basalts and basanites similar to those of the Mauchline Basin and interbedded sedimentary units. Conglomeratic sandstones and breccias below the lavas, and beyond the present lava outcrop, contain angular fragments of basalt indicating earlier, possibly more extensive, flows. Although some basalts incorporate wind-blown sand in their matrix, the sedimentary rocks interbedded with and overlying the volcanic rocks are predominantly fluvial. Aeolian desert conditions did not become fully established here until well after the volcanic period. Small outliers of olivine basalt rest upon Middle Coal Measures at the southeast end of the Sanquhar Basin and five small necks pierce the Coal Measures nearby.

Across the North Channel, in a borehole at Larne in Northern Ireland, over 600 m of basic volcanic rocks were proved at a depth of over 2000 m, beneath an undoubted Permo–Triassic succession (Penn *et al.*, 1983). A K-Ar whole-

rock date of 245 ± 13 Ma is almost certainly too young and the authors suggested an Early Permian age. However, there are marked petrological differences between these lavas (which have possible tholeiitic affinities) and those of south-west Scotland. They occupy a separate sedimentary basin and are certainly a separate lava field.

Offshore

In the centre of the East Irish Sea Basin, a borehole has penetrated 45.5 m of altered basalts overlain by 22 m of volcaniclastic rocks at the base of the Permian succession (Jackson *et al.*, 1995, 1997). These Tormentil Volcanics occur on a high that trends north-east towards south Cumbria, where clasts of olivine-dolerite and vesicular basalt are abundant in basal Permian conglomerates in the Humphrey Head Borehole (Adams and Wadsworth, 1993). The source of these clasts is not known, but they are likely to be Carboniferous to Early Permian in age and relatively local. Thin subaerial basaltic flows are also recorded from the Lower Permian rocks of the North Sea Basin (Dixon *et al.*, 1981).

Highlands and Islands (Early Permian)

On the Isle of Arran, the sequence at the head of the Sliddery Water that includes possible Passage Formation volcanic rocks (see above), passes up into gritty feldspathic sandstones and slaggy basaltic lavas with thin tuffs that have been assigned to the base of the Permian succession on the current British Geological Survey 1:50 000 map (1987).

A 120 m-thick Permian succession is exposed on the small island of Glas Eilean in the Sound of Islay, between the Isles of Islay and Jura (Pringle and Bailey, 1944; Upton *et al.*, 1987) (Figure 4.2). Above a basal conglomerate and sandstone (7 m thick), which contain basaltic clasts, most of the succession comprises subaerial basaltic lavas. There are many individual flows, up to 2 m thick and with slaggy amygdaloidal tops. The flow thickness decreases upwards as intercalations of shallow-water sedimentary rocks increase. The lavas are all mildly alkaline olivine-microphyric basalts that are hypersthene- or nepheline-normative and the lower flows are relatively primitive with high MgO, Ni and Cr contents. The succession appears to overlie Dalradian rocks unconformably to the ENE, and dips WSW at *c.* 30°, towards an inferred NNW-trending fault along the sound. It therefore seems to occupy a half-graben, a possible transverse extension off the northern end of the Rathlin Basin, which may have been active at the time of the sedimentation and volcanism (Fyfe *et al.*, 1993; Anderson *et al.*, 1995). A K-Ar whole-rock date of 285 ± 5 Ma appears to confirm the Early Permian age.

Evidence of more widespread Early Permian volcanism in the Highlands and Islands comes from the distribution of small sub-volcanic necks (Figure 4.4), composed largely of explosion breccia, but characterized by the presence of monchiquite, either as clasts, or as a magmatic matrix, or in associated minor intrusions (Rock, 1983). They are thus correlated petrographically with the even more widespread camptonite and monchiquite dykes swarms that are well established as being of Early Permian age (see Chapter 5; Figure 5.2). Nine necks, including that at Stob a'Ghrianain (Hartley and Leedal, 1951), seem to define a NW-trending

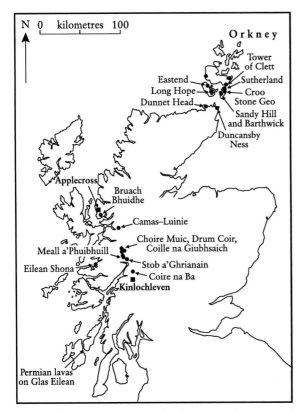

Figure 4.4 Map showing the location of plugs and vents of Carboniferous to Permian age in the Highlands. The Early Permian lavas of Glas Eilean are also indicated. After Rock (1983).

lineament between Coire na Ba, near Kinlochleven (Wright in Bailey and Maufe, 1960) and Toscaig, near Applecross (Rock, 1982). Most others form a cluster around south-east Orkney (Mykura, 1976) which includes the neck at Duncansby Ness, dated at around 270 Ma by K-Ar whole-rock dating (Macintyre *et al.*, 1981). Like the dykes, many of the necks are a valuable source of inclusions derived from the lower crust and upper mantle (e.g. Chapman, 1975) (see Chapter 1).

EAST FIFE COAST, FIFE (NO 408 024–NO 444 020 and NO 454 006–NO 526 015)

I.T. Williamson

Introduction

The coastal section between Lundin Links and St Monance in the East Neuk of Fife, which comprises the East Fife Coast GCR site, includes numerous volcanic necks (Figure 4.5). Excellent exposures and a wide variety of volcanic features within a relatively small area make this a valuable site for both research and educational purposes. It is well known internationally, regularly visited by field parties, and is much cited in scientific literature.

In many instances the three-dimensional relationships within the necks and between necks and country rock are clearly seen. Associated strata include bedded and massive, pyroclastic and volcaniclastic deposits; all are cut by minor intrusions and a few necks have a central intrusive plug. The volcanism was commonly phreatic or phreatomagmatic, reflecting the interaction of magma with water, and there are many examples of localized magma–sediment interaction.

In East Fife in general there are more than 100 known volcanic necks, which cut Carboniferous strata ranging from the Pathhead Formation (top Visean) to Middle Coal Measures (Westphalian B). Radiometric ages on associated intrusions span the Late Carboniferous (Stephanian)–Permian boundary, but some may be contemporaneous with earlier volcanic beds in the local Namurian to Westphalian succession. Some necks are associated with the Ardross Fault, an important ENE-trending strike-slip structure that extends for about 8 km, more-or-less axial to the Midland Valley. It possibly exerted control on

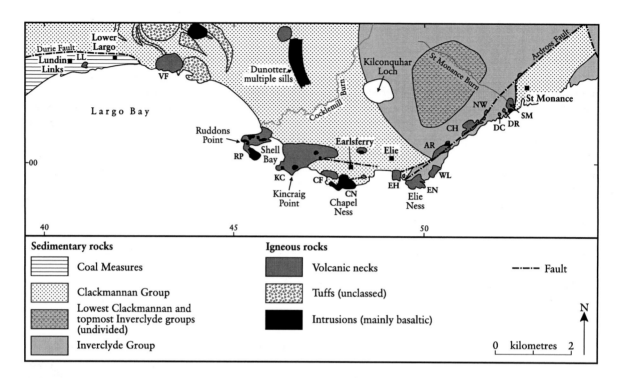

Figure 4.5 Map of the south-east Fife coast, showing the distribution of volcanic necks. The named volcanic necks lie within the East Fife Coast GCR site. (Volcanic necks, from west to east: LL = Lundin Links; VF = Viewforth; RP = Ruddons Point; KC = Kincraig; CF = Craigforth; CN = Chapel Ness; EH = Elie Harbour; EN = Elie Ness; WL = Wadeslea; AR = Ardross; CH = Coalyard Hill; NW = Newark; DC = Dovecot; DR = Davie's Rock; SM = St Monance.) Based on Geological Survey 1:50 000 Sheet 41, North Berwick (1970).

the location of the volcanism and is thought to be a re-activated Caledonian basement structure.

Both fragmental and crystalline intrusive rocks in a number of the necks contain xenoliths and megacrysts of lower-crustal and upper-mantle material. Their study has provided a major contribution to knowledge of the deep structure of northern Britain and has given an insight into the genesis of the Carboniferous–Permian magmas (see Chapter 1). They have also provided a source of material for numerous detailed studies of individual minerals such as garnets and zircons.

The necks have long attracted the attention of geologists and were first described by Geikie (1880, 1897, 1902) and Wallace (1916). Important work was done by Balsillie (1920a,b, 1923, 1927) and Cumming (1928, 1936), but it is mainly the detailed work of E.H. Francis to which we owe most of our present knowledge (Francis, 1960, 1968a,b, 1970b; Francis and Hopgood, 1970). Comprehensive details of the field relationships of the necks and their interpretation in terms of Silesian volcanic processes

were published by Francis in Forsyth and Chisholm (1977). They are featured in several reviews (Upton, 1982; Cameron and Stephenson, 1985; Francis, 1967, 1978a, 1991) and excursion guides (Francis and Hopgood in Upton, 1969; MacGregor, 1996). Detailed studies of the xenoliths and megacrysts include those by Colvine (1968), Chapman (1974, 1976), Chapman and Powell (1976), Macintyre *et al.* (1981), Donaldson (1984), Aspen *et al.* (1990), Hinton and Upton (1991) and Upton *et al.* (1999).

Description

The East Fife Coast GCR site comprises two extensive sections of the East Fife coast. The larger section extends for nearly 10 km from Ruddons Point to St Monance harbour, and the shorter section, west of this, extends for a little under 4 km around Largo Bay from Lundin Links to Viewforth. Of additional geological interest at the site are the local sedimentary sequence, fish and amphibian fossils (Dineley and Metcalfe, 1999), raised beaches, and mineral localities.

A total of 15 or so volcanic necks with associated plugs and minor intrusions, crop out within the site. Most are well exposed in the intertidal zone though exposures vary from time to time. The field relationships of individual necks are described in great detail by Francis (in Forsyth and Chisholm, 1977) and a summary of their main lithological units and structural features is shown here in Table 4.1. The original relationships of these lithologies and structures within the original volcanoes may be conveniently illustrated in a hypothetical cross-section (Figure 4.6).

Lithological components of the necks

Pyroclastic rocks form the principal component of all the necks. The dominant clasts are grey to greenish-grey alkali basalt and basanite, which vary in size from coarse ash to lapilli with rare larger bombs. They are predominantly of the ragged-edged, chilled juvenile type but there are also accessory lapilli and blocks. Other clasts are massive or thinly bedded tuffs and sedimentary rock debris. Fragments of woody material have been recorded in some necks. All are set in an altered greenish-grey matrix of basaltic coarse tuff.

Bedded tuffs appear to be more common than massive tuffs, but the two are intimately associated in the necks and commonly pass laterally into one another. The bedded tuffs are usually medium to thickly bedded and individual beds are moderately sorted. Sedimentary structures include graded bedding and cross-bedding. The massive tuffs are considerably more heterogeneous. They may be either moderately sorted or unsorted and chaotic. The less well-sorted tuffs generally occur towards the centre of necks.

Pyroclastic breccias in which the clasts are predominantly angular and almost exclusively of basalt, are commonly located in the more central portions of the necks. In some cases they grade into marginal basalt-dominated bedded tuff and agglomerate or into coherent basaltic intrusions.

Sediment-derived tuffs are most commonly located at the margins of a neck. Here they either grade outwards into country rock or are bound on both sides by ring-fractures. These tuffs are grey to greenish in colour and are composed mostly of fragments of brecciated country rock, most commonly sandstone, ranging in size up to blocks. In addition, there may be a small but variable population of basaltic clasts and

Table 4.1 Lithological units and features of the volcanic necks between Lundin Links and St Monance, East Fife Coast. (Abbreviations: **LL** = Lundin Links; **VF** = Viewforth; **RP** = Ruddons Point; **KC** = Kincraig; **CF** = Craigforth; **CN** = Chapel Ness; **EH** = Elie Harbour; **EN** = Elie Ness; **WL** = Wadeslea; **AR** = Ardross; **CH** = Coalyard Hill; **NW** = Newark; **DC** = Dovecot; **DR** = Davie's Rock; **SM** = St Monance.) Based on Francis in Forsyth and Chisholm, 1977, figs 20–24; Upton *et al.*, 1999.

Lithological units / Necks	LL	VF	RP	KC	CF	CN	EH	EN	WL	AR	CH	NW	DC	DR	SM
Basaltic tuff and agglomerate (bedded)		•	•	•		•	•	•	•		•				•
Basaltic tuff and agglomerate (unbedded)	•	•	•	•			•	•	•	•	•	•			•
Basaltic breccia				•		•									
Sediment-derived tuff						•				•	•	•			
Tuffisite breccia				•	•	•	•	•		•	•			•	•
Tuffisite dyke(s)		•	•	•		•		•				•		•	
Tuffisite intrusion(s)									•	•		•	•		
Basaltic dyke(s)	•				•			•	•	•		•			
Basaltic intrusion(s) (not specified)	•		•	•							•			•	•
Olivine basalt and basanite intrusion(s)					•	•						•			
Olivine-dolerite intrusion(s)					•	•									
Sandstone (large xenoliths and rafts)		•	•			•				•	•		•		•
Carboniferous sedimentary rocks	•	•	•	•	•	•	•	•	•	•	•	•	•	•	•
Bedding: •=collapsed; ○=centroclinal		•	○	•	○		○	•○	○						
Marginal ring-faults or shear zones	•	•		•		•					•				•
Cryptovolcanic structures				•	•							•			
Megacrysts and xenoliths				•				•			•	•			

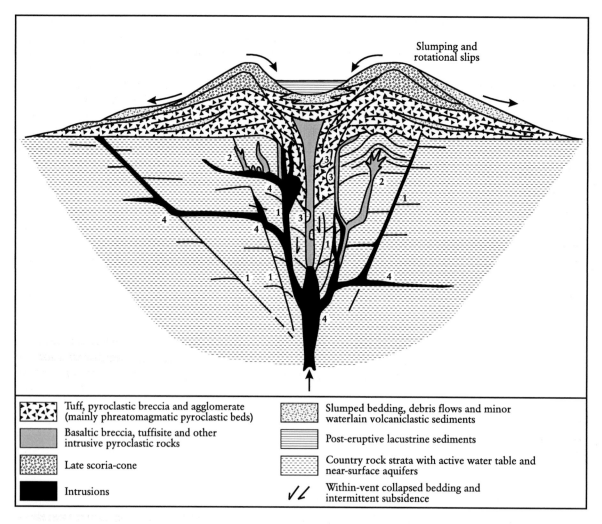

Figure 4.6 Schematic cross-section through an evolving tuff-ring, illustrating some of the volcanic processes thought to have been involved in the emplacement of the East Fife volcanic necks. The exposed necks within the GCR site may be interpreted in terms of sub-horizontal sections through this structure. (Features marked on the diagram: 1 = ring-faults with marginal tuffisite and breccia, or basaltic dykes; 2 = tuffisite within country rock – may develop adjacent to sills or dykes; 3 = large foundered bodies of country rock within vent and entrained within breccias and tuffisite; 4 = minor intrusions emplaced along bedding and fault planes.) Based on Forsyth and Chisholm (1977, fig. 17 after Francis, 1970b and Lorenz, 1973); Lorenz (1986); and Godchaux *et al*. (1992).

even some basaltic bombs; examples of the latter are seen in the Craigforth Neck. The matrix is generally also derived from the country rock and comprises comminuted lithic fragments and crystals.

Tuffisites (intrusive tuffs) were emplaced along radial and concentric fractures within most of the East Fife necks and they are common on the inside of marginal ring-fractures. They also occur as a marginal facies to associated basaltic intrusions. A characteristic feature is a strong flow foliation, especially at the margins. When derived from a mainly sedimentary source, tuffisite commonly veins or acts as the

matrix to many of the breccias and sediment-derived tuffs associated with the volcanic necks.

Minor intrusions of basalt, basanite and dolerite are commonplace in and near the volcanic necks. Many are highly irregular. They range from minor dykes and sheets, commonly occupying ring-faults or radial fractures, to central plug-like bodies. The larger intrusions exhibit columnar jointing, indicating slow and uninterrupted cooling. Some basaltic dykes intruding the adjacent, locally carbonaceous, country rock are extremely altered. Their very pale and bleached appearance is due to replacement by carbonates and the rock-type is traditionally referred to as 'white trap'.

Structural features of the necks

Most of the necks have an irregular, but broadly oval, plan and vary in size from a few tens of metres to hundreds of metres across. Their margins are usually inwardly dipping and are commonly ring-faults.

Within the tuff and agglomerate of many necks, there are small areas, usually ill-defined, where the attitude of the bedding and of large rafts of fractured bedded tuff, has been disturbed, re-orientated and even overturned. Some beds appear to have flowed or deformed plastically. Where bedding is relatively undisturbed it is centroclinal, i.e. inclined inwards towards a central focus, with the higher dips close to the neck margins.

Cryptovolcanic ring-structures are noted sporadically among the country rocks near some necks. These are circular or oval areas of variably brecciated strata that vary considerably in size from 3 m to 200 m in diameter. The breccias are composed entirely of angular clasts of sedimentary rock up to several metres across in a variable amount of matrix that consists of tuffisite of mainly sedimentary origin. The degree of fragmentation varies from simply fractured in the smaller structures, through in-situ breccias with increasingly disoriented clasts, to coarse breccias with a higher proportion of matrix and veins of tuffisite in the larger structures. Thin dykes of bleached basalt feature in some. The structures range from small swells and gentle domes to larger vertically sided ring-structures in which blocks become orientated parallel to the contacts.

The individual necks

The necks may be conveniently divided into those associated with the Ardross Fault and those that are not.

Only the necks in the eastern half of the GCR site are associated with the Ardross Fault. They are the Elie Harbour Neck (NO 4930 9955), Elie Ness Neck (NO 498 994), Wadeslea Neck (NO 503 997), Ardross Neck (NO 5045 0020), Coalyard Hill Neck (NO 5120 0085), Newark Neck (NO 516 012), Dovecot Neck (NO 5095 0115), Davie's Rock Neck (NO 5210 0125) and St Monance Neck (NO 5225 0140). The last three are situated south-east of the Ardross Fault but are still loosely aligned along its trend.

The *Elie Harbour Neck* consists of tuffs, lapillistones and agglomerate, traversed by a few impersistent basaltic dykes. The agglomerate consists of large blocks and bombs of scoriaceous basalt and sedimentary rock, including, in the central part of the neck, a large raft of sediment-derived tuffisite. Geikie (1902) also noted fragments of wood and coal. The Ardross Fault separates the Elie Harbour Neck from the *Elie Ness Neck*. The latter, orientated crudely north-east–south-west, comprises well-bedded, inward-dipping (centroclinal) basaltic tuffs and agglomerates. Sedimentary structures include cross-bedding, graded bedding and slump-bedding, and deformation caused by the impact of volcanic ejecta and contemporaneous collapse (Figure 4.7). The pyroclastic rocks also contain 'breadcrust' bombs of basalt and blocks of sedimentary rock, but it is for its exotic clasts that the neck is perhaps best known. These include various xenolithic nodules and xenocrysts. The latter include pyrope garnet (so-called 'Elie Ruby'), zircon and alkali feldspars. The Elie Ness Neck is separated from the *Wadeslea Neck* by a narrow outcrop of folded sedimentary rocks, and minor tuffisite breccia. The *Ardross Neck*, on the opposite side of the Ardross Fault to the Wadeslea Neck, is comparatively simple and comprises only massive and bedded tuff and agglomerate. A series of *en échelon* dykes of xenolithic basalt, penetrated locally by sediment-derived tuffisites, is present in the northern part. Divorced from the main body of the Ardross Neck, but situated a short distance to the north-east along the line of the Ardross Fault, are two small outcrops of tuffisite. These are important because their orientation, and also that of the materials within them, mirrors that of the fault, strongly suggesting that their emplacement had strong tectonic control.

The *Coalyard Hill Neck* is described by Francis (in Forsyth and Chisholm, 1977) as a composite structure, consisting of outer and inner necks. These are very different in form and lithology, but collectively they demonstrate the structure and evolution of a typical Late Carboniferous Midland Valley volcanic neck. The outer neck, which is the older, is only 100 m wide but extends for about 700 m along the north-western side of the Ardross Fault. It is dominated by sediment-derived tuff but there is scattered basaltic material within it. It is cut by tuffisite veins, and flow-banded tuffisite commonly flanks the larger clasts and rafts (Figure 4.8), including some large blocks of crinoidal limestone at the western margin. The inner neck consists of

Figure 4.7 Basaltic bomb showing impact effects in the underlying tuffs, Elie Ness Neck, East Fife Coast GCR site. The hammer head is about 15 cm long. (Photo: British Geological Survey, No. MNS1635, reproduced with the permission of the Director, British Geological Survey, © NERC.)

Figure 4.8 Flow-banding in tuffisite (below hammer) intruded into a large raft of sandstone (on which the hammer rests) in the north-eastern part of the Coalyard Hill Neck, East Fife Coast GCR site. The pale fragments elongated parallel to the edge of the sandstone are of bleached basalt. The hammer shaft is about 35 cm long. (Photo: British Geological Survey, No. D1680, reproduced with the permission of the Director, British Geological Survey, © NERC.)

massive, basaltic tuffs and agglomerates with ill-defined masses of basaltic breccia and minor basaltic intrusions. A small intrusion of basanite at the south-western contact contains xenoliths of spinel lherzolite and also rare wehrlite and pyroxenite (Table 4.2). Only a small area of the *Newark Neck* is exposed on the north-western side of the Ardross Fault. It mainly comprises sediment-derived tuffs although locally the matrix carries fragments of juvenile basalt. These tuffs grade imperceptibly into bedded basaltic tuffs and agglomerates forming the central zone of the neck.

The small *Dovecot Neck* provides good examples of neck-margin phenomena such as the localized thrusting, deformation and induration of country rock and intrusions of flow-aligned tuffisite. One large raft of sandstone, penetrated from below by flow-aligned tuffisite, may have formed part of the stoped roof of a cryptovolcanic ring-structure. The *Davie's Rock Neck* is emplaced in the crest of an anticline and consists of a central plug-like mass of nepheline basanite surrounded by tuffisitic breccia. Francis interpreted the exposures as a deep section through another large cryptovolcanic structure. The *St Monance Neck* is the most easterly neck in the GCR site. It consists almost entirely of massive, unbedded lapilli-tuff and agglomerate cut by a series of cross-cutting monchiquitic dykes (Figure 4.9). Large clasts of sedimentary rock, some with tuffisite veining, are common towards the margins.

Figure 4.9 Western margin of the St Monance Neck, East Fife Coast GCR site, showing tuff and agglomerate (right), upturned, disorientated sediments (top left) and a monchiquitic dyke emplaced along part of the margin (top centre). The hammer shaft is about 35 cm long. (Photo: British Geological Survey, No. D1679, reproduced with the permission of the Director, British Geological Survey, © NERC.)

Table 4.2 Distribution of accidental xenoliths and megacrysts in the East Fife necks (* = fragmental pyrope garnets – the famous, so-called 'Elie Ruby') (additional minor xenocryst phases are listed in the text). (Abbreviations: **RP** = Ruddons Point; **EN** = Elie Ness; **CH** = Coalyard Hill; **AR** = Ardross.)

Volcanic Neck	RP	EN	CH	AR
Xenoliths				
Hydrated ultramafic rock		●		●
Spinel lherzolite	●		●	
Wehrlite	●		●	
Biotite-amphibole pyroxenite	●		●	
Anorthoclasite	●	●		
Pyroxene granofels and gneiss	●			
Quartzo-feldspathic granofels and gneiss		●		
Garnetiferous quartzo-feldspathic granofels and gneiss			●	
Garnetiferous ultramafic rock		●		
Principal megacrysts and xenocrysts				
High-temperature feldspar – mainly anorthoclase	●	●	●	●
Garnet *		●		
Corundum	●			
Zircon		●		

Necks that are not associated with the Ardross Fault are all situated north-west of the fault. They are the Lundin Links Neck (NO 411 024), Viewforth Neck (NO 431 024), Ruddons Point Neck (NO 454 004), Kincraig Neck (NO 466 998), Craigforth Neck (NO 475 996) and Chapel Ness Neck (NO 4755 9935).

The *Lundin Links Neck* is the most westerly within the GCR site. It is comparatively small and cuts the Middle Coal Measures some 30 m below the Barncraig Coal. The *Viewforth Neck*, farther east around Largo Bay, is composed solely of frag-mental deposits. It has steeply dipping, inwardly inclined margins against Passage Formation strata. The *Ruddons Point Neck* forms a rocky promon-tory between Largo Bay and Shell Bay and is formed of approximately equal proportions of pyroclastic rocks and basaltic intrusions. The main plug is one of the largest in East Fife. The intrusions carry xenocrysts (Table 4.2). On the opposite side of Shell Bay the *Kincraig Neck*, measuring 1.5 km in length, is the largest of the coastal necks in East Fife. It contains most of the elements and features listed in Figure 4.6 and provides a unique opportunity to determine the three-dimensional relationships between neck materials, intrusions and country rock. The largest

intrusion is a flat-based boss or sill-like body of basalt with exceptionally well-developed columnar jointing (Figure 4.10). Both the *Craigforth Neck* and the *Chapel Ness Neck* are comparatively small structures. The latter is unusual in that it mainly comprises an irregular-shaped intrusion of olivine basalt and basanite. Elie Bay to the east contains at least three cryptovolcanic ring-structures.

The Ardross Fault

The surface trace of the Ardross Fault is most readily seen in the shore sections between the Elie Ness, Wadeslea, Ardross and Coalyard Hill necks. The line of the fault is traceable by litho-logical contrasts on either side, and locally by an ill-defined weathered-in zone. The style of the folding in the adjacent country rock is broad and open on one side, and tight, locally isoclinal, on the other; the intensity of folding dies out abruptly away from the fault. The fault shows dextral lateral movement and there is a consis-tent sense of vertical drag with a downthrow to the north-west (Francis and Hopgood, 1970). Although the fault appears to control the siting of many of the necks, the principal fault movements demonstrably post-date neck emplacement.

Figure 4.10 Curved columnar jointing in basalt intrusion within the Kincraig Neck, East Fife Coast GCR site. (Photo: British Geological Survey, No. D1684, reproduced with the permission of the Director, British Geological Survey, © NERC.)

The xenolith, cumulate inclusion and megacryst suites

In addition to the dominant clasts of juvenile or 'parental' basaltic material, some tuffs and intrusions in the necks contain sparse, more exotic clasts such as large, accidental crystals and various mafic and ultramafic rocks. Similar material also occurs as megacrysts and xenoliths in associated intrusions (Table 4.2). The Ruddons Point, Elie Ness, Ardross and Coalyard Hill necks are internationally famous in this respect, and this extremely important feature of the Carboniferous–Permian Igneous Province of northern Britain is discussed more fully in Chapter 1.

The majority of exotic inclusions and xenoliths in the Elie Ness and Ardross necks are hydrated ultramafic rocks (Chapman, 1976), including both feldspar-free and albite-bearing pyroxenites. In the Ruddons Point and Coalyard Hill necks the commonest type is a spinel lherzolite but there are also scarce iron-rich wehrlites as well as biotite- and amphibole-rich pyroxenites, rare composite wehrlite–lherzolites, websterites and garnet-bearing pyroxenites (Chapman, 1974). Other rock-types include metamorphic rocks such as granulite-facies mafic gneisses and both garnetiferous and quartzo-feldspathic gneisses. Examples of the latter, with plagioclase porphyroblasts, are recorded from the Coalyard Hill Neck.

Anorthoclase, a high temperature alkali feldspar, is the commonest megacryst phase in the Fife necks (Chapman and Powell, 1976; Aspen *et al.*, 1990). Pinkish-white crystals, some over 10 cm in size, have been found in most necks. Anorthoclase-dominated composite megacrysts grade into anorthoclasites with subordinate zircon, chlorite pseudomorphs after clinopyroxene, corundum and an yttro-niobate rich in the heavy rare-earth elements uranium and thorium (Upton *et al.*, 1999). The Ruddons Point Neck contains the broadest compositional range of anorthoclase megacrysts, with lesser ranges in the Elie Ness, Coalyard Hill and Ardross necks. The Elie Ness Neck is noted for its fresh, orange-brown, fractured, but inclusion-free, pyrope garnets (Colvine, 1968; Donaldson, 1984). They are known locally as 'Elie Rubies' and occur mostly as fragments from 0.25 mm to 25 mm in size. Sub-calcic augite, kaersutite, magnetite, apatite and zircon (the latter rarely up to up to 5 mm in size) have also been recorded at Elie Ness. Orthopyroxene has been recorded at Ruddons Point (Balsillie, 1927), Davie's Rock and Coalyard Hill.

Timing of volcanic activity

The age of the East Fife necks has been the subject of considerable debate. Country rocks range from Dinantian (Asbian–Brigantian) Pathhead Formation strata at, and east of, the Elie Ness Neck, to (Westphalian B: Duckmantian) Middle Coal Measures strata at the Lundin Links Neck. Tuffs interbedded with the local sedimentary succession demonstrate that East Fife had an almost unbroken history of volcanic activity from early Namurian to mid-Westphalian times, so it is possible and indeed likely that the necks span a similar range.

K-Ar whole-rock ages of intrusions within East Fife necks (Forsyth and Chisholm, 1977; Forsyth and Rundle, 1978) show a range from Stephanian to Early Triassic. The youngest (244 ± 6 Ma), was obtained from a minor intrusion within the Lundin Links Neck but is perhaps anomalous due to argon loss. However, the five oldest results, from St Monance, Chapel Ness, Davie's Rock and Largo Law, are indistinguishable within the limits of analytical error within the range 295–288 Ma and hence the best estimate for the time of emplacement is close to the Stephanian–Permian boundary (Forsyth and Rundle, 1978; Wallis, 1989). Other K-Ar whole-rock dates for intrusions from Kincraig (De Souza, 1979) and from the Ruddons Point, Kincraig and Chapel Ness necks by Wallis (1989) all seem to be anomalously young.

K-Ar dating of both inclusions and intrusions associated with the Ruddons Point, Kincraig, Elie Harbour, Elie Ness, Ardross and Coalyard Hill necks was carried out by Macintyre *et al.* (1981). The results suggest that basanites in both of the Elie necks have a probable minimum emplacement age of 276 ± 4 Ma (Early Permian). Anorthoclase megacrysts from the Ruddons Point, Elie Ness, Ardross and Coalyard Hill necks appear to have crystallized by 294 ± 3 Ma (Stephanian). However dating of ultramafic cumulate xenoliths from the Elie Ness and Kincraig necks suggests that the inclusions formed or last equilibrated much earlier, at 315 Ma (Namurian to Westphalian boundary) and at shallow depth. Similar ages have been obtained from megacrysts at Elie Ness; around 318 Ma by U-Pb on zircons (Macintyre *et al.*, 1981) and a plateau age of 311 ± 3 Ma by Ar-Ar on kaersutite (M. Timmerman, pers. comm., 2002).

Interpretation

The location of several volcanic necks within the East Fife Coast GCR site appears to have been controlled by the Ardross Fault. This high-level fault probably resulted from the re-activation of a deep-seated Caledonian structure and is considered to have been active intermittently throughout the Carboniferous and perhaps into the Permian Period (Francis and Hopgood, 1970). The radiometric ages of the necks suggest that they were probably emplaced during Stephanian to Early Permian times. During this time shallow-water environments persisted (Forsyth and Chisholm, 1977) and this had a pronounced effect upon the style of the contemporaneous volcanism.

The present-day outcrop of each neck represents a horizontal slice through the sub-volcanic plumbing of a small- to medium-sized volcano. These volcanoes were the result of violent eruptions and produced mainly fragmental pyroclastic products rather than lavas. There is considerable evidence to suggest that many of these eruptions were steam-driven phreatic and phreatomagmatic explosions, as bodies of ascending magma came into contact with aquifers, wet sediments or bodies of standing water such as shallow seas and lakes. The ash cones that typically form in such conditions have a wide diameter and relatively low height and are termed tuff-rings or maars (Lorenz, 1973, 1986). This type of activity is often compared to Surtseyan-style volcanism of marine areas, as summarized by Kokelaar (1986) and White and Houghton (2000). Phreatomagmatic volcanoes in general range from subaqueous to emergent to subaerial (Godchaux *et al.*, 1992), but the Fife volcanoes most readily fit the transition from emergent to subaerial.

Much of the form and structure of the volcanoes has been preserved due to post-eruptive processes, especially the foundering of sequences within the funnel-shaped conduits that now constitute the necks. Areas of collapsed and centroclinal bedding are thought to be due to the intermittent and progressive inward collapse of unconsolidated fragmental deposits as the magma withdrew to depth. The dominant centroclinal bedding in any one neck is related to the final stages of collapse, generally at the end of the last episode of volcanic activity at that site. The margins of many necks are ring-fractures and it is thought that some of the Fife volcanic sequences may have subsided by up to 500 m, revealing a variety of original structural levels at current erosion levels. However, ring-fracturing may have been an intermittent phenomenon with several generations of subsidence (Lorenz, 1973, 1986; Francis, 1991). The intermittent nature of the volcanicity is indicated by the abundance within the necks of obviously recycled clasts, such as blocks of bedded tuff and volcaniclastic breccia.

The necks are filled by pyroclastic and volcaniclastic rocks that formed sequences of volcanic ejecta in and around the volcanic craters. The presence of bedding, along with fragments of wood, volcanic bombs and clasts of contemporary sedimentary origin, some with interbedded coals, all strongly imply a mainly subaerial origin. The basal facies of subaerial volcanoes such as these usually contain much non-juvenile, country-rock material, commonly as large blocks. Such lithologies are well represented in most of the East Fife necks. Beds of massive tuff within otherwise bedded sequences may be high-concentration base-surge deposits (Chough and Sohn, 1990). Base-surge activity may also have formed some of the hummocky cross-bedding. Other cross-bedding may be due to reworking with the development of slump or debris sheets and lahar-like slurries.

Tuff sequences that are unbedded or with only minor bedded units suggest a more subaqueous origin. This is a common feature in the basal facies of small phreatic to phreatomagmatic volcanoes (Godchaux *et al.*, 1992), where initial activity is accompanied by chaotic deposits and some mobilization, often resulting in slumps and debris flows. The highly degraded state and green colouration of many of the basaltic clasts may reflect the formation of basaltic glass due to quenching by the water, followed by rapid alteration to palagonite and subsequently to chloritic residues. Since there are no known pillow lavas and associated hyaloclastite breccias in the Fife necks at their present levels of exposure, this subaqueous phase was probably short-lived. The phreatomagmatic phase was probably followed by more dominantly magmatic activity in which basaltic pyroclastic eruptions occurred subaerially or in shallow water.

The cryptovolcanic ring-structures are believed to represent incipient neck formation, the breccias forming in country-rock strata above magma bodies that failed to breach the surface to form volcanic cones. Where this explosive brecciation of both country rock and contemporaneous volcanic products was followed by their mobilization through gas/steam fluidization or fluxion processes, bodies of tuffisite were emplaced.

Magmas failing to reach the surface were emplaced as sub-surface intrusions. Most were intruded as dykes, thin sheets and irregular masses, but some formed solid plug-like structures to the main volcanic vents. The Ruddons Point intrusion, for example, is one of the largest in East Fife. The basaltic breccias that are common in the central parts of the necks may be interpreted as either pyroclastic breccias or as masses of intrusive basalt brecciated *in situ* by subsequent intrusions and violent gas and stream-driven eruptions. There is no conclusive proof of subaerial lavas having developed, though these might have been a natural consequence of the later evolution of the volcanoes. Some dykes and plugs may have fed lavas, though no direct evidence for this exists.

The 'exotic' inclusions, xenoliths and megacrysts that occur within the necks and associated intrusions are thought to have been derived from the lower crust and the lithospheric upper mantle. Assemblages from several of the East Fife necks (Table 4.2) have played a leading part in formulating ideas as to the deep structure of the Midland Valley (e.g. Upton *et al.*, 1984) and also in the construction of complex petrogenetic models (e.g. Macintyre *et al.*, 1981; Upton *et al.*, 1999) (see Chapter 1). Chapman (1976) interpreted the various igneous xenoliths from the Elie Ness Neck as within-mantle and within-crust differentiates of alkali basalt magmas. Studies of the pyrope garnet megacrysts ('Elie Rubies') by Colvine (1968) and Donaldson (1984) suggest that the magmas contained significant water and were cooler than had been supposed previously. Aspen *et al.* (1990) considered that the anorthoclase megacrysts represent syenitic (salic alkaline) vein deposits crystallized from magmas in the upper mantle, and Upton *et al.* (1999) concluded that they and the associated anorthoclasites may also occur as pegmatitic veins traversing pyroxenitic wall-rocks.

Conclusions

The East Fife Coast GCR site contains no less than 15 volcanic necks, the eroded remains of a series of small Late Carboniferous to Early Permian volcanoes. These exceptional exposures are of international value as they enable reconstructions of the original form of the volcanoes, their mechanisms of emplacement and the environments in which they formed. Exposure is excellent and, as the necks are exposed at different structural levels, three-dimensional relationships are clear. The site is consequently much used for research, and is a popular venue for educational field parties.

The necks are thought to represent the roots of low cinder and ash cones known as tuff-rings or maars, formed during violent (phreatomagmatic) eruptions due to the explosive interaction of magma with groundwater and surface water. The presence of intrusive fragmental rocks (tuffisites) containing much country-rock material, points to the importance of gas-streaming by water vapour generated during the eruptions. Adjacent sedimentary country rocks are commonly disrupted by folding and brecciation. Although there is no evidence that magma was ever erupted as lava, many of the necks contain minor intrusions and larger plugs of basalt, representing magma that solidified relatively close to the surface.

Some of the necks are aligned along the Ardross Fault which, although demonstrably active during and after the volcanism, is thought to be a re-activation of a deeper Caledonian basement structure and probably acted as one of a number of factors controlling the sites of the volcanoes.

Several of the necks contain suites of rocks and crystals (xenoliths and xenocrysts) brought up from great depths by the rising magmas. By studying these assemblages it is possible to investigate the high-pressure–high-temperature processes that operated beneath the volcanoes, in the lower part of the Earth's crust and the underlying upper mantle beneath the Midland Valley. The results have an important bearing upon the origin of the magmas that produced the Carboniferous–Permian Igneous Province of northern Britain.

HOWFORD BRIDGE, EAST AYRSHIRE (NS 512 254–NS 516 255)

I.T. Williamson

Introduction

The River Ayr at Howford Bridge, 1 km west of Catrine, East Ayrshire, affords a representative section through some of the youngest volcanic rocks in the Carboniferous–Permian Igneous Province of northern Britain (Figure 4.11). The lavas and tuffs of this GCR site form part of the Mauchline Volcanic Formation, which comprises the lower part of the Permian succession in the Mauchline Basin. The upper part comprises continental red bed sandstones of the Mauchline Sandstone Formation and the whole succession is 610 m thick at its maximum.

The Mauchline Basin has a simple form in which the more resistant, volcanic rocks form a low ridge surrounding a broad, shallow topographical depression. The volcanic rocks thicken eastwards from 100 m to 238 m and are probably part of a more extensive volcanic field that extended originally to the south-east, across the Southern Upland Fault, to include the Carron Basalt Formation of the Sanquhar and Thornhill basins (see **Carron Water** GCR site report).

Regionally, the Mauchline Volcanic Formation rests unconformably, but with no marked discordance, upon reddened Upper Coal Measures sedimentary rocks. Fossil plant remains from intercalated sedimentary beds elsewhere in the basin suggest an earliest Permian age (Wagner, 1983), and hence the volcanic rocks have considerable potential importance for dating the Carboniferous–Permian boundary. K-Ar whole-rock dates of around 286 ± 7 Ma were obtained from the lavas by De Souza (1979, 1982), and Wallis (1989) reported a K-Ar date of 291 ± 6 Ma from an associated neck intrusion. Palaeomagnetic measurements support an age of emplacement close to the Carboniferous–Permian boundary (Du Bois, 1957; Harcombe-Smee *et al.*, 1996).

The section was first described by Geikie (1866) (his Ballochmyle section) and subsequently by Eyles *et al.* (1949) in the Geological Survey memoir and by Mykura (1967). Excursion guides for the Glasgow district have included this key section (e.g. Weedon and Mykura in Lawson and Weedon, 1992). Detailed

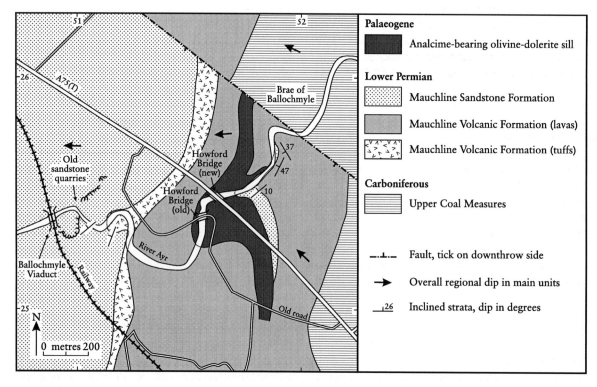

Figure 4.11 Map of the area around the Howford Bridge GCR site. Based on Geological Survey 1:10 560 sheets NS 52 NW (1966); and NS 52 SW (1964).

petrographical descriptions of the formation were given by Tyrrell (1928a), and analyses of the lavas were included in studies of Silesian and Permian magmatism of northern Britain by Macdonald *et al.* (1977) and Wallis (1989). A stream-sediment survey of the Mauchline Basin has revealed significant amounts of gold, possibly derived from the volcanic rocks and precipitated from hydrothermal solutions in the red beds (Leake *et al.*, 1997).

Description

The Mauchline Volcanic Formation is extremely variable in lithology, but comprises mainly lenticular basic lavas, with intercalated beds of tuff, tuff-breccia, agglomerate, aeolian sandstone and mudstone. The lavas are mainly olivine-microphyric and olivine-clinopyroxene-microphyric basalts with some nepheline basanites, analcime basanites and olivine nephelinites (Eyles *et al.*, 1949), though whole-rock analyses reveal many basaltic hawaiites and hawaiites (Wallis, 1989). There is a variable, localized basal unit of tuffs and volcaniclastic sandstones. The overlying Mauchline Sandstone Formation comprises brick-red sandstones with large-scale, dune cross-bedding and is characterized by the presence of wind-rounded grains.

Lavas and interbedded sedimentary rocks are exposed in the river bed and on the south bank upstream (east) of the new road bridge. The dip here is about 10° to the west. Lavas on the north bank, beneath the new bridge, are difficult to access. The best section of the upper part of the volcanic formation is seen in the cliff below the old road, downstream (west) from NS 512 254 (Figure 4.12). Here tuffs, some containing wind-rounded sand grains, are interleaved with and overlain by the Mauchline Sandstone Formation. The latter is very well exposed in old quarries and cliffs around NS 511 254, where the large-scale dune bedding can be seen.

Most flows appear to be altered to a greater or lesser degree, and colour varies between grey and a purplish-red, although some very fresh material is preserved. Pseudomorphed olivines are a common feature on weathered surfaces, giving the rocks a characteristic speckled appearance. The lavas are fine grained, usually highly scoriaceous and amygdaloidal with mainly calcite and zeolite infills. Some flows contain larger cavities and preserve fossilized surface cracks infilled with reddish-brown sandstone.

The fragmental volcanic rocks are predominantly lithic tuffs and volcaniclastic breccias. They usually comprise sub-angular to angular lapilli and blocks of olivine basalt, which are commonly amygdaloidal, in a matrix of finer material derived from weathered ash and lava. Some crystal-lithic tuffs may be present. Sedimentary rocks interbedded with the lavas are orange-red or brick-red, generally fine- to medium-grained, commonly pebbly, sandstones and less commonly siltstones and mudstones. Clasts in the sandstones are mostly basalt, reflecting weathering of contemporaneous lavas, tuffs and vent agglomerates. Some, but not all, sandstones also contain wind-rounded quartz grains.

The geochemical studies by Macdonald *et al.* (1977) and Wallis (1989) have provided many whole-rock analyses of the Mauchline lavas, 28 of which are from the Howford Bridge area. All of the latter are basalts or basanites. In contrast to the majority of lavas from earlier Carboniferous volcanism in the Midland Valley, these lavas have strongly alkaline characteristics and are mainly strongly silica-undersaturated (nepheline-normative), although Macdonald *et al.* (1977) and Wallis (1989) also identified some mildly alkaline, transitional (hypersthene-normative) types. They have distinctive isotopic and trace-element signatures (see 'Introduction' to this chapter).

Also notable at this site is an irregular sill of analcime-bearing olivine-dolerite that cuts the lavas (Geikie, 1897; Tyrrell, 1912, 1928b). It forms a cliff on the north bank of the river, between the old and new bridges, and is probably between 25 m and 30 m thick. It appears to have been intruded partly along the plane of relative weakness afforded by an intercalation of fissile sandstone and has chilled upper and lower margins. Xenolithic bodies of sandstone and basalt lava occur close to the sill's margins and pale-coloured segregation veins of analcime-syenite are well seen. Although this sill was formerly assumed to be contemporaneous with the Lugar Sill and hence only slightly younger than the lavas, it is now considered to be part of the Prestwick–Mauchline Sill-complex, of Palaeogene age (Mykura, 1967). A K-Ar mineral date of 58.4 ± 1.4 Ma from Howford Bridge (De Souza, 1979, recalculated by Wallis, 1989) is the main evidence for the age of this complex, although earlier studies of palaeomagnetism from several localities had reached the same conclusion (Armstrong, 1957).

Figure 4.12 Cliffs of the River Ayr near Howford Bridge, showing aeolian sandstones of the Mauchline Sandstone Formation, overlying poorly bedded tuffs of the Mauchline Volcanic Formation. (Photo: British Geological Survey, No. C2917, reproduced with the permission of the Director, British Geological Survey, © NERC.)

Interpretation

The Early Permian volcanic activity appears to have been a mixture of effusive and explosive events, interrupted by periods of relative quiescence during which sediments were deposited. Various features of the lavas, for example the scoriaceous surfaces and the presence of surface fissures infiltrated by sandstone, suggest that they were emplaced subaerially and no pillow lavas or hyaloclastites have been reported.

Lateral variations in thickness, lithology and facies are a feature of the Mauchline Volcanic Formation. This strongly suggests that lavas were probably erupted as localized events from a number of separate centres. Some 60 or so volcanic necks, many with intrusions of highly silica-undersaturated rock-types, including olivine analcimite and monchiquite, occur within a radius of 30 km and these may well have been the sources of both the lavas and the pyroclastic rocks. Many basic alkaline sills and dykes in the western Midland Valley are also thought to be contemporaneous with this volcanism (e.g. see **Lugar** GCR site report).

The composition, irregular lithofacies alternation, and sedimentary structures of the sedimentary rocks point to a mixture of aeolian and subaqueous deposition. Hence the overall palaeoenvironment appears to have been one of a spasmodically active volcanic field combined with increasingly arid, desert conditions, punctuated by seasonal periods of rainfall giving rise to sheet-floods and local lakes. Topography is thought to have been subdued with the lavas erupted on to a floodplain.

Howford Bridge

The strongly silica-undersaturated nature of these lavas was one line of evidence that led MacGregor (1948) to propose that volcanism in the Scottish sector of the Carboniferous–Permian Igneous Province of northern Britain became increasingly silica-understaurated with time. This was refined by Macdonald *et al.* (1977), who identified two magmatic or thermal cycles, each beginning with the production of hypersthene-normative magmas which then gave way to increasingly nepheline-normative types. The Mauchline lavas are part of the second of these cycles, but more recent work has suggested that this model is over-simplified (see Chapter 1).

Analyses of these lavas have contributed greatly to the overall model for the generation and evolution of Silesian and Early Permian magmas proposed by Wallis (1989) and summarized in Chapter 1. More specifically, they exhibit reduced levels of the most incompatible trace elements, because the lithospheric mantle, the usual source of such elements in the Midland Valley igneous rocks, had already been depleted by partial melting in late Namurian times which had resulted in the Troon Volcanic Member. However, Sr and Nd isotope ratios do still indicate some lithospheric interaction, in marked contrast to late Stephanian–Early Permian igneous rocks in areas such as Fife and East Lothian, which had been affected by partial melting responsible for the Stephanian tholeiitic intrusions (see Chapter 6).

A north-west–south-east to WNW–ESE structural control for both volcanism and sedimentation in the Permian basins of south-west Scotland was inferred by MacGregor (1948) and Mykura (1967) respectively and this has generally been interpreted as being a reflection of north-west–south-east and north–south rifting (McLean, 1978). More recent interpretations have related the basin development to the presence and re-activation of Caledonian structures in the underlying basement rocks (Anderson *et al.*, 1995; Coward, 1990, 1993, 1995). Coward's (1993) model of the tectonic evolution of the Midland Valley envisaged sinistral strike-slip movement on the Highland Boundary and Southern Upland faults continuing throughout the Carboniferous Period but being replaced by dextral strike-slip movement during end-Carboniferous and Early Permian times. The Mauchline Basin is situated between the ENE- to NE-trending Inchgotrick Fault in the north and the NE-trending Kerse Loch Fault to the south, and Rippon *et al.*

(1996), whilst generally supporting Coward's model, suggested that these faults may have acted as extensional structures controlling basin formation and volcanism. However, they pointed out that, as dykes with petrological affinities to the Mauchline lavas and also the Late Carboniferous tholeiitic dykes have east–west trends, the extension may have been north–south.

Conclusions

The volcanic rocks that crop out at the Howford Bridge GCR site are representative of the Mauchline Volcanic Formation, the extrusive product of one of the youngest magmatic events in the Carboniferous–Permian Igneous Province of northern Britain. Many volcanic necks, plugs and sills in and around the Mauchline Basin are related to these rocks and they may have formed part of a larger volcanic field that included the comparable sequences of the Thornhill and Sanquhar basins to the south-east.

Old quarries that expose wind-deposited, dune-bedded, red sandstones of the overlying Mauchline Sandstone Formation are an added attraction at this site. The intimate association of these continental red beds with the volcanic rocks was a factor that first led geologists to suggest a Permian age for the volcanism, and plant remains have subsequently been found elsewhere in the Mauchline Basin that confirm an Early Permian age. Since both lithological and palaeontological evidence suggests that the volcanic rocks were erupted close to the Carboniferous–Permian boundary, they have international importance as a source of material for radiometric dating, and recently obtained dates have contributed to the currently accepted boundary age of 290 million years.

The lavas and tuffs at this site are mainly basaltic and some are very deficient in silica (basanites). They are some of the most silica-undersaturated and alkaline in the whole igneous province and hence are of considerable interest. They play an important role in developing a consistent model for the magmatic origin and development of the province, which in turn is of great relevance to the broader aspects of magmatism and basin development in Britain and north-west Europe during Late Palaeozoic times. An alkali dolerite sill in the eastern part of the site is of much younger, Palaeogene age and is related to similar sills on the Isle of Arran.

CARRON WATER, DUMFRIES AND GALLOWAY (NS 885 017–NS 887 024)

I.T. Williamson

Introduction

The gorge of the Carron Water, 4 km NNE of Carronbridge, Nithsdale and 0.5 km downstream from Jenny Hair's Bridge, is the type section for the Early Permian Carron Basalt Formation (Figure 4.13). The site is continuous with the Hapland Burn GCR site that represents the associated fluvial and aeolian sedimentary rocks (see Benton *et al.*, 2002).

The Carron Basalt Formation, defined by Brookfield (1978) from this type section, comprises basaltic lavas and some interbedded sedimentary units. It is restricted to the Thornhill Basin, a small N–S-elongated fault-bound outlier of Carboniferous and Permian rocks within the Southern Uplands, and to very small outliers in the adjoining Sanquhar Basin. Originally these lavas may have formed part of a more extensive volcanic field that included the volcanic rocks in the Mauchline Basin (see **Howford Bridge** GCR site report).

These volcanic rocks were identified by Geikie (1866, 1897) and were first described in some detail in the Geological Survey memoir for the Sanquhar and Thornhill coalfields (Simpson and Richey, 1936). A general description of the Thornhill Basin appears in the memoir for the adjacent Sheet 9 (McMillan, 2002) and aspects of the Permian sedimentology and stratigraphy were discussed by Brookfield (1978, 1980) and McMillan and Brand (1995). The basalts have been included in geochemical studies of Silesian and Permian igneous rocks of southern Scotland by Macdonald *et al.* (1977) and Wallis (1989) and have also been investigated as a potential source of gold that occurs as trace amounts in the associated red beds (Leake *et al.*, 1997). Brief descriptions of the GCR site and nearby localities have been included in field excursion guides (Brookfield, 1981; McMillan in Stone, 1996).

Description

The Carron Basalt Formation is exposed only intermittently within the northern and western parts of the Thornhill Basin. The sequence of lavas with associated thin breccias and sand-

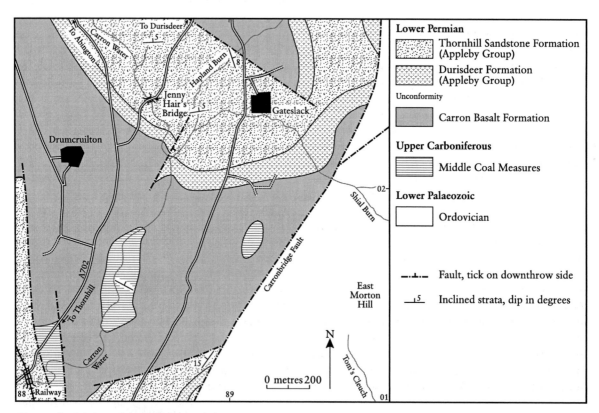

Figure 4.13 Map of the area around the Carron Water GCR site. Based on British Geological Survey 1:10 000 Sheet NS 80 SE (2000).

170

stones is no more than 50 m thick at maximum, though thicknesses of 20 m are most usually quoted (e.g. McMillan, 2002). It unconformably overlies mainly reddened Middle Coal Measures strata, though in the south-east it rests upon Lower Palaeozoic rocks. It is succeeded by the Durisdeer Formation and the Thornhill Sandstone Formation of the Lower Permian Appleby Group.

The Carron Water GCR site is the type locality for the Carron Basalt Formation, where 20 m or so of lavas and sedimentary rocks dip gently to the north. The type succession of the formation (after Simpson and Richey, 1936) is shown below.

Top
Sandstone, brick-red with occasional 'blocks' of basalt
Sandstone, brick-red, cross-bedded, aeolian
Breccia, basaltic
Non-exposed gap
Olivine basalt, amygdaloidal; 2 flows, each with fissured upper surfaces
Sandstone, red, fine grained
Olivine basalt, amygdaloidal
Sandstone, very fine-grained, with basaltic pebbles in upper part
Non-exposed gap
Carboniferous sedimentary rock
Bottom

Locally, the base of the volcanic formation is a breccia with small angular clasts of greywacke and basalt in a sandy matrix. The presence of basaltic clasts indicates that lavas were already present and were being eroded elsewhere in the basin. Some basalts incorporate wind-blown sand in their matrix (Brookfield, 1980). The lavas, for the most part, comprise deeply and extensively weathered olivine basalts, 1–3 m thick (Figure 4.14). Olivine microphenocrysts and other ferro-magnesian phases are easily seen on weathered surfaces as they are pseudomorphed by amorphous mixtures of 'serpentine', haematite, chlorite and clay minerals, giving a red speckled appearance to the rock. All three flows are amygdaloidal to a greater or lesser degree, but locally they have a slightly more massive facies overlain by a thicker amygdaloidal zone. This upper part is often reddened and fissured. Where the flows are overlain by contemporaneous sedimentary rocks, these fissures have been partially infilled, and neptunian dykes of sandstone are quite common. The top of the formation is a basalt breccia, irregularly overlying fissured, amygdaloidal basalt. However, the contact between basalt and breccia cannot be seen.

The top of the Carron Basalt Formation interdigitates with the base of the Durisdeer Formation. The latter comprises a variable unit, some 70 m thick in the Hapland Burn, of arenaceous sedimentary rocks dominated by polymict conglomerates, pebbly sandstones, cross-bedded sandstones and tabular sandy breccias (Brookfield, 1978). Clasts in the conglomerates and breccias are dominated by locally derived basalt, up to boulder size, but also include local Carboniferous and Lower Palaeozoic sedimentary rocks. These coarse-grained fluvial lithologies interdigitate with and pass upwards into aeolian dune-bedded sandstones that typify the overlying Thornhill Sandstone Formation.

There are few analyses of lavas from the Thornhill Basin (Macdonald *et al.*, 1977; Wallis, 1989). Although the latest Carboniferous and Early Permian igneous rocks of south-west Scotland are dominantly alkaline and silica-undersaturated, the lavas of the Thornhill Basin, like those of the Mauchline Basin, show a range of compositions from hypersthene-normative (transitional) basalts to nepheline-normative alkali basalts and basanites.

Interpretation

Because of its association with red fluvial and aeolian strata, the Carron Basalt Formation has long been considered to be Permian in age (Geikie, 1866, 1897; Simpson and Richey, 1936). Plant remains in beds intercalated with similar flows in the Mauchline Basin have been assigned to the earliest Permian (Wagner, 1983), and by inference the Carron Basalt Formation is probably also of earliest Permian age. Being so close to the Carboniferous–Permian boundary, the basalts therefore have potential international significance as a source of material for radiometric dating, although finding fresh material could be difficult.

The palaeoenvironment of the Thornhill Basin during the volcanic period is best assessed by considering both the lavas and the facies of the associated sedimentary rocks. The volcanism appears to have been short-lived and intermittent. Locally, flows show reddened upper surfaces suggesting atmospheric weathering, and the incorporation of unconsolidated sand into the matrix of some flows and the sandstone dykes in fissures also point to surface exposure. The lavas were emplaced subaerially; there is no evidence by way of pillow structures or

Figure 4.14 Residual 'core' within heavily-weathered basalt lava of the Carron Basalt Formation on the west bank of the Carron Water GCR site. (Photo: K.M. Goodenough.)

hyaloclastites for the existence of bodies of standing water, despite the presence of inter-bedded, waterlain sedimentary rocks.

The lower sandstones and those infilling fissures on the flow surfaces contain mainly sub-angular grains, typical of immature fluvial facies. Brookfield (1978, 1980) and McMillan and Brand (1995) have interpreted the basal breccias and conglomerates of the Durisdeer Formation as piedmont and minor stream-flood deposits with some alluvial fan sheet-flood sands and breccias and marginal fluvial facies. There are some interbedded aeolian sandstones and climatic conditions became progressively more arid, but true desert conditions may not have been fully established until well after the volcanic period. The succeeding beds of the Thornhill Sandstone Formation contain mainly well-rounded grains and polished and faceted pebbles. They are dominated by desert dune sands and a few interdune sheet deposits.

The Thornhill Basin is one of a number of now isolated Permian sedimentary basins in the Southern Uplands that are orientated perpen-dicular to the north-east–south-west Caledonian fabric of the underlying rocks. They developed under extensional regimes, with their shape and orientation controlled by the re-activation of deep-seated structures in the basement

(Anderson *et al.*, 1995). Limited transitional to alkaline volcanism was associated with the early phases in the rift-history of the basin and may have been contiguous with other Permian volcanic sequences in southern Scotland, for example the Mauchline Volcanic Formation (see **Howford Bridge** GCR site report).

Conclusions

The Carron Water GCR site contains the type section for the Carron Basalt Formation, a series of subaerial, olivine basalts within the Early Permian 'red bed' sequence of the Thornhill Basin. The interaction between volcanism and contemporaneous sedimentation is a feature of the site that enables reconstructions of both palaeoenvironment and palaeogeography.

The basalts are among the youngest products of the Carboniferous–Permian Igneous Province of northern Britain and hence are important in any consideration of the overall magmatic evolution. Together with interbedded fluvial and aeolian sedimentary rocks, they are also critical to a full understanding of the complex interplay between magmatic events, sedimen-tation and basin tectonics in northern Britain and throughout north-west Europe during Early Permian times.

Chapter 5

Alkaline basic sills and dykes of Scotland

Introduction

INTRODUCTION

D. Stephenson

Sub-volcanic minor intrusions, such as plugs, dykes and sills, form an integral part of all eruptive centres and a genetic association is usually clear from close geographical links and from petrological similarities. Descriptions of such intrusions within the Scottish volcanic fields are included, where relevant, in chapters 2, 3 and 4. More-extensive sill-complexes and regional dyke-swarms, representing voluminous injections of alkaline basic magma, are also widespread in parts of Scotland. Some may well be contemporaneous with local extrusive events, but others occur well outside known volcanic fields or are demonstrably younger than any local volcanic rocks.

Most of the major sill-complexes and regional dyke-swarms are of Namurian age or younger and hence post-date the most voluminous outpourings of lava that occurred during Visean time, but they are coeval with intermittent, more localized volcanic events that continued until Early Permian times. The tectonic development of the region during this period is described in Chapter 1. It has been argued that the increasing thicknesses of geotechnically weak sediments in the rapidly developing Silesian basins of the Midland Valley were of too low density to support columns of magma, which were unable to rise to the surface, and hence they spread laterally to form sills (Francis, 1991). Their distribution throughout the Midland Valley is shown on Figure 5.1. Associated regional dyke-swarms of alkaline basic rocks are not recognized in the Midland Valley, except in the Ayrshire Basin where alkali dolerite dykes, some of which may be contemporaneous with the sills, occupy a wide range of fracture directions. In contrast, in the more competent 'basement' rocks of the north-west Highlands, and to a much lesser extent in the Southern Uplands, there are several alkaline basic dyke-swarms but no sills (Figure 5.2).

The alkaline intrusions represent a major component of Carboniferous–Permian igneous activity in Scotland; Macdonald (1980) has estimated a total volume of 1200–1500 km^3. Most of these are probably post-Dinantian in age, and hence their volume significantly exceeds the known volume of Silesian and Permian extrusive rocks – less than 500 km^3, according to the calculations of Tomkeieff (1937) – and probably increased only moderately by newer information from mining and boreholes.

Emplacement mechanisms

The large sill-complexes in Scotland were almost all emplaced into developing sedimentary basins, and in many cases the greatest sill thicknesses have been shown to occur in the deepest parts of the basins (Francis and Walker, 1987). From a detailed study of Namurian sills in western and central Fife, Francis and Walker (1987) concluded that magma had flowed down bedding planes that were already dipping inwards at up to 5° at the time of intrusion. Magma accumulated in the bottoms of the basins and in some cases flowed up-dip on the opposite side, due to hydrostatic pressure. In this respect the model is similar to that proposed by Francis (1982) for the later tholeiitic sill-complex (see Chapter 6). However, whereas the tholeiitic magma rose along dykes that extended above the sills without reaching the surface and hence provided the head of magma, there are no known dykes associated with the alkali sills. Instead, there is a close geographical and petrological association with volcanic necks that mark the sites of conduits for surface eruptions (Figure 5.3). Francis and Walker (1987) suggested that it was degassed magma in the volcanic pipes that provided the feeders for the alkali sills, bursting out along radial and concentric minor fractures to flow down-dip when the pipes became plugged following an eruption (Figure 5.4). Synsedimentary extensional faults within the basins acted as structural controls of sill emplacement; they limited the extent of some sills and acted as near-vertical channels by which the sills changed level by up to 400 m.

Most of the volcanism at this time was phreatomagmatic, driven by the interaction of magma and water within the sedimentary pile (see Chapter 4). The effects of this interaction are well exhibited at the advancing edges of some sills, where peperitic textures occur, such as isolated blobs of magma within reconstituted sediment and plastically deformed inclusions of vesiculated, heterogeneous sediment within dolerite (Walker and Francis, 1987). The contact effects are particularly dramatic where sills have been emplaced along planes of weakness created by seams of wet lignite (now coal), a common feature of the Scottish coalfields (e.g. Mykura, 1965). At one contact, Walker and Francis (1987) recorded compositionally banded tuffisites, rich in basalt clasts and coal fragments, and identical to those seen in some volcanic pipes (Figure 5.5) and

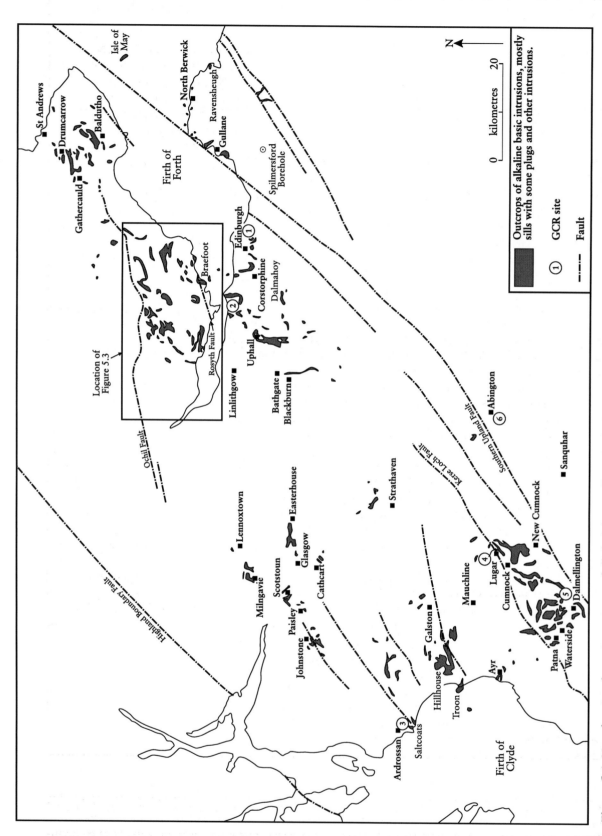

Figure 5.1 Map showing the main outcrops of alkali dolerite sills and dykes of Carboniferous and Early Permian age in central and southern Scotland. GCR sites: 1 = Arthur's Seat Volcano (Salisbury Craigs Sill); 2 = South Queensferry to Hound Point (Mons Hill Sill); 3 = Ardrossan to Saltcoats Coast; 4 = Lugar; 5 = Benbeoch; 6 = Craighead Quarry. The Dubh Loch GCR site lies outside the range of this map (see Figure 5.2). After Cameron and Stephenson (1985).

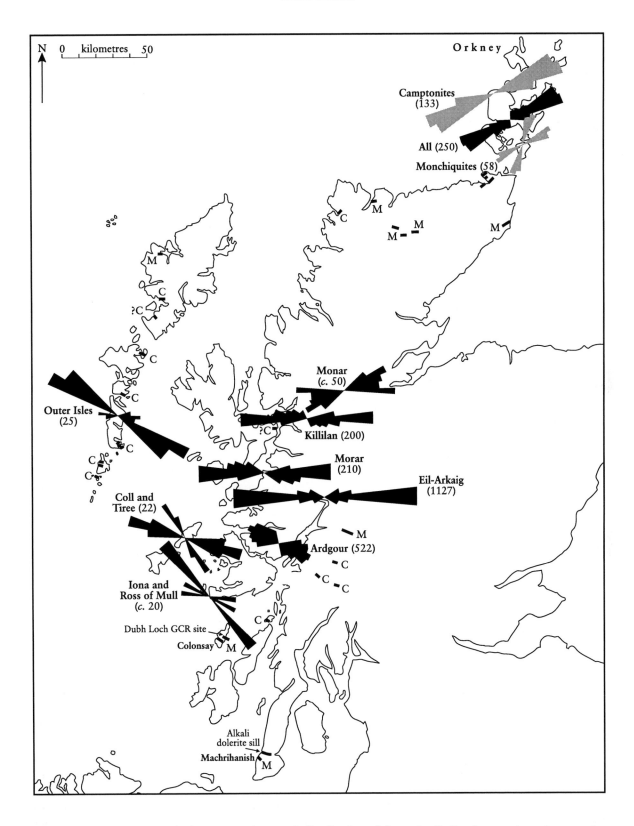

Figure 5.2 Map showing the location and azimuth distribution of the main alkaline lamprophyre (camptonite and monchiquite) dyke-swarms of the northern Highlands. Azimuth distributions are presented as total percentage of dykes in each swarm with a particular orientation; thus long arms indicate swarms trending more uniformly than short ones. The number of dykes recorded in each swarm is shown in brackets. Isolated occurrences of monchiquite and camptonite are shown by M and C respectively. After Rock (1983).

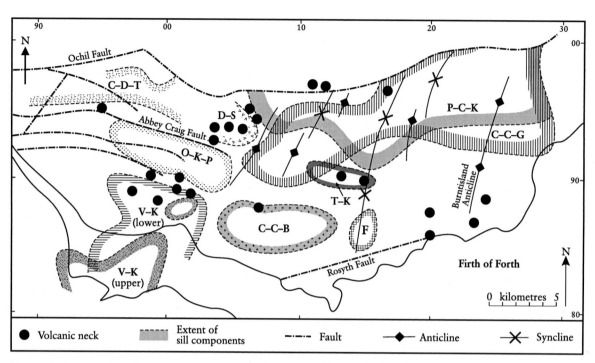

Figure 5.3 Map showing the components of the west and central Fife sill-complex, illustrating their close relationship with volcanic necks. Named sill components: C–C–B = Crombie–Cairneyhill–Bellknowes; C–C–G = Craigluscar–Cluny–Glenrothes; C–D–T = Cairnfolds–Dollar–Tillicoultry; D–S = Dunnygask–Steelend; F = Fordell; O–K–P = Oakley–Kinneddar–Parklands; P–C–K = Parkhill–Cowdenbeath–Kinglassie; T–K = Townhill–Kingseat; V–K = Valleyfield–Kinnell. After Francis and Walker (1987).

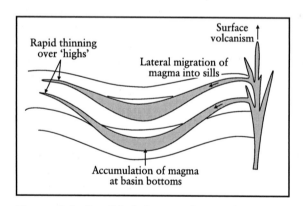

Figure 5.4 Simplified diagram showing how large-volume multi-leaf sills were envisaged by Francis and Walker (1987) as having been fed from magma rising up volcanic pipes.

Lumsden (1967) described fluidized coal infilling joints to over 40 m above a sill. The dolerite is commonly altered to 'white trap' (see below) and productive coal seams may be totally replaced or 'burnt' (i.e. coked). In contrast, some seams close to sills have been converted to a higher grade of coal (anthracite), so enhancing their economic value (see **Benbeoch** GCR site report).

Petrography

The sills and dykes are mostly varieties of alkali basalt, dolerite or gabbro, with some basanites, foidites and alkali lamprophyres. More fractionated rocks occur only as minor segregations in essentially basic sills. The basic rocks exhibit a remarkable range of mineralogy and textures and, in the past, have been given a plethora of names in an attempt to classify the varieties and understand their distribution. A complex classification scheme was adopted by early Geological Survey publications (e.g. Richey *et al.*, 1930; Macgregor and MacGregor, 1948; Eyles *et al.*, 1949) and was simplified and translated into more modern terms by Cameron and Stephenson (1985). In this volume the terminology has been simplified further, following the IUGS recommendations (Le Maitre, 2002), as modified by the British Geological Survey (Gillespie and Styles, 1999). Many names have been shown subsequently to have little or no petrogenetic significance and hence do not aid interpretation (Henderson *et al.*, 1987). In particular, much significance has been given

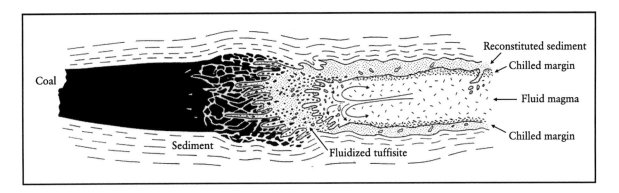

Figure 5.5 A schematic diagram illustrating the effects of coal–magma interaction, as observed in the basic alkaline sills of Fife. After Walker and Francis (1987).

historically to the distinction between 'theralitic' rocks, with essential nepheline, and 'teschenitic' rocks, with essential analcime, whereas it is now generally regarded that most, if not all, analcime in these rocks is a sub-solidus replacement of nepheline (Henderson and Gibb, 1983). The terms 'theralitic' and 'teschenitic' are retained to aid cross-referencing to previous literature, but more descriptive names such as nepheline-dolerite and analcime-dolerite are preferred.

Groups of related lithologies can be summarized as follows:

1. Olivine-dolerite, basalt and basanite, mildly silica-undersaturated, but with no modal nepheline and little analcime. These are commonly microporphyritic (olivine ± augite), resembling local basaltic lavas of 'Dalmeny' type.
2. More strongly silica-undersaturated basic rocks with modal nepheline and/or analcime. These include analcime-dolerite/gabbro (formerly 'teschenite'), nepheline-dolerite/gabbro (formerly 'theralite') and nepheline-monzogabbro (formerly 'essexite'), together with olivine-rich picritic variants and rare peridotite. In the western Midland Valley, most of the theralitic rocks are characterized by abundant olivine (10–40%) and were formerly classified as 'kylitic' types.
3. Strongly silica-undersaturated, highly alkaline, feldspar-poor or feldspar-free rocks, mostly fine-grained basanite, foidites and alkaline lamprophyres (all formerly classified as 'monchiquitic' types). Typically they comprise phenocrysts of olivine and augite in

a mesostasis of glass, analcime or nepheline and are best termed 'olivine analcimite' and 'olivine nephelinite'. With increasing ground-mass feldspar they grade into analcime basanite, nepheline basanite and, rarely, leucite basanite. The alkaline lamprophyres, camptonite and monchiquite, are characterized by phenocrysts of amphibole. Rock-types of this group tend to occur in thinner sills and in dyke-swarms.
4. Some olivine-bearing dolerites defy classification, particularly where they have suffered alteration. Some have residual analcime and many have secondary quartz, whereas primary quartz and other petrographical features in a few sills suggest possible affinities with the Stephanian tholeiitic intrusive suite.

Alteration is particularly intense close to fault planes and adjacent to sedimentary rocks that were probably saturated with water at the time of intrusion. Zones of 'white trap', in which the normal rock is transformed into a pale-cream or yellowish-brown alteration product, are seen particularly well for example in the **Ardrossan to Saltcoats Coast** and **South Queensferry to Hound Point** GCR sites (Figure 5.8). The primary igneous texture is usually preserved, but the constituent minerals are pseudomorphs, comprising kaolinite, chlorite, leucoxene, amorphous silica and carbonate minerals. 'White trap', commonly containing solid or viscous hydrocarbons on joint surfaces, is particularly widespread in dolerites that are associated with carbonaceous mudstones, coals or oil-shales. It has been suggested that the alteration was caused by volatiles released during the distillation of such rocks by heat from the intrusions (Day, 1930a; Mykura, 1965).

The alkaline sills of the Midland Valley in particular have been the subject of many detailed petrological and geochemical studies that have contributed greatly to developing theories for the origin and evolution of alkaline basic magmas. The wide variety of rock-types within composite or differentiated intrusions such as the Lugar and Saltcoats Main sills in Ayrshire (see **Lugar** and **Ardrossan to Saltcoats Coast** GCR site reports) and the Braefoot Outer Sill in Fife attracted many early petrologists, such as Flett (1930, 1931a,b, 1932), Campbell *et al.* (1932, 1934), Patterson (1945, 1946), Higazy (1952) and Tyrrell (1917b, 1948, 1952), with more recent work on the Benbeoch Sill (Drever and MacDonald, 1967) and the sills of Fife (Walker, 1986). The observed ranges in lithology have been variously attributed to differentiation *in situ* aided by gravitational settling of crystals; to multiple injections of magma; to enrichment in residual liquid and volatiles; or to some combination of these. Most modern interpretations invoke multiple pulses of progressively more primitive magma from a deeper, fractionating magma chamber, followed by limited further fractionation *in situ* (e.g. Henderson and Gibb, 1987). Further details on the mode of emplacement of these heterogeneous intrusions are discussed in the **Benbeoch, Lugar** and **Ardrossan to Saltcoats Coast** GCR site reports.

Eastern Midland Valley

Major alkali dolerite sills are widespread throughout Fife and the Lothians, where there are also numerous minor intrusions associated with the local volcanic centres. In the Lothians, the major sills cut strata as low as the Ballagan Formation and extend up to the Lower Limestone Formation, whereas in west and central Fife they extend up to the Upper Limestone Formation (Figure 1.2, Chapter 1). They are not present in the overlying Passage Formation, nor in the Coal Measures, and it has been suggested therefore that they are of late Visean to Namurian age, contemporaneous with volcanism at Burntisland, the Bathgate Hills and western Fife. In the latter area,

many of the sills seem to be located along the same hinge lines that control the volcanic necks (see Chapter 4) and there is field and borehole evidence to suggest that sills were emplaced into near-surface Namurian sediments that were still saturated with water and not fully consolidated (Francis and Walker, 1987; Walker and Francis, 1987). Some individual sills and the marginal facies of others are of olivine-microphyric basalt or basanite, with strong petrographical and geochemical similarities to the local lavas ('Dalmeny' type) (Walker, 1986). However, many of the thicker sills are of analcime-dolerite ('teschenite') that is more silica-undersaturated and may comprise a separate, slightly later group. A possible upper age limit is provided by quartz-dolerite dykes of the Stephanian tholeiitic swarm that cut analcime-dolerite sills on the island of Inchcolm and near Linlithgow.

The few available K-Ar whole-rock radiometric dates must be treated with caution. Four determinations from Lothian sills fall within the range 317 ± 9 Ma to 308 ± 7 Ma (De Souza, 1974, 1979, recalculated by Wallis, 1989), suggesting that the intrusive activity may have continued into mid Westphalian times. However, recent Ar-Ar dates on biotite separated from three of these sills give late Visean ages in the range 332–329 Ma (A.A. Monaghan and M.S. Pringle, pers. comm., 2002). Five determinations from East Fife fall in the range 310 ± 6 Ma to 280 ± 8 Ma (Forsyth and Rundle, 1978, recalculated by Wallis, 1989), suggesting that although some of the larger sills may be Namurian to Westphalian in age, others may be of Early Permian age, coeval with the minor intrusions in volcanic necks of this area (see Chapter 4). Unfortunately, the petrographical divisions of the sills and the clear geochemical divisions on the basis of silica-saturation and incompatible elements, recognized by Wallis (1989), show no meaningful correlation with currently available age determinations.

Analcime-dolerite sills, up to 137 m thick, are widespread in East and West Lothian and within the city of Edinburgh, but are absent from the Midlothian Basin. Detailed descriptions were given in earlier Geological Survey memoirs by Bailey (in Clough *et al.*, 1910) and Flett (in Peach *et al.*, 1910), and summaries and updates were given in subsequent editions, in particular

Introduction

McAdam and Tulloch (1985) and Davies *et al.* (1986). There have also been numerous studies on individual intrusions, which are given below. They are represented in this volume by the Salisbury Craigs Sill in the **Arthur's Seat Volcano** GCR site and the Mons Hill Sill in the **South Queensferry to Hound Point** GCR site (Walker, 1923; Flett, 1930). Other major 'teschenitic' sills include those at Ravensheugh (Day, 1930f), Gullane (Young, 1903; Day, 1914), Gosford Bay, Point Garry (Day, 1932a), Blackness (Flett, 1931b, 1934), Blackburn, Corstorphine Hill and Stankards (Flett, 1932). The last three are noted for their thick picritic layers. One of the thickest sills recorded in the eastern Midland Valley (114.5 m) is an olivine basalt, porphyritic in parts with augite and olivine phenocrysts, that was penetrated in the Spilmersford Borehole (McAdam, 1974).

In the Firth of Forth, sills of analcime-dolerite form the Isle of May (Walker, 1936) and Inchcolm island, where there is a marked picritic facies (Campbell and Stenhouse, 1908).

In west and central Fife, sills of olivine-dolerite and analcime-dolerite are well known from coal workings and boreholes as well as from extensive surface outcrops. Most of the sills lie within an area limited to the north and south by the Ochil and Rosyth faults, and to the east and west by major sedimentary basins. These constitute a major sill-complex, extending over 750 km² and having a total volume of 7.25 km³ (Francis and Walker, 1987). Francis and Walker have correlated the many individual leaves and recognized nine component sills, some of which may originally have been joined (Figure 5.3). Walker (1986) also recognized distinctive geochemical signatures, based particularly on incompatible trace-element ratios such as Zr/Nb and the pyroxene geochemistry, which represent at least three separate pulses of magma injection, not necessarily widely separated in time.

The Craigluscar–Cluny–Glenrothes Sill is the most extensive and also possibly the oldest, having geochemical affinities with the late Visean Kinghorn Volcanic Formation of the Burntisland area. Intrusive relationships of one leaf of this sill were described in detail by Walker and Francis (1987). The Dunnygask–Steelend and Oakley–Kinneddar–Parklands sills were both correlated with basanitic plugs associated with the early Namurian Saline Hills volcanic rocks, and the Cairnfold–Dollar–Tillicoultry Sill was correlated with mid-Namurian basalts just north of Saline. The second most extensive and thickest sill, at 190 m, is the Parkhill–Cowdenbeath–Kinglassie Sill. Others are the Valleyfield–Kinneil Sill, the Crombie–Cairneyhill–Bellknowes Sill, the Townhill–Kingseat Sill, and the Fordell Sill, which has an atypical nepheline basanite petrography (Allan, 1931) and a unique geochemical signature (Walker, 1986).

At lower stratigraphical levels in the core of the Burntisland Anticline, the Raith–Galliston Sill (Allan, 1924) may be a lower leaf of the Craigluscar–Cluny–Glenrothes Sill, but the Braefoot Outer Sill occurs much lower in the succession, near the base of the Visean Series. The latter is well documented petrologically on account of its layered structure attributable to gravitational sinking of olivine, a pegmatitic dolerite facies and well-developed chilled margins (Campbell *et al.*, 1932, 1934; Higazy, 1952). Layering in part of the Oakley–Kinneddar–Parklands Sill was attributed by Flett (1931a) either to gravitational sinking after emplacement, or to separation of olivine crystals by elutriation in a feeder conduit.

In East Fife, more than 30 sill-like bodies of alkali dolerite, up to 115 m thick, have been recorded, forming a sill-complex of considerable extent (Forsyth and Chisholm, 1977, fig. 16). There is a wide range of petrographical varieties, a feature that was commented upon by Balsillie (1922), who was also the first to recognize the major distinction between the alkaline olivine-dolerites and the tholeiitic quartz-dolerites. Forsyth and Chisholm (1977) recognized a crude zonal distribution to the sills, but this is independent of any obvious geological structure and hence the significance is not apparent. Ophitic, non-ophitic and olivine-microphyric olivine-dolerites form sills at Balcarres, Kilbrackmont, Baldutho, Gilston, Drumcarrow, Gathercauld, Greigston and Wilkieston. More silica-undersaturated 'teschenitic' types, which include analcime-dolerite, analcime basanite, picrite and analcime-monzogabbro, occur at Lathones, Crossgates, Radernie, Craighall, Kingask and Lingo. Considerable vertical differentiation is recorded in 'teschenitic' sills at Higham, Dunotter, Lochty and Kinaldy and is probably present elsewhere (Forsyth and Chisholm, 1968).

Western Midland Valley

A wide petrographical range of alkali dolerites occurs as both sills and dykes in the Ayrshire Basin and analcime-dolerite ('teschenite') sills are abundant in the Glasgow–Paisley area. Although individual intrusions cut strata as low as the Lawmuir Formation, just above the Clyde Plateau Volcanic Formation, representatives of most types cut Coal Measures and many cut Upper Coal Measures. Thus, although some individuals may be coeval with the Namurian volcanism of north Ayrshire (see Chapter 4), most are of late Westphalian age or younger.

In the Ayrshire Basin, most of the transitional to mildly silica-undersaturated olivine-dolerites ('Dalmeny' type) have a petrographical and spatial association with the Troon Volcanic Member and only cut rocks of that member and older; they are probably Namurian in age. The more strongly silica-undersaturated dolerites, basanites and foidites (former 'teschenitic', 'kylitic' and 'monchiquitic' types) cut Coal Measures, but none cut the Mauchline Sandstone Formation that overlies the Early Permian Mauchline lavas. They are all therefore assumed to be slightly older than, or broadly coeval with, the Early Permian volcanism. The most reliable K-Ar radiometric dates on separated minerals from these last types are within the range 303–278 ± 7 Ma (late Westphalian to earliest Permian) (De Souza, 1979, recalculated by Wallis, 1989). More-precise Ar-Ar ages within this range have also been obtained: 288 ± 6 Ma from the Lugar Sill (Henderson *et al.*, 1987), and 295.2 ± 1.3 Ma and 298 3 ± 1.3 Ma from sills at Carskeoch and Ardrossan (A.A. Monaghan and M.S. Pringle, pers. comm., 2002).

There is also some field evidence that, within this latest group of intrusions, there are significant age differences. For instance, underground records have revealed that most sills post-date most faults apart from a late NW- to WNW-trending set, but that there are some sills that post-date all major faults (Eyles *et al.*, 1949; Mykura, 1967). Some sills are cut by necks and dykes associated with the Early Permian volcanic rocks, and their rock-types occur as blocks in the necks. However, the most strongly silica-undersaturated and alkaline intrusions of the Ayrshire Basin have strong petrographical and geochemical similarities with these volcanic rocks and hence have to be regarded as

comagmatic and coeval. Palaeomagnetic data on some of the sills also support a Permian age (Armstrong, 1957).

Much of the early general work on the alkali intrusions of the western Midland Valley was by Tyrrell (1909a, 1912, 1923, 1928a,b) and details of the Ayrshire sills are given in Geological Survey memoirs (Richey *et al.*, 1930; Eyles *et al.*, 1949; Monro, 1999). Unlike in the eastern Midland Valley, only a few of the sills have been studied in detail, but these have acquired international recognition. Several are composite and have provided continuous sections, variously interpreted as showing sequential intrusion of differentiates from an alkali basalt magma and/or differentiation of the magma *in situ*. The earliest study was by Tyrrell (1917b) on the Lugar Sill, which was followed by that of Patterson (1945, 1946) on the Saltcoats Main Sill and by further definitive work on the Lugar Sill that took advantage of two continuous borehole cores (Tyrrell, 1948, 1952). These studies became textbook examples and prompted further work (e.g. Phillips, 1968), culminating in the comprehensive model of Henderson and Gibb (1987), which is based on a further 49 m continuous core through the Lugar Sill. According to this model, the sill formed by up to four multiple injections of progressively less evolved alkali basalt magma, followed by a large pulse of olivine-rich magma that differentiated *in situ*. Upward enrichment of residual liquids and volatile fractions gave rise to late-stage veins. These key intrusions are represented in this chapter by the **Lugar** and **Ardrossan to Saltcoats Coast** GCR sites. The latter site includes several other sills that exhibit a wide variety of field relationships and petrographical features. Other notably composite sills occur at Carskeoch, Kilmein Hill and Craigens–Avisyard.

The Benbeoch Sill (**Benbeoch** GCR site) is one of a dense cluster of sills in the Patna–Dalmellington–Cumnock area, between the Kerse Loch and Southern Upland faults, and is one of the thickest sills at over 65 m. It was the type locality for the 'kylitic' types of sill, characterized by olivine-rich nepheline-dolerite, and typically contains about 35% olivine, rising to 55% in picritic layers (Drever and MacDonald, 1967). Other notably picritic sills occur at Craigdonkey and Benquhat. A further concentration of sills occurs in the Dundonald area, between Galston and Troon, where dolerite crops out over some 16 km² and has been quarried extensively. Most of the outcrops are part of two large sills, the Caprington Sill of analcime-dolerite and the 58 m-thick Hillhouse Sill, dominantly of nepheline-dolerite.

Sills of the strongly silica-undersaturated 'monchiquitic' types are never more than 2 m thick and are all closely associated with volcanic necks of the Mauchline lava field (see 'Introduction' to Chapter 4). Notable examples occur at Meikleholm Glen, Dunaskin Glen and Carskeoch.

Numerous dykes of alkali dolerite and basalt, with a variety of trends, are exposed in coastal sections of Ayrshire and were recorded in underground workings. They are clearly younger than the Coal Measures and some must be late Westphalian to Early Permian in age, but many are members of the extensive Palaeogene dyke-swarms that cross the area. Some attempt has been made to divide the dykes on the basis of their trends and cross-cutting relationships with other dykes and with faults (Eyles *et al.*, 1949; Mykura, 1967), but with only limited success. It is assumed that most of the NW-trending dykes are of Palaeogene age, though some near West Kilbride are cut by other dykes orientated east–west. In this area, dykes of all ages can be very fresh and petrography is not a reliable indicator of age, except for the alkali lamprophyres and foiditic types, which can be compared with the Early Permian volcanic rocks. Hence it is seldom possible to assign an age to an individual dyke with any confidence in the absence of radiometric or palaeomagnetic dates, or of diagnostic trace-element and isotope ratio data (Palaeogene magmas were generally depleted in incompatible elements relative to earlier magmas in the same area; e.g. Thompson, 1982). Many dykes are analcime-bearing olivine-rich dolerites with coarsely ophitic titanaugite, such as are very common in the Palaeogene swarms. However, few have sufficient analcime or nepheline to compare with the 'teschenitic' sills, which has led to general statements that there is no dyke-swarm associated with the late Westphalian to Early Permian alkali dolerite sills (e.g. Cameron and Stephenson, 1985). However, Richey *et al.* (1930) have described east- to ESE-trending dykes that appear to rise from a 'teschenitic' sill and are not present in coal workings below.

In the Glasgow–Paisley area, four major sill-complexes, some consisting of up to three leaves and up to 80 m thick, can be traced over wide areas (Clough *et al.*, 1925; Hall *et al.*, 1998). These occur in the Johnstone–Howwood area; between Paisley and the River Clyde at Scotstoun (the Hosie and Hurlet sills); around Cathcart; and between the Necropolis Hill, Glasgow and Easterhouse. All are 'teschenitic' analcime-dolerites and some contain appreciable amounts of nepheline in addition to analcime. A particularly striking melanocratic nepheline-dolerite at Barshaw has abundant titanaugite and red-brown alkali amphibole (kaersutite); it was formerly classified as a 'bekinkinite' by comparison with a similar rock from Madagascar (Tyrrell, 1915). Three of these sills have yielded K-Ar radiometric dates, based on separated amphibole or biotite, that are tightly grouped in the range 279 ± 9 Ma to 276 ± 8 Ma (De Souza, 1979, recalculated by Wallis, 1989) implying an association with the Early Permian volcanism of Ayrshire. However, an Ar-Ar re-determination of one of these gives a more precise but significantly older age of 292.1 ± 1.1 Ma (A.A. Monaghan and M.S. Pringle, pers. comm., 2002). Two plug-like intrusions, close to the Campsie Fault at Lennoxtown, are of a distinctive augite-phyric nepheline-monzogabbro (Clough *et al.*, 1925; Forsyth *et al.*, 1996), similar to that of the Crawfordjohn dyke in the Southern Uplands (see **Craighead Quarry** GCR site report). One of the plugs has been dated at 276 ± 7 Ma (De Souza, 1979, recalculated by Wallis, 1989), suggesting an Early Permian age for both the Lennoxtown and the Crawfordjohn intrusions, but the Lennoxtown intrusion also gives a significantly older date of 292 ± 2.7 Ma by Ar-Ar (A.A. Monaghan and M.S. Pringle, pers. comm., 2002). Alkali dolerite dykes are rare in this area, which lies well to the north-east of the sharply defined limit of the main Palaeogene dyke-swarms (Cameron and Stephenson, 1985). Hence, the few very fresh olivine-dolerite dykes that are present are probably related to the Early Permian sills.

Highly altered sills around Milngavie, up to 30 m thick, consist of olivine-free dolerite with small patches of quartz (probably secondary), but their mafic minerals (purplish augite, red-brown amphibole and biotite) are of the type found in the alkali dolerites (Clough *et al.*, 1925; Hall *et al.*, 1998).

Southern Uplands

In the Sanquhar Basin, thin sills of analcime-dolerite cut Coal Measures (Simpson and Richey, 1936). Most are altered, commonly to 'white trap', but some have been described as 'camptonitic' and presumably contain abundant alkali amphibole. A few NW-trending dykes of 'monchiquite' and 'camptonitic dolerite' are also recorded in the coalfield, and both dykes and sills are presumed to be related to the Early Permian volcanic rocks that are preserved as small outliers in the basin (see 'Introduction' to Chapter 4 Figure 4.2).

The Lower Palaeozoic rocks of the Southern Uplands are cut by rare 'monchiquite' dykes and by two 'essexites' near Wanlockhead and Abington. The latter, an attractive nepheline-gabbro that was formerly well known as the Crawfordjohn 'Essexite' (Scott, 1915), is represented in this volume by the **Craighead Quarry** GCR site. It is very similar petrographically to the nepheline-monzogabbro at Lennoxtown, north of Glasgow which has been dated radiometrically at 292 Ma. Most of the dykes are NW-trending, although a NE-trending 'monchiquite' has been recorded in Lauderdale (Walker, 1925). The area is also cut by NW-trending dykes of the Palaeogene regional swarm, but this swarm is not known to include strongly silica-undersaturated rocks such as the 'monchiquites' and nepheline-gabbros.

Highlands and Islands

North-west of the Highland Boundary Fault, Early Permian extrusive rocks occur only in the Sound of Islay, but sub-volcanic necks occur in a linear zone between Kinlochleven and Applecross and in a cluster around south-east Orkney (see Figure 4.4, Chapter 4). A 60 m-thick sill of alkali olivine-dolerite intruded into Coal Measures at Machrihanish is probably of similar age. Much more widespread are dykes of alkaline lamprophyre (camptonite and monchiquite), with subordinate associated foidite, basanite and basalt (Figure 5.2), which have long been assumed to be of Carboniferous to Permian age (rather than of Caledonian or Palaeogene age) on petrographical grounds (e.g. Richey, 1939). In the western Highlands, camptonite dykes cut quartz-dolerite dykes of the Stephanian suite (see Chapter 6).

The Orkney dykes have been described in great detail by Flett (in Wilson *et al.*, 1935; Flett, 1900) and those of the Eil–Arkaig, Monar and Ardgour areas were described by Leedal (1951), Ramsay (1955) and Gallagher (1963) respectively. Several individual dykes have been studied, largely because of their varied content of mantle and crustal inclusions (see below) (Walker and Ross, 1954; Praegel, 1981; Upton *et al.*, 1992, 1998, 2001). In a major review of the whole suite, Rock (1983), recognized over 3000 dykes which he divided into nine swarms, with a few widely scattered individual dykes elsewhere (Figure 5.2). There are three principal trends: north-west–south-east, dominant in the western and south-western Highlands and Islands; east–west, dominant in the central part of the northern Highlands; and WSW–ENE in the Orkneys.

The age of these dyke-swarms was the subject of one of the first ever radiometric studies, by Urry and Holmes (1941), who determined the age of two monchiquite dykes on Colonsay by the pioneering Helium Method. One of these dykes now represents the suite in this chapter (see **Dubh Loch** GCR site report). Subsequently many K-Ar studies appeared to confirm a Late Carboniferous to Permian age (Beckinsale and Obradovich, 1973; Brown, 1975; Mykura, 1976; Halliday *et al.*, 1977; De Souza, 1979; Speight and Mitchell, 1979). A review of these works, together with further K-Ar determinations, by Baxter and Mitchell (1984) led to the suggestion that the three trends may represent three separate tectonomagmatic events:

1. late Visean age (326 Ma, measured on the E–W-trending Morar and Eil–Arkaig swarms). A comparable date for these swarms was obtained by palaeomagnetic measurements (Esang and Piper, 1984)
2. late Stephanian to Early Permian age (290 Ma, measured on the NW-trending Ardgour Swarm). A NNW-trending dyke on Mull has yielded an Ar-Ar age of 268 ± 2 Ma (Upton *et al.*, 1998)
3. Late Permian age (250 Ma, measured on the WSW-trending Orkney Swarm).

This correlation of trend with age may be broadly applicable in terms of the various swarms, but individual dykes commonly follow pre-existing structures and hence it cannot be applied to individual dykes. The problem is compounded in Ardgour and the Inner and Outer Hebrides, where swarms of Caledonian calc-alkaline lamprophyres and Palaeogene alkali olivine-dolerites cross the same area as the Ardgour Swarm and occupy the same fracture sets (Morrison *et al.*, 1987). Criteria for distinguishing the dykes of various ages are listed by Rock (1983).

Collectively, these dykes are the most silica-undersaturated, the most highly alkaline and the most primitive suite of basic igneous rocks recorded anywhere in Britain. They are a vital source of information on late Visean to Permian magma genesis and the nature of the upper mantle over a far wider area than that sampled by the more voluminous magmatism of the Midland Valley of Scotland (Baxter, 1987; Upton *et al.*, 1992). They commonly contain xenoliths and xenocrysts from their source region, but also include material from the overlying lithospheric upper mantle and lower crust. Together with the coeval volcanic necks, the dykes are the most prolific source of such material, which is discussed in detail in Chapter 1.

SOUTH QUEENSFERRY TO HOUND POINT, CITY OF EDINBURGH (NT 137 784–NT 159 794)

S.C. Loughlin and I.T. Williamson

Introduction

Major basic sills of both alkaline and tholeiitic affinity are prominent within many parts of the Midland Valley of Scotland. The southern shore of the Firth of Forth, to the east of the famous railway bridge, provides a unique opportunity to examine both types of sill in close proximity, where they intrude mudstones and sandstones of the Gullane Formation (Strathclyde Group). The superb exposures and great diversity of features make this a valuable site for educational purposes and it is a favoured field excursion venue (e.g. MacGregor, 1973; McAdam in McAdam and Clarkson, 1986).

The site has been a source of interest and debate since the 19th century. Some of the more important early studies include Howell and Geikie (1861), Geikie (1880, 1897), Stecher (1888), Flett (in Peach *et al.*, 1910) and Walker (1923). The alkaline Mons Hill Sill, formerly classed as a 'teschenite', exhibits considerable petrographical variation but mainly comprises

analcime-dolerite. It shows many features characteristic of other alkali dolerite sills in the eastern Midland Valley (e.g. Flett, 1930, 1931a,b, 1932; Campbell *et al.*, 1932, 1934; Higazy, 1952), but also has slight petrographical differences that are of academic interest. The tholeiitic Hound Point Sill comprises mainly quartz-dolerite and is a component of the Midland Valley Sill-complex (see Chapter 6). It is petrographically and geochemically similar to other quartz-dolerite sills in the eastern Midland Valley (e.g. Falconer, 1906; Tyrrell, 1909b; Bailey in Clough *et al.*, 1911) and shows typical features such as the development of a coarse-grained and slightly evolved facies just above mid-height, and segregation veins. Near the railway bridge smaller doleritic sills, intruded into a sequence of carbonaceous mudstones and oil-shales, have been altered to a distinctive rock-type known as 'white trap' (Day, 1930a). 'White trap' is relatively common in the Edinburgh district but this is a particularly well-exposed example.

There is no precise field evidence for the age of the sills within the South Queensferry to Hound Point GCR site, or for their age relative to each other. Alkaline basic sills were emplaced during various magmatic episodes from Visean to Early Permian times. In Fife and the Lothians many olivine-dolerites may be Visean or Namurian, as they are petrographically and geochemically similar to neighbouring extrusive rocks of that age (e.g. the Bathgate Hills Volcanic Formation). Some radiometric dates confirm this correlation (De Souza, 1979, 1982). The distinctive 'teschenitic' sills (analcime-dolerites) were thought to be younger, possibly Namurian to Westphalian in age, as appeared to be confirmed by a K-Ar whole-rock date of 308 ± 7 Ma on the Mons Hill Sill (De Souza, 1979, recalculated by Wallis, 1989). However, a re-determination of this sample by Ar-Ar dating has yielded a latest Visean age of 329.3 ± 1.3 Ma (A.A. Monaghan and M.S. Pringle, pers. comm., 2002). Radiometric dates on the tholeiitic Midland Valley Sill-complex elsewhere suggest a Stephanian age on current timescales (see Chapter 6).

Description

Walker (1923) mapped this site in some detail (Figure 5.6), slightly modifying the linework of the 1910 edition of the Geological Survey one-inch Sheet 32 on which some quartz-dolerite

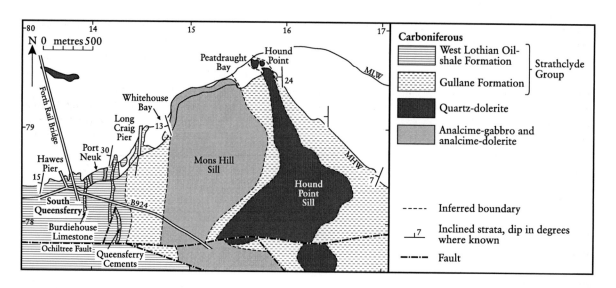

Figure 5.6 Map of the area around the South Queensferry to Hound Point GCR site. After McAdam (in McAdam and Clarkson, 1986).

outcrops had been mapped as 'teschenite'. He recognized that the quartz-dolerite commonly shows spheroidal weathering and crude columnar jointing whereas the analcime-dolerite does not have such distinctive weathering but does have well-developed, sharp-edged columnar joints. In addition, analcime-dolerite is more leucocratic in appearance than quartz-dolerite and ferromagnesian minerals are usually fresher. Analcime-dolerite commonly contains irregularly shaped cavities (druses) into which euhedral crystals of the rock project.

The section is described from east to west, up the succession.

The Hound Point Sill (tholeiitic)

Hound Point, at the eastern extremity of the site (NT 158 796), and rocks on the shore to the north, are composed of a gently westward-dipping (*c.* 15°) quartz-dolerite sill. Here the sill is 20–30 m thick, but it thickens inland. Crude columnar jointing is developed and pale-grey, curvi-planar segregation veins are well displayed locally as a result of differential weathering. The sill intrudes sandstones and black mudstones belonging to the Gullane Formation (formerly part of the 'Queensferry Beds').

The base of the sill is exposed on the east side of Hound Point, where it lies on indurated mudstones and sandstones. The more arenaceous beds are baked to quartzite, whereas black carbonaceous mudstone has been altered to a cordierite-bearing hornfels. The cordierite is commonly pseudomorphed by calcite or altered to micaceous material and gives the altered mudstones a spotted appearance (Flett in Peach *et al.*, 1910; Day, 1928b). Two thin sheets of quartz-dolerite with chilled margins occur below the main body of the sill (MacGregor, 1973). These are probably apophyses from the main sill. The sill becomes finer grained towards its base and has a chilled margin. At one place the base of the main sill has wedged into the bedded sediments producing a transgressive contact (Figure 5.7) that resembles Hutton's famous locality at Salisbury Craigs (see **Arthur's Seat Volcano** GCR site report). Above this contact a thin sheet-like body of quartzite within the sill, which superficially resembles a quartzo-feldspathic segregation vein, has chilled basalt on each side.

Basalt exposed in reefs close to the low-water mark north-west of Hound Point is presumed to represent the chilled margin at the top of the sill.

The Mons Hill Sill (alkaline)

Just above the horizon of the Hound Point Sill the Gullane Formation is intruded by another major basic sill known as the 'Mons Hill Sill' (e.g. Flett in Peach *et al.*, 1910; Walker, 1923; MacGregor, 1973). Virtually the whole thickness of the sill is seen in well-exposed sections from

Figure 5.7 Base of the Hound Point quartz-dolerite sill at Hound Point, forcing up the underlying beds of sandstone. The hammer shaft is about 35 cm long. (Photo: British Geological Survey, No. D1917, reproduced with the permission of the Director, British Geological Survey, © NERC.)

the west side of Peatdraught Bay (NT 154 794) to Whitehouse Point (NT 147 789). Inland, the sill forms the upstanding ridge of Mons Hill, from which it takes its name, and it is seen in several, now disused, quarries. Jointing in the sill suggests a dip of about 11° to the west, more-or-less conformable with the country-rock strata, which here dip westwards at 13°–19°. Original estimates of the thickness were 150–155 m, but undulations in the dip, suggested by the jointing, mean that it may be thinner (McAdam and Clarkson, 1986).

The basal contact of the sill is obscured by sand and the upper contact is accessible only during exceptionally low tides. The upper few metres of the sill are vesicular and well jointed. Contact-altered spotted mudstones and indurated sandstones of the Gullane Formation are exposed close to the supposed locations of both contacts and a good section through these beds is exposed intermittently for 25–35 m along the top of the beach on the east side of Whitehouse Bay (MacGregor, 1973).

This 'teschenitic' sill is composed mainly of analcime-dolerite and analcime-gabbro, with some nepheline-dolerite. In common with other alkaline sills of the Midland Valley, internal contacts separate a number of distinct sheets showing variations in texture, petrography and chemical composition. The description of the coastal section (see below), is based largely on Walker (1923), who distinguished what he termed 'modifications', but apparently was unable to give precise thicknesses.

Top

1. **Nepheline-dolerite**, dark, medium grained with idiomorphic kaersutite needles, black and pink segregation veins and a vesicular top; angular jointing

Contact fairly sharp but not chilled

2. **Analcime-dolerite**, compact, medium grained, sub-ophitic, fresh with mottled appearance and no segregation veins

Sharp contact seen at Whitehouse Point

3. **Analcime-gabbro**, coarse grained and very coarse-grained, mottled; large ophitic titaniferous augite crystals, plagioclase partly altered to analcime, much chlorite; pink segregation veins; calcite-filled cavities and conspicuous zeolitic drusy cavities; rounded jointing. Forms the bulk of the sill, between a point 300 m west of Peatdraught Bay and Whitehouse Point

Sharp contact

4. **Analcime-dolerite**, dark, medium grained, sub-ophitic; angular jointing

Uncertain contact

5. **Nepheline-dolerite**, pale, medium grained, with small kaersutite needles

Merging contact

6. **Kaersutite analcime-gabbro**, coarser grained than the nepheline- and analcime-dolerites above. Seen just east of a small sea-stack

Sharp contact, not chilled

7. **Analcime-dolerite**, dark, medium grained, idiomorphic titaniferous augite; angular jointing

Base

The analcime-gabbro that comprises the main part of the sill (layer 3 above) contains distinctive ophitic titaniferous augites measuring up to 2 cm × 15 cm and enclosing strongly zoned plagioclase that is partially replaced by analcime. Chlorite is also prominent and there are rare pseudomorphs after olivine. Alkali feldspar, analcime, natrolite and large skeletal ilmenite occur as prominent accessories along with some biotite and apatite. The kaersutite analcime-gabbro towards the base of the sill (layer 6 above) contains sub-ophitic titaniferous augite and variably sized kaersutite prisms. There is much chloritization and no nepheline.

The analcime-dolerite (layers 2 and 4 above) contains sub-ophitic titaniferous augite and plagioclase, most of which is altered to analcime. Pseudomorphs after olivine are common, as is biotite but there is no kaersutite. A variety of analcime-dolerite with idiomorphic rather than ophitic titaniferous augite comprises layer 7.

The nepheline-dolerite (layers 1 and 5 above) is dominated by idiomorphic kaersutite and green-rimmed (presumably slightly sodic)

titaniferous augite. In layer 5 the kaersutite forms prominent needles. The groundmass comprises zoned plagioclase (labradorite to oligoclase), alkali feldspar, analcime, nepheline (mostly altered), titaniferous magnetite and pyrite with accessory apatite and biotite. There are also rare pseudomorphs after olivine.

Distinctive pink segregation veins occur in layers 1 and 3. They are medium grained, non-porphyritic and contain biotite, alkali feldspar, analcime and rare euhedral nepheline. Two varieties of black fine-grained segregation vein occur in layer 1: a ferromagnesian-rich variety with ocellar structure, and a modification of this with large phenocrysts of plagioclase and titaniferous augite.

The inland continuation of the Mons Hill Sill was proved in two boreholes sunk during the early decades of the 20th century, one at Easter Dalmeny (*c.* NT 150 775) and the other about 320 m farther west (Flett, 1930). These boreholes proved a layered sequence of over 85 m that includes analcime-gabbro and, notably, some picritic (olivine-rich) variants that are not present in the coastal section of the sill. In neither case was the top of the intrusion seen.

'White trap'

The rocky shoreline between Long Craig Pier (NT 144 789) and Port Neuk (NT 138 784) comprises a succession of mudstones, siltstones, sandstones, oil-shales and ferran dolostones ('cementstones') belonging to the Calders Member of the West Lothian Oil-shale Formation. Within this succession, there are two thin, slightly transgressive sills, roughly 100 m apart, which have been altered to a light-coloured calcareous clay-rich material known as 'white trap' (Figure 5.8). The eastern sill, 60 cm thick, is a cream-coloured rock with brown margins; the western sill, 90 cm thick, is pale grey and weathers buff-brown. The margins of both sills are indistinct in places because the host sandstones are of a similar pale colour, but the sills may be distinguished by their polygonal jointing. Carbonaceous mudstones, even where bleached, are slightly darker and hence contacts with them are quite distinct; they may be brecciated or smooth (MacGregor, 1973; McAdam and Clarkson, 1986).

The 'white trap' sills are composed almost entirely of calcium-magnesium-iron carbonates, kaolin, muscovite and quartz. Relict igneous

Figure 5.8 Basic sill intruding and transgressing sedimentary rocks of the West Lothian Oil-shale Formation and altered to 'white trap', South Queensferry shore. The hammer shaft is about 35 cm long. (Photo: A.D. McAdam.)

textures are preserved in places, but commonly only 'ghosts' of the original feldspar crystals remain, having been altered to aggregates of kaolin, isotropic silica, calcite, chalybite and some dolomite. Skeletal ilmenite and magnetite remain as accessories, particularly in the chilled margins (Stecher, 1888; Flett in Peach *et al.*, 1910; Day, 1930a).

Interpretation

The quartz-dolerite sill at Hound Point is a member of the Midland Valley Sill-complex, which is discussed at length in Chapter 6. Several other component sills of the complex are described as GCR sites and interpretations of their magmatic origin, evolution, structural setting and mode of emplacement apply equally to Hound Point. Consequently they are not repeated here. These tholeiitic sills do not have any known extrusive equivalents and were emplaced along E–W-trending fractures during a brief change in the stress regime that occurred in Late Carboniferous times (Francis, 1978b, 1982).

Walker (1923) described the petrographical variation within Mons Hill Sill in some detail,

including the 'finer-grained marginal modifications' between the main rock-types. Despite the finer grain-size he did not observe glassy chilled margins towards the internal contacts and considered this as evidence for differentiation *in situ* rather than for separate injections of magma. Other alkaline basic sills of the Midland Valley are similarly composite, with a lithological range in some cases greater than that at Mons Hill. It is likely that some of the mechanisms that have been proposed for these sills also hold true for the Mons Hill Sill (see **Lugar**, **Ardrossan to Saltcoats Coast** and **Benbeoch** GCR site reports).

Numerous examples of the alteration of dolerite to 'white trap' have been recorded in the Edinburgh district. In most cases the original affinity of the dolerite cannot be determined, but the process is known to affect both alkaline and tholeiitic dolerites. Day (1930a) studied examples of 'white trap' within carbonaceous mudstones, oil-shales and coals from Dalmeny (this site), Granton, Weak Law and North Berwick and observed considerable variations in the chemical composition. He recognized a series of gradations between two end-members; one is clay-rich and retains some original igneous texture and the other is a more carbonated rock in which virtually nothing remains of the original rock. Flett (in Peach et al., 1910) recognized that the presence of remnant igneous textures implies that the rock was fully crystallized prior to alteration. He proposed that heat from the intrusion distilled gases and solutions from the carbonaceous mudstones. Organic gases cannot affect rock-forming silicates at high temperatures and therefore modification occurred after the dolerite had solidified and the temperature had dropped. Day (1930a) proposed that the metasomatic process took place in two stages; first, kaolin and isotropic silica appeared as a result of the decomposition of feldspars and ferromagnesian minerals. This was followed by the gradual replacement of the whole rock by carbonates.

Conclusions

The South Queensferry to Hound Point GCR site contains both a tholeiitic, quartz-dolerite sill and a distinctive alkaline basic ('teschenitic') sill. Each represents a major intrusive suite in the Midland Valley of Scotland and was the subject of early studies. The alkaline Mons Hill Sill was emplaced during latest Visean times, possibly concurrent with volcanic rocks of this age that are preserved in the Bathgate Hills and west Fife. In contrast, the quartz-dolerite sill at Hound Point was emplaced as part of the Midland Valley Sill-complex during a very brief period in early Stephanian time when there was no known surface volcanism in the area (see Chapter 6).

Internal variations in mineralogy and texture are well developed in the Mons Hill Sill and details of internal contact relationships between distinctive lithologies are also clear. The Hound Point Sill exhibits the regular gradational zonation that is typical of Midland Valley quartz-dolerite sills. These factors, coupled with geochemical data, provide many clues as to the processes of magma generation and evolution responsible for both suites. The different geochemical characteristics of the two sills probably reflect magma generation at different depths below the Earth's crust and/or at different pressures and temperatures.

There is abundant evidence of the effect of heat upon the sedimentary host rocks adjacent to the major sills, and smaller sills show excellent examples of the alteration of dolerite to 'white trap', due to fluids and gases distilled out of carbonaceous mudstones and oil-shales by the heat of the intrusions.

ARDROSSAN TO SALTCOATS COAST, NORTH AYRSHIRE (NS 246 409–NS 224 417)

J.G. MacDonald

Introduction

South Bay, between Ardrossan and Saltcoats on the north Ayrshire coast (Figure 5.9), is flanked by promontories formed by resistant igneous rocks, products of Late Palaeozoic basic extrusive and intrusive activity. At Saltcoats, Coal Measures strata, resting on the Namurian Ayrshire Bauxitic Clay Member and lavas of the Troon Volcanic Member, have been intruded by the Inner Nebbock Sill of analcime-dolerite ('teschenite') and most notably by the Saltcoats Main Sill, a composite intrusion of analcime-dolerite and picrite. The latter has much in common with the better known and more studied Lugar Sill (see **Lugar** GCR site report) some 39 km to the SSE. Also of note, in the intertidal platform between the two sills, are fossil tree stumps of sigillarian type (Yuill, 1963). The headland of Castle Craigs, Ardrossan is also formed from a composite sill of dolerite and picrite which may be an extension of the Main Sill, displaced by a WNW-trending fault. On the north (inland) side of this fault, a separate sill of analcime basanite extends northeastwards to form Castle Hill; it is intruded into Visean lavas, tuffs and sedimentary rocks. The area is cut by NW-trending basaltic and andesitic dykes of Palaeogene age.

Some of the sills were described by Geikie (1897) and Falconer (1907), and they were all described in relation to other intrusions in the north Ayrshire area in Geological Survey memoirs (Richey et al., 1930; Monro, 1999). A detailed account of the petrography and geochemistry of the Saltcoats Main Sill was given by Patterson (1945, 1946). The area is frequently visited by field parties and features in excursion guides (Bassett in Bluck, 1973; Weedon in Lawson and Weedon, 1992). A K-Ar determination on the Castle Craigs Sill yielded an Early Permian age of 272 ± 7 Ma (c. 278 Ma using new constants) (De Souza, 1979), but a re-determination of the same sample by Ar-Ar gave a more precise, significantly older, Stephanian age of 298.3 ± 1.3 Ma (A.A. Monaghan and M.S. Pringle, pers. comm., 2002).

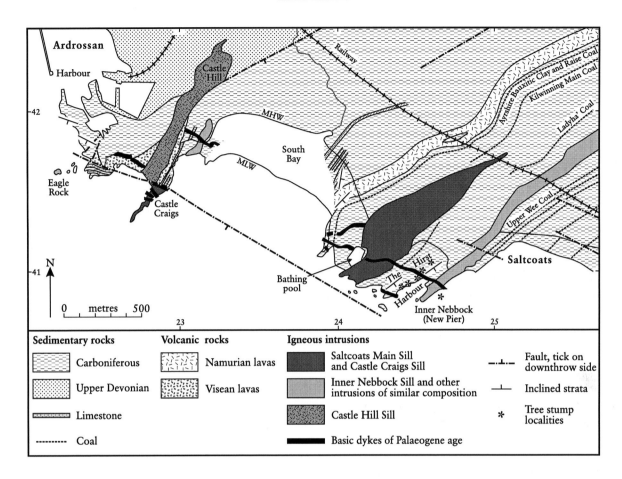

Figure 5.9 Map of the area around the Ardrossan to Saltcoats Coast GCR site. After Bassett (in Bluck, 1973).

Description

Namurian volcanic rocks

Near low-water mark, west of the Saltcoats Bathing Pool (NS 241 411), there are poor exposures of the Ayrshire Bauxitic Clay and the underlying Troon Volcanic Member, which together form the main part of the Passage Formation at the top of the Namurian Series in north Ayrshire (Monro, 1999).

The Troon Volcanic Member is over 50 m thick in the Saltcoats area but only the highly decomposed topmost few metres are exposed within the GCR site. Less altered samples from neighbouring localities have been identified as being composed dominantly of olivine basalt similar in character to the 'Dalmeny'-type basalt of the Visean Clyde Plateau Volcanic Formation.

The Ayrshire Bauxitic Clay Member varies in thickness up to about 20 m. On the Saltcoats shore it consists of approximately 1.2–1.5 m of massive light-grey to buff-coloured kaolinitic clayrock with ooliths and pisoliths that grades downwards into altered basalt. The highly oolitic upper portion passes downwards into a pale-brown to reddish clayrock containing specks of sphaerosiderite. Fragmentary plant remains are common. This is one of the few natural sections of this member available for study.

Saltcoats Main Sill

The Saltcoats Main Sill crops out on the foreshore south of the bathing pool, where it is about 18 m in thickness. It dips to the southeast in conformity with the Coal Measures strata. The base is in contact with the Kilwinning Main Coal that has been baked to a columnar coke (Figure 5.10). The outcrop can be subdivided into four distinct units (Figure 5.11) that occur in downwards succession from southeast to north-west as follows (Patterson, 1945, 1946):

191

Figure 5.10 The contact between the base of the Saltcoats Main Sill (pale weathering) and baked coal-bearing sedimentary rocks (dark). The sill has been altered to form 'white trap' adjacent to the coal. The hammer is 28 cm long. (Photo: C. MacFadyen.)

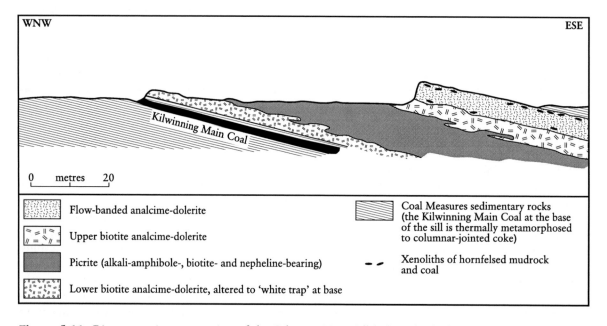

Figure 5.11 Diagrammatic cross-section of the Saltcoats Main Sill below the bathing pool. After Patterson (1946).

1. **The top flow-banded analcime-dolerite** ('teschenite'), which varies in thickness from about 1.8 m to 2.7 m, is generally fine grained with microphenocrysts of titanaugite and serpentinized olivine. The groundmass consists largely of microlites and laths of plagioclase, brown amphibole and abundant interstitial analcime. The rock has a characteristic brown colour on exposed surfaces and has well-developed flow-banding roughly parallel to the upper contact. The overlying fissile mudrocks have been baked and hardened. Xenoliths of hornfelsed mudrock occur towards the top of the unit indicating that they were broken off during intrusion. Some xenoliths of mudrock and coal occur near the bottom of the unit where it is in contact with the underlying biotite analcime-dolerite. There appears to be some marginal chilling of the base of the flow-banded analcime-dolerite close to the lower contact.

2. **The upper biotite analcime-dolerite** ('biotite-teschenite') is a little less than 3 m in thickness. It crops out as smooth rounded masses of black rock with cross-cutting segregation veins and patches rich in pale-pink analcime. The rock consists essentially of labradoritic plagioclase laths up to 2 mm in length, and titanaugite with lesser amounts of red-brown amphibole, and analcime. Biotite occurs as numerous small flakes moulded on feldspar and titanaugite. Olivine is variable in abundance but usually in small amounts and is invariably altered to 'serpentine'. There are a few small euhedral crystals of nepheline.

   The segregation veins contain elongate crystals of alkali amphibole, euhedral titanaugite and sparse flakes of biotite; plagioclase, zoned from oligoclase to albite, has largely been replaced by secondary analcime and chlorite. Within the veins there are also patches of analcime, vestiges of K-feldspar and a little nepheline. Similar veins occur in the Lugar Sill, where they have been termed 'lugarite' (see **Lugar** GCR site report), but at Saltcoats the rock is richer in potassium.

   It would appear that the underlying picrite has penetrated the base of the dolerite, prising off slabs, from which it has been concluded that the picrite was intruded after the dolerite (Patterson, 1946). However 'lugaritic' segregation veins originating in the alkali dolerite penetrate the picrite in a few instances – an indication that the picrite was intruded prior to the complete solidification of the dolerite.

3. **The central picrite**, about 9 m in thickness, is composed essentially of abundant serpentinized olivine with somewhat lesser amounts of alkali amphibole (red-brown barkevikite), augite and much-altered plagioclase. Patches of analcime may be primary in origin or may in part be derived from the breakdown of plagioclase. Biotite and opaque oxides occur as accessory minerals along with rare prisms of apatite.

   Both the upper and lower contacts with biotite analcime-dolerite are abrupt although neither the picrite, nor the units above and below, show signs of chilling. At both contacts there is a marginal gradation of the picrite into picrodolerite, marked by a decrease in the abundance of olivine and an increase in the proportion of feldspathic minerals. An 8 cm-thick 'lugaritic' vein, 60 cm below the upper contact, differs from those cutting the upper biotite analcime-dolerite in the presence of olivine and lack of biotite. Primary plagioclase has been replaced to a major extent by analcime, thomsonite and prehnite.

4. **The lower biotite analcime-dolerite** ('biotite-teschenite'), about 3.5 m in thickness, is intensely altered to yellowish 'white trap' for about 1.5 m above the lower contact as the result of carbonation by fluids produced by the thermal metamorphism of the underlying coal (Figure 5.10). Dark slabs of coal, prised off during intrusion, occur within the 'white trap'. Above this the unit is composed of much fresher rock, similar to the upper biotite analcime-dolerite, with analcime-rich patches and 'lugaritic' segregation veins.

The Inner Nebbock Sill

A substantial sill of 'teschenitic' alkali dolerite forms the south-west side of Saltcoats Harbour at the Inner Nebbock (NS 245 409); similar rock occurs offshore as the Outer Nebbock islet. Sedimentary rocks above the sill are noticeably hornfelsed. Although the sill is largely concealed by the harbour wall (New Pier) it is exposed in a railway cutting about 1 km to the north-east where it is seen to consist of three layers, each 3–4 m thick; a central picrite is flanked above and below by analcime-dolerite. At a quarry nearby, in the same intrusion, the coarse-grained picritic layer was at one time worked for 'osmond stone', a term used to denote rock suitable for the soles of bakers' ovens (Richey *et al.*, 1930). The sill can be traced inland to Stevenston as a topographical feature and still farther east in boreholes.

The Castle Craigs Sill

The low rocky promontory of Castle Craigs (NS 228 415) at Ardrossan is formed by a composite layered intrusion (Falconer, 1907). A lower, marginal layer of 'olivine-feldspar rock' is overlain by coarse-grained amphibole-bearing picrite. The upper part comprises a thin layer of amphibole-bearing dolerite overlain by finer-grained banded biotite analcime-dolerite. The latter becomes less olivine-rich upwards and develops alkali amphibole as it passes up into a metre-thick margin of analcime-basalt.

Another small alkali dolerite sill occurs on the beach about 400 m to the north-east of Castle Craigs.

Interpretation

Namurian volcanic rocks

The outcrop of the Troon Volcanic Member at Saltcoats is the north-western limit of a 40 km-wide Namurian volcanic field in north Ayrshire. Borehole evidence indicates a maximum thickness of about 160 m north of Troon. The resulting volcanic land surface that emerged from the surrounding deltaic environment, is much decomposed, consistent with the near-equatorial tropical latitude that has been inferred for this part of the Scottish crust at this time.

The Ayrshire Bauxitic Clay Member, which rests directly on top of the weathered surface of the Troon Volcanic Member, is considered to have resulted from a prolonged period of post-volcanic subaerial lateritic weathering under wet tropical conditions. Although in some areas a complete gradation of the claystone downwards into underlying lava is indicative of residual weathering *in situ*, the claystone is commonly interbedded with other sedimentary rocks including coal and laminated mudrock. It is thus considered that much of the deposit has resulted from transport of the products of weathering and their deposition in shallow pools on the uneven surface of the underlying lavas (Monro *et al.*, 1983; Monro, 1999).

Sills

A reconstruction of the order of intrusion of the various units of the Saltcoats Main Sill by Patterson (1946) suggested that the top flow-banded analcime-dolerite (unit 1) was intruded first. A viscous, volatile-poor magma was intruded along a horizon at or just above the top of the Kilwinning Main Coal, with xenoliths of sedimentary rocks being incorporated into the basal and upper parts of the intrusion; the flow-banding is consistent with this. There was insufficient heat to cause major alteration of the underlying coal. This may be explained, at least in part, if the intrusion took place mainly in the fissile mudrock immediately above the coal. This first unit had probably completely solidified when further alkali basalt magma was intruded below it, but still above the partly disturbed coal, forming a sill over 6 m in thickness (units 2 and 4). The greater thickness of the second intrusion provided a more long-lasting heat source which led to the destructive distillation of the coal at its base to produce carbonate-rich volatiles that altered the base of the intrusion to 'white trap'. As the magma solidified, a volatile- and alkali-rich fraction became segregated to form the 'lugaritic' veins.

While it was still hot, and before there had been time for complete solidification, the biotite analcime-dolerite of units 2 and 4 was intruded by a third and final pulse of magma. Picritic magma (unit 3) split the dolerite a little more than halfway up, along the plane of weakness that would have existed where it was not yet entirely solidified. Some xenoliths detached from the dolerite contained still unconsolidated patches of alkali-rich differentiates, some of which penetrated the picrite. The high temperature of the enclosing rock delayed the cooling of the picrite, hence the lack of internal chilled margins between the units. The picritic magma was already partly solidified at the time of emplacement and was thus intruded as a mush of crystals. The crystallization of the groundmass led to a concentration of alkalis in the volatile-enriched residual liquid. This led to a further set of 'lugaritic' segregation veins. As the intrusion cooled, hydrothermal fluids expelled from the residual liquid attacked the olivine, converting most of it to 'serpentine'.

The clear evidence that the picrite was intruded soon after the alkali dolerite and the similarity of their respective residual liquids suggest a close genetic relationship. It is thus likely that they were each derived from the same parent magma by gravitational separation of olivine prior to intrusion of the resulting differentiated fractions (Patterson, 1946). However, the relationship of the flow-banded analcime-dolerite to the rest of the intrusive complex is unclear.

Evidence for successive intrusion of pulses of genetically related magmas to form composite sills is also found in the Inner Nebbock and Castle Craigs sills. The similarity of the main lithologies in the latter to those in the Saltcoats Main Sill, in particular the biotite analcime-dolerite and the amphibole-bearing picrite, led Richey *et al.* (1930) to suggest that the two outcrops are part of the same sill displaced by the WNW-trending Ardrossan Harbour Fault. However, the arrangement of the units is not directly comparable and Falconer (1907) considered that the doleritic facies was emplaced later than the picrite at Castle Craigs, which is the opposite to the order deduced for the Main Sill. A re-investigation of the field relationships and petrogenesis of the intrusions is clearly needed to resolve this and several other outstanding problems.

Conclusions

The Saltcoats Main Sill is representative of the analcime-dolerite ('teschenitic') varieties of Late Carboniferous to Early Permian basic alkaline sills in the west of the Midland Valley of Scotland and is an excellent example of a composite mafic to ultramafic intrusion. It provides evidence of successive pulses of magma that are likely to have had a common origin. Other basic sills within the area of the Ardrossan to Saltcoats Coast GCR site are also composite, but they all differ in detail from other sills of the same age and petrographical affinity (e.g. see **Lugar** GCR site report). In addition to a variety of mafic and ultramafic rock-types, the exposures show excellent examples of internal contacts between separate intrusive phases and external contacts with country rocks. Mudstones are baked, coal seams are reduced to coke, and volatiles expelled from the coals have altered the margins of some sills to a pale rock termed 'white trap'.

The site is also representative of the Troon Volcanic Member, the most extensive product of Namurian volcanism in the western Midland Valley (see 'Introduction' to Chapter 4). Exposures of these rocks are poor, but the basalt

lavas exhibit evidence of deep weathering under wet tropical conditions soon after they were erupted. They grade upwards into the Ayrshire Bauxitic Clay Member, a pale aluminium-rich clayrock derived partly *in situ* and partly by accumulation of the products of weathering in hollows on the lava surface. This is one of few places where these deposits can be studied in natural sections.

LUGAR, EAST AYRSHIRE (NS 599 216–NS 601 213)

I.T. Williamson

Introduction

It is widely held that many of the alkaline basic sills and sill-complexes in the west of Scotland are probably comagmatic with the Early Permian Mauchline Volcanic Formation (see **Howford Bridge** GCR site report). Almost all the sills are olivine-bearing doleritic rock-types. Some are thick, differentiated, composite bodies showing a layering attributed to a variety of magmatic processes such as gravitational settling and upward volatile enrichment, elutriation (flow differentiation) and multiple intrusion.

A classic, textbook example of just such an intrusion is the Lugar Sill in the south-west of the Midland Valley. It is exposed in the valley of the Lugar and Glenmuir waters (Figure 5.12) and takes its name from the nearby village of Lugar, 3 km north-east of Cumnock. Historically this sill has played a very important role in developing the concept and mechanisms of magmatic differentiation and is regularly visited for the purposes of education and research. A field excursion was described by Weedon and Mykura (in Lawson and Weedon, 1992).

Although much of our knowledge of this sill is due to the early work of G.W. Tyrrell, his descriptions and interpretations were not the first published accounts. In a paper dealing with the classification of post-Carboniferous intrusions in the west of Scotland (Tyrrell, 1909a), he presented an outline of the Lugar Sill, but fully acknowledged the '...valuable and comprehensive paper on the Lugar intrusions...' by Boyle (1908). The petrography and field relationships of the sill, based upon the Glenmuir Water section, were described by Tyrrell (1917b), and his later papers (1948, 1952) concentrated upon nearby boreholes at

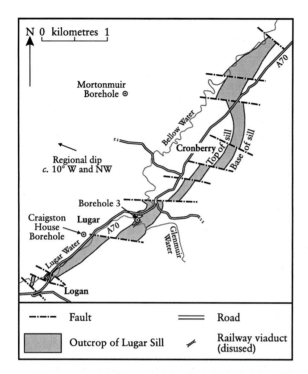

Figure 5.12 Map showing the outcrop of the Lugar Sill and the locations of boreholes through the sill. After Henderson and Gibb (1987).

Mortonmuir and Craigston House respectively. Tyrrell's work was augmented by the Geological Survey memoir (Eyles *et al.*, 1949), and later mineralogical and geochemical studies by Phillips (1968) and Henderson and Gibb (1987) have resulted in more refined models for the petrogenesis of the sill. Radiometric dates obtained by De Souza (1979) and Henderson *et al.* (1987) suggest an earliest Permian age.

Description

The Lugar Sill comprises two principal lithological units. Marginal analcime-dolerites (formerly termed 'teschenites') are separated by a central thick composite unit of nepheline-dolerite, kaersutite nepheline-dolerite and picrite (formerly termed 'theralites'). In detail, the analcime-dolerites are made up of a number of separate intrusions or magmatic pulses. Henderson and Gibb (1987) recognized four such pulses in each of the upper and lower units that form 'mirror images' on either side of the central unit, which was emplaced later as a single pulse. Hence the full composite section comprises nine units, which represent at least five separate intrusive pulses. Later differentiates cut all of these units.

The stream section

The best natural section is afforded by steep cliffs in the Glenmuir Water (Figure 5.13), which cuts through the sill between NS 6006 2134 and the confluence with the Bellow Water at NS 5988 2152. After this confluence, the stream is known as the 'Lugar Water'. Most units of the sill are exposed here and, although access is difficult in places, boulders in the stream bed provide excellent examples of most lithologies. The sill is here about 43 m thick and intrudes arenaceous strata of the Namurian Passage Formation, which dip regionally to the west or NNW at about 10°. The details of the Glenmuir Water section given by Tyrrell (1917b) remain the most comprehensive. They are not repeated here and should be consulted for specific locations. The following short descriptions are mainly taken from Weedon and Mykura (in Lawson and Weedon, 1992).

The basal contact of the sill, which is chilled against pale baked sandstone, is seen in the bed of the stream at NS 6006 2134. The basal facies of the sill is some 3 m thick and comprises basalt and analcime-dolerite with numerous layers of differing texture and colour, but there appears to be an upward gradation into more granular analcime-dolerite.

Downstream, to the north-west, this is followed up the sequence by peridotite and picrite, which form extensive, but deeply weathered cliff exposures, mostly on the outer bends of the stream (Figure 5.13) down to the disused railway viaduct (NS 5991 2142). No contact between the dolerite and the ultramafic facies is visible. North-west of the viaduct, the picrite is in contact with a dark-grey nepheline-dolerite. Neither the top nor the base of the nepheline-dolerite is well exposed. The lower part contains abundant amphibole (kaersutite) and is slightly coarser grained. The upper part is veined by a paler analcime-bearing variety. The contact with the overlying analcime-dolerite is not visible here, though elsewhere it is known to be sharp and chilled.

The upper marginal facies of the sill is, like the base, an analcime-dolerite or gabbro. Both medium- and coarse-grained varieties are exposed downstream from the viaduct and the upper contact with white thermally altered sandstones is exposed on the south bank of the stream, where it is joined by the Bellow Water to become the Lugar Water (NS 5986 2151).

Figure 5.13 Cliff exposures of the picritic central part of the Lugar Sill in the Glenmuir Water, upstream from the railway viaduct, Lugar GCR site. (Photo: K.M. Goodenough.)

This section is also the type locality for an unusual rock-type. This is a kaersutite- and/or augite-rich nepheline-gabbro or nephelinolite that has been termed 'lugarite'. In hand specimen it can be very striking as it is essentially a coarse-grained pegmatitic rock (Figure 5.14). It is exposed in the west bank of the Glenmuir Water 15 m north of the viaduct, close to the picrite–nepheline-dolerite contact, where it occurs as segregation patches up to 1.2 m thick. It also occurs as irregular, anastomosing veins, 2–12 cm wide, which cut the picrite.

Boreholes

Most of the detailed descriptions and interpretations of the Lugar Sill are based on the examination of borehole core. To date, three holes have specifically intersected the sill (Figure 5.12). These are at Mortonmuir (NS 5984 2337) (Tyrrell, 1948), Craigston House (NS 5908 2130) (Tyrrell, 1952) and Lugar Water (NS 5990 2150) (Henderson and Gibb, 1987). There is overall internal consistency between the boreholes in both the relative positions and the thickness of

the majority of lithologies (Figure 5.15). However, they show that the sill has a much more complex internal structure than is revealed by the natural exposures alone. In detail, there are clear differences within the nepheline-dolerite facies and in the presence and position of lugarites (kaersutite-augite-rich nepheline-gabbro).

The Lugar Water Borehole, detailed by Henderson and Gibb (1987), was located at the junction of the Glenmuir and Bellow waters and hence the section closely resembles and significantly augments the natural section. Important additional details seen in the borehole core concern the complexity and nature of the internal contact relationships. The thicknesses of the upper and lower marginal analcime-dolerites are 4.45 m and 8.90 m respectively. Each comprises several distinct units of layered analcime-dolerite, which show chilled internal contacts with one another. Superimposed upon an overall inward-coarsening profile through the analcime-dolerites, these smaller units also coarsen individually into the sill. The 35.5 m-thick central part of the sill comprises a complex unit of nepheline-dolerite and picrite. The

Figure 5.14 Polished sample of pegmatitic kaersutite-augite-rich nepheline-gabbro or nephelinolite ('lugarite') from the Lugar Sill. Note the long acicular crystals of kaersutite, particularly well developed in the marginal zone, and smaller, more equidimensional augite. Grant Institute of Geology and Geophysics (University of Edinburgh) collection. (Photo: British Geological Survey, No. P505645, reproduced with the permission of the Director, British Geological Survey, © NERC.)

upper part of this consists of 2.25 m of relatively fine-grained nepheline-dolerite, which has a sharp, chilled contact with the overlying analcime-dolerite. Below, but gradational into the nepheline-dolerite, is a substantial unit of kaersutite nepheline-dolerite that extends downwards for a further 13 m or so. With a downward increase in olivine and a concomitant decrease in kaersutite, this passes into picrite. The picrite unit is about 20 m thick. The lower few metres, though showing mineralogical

changes and a slight downward decrease in grain size, are not chilled like the top of the central unit. Lugarite is present as four thin units interbedded within the upper part of the kaersutite nepheline-dolerite unit. These comprise both kaersutite- and kaersutite-augite-rich variants and each has a sharp contact with adjacent rock. They occur in the same position within the sill as in the exposed stream sections. Pink aplitic veins (probably microsyenitic) cut all the analcime-dolerite units.

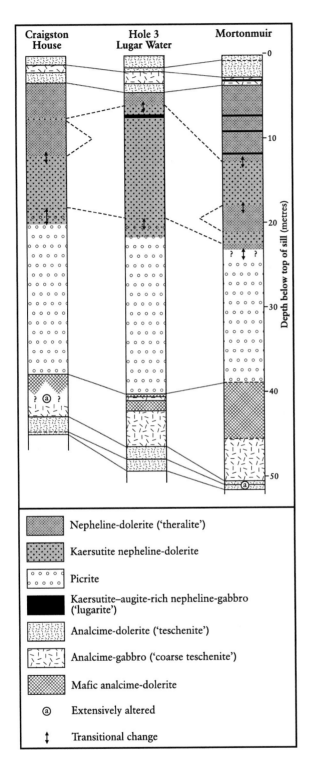

Craigston House Hole 3 Lugar Water Mortonmuir

Depth below top of sill (metres)

Nepheline-dolerite ('theralite')

Kaersutite nepheline-dolerite

Picrite

Kaersutite–augite-rich nepheline-gabbro ('lugarite')

Analcime-dolerite ('teschenite')

Analcime-gabbro ('coarse teschenite')

Mafic analcime-dolerite

ⓐ Extensively altered

↕ Transitional change

Figure 5.15 Correlation of borehole sections through the Lugar Sill. After Henderson and Gibb (1987). See Figure 5.12 for locations.

attributed to the effects of varying dip. There are thickness changes in some of the units, for example the lower analcime-dolerites also thicken eastwards. The principal contrasts in lithology between the Lugar Water and Mortonmuir boreholes are seen in the relationship between the nepheline-dolerite and its kaersutite-bearing variant. In both boreholes these dolerites have similar thicknesses, but in the Mortonmuir Borehole, there are two kaersutite-bearing units and their total thickness is considerably less than at Lugar Water. Also, there are no lugarites in the Craigston House section as opposed to the complex multiple unit at Lugar and the three at Mortonmuir; at the latter, the upper two units are augite-rich varieties and the lower unit is a 'normal' kaersutite-augite-rich variety.

Internal variations in mineralogy and geochemistry

The gross petrographical variation from top to base through the Lugar Sill is, not surprisingly, mirrored by variations in both mineralogy and whole-rock geochemistry. These systematic variations have been documented comprehensively by Henderson and Gibb (1987). The following summarizes some of the essential points of their study.

The mineral compositions reflect an overall evolutionary trend from picrite, through kaersutite nepheline-dolerite and nepheline-dolerite to the kaersutite-augite-rich nephelinolite (lugarite) in the thick, central part of the sill. The earlier, marginal analcime-dolerites are even more evolved. The mafic phases (olivine, clinopyroxene, kaersutite and biotite) are compositionally zoned and, generally, all show maximum magnesium content within the picrite and kaersutite nepheline-dolerite of the central unit. Biotite and amphibole compositions show markedly symmetrical distribution patterns throughout the sill, becoming less magnesian towards both upper and lower margins (Henderson and Gibb, 1987, fig. 4). The main feldspar in the sill is a zoned plagioclase. The range of zoning, from anorthite-rich ($c.$ An$_{70-80}$) to orthoclase-rich ($c.$ Or$_{42}$) compositions, is considerable, but similar, in the marginal layered analcime-

The profiles of the other boreholes illustrate an apparent slight increase in overall thickness eastwards, from Craigston House (44.7 m), through Lugar (50.2 m; cf. Tyrrell's field estimate of 42.7 m) to Mortonmuir (51.4 m). These are considered real, but in part they could also be dolerites, the kaersutite nepheline-dolerite and the lower parts of the picritic unit. There is a much more restricted range in the rest of the picritic unit. Alkali feldspar occurs in the more marginal units (Henderson and Gibb, 1987, fig. 8) and it is likely that primary nepheline was originally present in all lithologies.

Alteration of both mafic and felsic minerals is common. Olivines are typically pseudomorphed by serpentine minerals, especially in the analcime-dolerites, and the feldspars, nepheline and interstitial areas are converted to analcime, zeolite and chlorite associations. Pyroxenes are generally unaffected, except in the lower analcime-dolerites.

The general pattern of variation in whole-rock chemistry with position in the sill is fairly symmetrical for most elements, with the marginal analcime-dolerites having the most extreme values (Henderson and Gibb, 1987, fig. 11; Figure 5.16). The main control over the major element trends is the variation in modal olivine during the early fractionation, with clino-pyroxene controlling formation of the analcime-dolerite and later differentiates. The highest MgO contents occur near the middle of the central picrite–nepheline-dolerite unit, with progressive decreases in concentration from the centre outwards. The total Fe (FeO + Fe_2O_3) trend closely parallels this but the other major element trends are antipathetic to the MgO trend, i.e. with lowest concentrations in the middle of the picrite–nepheline-dolerite unit and increasing

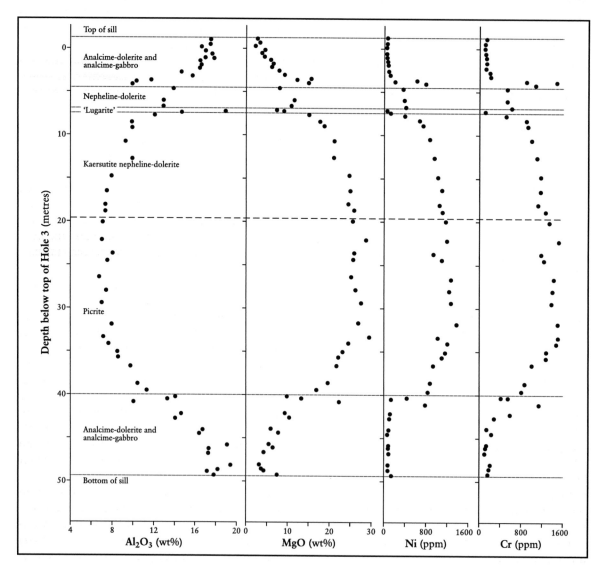

Figure 5.16 Variations of key major and trace elements in a vertical section through the Lugar Sill (Borehole 3). After Henderson and Gibb (1987). See text for details.

outwards. The lugarites have evolved compositions with low MgO and CaO and high Al_2O_3 and Na_2O values. These, the last-intruded rocks, represent a late-stage liquid. However, the most evolved compositions, in terms of major-element chemistry, are the first-intruded, upper and lower marginal analcime-dolerites.

The variation patterns for Ni and Cr in the central unit are also controlled by the olivine and chrome-spinel inclusions within the olivine and hence follow the MgO trend. Other trace elements, for example Zr, Sr, Rb, Ba, Nb, Y, La, Ce and Nd, show patterns similar to that of Al_2O_3 (i.e. antithetic to the MgO trend; Figure 5.16). There are discontinuities and some complications in the marginal facies, but overall, these incompatible elements increase towards the margins of the sill. Since Sr, Ba and Rb contents are normally controlled by feldspar composition and distribution, their incompatible behaviour suggests that feldspar played only a subordinate role during fractionation (Henderson and Gibb, 1987).

Age

Henderson *et al.* (1987) presented a new Ar-Ar plateau age of 288 ± 6 Ma for a kaersutite separated from the main picrite–nepheline-dolerite unit of the Lugar Sill. This age is preferred to the 'total gas' ages in the same study. These gave a result of 292 ± 7 Ma, which is broadly in agreement with the earlier K-Ar determinations, on kaersutite from a 'lugarite' vein, by De Souza (1979), which yielded ages of 297 ± 7 Ma (as recalculated by Wallis, 1989). The preferred age is Early Permian, but very close to the Carboniferous–Permian boundary.

Interpretation

The Lugar Sill is a complex, multiple intrusion that has contributed significantly to theories of magma evolution and emplacement over the past century. The following summary is based largely upon the most recent petrogenetic model of Henderson and Gibb (1987), who also include a comprehensive review of earlier models.

It has long been supposed that the lithologies that make up the Lugar Sill were all derived from a common parent. This is reasoned to have been a primary, relatively alkali-rich, picritic magma, likely to have originated in the upper mantle. It rose through the crust before fractionating in a low-level magma chamber. Here, gravitational settling of olivine, accompanied by ascent of the lower density residual melt, produced a vertically stratified column, with the denser, more mafic and therefore less-fractionated magmas, towards the bottom.

The earliest intrusion was formed when the more-fractionated magmas, towards the top of the chamber, were evacuated in a series of pulses. These had an analcime-dolerite composition. A final larger pulse emplaced the less-fractionated olivine-rich magma from deeper in the chamber to form the picrite–nepheline-dolerite unit. This has regionally transgressive margins in contact with the analcime-dolerites, the top margin being notably chilled, but has gradational internal contacts. The proportion of suspended olivine crystals increased during emplacement, as the magma chamber was purged of progressively more olivine-rich magma, so that the central part of the unit, the last to be emplaced, is the most olivine-rich. Thus, in simple terms, the profile of the sill was formed in sequence from more evolved analcime-dolerite, through nepheline-dolerite, to less evolved picrite.

Differentiation then continued *in situ* with gravitational settling and equilibration of the olivine crystals that were suspended in a liquid phase of nepheline-dolerite composition. This later settling explains the zonation of the unit from nepheline-dolerite to picrite and the fact that the greatest concentration of magnesium-rich olivines in the sill occurs just below the middle part of the central unit.

The segregations and veins of lugarite (kaersutite-augite-rich nepheline-gabbro or nephelinolite) were interpreted by Henderson and Gibb (1987) as auto-intruded, late-stage fractionation products of the central unit, involving in-situ differentiation and upward enrichment in residual liquid and volatiles. The aplitic veins cutting the analcime-dolerites were similarly interpreted as late-stage, in-situ differentiation products from the earlier analcime-dolerite magma.

Post-magmatic alteration is common across the entire sill. However, this phenomenon is most prominent and pervasive within the lowermost units. Henderson and Gibb (1987) suggested that circulating, super-heated groundwater below the sill may have accounted for this.

Conclusions

The Lugar Sill has a long-standing, international reputation as an example of a composite, differentiated, basic alkaline intrusion and is frequently visited for both teaching and research purposes.

It was probably emplaced in very early Permian time as a series of pulses of magma from a compositionally stratified magma chamber situated deep in the Earth's crust, below the final level of the sill. The more evolved, less dense magmas residing at the top of the magma chamber were the first to be evacuated, followed by successive pulses from sequentially deeper levels and hence more mafic magmas. The first phase of sill formation involved the intrusion of progressively less evolved analcime-dolerite magmas. This phase was then followed by the intrusion, into this early sill, of a large-volume pulse of olivine-rich nepheline-dolerite magma. Continued crystallization and settling of crystals *in situ* and an upward enrichment in residual liquids and gases subsequently gave rise to an unusual rock-type, a spectacular nepheline-gabbro with large crystals of pyroxene and amphibole. This has been given the local name of 'lugarite', from this, the type locality.

BENBEOCH, EAST AYRSHIRE (NS 484 085–NS 498 081)

J.G. MacDonald

Introduction

A suite of basic alkaline intrusions was intruded into the sedimentary basins that now comprise much of the Midland Valley of Scotland (Cameron and Stephenson, 1985). In the west of the Midland Valley, where the intrusions are mostly of Late Carboniferous to Early Permian age, they include the Saltcoats and Lugar sills (see **Ardrossan to Saltcoats Coast** and **Lugar** GCR site reports) and many others in the area between Patna and Dalmellington. These sills are typically olivine bearing and contain a variety of rock-types, with varying proportions of olivine or augite enrichment in the main parts of the intrusion.

The sill of dolerite and picrodolerite that forms Chalmerston Hill, 3 km north-east of Dalmellington (Figure 5.17), provides a good example of a type in which the petrography is dominated by olivine enrichment. The columnar-jointed crags of very fresh dolerite at Benbeoch, which form a distinctive feature at the eastern extremity of the hill, provide a continuous section, about 65 m in vertical

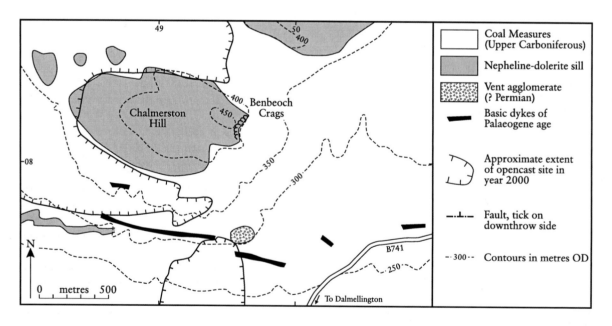

Figure 5.17 Map of the area around the Benbeoch GCR site. Based on Geological Survey 1:10 560 Ayrshire sheets 67NW; and 66NE (both 1910); and 1:63 360 Sheet 14, Ayr (1933).

thickness, through the greater part of the intrusion (Figure 5.18). Most of the western part of Chalmerston Hill has been excavated as part of a vast opencast coal development and the original land surface no longer exists. However, the opencast working has exposed the base of the sill, which was previously unseen, and a section through the lowest 30 m of sill is to be preserved and landscaped.

The rocks of the Benbeoch Sill are typically 'theralitic', in that they contain significant nepheline, with lesser amounts of analcime, and hence should be classed as nepheline-dolerites. They are also rich in fresh olivine and the sill was selected by Tyrrell (1912) as the type example of a rock-type he termed 'kylite', which is well developed in this part of south Ayrshire. The term was adopted as part of the classification used by the Geological Survey (Eyles *et al.*, 1929, 1949) and hence is of historical significance, but it is no longer used. The most detailed study of the sill was that of Drever and MacDonald (1967), who documented the extent of internal modal, mineralogical and chemical variation.

Description

The Benbeoch Sill is intruded into strata of the Upper Coal Measures at the local base of the Barren Red Measures. It forms the main mass of Chalmerston Hill, the highest part of which, Benbeoch (463 m), is bound to the south-east by Benbeoch Crags (NS 496 082) where columnar-jointed picrodolerite occurs in a 40 m-high cliff (Figure 5.18). Here, the top part of the sill has been removed by glacial erosion. The base at Benbeoch Crags is concealed by scree and boulders but some detached slabs, one notably 3 m long, contain a decreasing amount of olivine along their length, passing into what was most likely a chilled margin and hence the base of the intrusion. One such boulder occurs only 12 m below the foot of the cliff, and hence provides a maximum for the amount of the sill that is unexposed at this locality.

Opencast coal workings on the western flank of Chalmerston Hill have exposed a good section of the basal part of the sill around NS 485 084. Other sills have been encountered below the main sill and many of

Figure 5.18 Benbeoch Crags from the south-east. Note the strongly developed columnar jointing in the nepheline-dolerite of the Benbeoch Sill. The top of the sill has been removed by erosion and up to 12 m at the base is covered by scree and boulders, but a 40 m-thick section is exposed. (Photo: Scottish Natural Heritage.)

the coals close to these sills have reduced amounts of volatiles, enhancing their value. As the bottom contact and the contact zone in the underlying sedimentary rocks is not seen anywhere else, a representative part of the section has been preserved to allow future study. The sedimentary rocks consist of pale-green mudstone resting on laminated sandstones of shallow-water fluvial origin. Obvious baking fades away from the contact within a few metres and there is localized brecciation of the country rocks. The chilled margin of the sill contains sparse small vesicles. Over a distance of less than 1 m above the contact, the rock increases in grain size to a very fresh bluish dolerite in which faint layering can be discerned on weathered surfaces, possibly reflecting very slight modal variations. The coarser-grained gabbro above this is intersected in places by white veins (up to 50 mm in width), containing dark needle-shaped crystals of amphibole. The veins emanate from coalescing patchy areas, have gradational margins and hence are most likely derived from late-stage concentrations of alkali- and volatile-rich residual liquids from the magma. Similar veins, containing large acicular crystals of the titanium-rich amphibole kaersutite, occur as late differentiates of the Lugar Sill (see **Lugar** GCR site report). Although some good columnar jointing occurs, the outcrop is dominated by a set of closely spaced, planar, vertical joints trending around 110°. These joints are invariably filled by apparently later zoned veins, dominated by clay minerals and chlorite and containing prehnite, but exhibiting pseudomorphs after plagioclase, clinopyroxene and rare olivine. They have sharp but irregular margins but seem to be due to hydrothermal replacement.

Near the top of Chalmerston Hill, at NS 490 083, a variety of picrite, exceptionally rich in olivine occurs in a small knoll. It was named 'kylite-picrite' by Tyrrell (1912).

The chilled margin exposed in the large slab below Benbeoch Crags contains equant microphenocrysts of carbonated and serpentinized olivine set in a dark turbid groundmass with a few small fresh feldspar laths. About 0.5 m above the margin the rock, although still fine grained, is little altered and contains abundant olivine with peripheral zoning, along with small euhedral zoned pink augites in a sub-ophitic relationship with zoned plagioclase laths.

Magnetite and analcime are also present. Both olivine and augite increase in grain size away from the chilled margin but while the augite decreases in abundance there is a corresponding increase in modal olivine (Figure 5.19).

The proportion of olivine in the main part of the Benbeoch Crags section varies only slightly from an average value of 35.5%, except at the top of the section where a decrease in olivine content and a corresponding increase in augite suggest a position only a few metres below the top contact prior to erosion. The olivine (Fo_{75}) is unzoned and occurs as rounded or subhedral crystals, in a few cases enclosed by augite. The strongly zoned, faintly pleochroic augite commonly displays hour-glass twinning. It is rich in titanium and appears to have

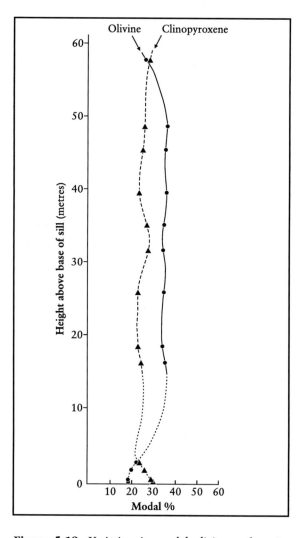

Figure 5.19 Variation in modal olivine and augite through the Benbeoch Sill.

commenced its crystallization prior to that of plagioclase in view of their sub-ophitic or intersertal relationship. The strongly zoned feldspar has cores of calcium-rich bytownite but grades to andesine at the margins. There is a small amount of fresh nepheline, and analcime and biotite occur as minor components. Tiny needles of apatite occur in the groundmass and as inclusions in the augite. The Chalmerston Hill picrite, estimated to be positioned about 15 m below the top of the sill, contains almost 55% olivine but both the olivine and the plagioclase have the same composition as in the rest of the sill although the augite is not so strongly zoned.

Whole-rock analyses of the Benbeoch and Chalmerston Hill picrodolerites and picrites, together with other 'kylitic' intrusions of Ayrshire, indicate a trend of high alkalinity and only moderate iron enrichment, relative to analcime-bearing olivine-dolerites such as those that are common in Palaeogene sill-complexes of Scotland (Drever and MacDonald, 1967). This could help to distinguish them from sills of Palaeogene age that crop out in adjacent areas of south Ayrshire (e.g. see **Howford Bridge** GCR site report).

Interpretation

In the Benbeoch Crags section, there is only minor inhomogeneity in the modal proportions of olivine and augite (Figure 5.19). This is matched by small variations in chemical composition. The apparent lack of internal chilled margins, or indeed any sudden discontinuities, suggests that the magma was emplaced in a single pulse. The observed variations in mode near the top and bottom of the sill make it clear, however, that the first intruded magma, as represented by the chilled margins, was significantly less enriched in olivine crystals than that which formed the main part of the sill. There is no evidence here of any measurable concentration of olivine by post-intrusive crystal settling, so such variation in olivine content as has been observed most likely arose in the magma prior to intrusion. The much greater abundance of olivine in the picrite at Chalmerston Hill at a level 'at or a little below the centre of the sill' (Tyrrell, 1912) could be evidence of a separate but contemporary pulse of magma, or an extreme of gradation, in either

case representing the last part of the magma to be intruded. The former explanation would resemble the relationships observed in the Lugar and Saltcoats sills, where the most olivine-enriched portions are emplaced last, without chilling.

The lack of zoning of the olivine crystals suggests slow growth under conditions approaching stable chemical equilibrium. The similarity in composition of the olivine in both the picrite and the picrodolerite suggests that both rocks originated from the same batch of differentiated magma. If there had been any significant differentiation *in situ* it would have been reflected by a higher magnesium content in the olivine of the picrite. This points to olivine enrichment by some process prior to intrusion or associated with the movement of the magma in the conduit during emplacement. However, lack of exposure renders the precise relationship of the picrite to the rest of the intrusion uncertain.

Conclusions

The Benbeoch Sill comprises distinctive olivine-rich varieties of nepheline-dolerite and nepheline-gabbro ('theralites') within the Late Carboniferous to Early Permian alkaline basic sill suite of the western Midland Valley. The chilled base of the sill has recently been exposed in opencast coal workings and good continuous sections through parts of the sill are exhibited here and in natural crags. In addition to vertical variations in mineral proportions, late-stage alkali-rich patches and veins and various types of jointing are well exhibited. The exceptionally fresh condition of the rocks affords the opportunity to expand knowledge of their whole-rock and mineral geochemistry, and hence gain a valuable insight into the origin of the magma and its subsequent evolution prior to, during and following emplacement and crystallization. When linked with detailed studies of similar but subtly different sills, such as that at Lugar, such studies could significantly increase our understanding of Carboniferous–Permian magmatism in northern Britain and also contribute to a wider understanding of the petrogenesis of alkali-rich basic rocks. A continuous drill core through the sill on this site would be particularly useful.

CRAIGHEAD QUARRY, SOUTH LANARKSHIRE (NS 919 238)

J.G. MacDonald

Introduction

A disused quarry on the west side of Craighead Hill, 2.5 miles east of Crawfordjohn, exposes steeply dipping Ordovician greywackes into which a dyke-like intrusion of a distinctive rock, known as the Crawfordjohn 'essexite' has been emplaced (Figure 5.20). This porphyritic alkali gabbro contains large well-shaped black crystals of augite that give it a distinctive coarsely spotted appearance, especially on surfaces on which the groundmass of the rock has weathered to a pale-creamy-grey colour. It was worked for curling stones which were manufac-

tured nearby in the village of Crawfordjohn in the 19th and early part of the 20th centuries (Figure 5.21a). The only other locality in Scotland where nearly identical 'essexite' occurs is at Lennoxtown, north of Glasgow, on the southern margin of the Campsie Fells, but Craighead Quarry is the only place where it has been quarried.

The rock was first described by Teall (1888) but the most detailed description is that of Scott (1915) who carried out petrographical studies and whole-rock chemical analyses. He concluded that the intrusion is probably 'an elongated plug or small boss' and confirmed the interpretation of Tyrrell (1912) that it is allied to the Late Palaeozoic alkali dolerites, rather than to the Palaeogene dykes of the area which, although they have a similar north-west–south-east trend, have tholeiitic affinities. Greig (1971)

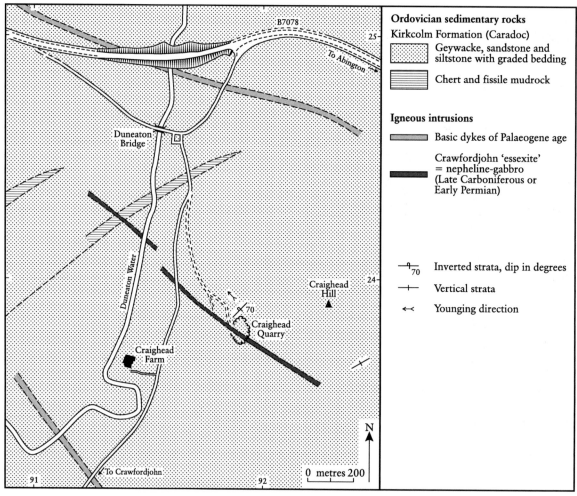

Figure 5.20 Map of the area around the Craighead Quarry GCR site. Based on Geological Survey 1:63 360 Sheet 15, Sanquhar (1937); and original mapping and proton magnetometer survey by J.J. Doody and J.G. MacDonald (2000).

Figure 5.21 (a) Curling Stone made of nepheline-gabbro ('essexite') from Craighead Quarry. Compare the texture with that seen in the photomicrograph (b). (b) Photomicrograph of nepheline-gabbro ('essexite') from Craighead Quarry. Ordinary light. The largest single phenocryst is 5 mm in diameter. (Photos: J.G. MacDonald.)

referred to the intrusion as a NW-trending dyke of 'theralitic essexite' and more recent geophysical work has confirmed the dyke-like form. The most appropriate modern term for the rock-type is nepheline-gabbro.

Description

Craighead Quarry is the main exposure of the Crawfordjohn 'essexite', but smaller quarries and exposures occur between 120 m and 200 m to the south-east. The 1870 and 1937 editions of the Geological Survey map (Sheet 15) show the intrusion as a dyke extending for about 1.2 km to the north-west, beyond Duneaton Water. It is not exposed in the river, but boulders of 'essexite' occur on the west bank approximately on the projected line of the quarry outcrops and a trial pit some 130 m farther to the north-west has produced similar rock. A preliminary proton magnetometer survey has indicated that a magnetic anomaly extends south-eastwards for about 450 m beyond the last exposures, where drift cover is shallow (less than 6 m). To the north-west the anomaly can be traced for at least 1.3 km and it is concluded that the intrusion is

in the overall form of a NW-trending dyke, 15 m to 25 m wide and at least 2 km long. The character of its dominant magnetization is consistent with a Permian field direction (D.W. Powell, pers. comm., 1971).

The main part of the quarry is entered along the line of the intrusion and a continuous cross-section is exposed in the main face at the south-east end (Figure 5.22). The intrusion margins are steeply inclined or near vertical and the width is somewhat variable, but at the quarry face it is about 24 m. At both contacts the intrusion is chilled against indurated sedimentary country rocks, which are tightly folded, near-vertical sandstone, siltstone and mudstone of the Ordovician (Caradoc) Kirkcolm Formation. Scott (1915) described the contact metamorphism in some detail. These greywacke facies rocks have been quarried extensively to the north of the main face where there is a major embayment on the north-eastern side of the quarry entrance.

In the main quarry face, there is a clear distinction between the chilled margins and most of the central porphyritic part. The margins are fine grained, with variable numbers

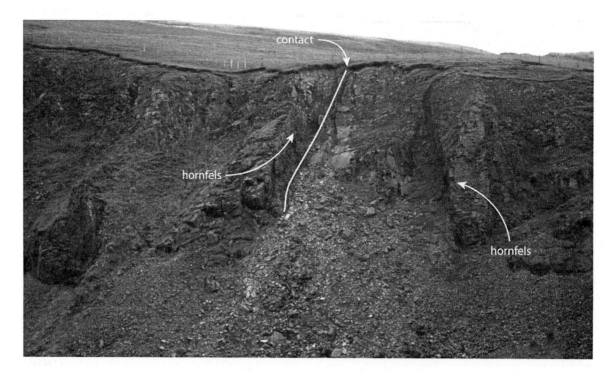

Figure 5.22 The south-east face of Craighead Quarry. The nepheline-gabbro ('essexite') dyke, here about 24 m wide, is exposed in the centre of the photo and the margins of thermally metamorphosed greywacke stand out on either side of the dyke. (Photo: J.G. MacDonald.)

of microphenocrysts of olivine, augite and rare plagioclase, set in an analcime-rich groundmass. This marginal rock was described as 'monchiquite' by Scott (1915) in view of its dominant feldspathoid. The central part of the intrusion, with its abundant large phenocrysts of augite, is separated from the marginal rock by a zone, a few centimetres in width, with few augite macrophenocysts. This zone, which was described by Scott (1915) as 'essexite-monchiquite', commonly has a spotted appearance due to abundant microphenocrysts of olivine and augite. These mafic minerals are set in a framework of plagioclase laths that tend to be flow-orientated parallel to the contacts. Olivine has been replaced by 'fibrous serpentine' and the augite displays varying degrees of alteration. Although the spotted zone has a well-defined non-gradational contact with the central part of the dyke, there is no sign of chill.

The bulk of the intrusion is strongly porphyritic (Figure 5.21a,b). The rock commonly comprises over 25% phenocrysts of titanaugite and more than 40% in places. The phenocrysts are equidimensional or slightly elongated, with well-developed crystal faces. They commonly exceed 5 mm and can exceed 10 mm in length. In thin section they have the purple coloration characteristic of titanium-rich augite and display both sector twinning and oscillatory zoning. Inclusions of groundmass minerals, including olivine, labradorite and apatite, are common and in many instances are aligned parallel to the crystal outlines. The groundmass consists dominantly of laths of labradorite, commonly exceeding 2 mm in length, and abundant rounded crystals of fresh olivine, generally less than 1 mm in diameter. Nepheline and analcime are fairly abundant, the latter as interstitial patches, and small grains of iron-titanium oxide make up about 5% of the rock. Small amounts of orthoclase, biotite and apatite also occur. (There is probably insufficient orthoclase to justify classification as nepheline-monzogabbro, the modern equivalent term for an essexite.)

Chemical analyses of the main part of the intrusion confirm the close affinity of the Crawfordjohn 'essexite' with that of Lennoxtown. The analyses are nepheline-normative and rich in alkalis, and Scott (1915) suggested that the rock has affinities with the 'theralitic' and 'kylitic' rocks of the western Midland Valley (see **Benbeoch** GCR site report).

Interpretation

There is little doubt that the Crawfordjohn 'essexite' was intruded as a NW-trending dyke. The only other major occurrence of a similar rock-type in Scotland is at Lennoxtown, where it occurs as a plug-like intrusion and an inclined sheet, and intrusions of any composition of this age are unusual in the Southern Uplands. The form of the intrusion may be related to its location within competent and well-lithified Lower Palaeozoic country rocks. These are deformed into tight folds with steeply inclined axial planes and are likely to have behaved differently, tectonically and structurally, from the water-saturated and perhaps not fully lithified Carboniferous sedimentary rocks of the Midland Valley into which the alkali dolerite sills of the same age were generally emplaced.

The lack of sharp internal boundaries indicates that the intrusion was emplaced as the result of the injection of a single pulse of magma. However, there must have been some fractionation during the ascent of the magma, which is reflected not just in the variable abundance of phenocrysts, but more notably in the compositional contrasts between the monchiquitic marginal rock and the porphyritic nepheline-gabbro of the main body. The presence of flow-textured feldspar laths in the transitional zone between the chilled margin and the main mass of the dyke provides clear evidence that much of the groundmass had already crystallized prior to intrusion. Hence the dyke must have been emplaced as a crystal mush in which as much as 50% of the material was already in solid crystalline form.

The abundance of large phenocrysts of titanaugite invites comparison with the highly mafic 'ankaramitic' lavas that commonly occur as members of alkaline to transitional volcanic sequences such as the Clyde Plateau and Arthur's Seat volcanic rocks (see Chapter 2). However, the highly developed oscillatory zoning of the phenocrysts in the nepheline-gabbro and their lack of resorption textures appear to indicate that they were in a closer state of chemical equilibrium with the groundmass than is common in many ankaramitic rocks. Inclusions of groundmass minerals within the augite crystals indicate that crystallization of the groundmass had begun prior to, or was taking place during, the growth of the phenocrysts, and small plagioclase laths have been trapped in the boundaries between individual crystals of augite in glomeroporphyritic clusters (Figure 5.21b).

The close resemblance of the main part of the intrusion to the porphyritic facies of the Lennoxtown 'essexite' indicates that the petrography is the result of processes, that, although unusual, were not unique in the petrogenesis of the Late Carboniferous to Early Permian alkali dolerites of Scotland.

Conclusions

The Crawfordjohn 'essexite' at Craighead Quarry constitutes an occurrence of an unusual and visually striking rock-type (a porphyritic nepheline-gabbro) that is known from only one other locality in Scotland. It is also a rare occurrence of an intrusion of Late Carboniferous to Early Permian age within the Southern Uplands. The quarry face provides easy access to fresh, little-weathered rock across the full width of the dyke, which exhibits significant variations in rock-type. Little of significance has been published on Scottish 'essexites' since the early part of the 20th century, and hence this site affords very significant potential for modern mineralogical and geochemical research which could throw light on the origin of augite-rich basic rocks of alkaline affinity. The site is also of historical significance in view of its use in the past as a source of rock for the manufacture of curling stones.

DUBH LOCH, ISLE OF COLONSAY, ARGYLL AND BUTE (NR 369 947)

B.G.J. Upton

Introduction

The Kilchatten Dyke is one of a pair of NW-trending Late Palaeozoic dykes on the Isle of Colonsay in the Inner Hebrides that are remarkable for their unusual compositions and their content of xenoliths and xenocrysts. Although both the Kilchatten and the nearby Riasg Buidhe dykes contain large biotite and amphibole crystals, the Kilchatten Dyke is the more spectacular of the two. The first detailed description of the dyke was provided by Flett (in Cunningham Craig *et al.*, 1911). The dykes also have considerable historical importance in that they were the subject of one of the earliest attempts at dating by radiometric methods (Urry and Holmes, 1941); detailed descriptions and

analyses were also included in the same paper. Brief descriptions of the xenolith and xenocryst inclusions were given within a general overview of inclusions of mantle and lower-crustal rocks brought up by alkaline basic dykes in the north of Britain (Upton *et al.*, 1983) and they provided material for a detailed trace-element and isotopic study of Scottish mantle material by Menzies and Halliday (1988).

Description

The Kilchatten Dyke cuts rocks of the Colonsay Group, an enigmatic Late Proterozoic metasedimentary sequence that has been variously assigned to the Torridonian and lower Dalradian (Bentley, 1988). It has a width of approximately 1 m and can be followed on a north-west trend for several hundred metres across the hills to the east of the Lower Kilchatten cottages (NR 367 949) (Figure 5.23). The most striking feature of the dyke is its content of large lustrous biotite crystals up to 4 cm in diameter (Figure 5.24). The biotites, although somewhat resorbed, tend to retain a subhedral morphology. The big mica crystals, together with other 'megacryst' species and included rock fragments, are concentrated in the more central parts of the dyke, with the marginal facies being essentially devoid of them. Associated megacrysts include kaersutitic amphibole and augite, which also occur as partly resorbed crystals up to several centimetres across. Apatite prisms over 1 cm long and fragments of magnetite megacrysts are also present. A range of ultramafic rocks is represented among the xenoliths, including spinel lherzolite (generally carbonated), olivine-pyroxenite, wehrlite, biotite- and kaersutite-pyroxenite and 'glimmerite' (biotite-rich ultramafic rock). Other xenoliths of granulite-facies, pyroxene-bearing meta-igneous rocks with gabbroic and dioritic compositions also occur, together with some metasedimentary xenoliths. The xenoliths rarely exceed a few centimetres in diameter.

The matrix of the dyke is composed of twinned augite prisms (exhibiting an hour-glass structure), magnetite and strongly pleochroic red-brown biotite in a mesostasis of analcime, calcite, apatite, zeolites (natrolite?) and chloritic interstitial material probably secondary after residual glass. Ocelli, up to 2 mm across, occur abundantly. These contain analcime and calcite, with subordinate alkali feldspar, biotite and augite.

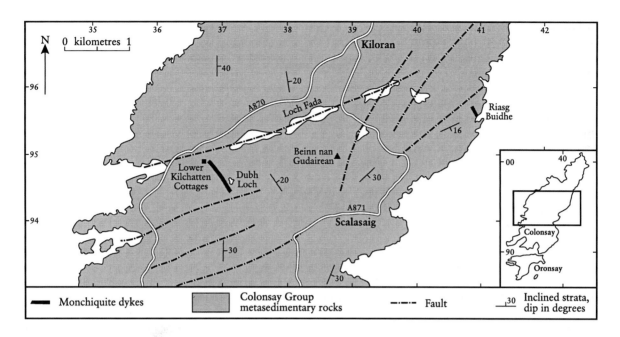

Figure 5.23 Map of the area around the Dubh Loch GCR site, Isle of Colonsay. Based on British Geological Survey 1:50 000 Provisional Series Sheet 35, Colonsay (1996). The inset shows the location of the main map.

Analysis of the dyke rock shows it to be strongly silica-undersaturated (less than 40% SiO_2) and distinctly potassic with $K_2O > Na_2O$. The rock could be described as a monchiquite, i.e. a feldspar-free lamprophyre containing silica-poor glass, commonly with analcime. However, typical monchiquites contain olivine (or pseudomorphs after olivine) whereas the Kilchatten Dyke, unlike the neighbouring Riasg Buidhe Dyke, is olivine-free. The term 'ouachitite', as used by Flett (in Cunningham Craig *et al.*, 1911), is similarly inappropriate and is now obsolete, so the rock is best referred to as an analcime monchiquite despite the qualifications.

Interpretation

The Kilchatten Dyke has long been regarded as one of a family of alkaline lamprophyric (mainly monchiquitic to camptonitic) dykes that traverse the western Highlands and Hebrides. The distinctive petrographical and geochemical features serve to distinguish these dykes from the more numerous dykes of Palaeogene age, which in many areas, including Colonsay, have an identical trend. Correlation of the lamprophyric dykes with the volcanic rocks of the Mauchline, Sanquhar and Thornill basins in south and central Scotland (see Chapter 4) suggested to Geological Survey workers that

they are of Late Carboniferous to Permian age. However, this could not be proved from field relationships and the Kilchatten and Riasg Buidhe dykes were selected as representatives of this problematic set of rocks by Urry and Holmes (1941) for radiometric age determination by the Helium Method (see also **Clee Hill Quarries** GCR site report). These workers obtained ages of 130 Ma and 125 Ma respectively for the two dykes which, given the crude timescale of the day, was thought to be in accord with that tentatively assigned on geological grounds. It at least established them as post-Carboniferous and pre-Tertiary. More recent K-Ar determinations on amphibole and biotite from the Kilchatten Dyke have yielded 266 ± 7 Ma and 283 ± 8 Ma respectively (De Souza, 1979). These give a mean of 281 ± 8 Ma using new constants (Baxter and Mitchell, 1984), and an Ar-Ar determination on an amphibole megacryst has yielded a weighted mean age of 280 ± 2.6 Ma (M. Timmerman, pers. comm., 2002), confirming the Early Permian age.

The dyke is typical of the very silica-deficient rocks with high contents of incompatible elements and volatiles (water and CO_2) that characterize this west of Scotland Late Palaeozoic swarm. They were probably generated by the melting of a geochemically enriched source in the lithospheric mantle as a result of pressure

Figure 5.24 Close-up view of the analcime monchiquite dyke at the Dubh Loch GCR site, showing xenoliths of pyroxenite (dull black) and biotite-rich ultramafic rock 'glimmerite' (glossy black) in addition to large megacrysts of biotite (black). The lens cap is about 50 mm in diameter. (Photo: M. Anderson.)

release related to extensional tectonics (Upton *et al.*, 1998). These volatile-rich magmas are inferred to have ascended at high velocities from depths of 70 km or more, breaking off fragments of both upper-mantle and lower-crustal side-walls as they arose and sweeping these up to shallow levels. The upper mantle (at depths of *c.* 60–30 km) is inferred to be of spinel lherzolite associated with younger veins and layers of wehrlite, olivine-pyroxenite, biotite- and/or amphibole-pyroxenite and 'glimmerite'. The xenoliths in the monchiquitic magmas are regarded as 'accidental' samples acquired from these sub-Moho depths, whereas the granulite-facies meta-igneous xenoliths are samples from the lower crust. The megacrysts were probably derived partly from the mechanical and thermal disaggregation of very coarse-grained (pegmatitic) facies in the upper mantle although some (especially the subhedral biotites) may represent large phenocrysts that were forming at depth in an earlier enriched magma fraction that was intercepted by the monchiquite magma.

The ocelli are likely to owe their origin to a process of separation of two liquid fractions as the magma ascended. They are inferred to represent a relatively water-rich alkali silicate immiscible melt that was deficient in Mg and Fe relative to the host monchiquite melt.

Conclusions

The Kilchatten Dyke exposed at the Dubh Loch GCR site is important in that it is a very distinctive representative of the Late Palaeozoic west Highland lamprophyric dyke-swarm. Although the nearby Riasg Buidhe Dyke shares many of the same characteristics, the Kilchatten Dyke is by far the most eye-catching on account of its large mica crystals. It is scientifically important because the geochemistry of the dyke provides information on the nature of the Earth's mantle from which the magmas were generated. Detailed study of the fragments of exotic rocks and minerals that it has picked up on its way to the surface also provides information about the rock-types present within the upper mantle and deep crust beneath Colonsay. The dyke is also significant historically in being one of the earliest rocks to be dated radiometrically in 1941.

Chapter 6

Tholeiitic sills and dykes of Scotland and northern England

Introduction

INTRODUCTION

S.C. Loughlin and D. Stephenson

The transitional to alkaline volcanism that dominated northern Britain throughout most of Carboniferous and Early Permian times (chapters 2–5) was interrupted in the Late Carboniferous by a short-lived period of tholeiitic magmatism during which basaltic magma was intruded into near-surface strata. The resulting intrusions comprise the Whin Sill-complex of northern England and the Midland Valley Sill-complex of Scotland, together with associated dykes (Figures 6.1 and 6.2). There are no associated extrusive rocks. Both sill-complexes were emplaced into major sedimentary basins and are associated with extensive ESE- to ENE-trending dyke-swarms that extend well beyond the basin limits both to the west and east. Dykes of quartz-dolerite occur in the Outer Hebrides in the west, and to the east they can be traced under the North Sea at least as far as the Central Graben (Smythe, 1994). Tholeiitic rocks of similar age in southern Scandinavia are probably related (e.g. Hjelmqvist, 1939; Weigand, 1975; Russell, 1976; Francis, 1978a,b; Russell and Smythe, 1983; Smythe et al., 1995) and the intrusions are clearly part of a substantial igneous province stretching across northern Europe.

The tholeiitic intrusions of northern England and the Midland Valley played an important part in the early development of the geological sciences in Great Britain. The word 'sill' was used in northern England to describe a flat-lying layer of rock, and 'whin' meant hard. Hence the term 'Whin Sill' may have been in use long before the origin of the rock was known and is most likely the first geological use of the word 'sill' (Randall, 1995b). In the Midland Valley, the origin of sills was the subject of controversy in the early part of the 19th century when 'Huttonians' and 'Wernerians' had different views on the subject. However, neither group considered that the sills might be intrusive. After Hall (1805) had pointed out the significance of glassy selvages on dykes at Vesuvius, Allan (1812), Rhind (1836) and Cunningham (1838) all described the fine-grained upper margins of sills in the Edinburgh district and their intrusive nature was eventually accepted (e.g. Howell and Geikie, 1861). The Great Whin Sill was recognized to be of igneous origin early in the 19th century (e.g. Trevelyan, 1823), but there was debate as to whether it was an intrusive sheet (Sedgwick, 1827) or a lava flow (e.g. Phillips, 1836; Hutton, 1838). The intrusive origin was finally established through the investigations of Clough (1876) in Teesdale, and of Tate (1867, 1871) and Topley and Lebour (1877) in Northumberland, and the Great Whin Sill became regarded as the type example of a sill.

Rocks of this tholeiitic suite were some of the earliest to be studied in detail using the petrological microscope, resulting in some interpretations and descriptions of features that we now take for granted. Allport (1874) pointed out the similarities between various sills in the Midland Valley thus establishing their close relationship. He also described the presence of quartz in the quartz-dolerite sill of North Queensferry but he was of the opinion that it was a secondary mineral. Further investigation of quartz from the Stirling Sill near Denny provided some evidence for its primary nature (Geikie, 1880) and Teall (1888), investigating rocks from Ratho Quarry, near Edinburgh, for his classic work on *British Petrography*, finally established quartz as a primary constituent of the dolerites. Teall also produced the first descriptions of micropegmatite and hypersthene from the quartz-dolerites of Scotland and pointed out the petrographical similarity between the Midland Valley Sill-complex and the Whin Sill-complex. His accounts of the petrography of the Great Whin Sill and associated dykes are early classics (Teall, 1884a,b).

By the early 20th century, the sills and dykes were well established in the literature and some of the most detailed accounts date from this period (Heslop, 1908, 1912; Holmes and Harwood, 1928; Wager, 1929a,b; Tomkeieff, 1929; Smythe, 1930a; Walker, 1934, 1935). More recent specialist studies of individual intrusions, records of borehole sections and age determinations are listed in the detailed sections that follow, but it is important to note the geochemical overviews of the Scottish dykes by Macdonald et al. (1981), the Whin Sill-complex by Thorpe and Macdonald (1985) and the whole tholeiitic suite by Howard (1999). Several general reviews are available of the Midland Valley Sill-complex and dykes (Walker, 1965), the Whin Sill-complex and dykes (A.C. Dunham, 1970; Randall, 1995b; Johnson and K.C. Dunham, 2001) and the whole suite (A.C. Dunham and Strasser-King, 1982; Francis, 1982).

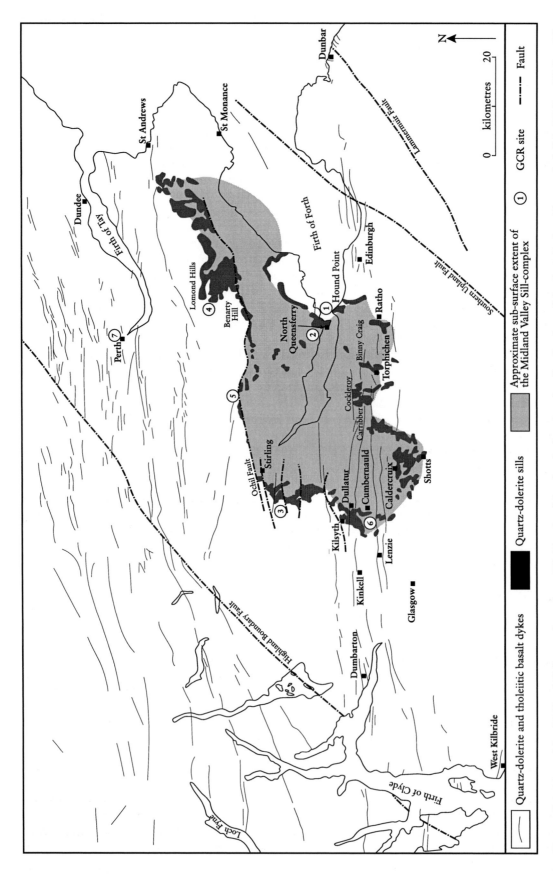

Figure 6.1 Map of the Midland Valley and southern Highlands of Scotland, showing the distribution of the Late Carboniferous tholeiitic Midland Valley Sill-complex and the associated dyke-swarm. GCR sites: 1 = South Queensferry to Hound Point (see Chapter 5); 2 = North Queensferry Road Cuttings; 3 = Wallstale; 4 = Lomond Hills; 5 = Gloom Hill, Dollar; 6 = Mollinsburn Cuttings; 7 = Corsiehill Quarry. After Cameron and Stephenson (1985).

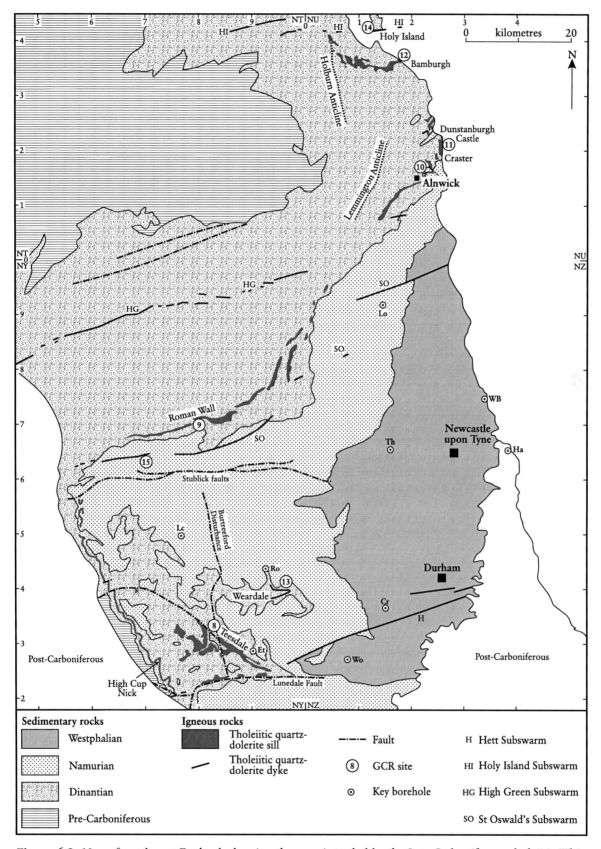

Figure 6.2 Map of north-east England, showing the area intruded by the Late Carboniferous tholeiitic Whin Sill-complex and associated dyke subswarms. GCR sites: 8 = Upper Teesdale; 9 = Steel Rigg to Sewingshields Crags; 10 = Longhoughton Quarry; 11 = Cullernose Point to Castle Point; 12 = Budle Point to Harkess Rocks; 13 = Greenfoot Quarry; 14 = Holy Island; 15 = Wydon. (Key boreholes: Cr = Crook; Et = Ettersgill; Ha = Harton; Lh = Longhorseley; Lo = Longcleugh; Ro = Rookhope; Th = Throckley; WB = Whitley Bay; Wo = Woodland.) After Francis (1982); and Johnson and K.C. Dunham (2001).

Tholeiitic sills and dykes of Scotland and northern England

Because the geological age of the Whin Sill-complex was well established as being quite close to the Carboniferous–Permian boundary, it was chosen by Arthur Holmes as a key component in his quest to construct a geological timescale using radiometric dates (Lewis, 2001). Thus it was the subject of one of the earliest attempts at radiometric dating using a Helium Method, which produced a date of 196 Ma (Dubey and Holmes, 1929). Much later, Miller and Musset (1963) used the K-Ar method on a number of samples from both the Great Whin Sill and the Little Whin Sill and produced an average age of 281 Ma (*c.* 287 Ma with new constants). However, a further examination of the samples revealed that all had undergone post-crystallization metasomatism and as a result Fitch and Miller (1964) suggested that the age be revised to 295 ± 19 Ma (*c.* 301 Ma with new constants).

Since then, the British tholeiitic intrusions have produced consistent K-Ar radiometric dates of *c.* 301–295 Ma (e.g. Fitch and Miller, 1967; Fitch *et al.*, 1970; De Souza, 1979; all recalculated with new constants) and recent, more precise Ar-Ar and U-Pb dates are within the same range (M. Timmerman, pers. comm., 2002; M.A. Hamilton and D.G. Pearson, pers. comm., 2002) (see **Upper Teesdale** and **Holy Island** GCR site reports). In the Oslo Graben, the earliest lavas and a NNW- to NNE-trending dyke-swarm are considered to be coeval with the British intrusions and have been dated at 297 ± 9 Ma (Rb-Sr mineral isochron; Sundvoll and Larsen, 1993). In addition, a WNW- to NW-trending swarm of dykes in southern Sweden (the Scania dykes) has been dated at *c.* 300 Ma (K-Ar; Klingspor, 1976, recalculated). The radiometric dates have been backed by palaeomagnetic studies of the Whin Sill-complex (Creer *et al.*, 1959; Storetvedt and Gidskehaung, 1969), the Holy Island Dyke (Giddings *et al.*, 1971; El-Harathi and Tarling, 1988) and the Midland Valley Sill-complex (Torsvik *et al.*, 1989) which indicate latest Carboniferous to earliest Permian pole positions. A more detailed study by Thomas *et al.* (1995) has led to the suggestion that, although the two sill-complexes are of broadly similar age, the Midland Valley Sill-complex was intruded fairly rapidly during the time that the Whin Sill-complex was being emplaced over a significantly longer period. Geological evidence for the age of emplacement of each complex is discussed in the individual sections.

There is some direct field evidence that the Midland Valley Sill-complex was fed by the associated E–W-trending dyke-swarm (Tyrrell, 1909b; Clough *et al.*, 1925; see **Mollinsburn Cuttings** GCR site report), and geochemical and petrographical evidence has supported this (e.g. Macdonald *et al.*, 1981). Despite a lack of field evidence, Holmes and Harwood (1928) and Anderson (1951) suggested that the Whin Sill-complex was also fed by its associated dyke-swarm, and here too the close relationship has subsequently been demonstrated by geochemical evidence (e.g. Thorpe and Macdonald, 1985). However, there are several examples of basaltic dyke-like intrusions cutting the Great Whin Sill, and Smythe (1930a) and Johnson and K.C. Dunham (2001) cited this as evidence that the dyke-swarm was a slightly later event. In both the Midland Valley and northern England, the dykes tend to occur on the flanks of basins rather than in their centres where the sills are thickest. Hence, some authors argued that the exposed dykes were not the feeders and invoked the presence of 'hidden feeders' located closer to the thickest sills (Smythe, 1930a; A.C. Dunham, 1970; Randall, 1995b).

The relationship of the dykes to the sills was explained by Francis (1982) in a single emplacement model that gained general acceptance (Figure 6.3). As had also been pointed out by A.C. Dunham and Strasser-King (1982), at the time of their emplacement the sills were at a lower structural level than the upper limit of dyke emplacement. Hence, Francis suggested that basaltic magma rose along the E–W-trending dykes at the outer margins of the basins until it reached hydrostatic equilibrium. The magma then flowed gravitationally downwards into the lower, central parts of the basins where it accumulated to form the thickest part of the sills, which assumed an overall saucer-shape. On the opposite side of the basin, the magma then advanced up-dip under the head of pressure, so that here the outer parts of the intrusion tend to be thin and steeper than bedding, pinching out as they approach the surface. This process should be reflected by magma flow directions in the dykes and sills, which can be determined from features such as fingers and tongues extending from contacts and from some highly unusual ropy flow structures that are preserved at the **Holy Island** and **Budle Point to Harkess Rocks** GCR sites. Of more widespread use is the technique of AMS (anisotropy of magnetic

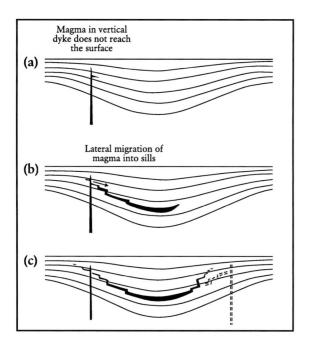

Figure 6.3 Diagram to illustrate the mechanism of intrusion of the Midland Valley Sill-complex and the Whin Sill-complex, suggested by Francis (1982). (a) dykes are intruded to 0.5–1.0 km below the surface; (b) lateral intrusion of magma leads to gravitational flow down-dip and accumulation of magma at the bottom of the sedimentary basin; (c) to achieve hydrostatic equilibrium, magma advances up-dip on the other side of the basin, with *en échelon* fingering at the leading edge. Broken lines indicate variation inherent in multiple dyke sources.

susceptibility), which measures the alignment of magnetic grains. Preliminary results, involving both AMS and macroscopic flow indicators within the Great Whin Sill, indicate a more complex pattern of magma flow than is suggested by the Francis model (Liss *et al.*, 2001). This is the first ever study of the magnetic fabric of a large sill and has significant potential for the understanding of emplacement mechanisms worldwide.

Petrography

Quartz-dolerites of the sill-complexes and dykes typically contain labradorite laths, sub-ophitic augite and Fe-Ti oxides with an intersertal intergrowth of quartz and alkali feldspar (commonly micropegmatitic). Minor constituents include hypersthene or pigeonite, hornblende, biotite, apatite and pyrite. Secondary quartz, carbonate and chlorite may occur. Fresh olivine has been found only in the Little Whin Sill (A.C. Dunham

and Kaye, 1965; A.C. Dunham and Wilkinson, 1992; see **Greenfoot Quarry** GCR site report) but pseudomorphs after olivine can be recognized in many sills and dykes, particularly in chilled margins. The rocks of the two sill-complexes are very similar, except that those of the Midland Valley Sill-complex have a slightly coarser grain-size overall (probably due to its greater thickness) and hornblende is more common (Walker, 1935, 1952; Francis *et al.*, 1970).

The finer-grained rocks that occur in chilled margins and in many dykes, particularly in Scotland, usually contain a variable amount of intersertal glass and have traditionally been termed 'tholeiites' (e.g. Walker, 1930, 1935). This is no longer used as a rock name, partly because of possible confusion with the geochemical use of the term 'tholeiitic'. Such rocks are more simply described as basalts or glass-bearing basalts (see **Corsiehill Quarry** GCR site report). The basalts ('tholeiites') are characterized by intersertal pale-brown microlitic glass, sporadic pseudomorphs after olivine (e.g. Allport, 1874) and an absence of Ca-poor pyroxene. In addition, skeletal ilmenite may occur in the glass and the distinctive amorphous chloritic material 'chlorophaeite' may be present in intersertal areas (chlorophaeite is a rich green colour when fresh but rapidly oxidizes to brown on exposure to air). Walker (1935) divided the 'tholeiites' into three petrographic types based on grain size, the abundance of glass and chlorophaite, and the presence or absence of pseudomorphs after early ferromagnesian minerals. However, geochemical and mineralogical differences between the basalt types and between basalts and dolerites are minimal and the textural differences almost certainly reflect differing rates of cooling and volatile contents of individual intrusions (Stephenson in Armstrong *et al.*, 1985).

The thicker sills show an increase in grain size from the chilled margins to the centre. Analysis of the grain-size distribution in the Great Whin Sill also reveals an increase in the percentage of microphenocrysts towards the centre (e.g. Harrison, 1968). Strasser-King (1973) proposed that the magma was intruded as a crystal mush and that flow differentiation caused phenocrysts to accumulate in the centre of a sill where flow rates are highest. However, Thorpe and Macdonald (1985) suggested that differences in trace-element geochemistry between the chilled margin and interior of the sill imply multiple intrusions rather than flow differentiation. Where the sill thickness is about 50 m or more, a pegmatitic zone may be developed about one-third of the way down from the top. This can be observed in the thickest parts of the Great Whin Sill around the **Upper Teesdale** GCR site and is common in the generally thicker sills of the Midland Valley (e.g. see **South Queensferry to Hound Point** GCR site report). The pegmatitic patches and veins are characterized by clusters of long feathery augite crystals in an intergrowth of quartz and alkali feldspar. Ca-poor pyroxenes are absent from the pegmatitic areas and iron-titanium oxides are rare, but biotite and hornblende are important minor constituents. Patches and veins of pink aplitic fine-grained quartzofeldspathic material with almost square phenocrysts of sodic plagioclase are also common throughout both sill-complexes. Late-stage veins of fine-grained basalt, presumably from later pulses of magma, have been recorded in both sills and dykes.

Geochemical evidence of in-situ differentiation is most commonly observed in the Midland Valley Sill-complex, which reaches a thickness of *c.* 200 m, and in some of the thickest dykes in the Midland Valley which can be up to 50 m wide (Falconer, 1906; Tyrrell, 1909b; Flett in Peach *et al.*, 1910; Bailey in Clough *et al.*, 1911; Robertson and Haldane, 1937; Walker; 1952). A sill from the Bathgate area ranges from 48% SiO_2 in the chilled margin, to 56% SiO_2 in patches of pegmatitic quartzo-feldspathic rock and 71% SiO_2 in quartzo-feldspathic segregation veins (Falconer, 1906).

Like the alkaline basic intrusions of the Midland Valley (see 'Introduction' to Chapter 5), the tholeiitic intrusions of both the Midland Valley and northern England are commonly altered to a pale-cream or yellowish-brown rock, particularly close to contacts, fault planes or mineral veins (see Figure 5.8, Chapter 5). The original mineralogy has been changed to assemblages of quartz, illite, kaolinite, muscovite, rutile, anatase and carbonates by hydrothermal solutions believed to be of juvenile origin (Wager, 1929b; Day, 1930a; A.C. Dunham and Kaye, 1965; K.C. Dunham *et al.*, 1968; Ineson, 1968). In the Midland Valley this is termed 'white trap', whereas in northern England it is 'white whin' (see **Mollinsburn Cuttings** and **South Queensferry to Hound Point** GCR site reports).

In addition to the zones of 'white trap'/'white whin', the quartz-dolerites commonly exhibit a suite of late-stage hydrothermal minerals developed mainly in joints during the final stages of cooling. Quartz-calcite-chlorite veins are abundant locally in many of the dykes and sills of Scotland and northern England, and the Great Whin Sill is particularly noted for its late-stage zeolites (this mineralization is distinct from the epigenetic lead-zinc-fluorite-baryte mineralization of the northern Pennines which also affects the intrusions – see below). Perhaps the best-known and most spectacular examples are the widespread occurrence of pectolite on joint surfaces, common in the High Force area (see **Upper Teesdale** GCR site report) and along the Roman Wall (see **Steel Rigg to Sewingshields Crags** GCR site report). Other zeolite-type minerals found within the late-stage veins include analcime, apophyllite, chabazite and prehnite (Young *et al.*, 1991). Smaller amounts of chlorite, bowlingite, sericite, stevensite, albite, anatase and titanite occur as part of this phase of mineralization, commonly accompanied by abundant quartz and calcite. Mineralized amygdales are found locally in parts of Northumberland (see **Cullernose Point to Castle Point**, **Holy Island** and **Budle Point to Harkess Rocks** GCR site reports).

Midland Valley Sill-complex and dykes

The Midland Valley Sill-complex is exposed at numerous outcrops around the inner Firth of Forth (Figure 6.1). Its scarp features form many prominent landmarks, such as the **Lomond Hills** (see GCR site report) and Benarty Hill in Fife, and Cockleroy Hill and Carriber Hill in the Bathgate Hills. At Stirling, the vertical cooling columns form impressive natural defences on Castle Rock, and Abbey Craig forms a natural plinth for the Wallace Monument (Figure 6.4). Other well-known sill locations include North Queensferry (**North Queensferry Road Cuttings** GCR site), Hound Point (**South Queensferry to Hound Point** GCR site), Ratho, the Caldercruix-Shotts area and Kilsyth. Many of the associated dykes form distinct, often wooded, craggy ridges. The rock is still quarried extensively, mainly for aggregate, in the Ratho and Shotts areas, and smaller quarries are worked elsewhere from time to time. Several disused quarries have been landscaped for recreational

Introduction

Figure 6.4 View from the air over Stirling. Outcrops of the SE-dipping Stirling Sill (Midland Valley Sill-complex) can be picked out by the tree-covered scarps that bound the golf course in the bottom right, Stirling Castle in the middle distance, and Abbey Craig (topped by the Wallace Monument) beyond. The Ochil Fault, which has fault-intrusions related to the sill-complex (e.g. the **Gloom Hill** GCR site) is responsible for the prominent south-facing scarp of the Ochil Hills in the distance. (Photo: British Geological Survey, No. D1940, reproduced with the permission of the Director, British Geological Survey, © NERC.)

use and many are, or have been, popular rock-climbing venues (e.g. Ratho, Ravelrig, Rosyth, Cambusbarron and Auchenstarry).

Dykes associated with the sill-complex cut rocks ranging from Archean to the Middle Coal Measures in age. The lowest stratigraphical horizon intruded by the sills is between the Knox Pulpit and Kinnesswood formations, at the Devonian–Carboniferous boundary, and the highest level is the Middle Coal Measures (Figure 6.5). Blocks of quartz-dolerite occur in sub-volcanic necks at Ardross and St Monance, which are considered to be late Stephanian in age (see Chapter 4), and plugs of olivine basalt

and basanite may cut a quartz-dolerite sill in central Fife although this relationship cannot be proven (see **Lomond Hills** GCR site report). The tholeiitic magmatism in Scotland can therefore be constrained to have occurred between Duckmantian (Westphalian B) and late Stephanian times. K-Ar radiometric dates are within the range 305 ± 7 Ma to 280 ± 9 Ma (Fitch *et al.*, 1970; De Souza, 1974, recalculated by Wallis, 1989), broadly coeval with those obtained from the Whin Sill-complex.

The dyke-swarm associated with the Midland Valley Sill-complex is more extensive than that associated with the Whin Sill-complex and

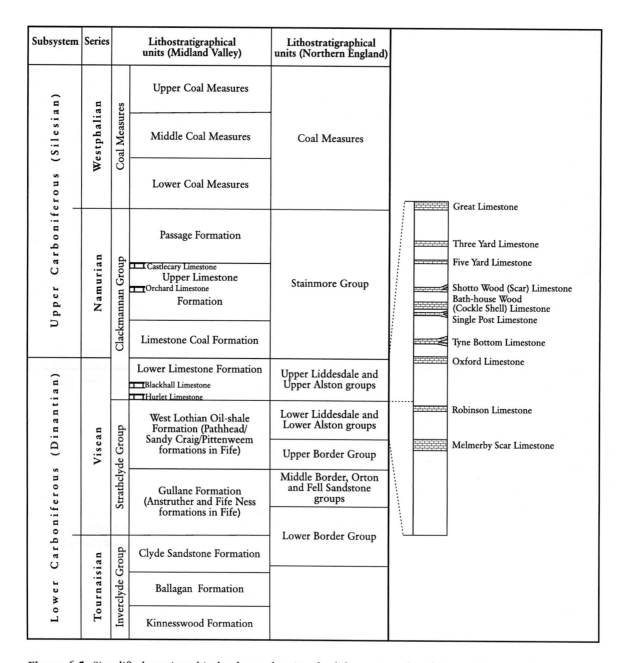

Subsystem	Series		Lithostratigraphical units (Midland Valley)	Lithostratigraphical units (Northern England)	
Upper Carboniferous (Silesian)	Westphalian	Coal Measures	Upper Coal Measures	Coal Measures	
			Middle Coal Measures		
			Lower Coal Measures		
	Namurian	Clackmannan Group	Passage Formation	Stainmore Group	Great Limestone
			Castlecary Limestone Upper Limestone Orchard Limestone Formation		Three Yard Limestone Five Yard Limestone Shotto Wood (Scar) Limestone Bath-house Wood (Cockle Shell) Limestone Single Post Limestone Tyne Bottom Limestone
			Limestone Coal Formation		Oxford Limestone
Lower Carboniferous (Dinantian)	Visean	Strathclyde Group	Lower Limestone Formation Blackhall Limestone Hurlet Limestone	Upper Liddesdale and Upper Alston groups	
			West Lothian Oil-shale Formation (Pathhead/ Sandy Craig/Pittenweem formations in Fife)	Lower Liddesdale and Lower Alston groups	Robinson Limestone
				Upper Border Group	Melmerby Scar Limestone
			Gullane Formation (Anstruther and Fife Ness formations in Fife)	Middle Border, Orton and Fell Sandstone groups	
				Lower Border Group	
	Tournaisian	Inverclyde Group	Clyde Sandstone Formation		
			Ballagan Formation		
			Kinnesswood Formation		

Figure 6.5 Simplified stratigraphical column showing the lithostratigraphy of Carboniferous rocks cut by the Stephanian tholeiitic sills and dykes of Scotland and northern England. In northern England, the Liddesdale Group is found in the Northumberland Basin whilst the Alston Group occurs on the Alston Block. The inset shows the position of major limestone bands that are transgressed by the Whin Sill-complex. After Browne *et al.* (1996); Chadwick *et al.* (1995); and Johnson (1997).

occurs across a 200 km-wide band stretching for over 300 km from the Outer Hebrides to the east coast of Scotland between Peterhead and Dunbar. The most comprehensive general review is that of Walker (1935), and details of individual dykes in some of the most dense parts of the swarm can be found in a preliminary paper (Walker, 1934) and in Geological Survey memoirs (Francis *et al.*, 1970; Armstrong *et al.*, 1985). Regionally the swarm is arcuate, trending 110° on the west coast, east–west in the central Midland Valley and 070° along the north-east coast. Locally some dykes are deflected to a north-east trend along the Highland Boundary Fault. In the Midland Valley, the dykes were emplaced partially along active or recently active

Introduction

E–W-trending fault planes (see **Mollinsburn Cuttings** GCR site report, which describes a road cutting through the Lenzie–Torphichen Dyke). Individual dykes may be traced as *en échelon* offsets and for up to 130 km (e.g. from Loch Fyne to Tayside). They average 30 m in width but may reach up to 75 m onshore (Richey, 1939). Geophysical modelling has suggested that some dykes may reach widths of at least 1 km offshore (Smythe, 1994), though it is likely that these are composite bodies.

Quartz-dolerite also occurs as fault-intrusions along the significant E–W-trending Ochil Fault and may be observed at the **Gloom Hill** GCR site (Francis *et al.*, 1970). The age of these intrusions dates the latest movement on the fault during the Late Carboniferous north–south extension event at *c.* 303 Ma (Forster and Warrington, 1985).

The Midland Valley Sill-complex underlies an area of about 1920 km². In places the thickness is *c.* 200 m, much greater than the Whin Sill-complex, but the total volume is less, at *c.* 125 km³ (Francis, 1982). The complex consists of several leaves, 25–100 m thick, which are linked by transgressive dyke-like intrusions along pre-existing fault planes ('fault risers'). A transgression can be seen clearly at the **Wallstale** GCR site where a vertical dyke-like intrusion links sills at two different structural levels. Other sills follow stratigraphical horizons for great distances, or are gently undulating forming long escarpments unaffected by faulting or sudden major transgressions (see **Lomond Hills** GCR site report).

There are a few sills that have been assigned tentatively to the tholeiitic sill-complex, but have atypical petrographical features. A sill of distinctive basalt at Binny Craig, West Lothian is mineralogically and geochemically similar to the quartz-dolerites, but is porphyritic, with small phenocrysts of plagioclase and augite (Lunn, 1928). Even more problematical is the Dalmahoy Sill, west of Edinburgh, which is olivine bearing but has many tholeiitic characteristics, including a glassy mesostasis extensively replaced by 'chlorophaeite'. A K-Ar date suggests a minimum age of 320 ± 7 Ma (*c.* 326 Ma with new constants) (De Souza, 1979), supporting an earlier Dinantian or Namurian age as was proposed by Campbell and Lunn (1925, 1927).

The sharp contacts of the sills with the host sedimentary rocks observed throughout the region provide evidence that the sediments were compacted and lithified prior to intrusion. Raymond and Murchison (1988) and Murchison and Raymond (1989) used borehole records to describe the thermal effects of sill emplacement on organic maturation in the Midland Valley. They found that thermal aureoles are extensive around the tholeiitic quartz-dolerite sills whereas there are limited thermal effects around earlier alkaline basic sills of similar thickness. The alkaline sills commonly show complicated relationships with the host sedimentary rocks indicating that these were unlithified on intrusion and still contained pore water (Walker and Francis, 1987).

Although the development of 'white trap' is widespread in both sills and dykes in the Midland Valley, mineralization is recorded from only a few tholeiitic dykes. The most instructive occurrences are in the Bathgate Hills, where boreholes have intersected several dykes, revealing an intimate relationship between faulting, multiphase dyke emplacement and mineralization (Stephenson, 1983). The dykes generally follow E–W-trending fault-lines, but they are also cut by sharply defined zones of fault-breccia implying both pre- and post-emplacement movement on the faults. Several dykes have broad zones of 'white trap', within which sticky black hydrocarbon occurs in calcite veins and as a coating to joints (Parnell, 1984). One dyke clearly shows at least two phases of intrusion, the earlier one being notably more affected by hydrothermal alteration and cut by calcite veins with baryte and traces of pyrite, chalcopyrite and fluorite; 'copper ore' is said to have been worked at one time from a baryte vein nearby. At Hilderston Mine a vein adjacent to a thin dyke contains two assemblages; Ni-Co-Ag-As adjacent to clastic sedimentary rocks, and Fe-Pb-Zn-S at a lower level adjacent to a limestone. Stephenson concluded that the dykes acted as both a heat source and a channel for the circulation of metalliferous brines that leached metals from the underlying oil-shale-bearing succession, local volcanic rocks and the intrusions themselves.

In the Renfrewshire Hills, near Lochwinnoch, copper was mined commercially in the mid-19th century from calcite-quartz-baryte veins on the margin of an E–W-trending quartz-dolerite dyke that cuts Dinantian lavas (Stephenson and Coats, 1983). In the Ochil Hills, lead- and silver-bearing veins seem to be closely associated with the Ochil Fault-intrusions (Francis *et al.*, 1970), particularly several of the veins in the Silver Glen, Alva, which occur on the margins of thin dykes parallel to the main intrusion (Hall *et al.*, 1982).

Whin Sill-complex and dykes

The quartz-dolerite of the Whin Sill-complex is generally tough and durable, weathering proud of the surrounding sedimentary rocks and forming spectacular crags and scarps that are a major feature of the scenery of north-east England (Warn, 1975). At the **Upper Teesdale** GCR site the Great Whin Sill forms the spectacular waterfalls on the River Tees at High Force and Cauldron Snout, both of which are major tourist attractions. In Northumberland, the Farne Islands, an important nature reserve, are outcrops of the Great Whin Sill, and both sills and dykes provide solid foundations for numerous castles, for example Dunstanburgh (**Cullernose Point to Castle Point** GCR site), Bamburgh (**Budle Point to Harkess Rocks** GCR site) and

Holy Island (**Holy Island** GCR site). The Romans utilized the sill, building an important segment of Hadrian's Wall along an extensive scarp just north of the Tyne Valley (Figure 6.6; and Figure 6.25 – **Steel Rigg to Sewingshields Crags** GCR site). The durable rock has been extensively quarried for setts, railway ballast and roadstone, and quarrying continues to the present day, principally for roadstone and aggregate. Many of the most instructive exposures occur in quarries; the majority of these are long abandoned but several remain active, such as in the vicinity of Belford, north Northumberland, at Barrasford, Keepershield, Great Swinburne and Divethill in the North Tyne valley and near High Force in Upper Teesdale. Inevitably, commercial and conservationist interests in the rocks of the Whin Sill have clashed on occasions over threats to both geological and landscape features.

The youngest strata cut by the Whin Sill-complex or its associated dykes are Late Carboniferous, Duckmantian (Westphalian B) in age and pebbles of quartz-dolerite are known

Figure 6.6 Hadrian's Wall capping north-facing crags of the Great Whin Sill at Housesteads, Northumberland. (Photo: British Geological Survey, No. L1512, reproduced with the permission of the Director, British Geological Survey, © NERC.)

Introduction

from breccias ('brockrams') in the Lower Permian (Saxonian) succession, near Appleby (Holmes and Harwood, 1928; K.C. Dunham, 1932). The intrusions were therefore probably emplaced during the time interval represented by the unconformity between the Upper Carboniferous (Westphalian) and Lower Permian rocks of the region (Randall, 1995b). This age of emplacement is re-inforced by K-Ar dating from a number of localities, suggesting a date of 301 ± 6 Ma (Fitch and Miller, 1967; recalculated with new constants), a U-Pb baddelyite date on the Great Whin Sill of 297.4 ± 0.4 Ma (M.A. Hamilton and D.G. Pearson, pers. comm., 2002), and an Ar-Ar plagioclase date of 294 ± 2 Ma on the Holy Island dyke-like intrusion (M. Timmerman, pers. comm., 2002). Two thin sheets of olivine-phyric dolerite that cut the Eycott Volcanic Group near Melmerby, west of the Pennines, have also been dated by K-Ar at 302 ± 8 Ma and have been interpreted as part of the Whin Sill-complex (Wadge et al., 1972; recalculated with new constants). However, their petrography and geochemistry do not match the complex (Thorpe and Macdonald, 1985) and if the date is interpreted as only a minimum age, they could be related to the Cockermouth Lavas (see **Little Mell Fell Quarry** GCR site report).

The relationships of the Whin Sill-complex and dykes to structural events have been summarized by Jones et al. (1980), Turner et al. (1995) and Johnson and K.C. Dunham (2001), all of whom demonstrated that the intrusions post-date WSW–ENE compressional structures such as the Burtreeford Disturbance and the Holburn and Lemmington anticlines that mark the end of thermal subsidence in late Westphalian times. Johnson and K.C. Dunham (2001) also showed that they pre-date regional low open domes that drape the Weardale and Cheviot plutons and have been attributed to the stress relief and ensuing isostatic uplift that led to inversion of the Carboniferous basins and erosion in Stephanian time. However, there are conflicting views on the type of structural regime that permitted emplacement of the intrusions (Chadwick et al., 1995). There is evidence of dykes having been intruded into strike-slip shear zones towards the end of the WSW–ENE compression (e.g. at Ratheugh Quarry near the **Longhoughton Quarry** GCR site). Or they may have been emplaced as a result of extension associated with the early stages of the uplift phase.

Dykes associated with the Whin Sill-complex are typically 3–10 m in width and follow north-east–south-west to ENE–WSW trends. Locally they form positive topographical features but many have now been quarried away and good quality natural exposures are rare. They occur in four widely separated subswarms, three of which could be regarded essentially as single discontinuous dykes with en échelon offsets (Figure 6.2). Some authors have actually used the term 'echelon' rather than 'subswarm'. The en échelon offsets have been attributed generally to the infilling of tensional fractures formed in response to regional compression, in a similar manner to small-scale tension gashes. However, geophysical investigations at the **Holy Island** GCR site have shown that some local offsets are caused by step-and-stair transgressions with short sill-like sectors. The most northerly subswarm, the Holy Island Subswarm, crops out to the north of the Great Whin Sill exposures and has en échelon offsets in a dextral sense (see **Holy Island** GCR site report). The High Green Subswarm extends for a distance of over 80 km south of the Cheviot Hills, converging slightly on the Holy Island Subswarm to cross the coastline at Boulmer. Its offsets are sinistral and some segments are c. 65 m in width. The St Oswald's Chapel Subswarm exhibits sinistral offsets on a broad scale and includes the Haltwhistle Dyke, well exposed at the **Wydon** GCR site where it forms a substantial feature on the banks of the River South Tyne. The Hett Subswarm includes several individual dykes to the south of Durham, near the southern limit of the Great Whin Sill exposures. A small group of dykes that cut the Berwickshire coast between Burnmouth and St Abb's have geochemical affinities with the Whin Sill-complex, rather than with the geographically closer Midland Valley dykes (Howard, 1999).

The Whin Sill-complex probably underlies at least 4000 km² of northern England (A.C. Dunham and Strasser-King, 1982), extending from the southernmost outcrops in Teesdale, west as far as the Pennine escarpment (most notably at High Cup Nick) and north to abundant exposures around Belford and the Farne Islands (Figure 6.2). There are also extensive exposures along the course of Hadrian's Wall and the Tyne Gap. Almost all of these natural exposures are of the Great Whin Sill, although this is known to split into several leaves in places. In Weardale, the Little Whin Sill is a

Tholeiitic sills and dykes of Scotland and northern England

distinctive separate intrusion represented by the **Greenfoot Quarry** GCR site. This slightly less fractionated sill, with olivine phenocrysts and slightly less SiO_2, is probably close in composition to the parental magma of the sill-complex and may have been intruded slightly earlier (A.C. Dunham and Kaye, 1965; Johnson and K.C. Dunham, 2001). A number of boreholes in the region have encountered the sills, for example at Crook (K.C. Dunham, 1948), Rookhope (K.C. Dunham *et al.*, 1965), Woodland (Harrison, 1968), Harton (Ridd *et al.*, 1970) and Throckley (A.C. Dunham *et al.*, 1972; Strasser-King, 1973; A.C. Dunham and Strasser-King, 1981). The thickest single leaf (73 m) crops out within the **Upper Teesdale** GCR site, but the Great Whin Sill is on average *c.* 30 m thick, with a tendency to thin towards its northern, western and southern margins (Francis, 1982). To the east, the sill splits into several leaves and occurs at three levels in the Harton borehole giving a total thickness of 90 m. The complete sill-complex has a volume of at least 215 km^3 and possibly much more, as it appears to thicken towards the east and may extend for some considerable distance under the North Sea (Francis, 1982).

The Great Whin Sill is considered to be saucer-shaped (Francis, 1982) and was intruded into a thick pile of Carboniferous strata ranging in age from Dinantian (e.g. Teesdale) to Westphalian (e.g. in the Midgeholme coalfield, north-east Cumbria). The intrusion changes stratigraphical level in a series of transgressive steps. This transgression of the sill may be observed clearly at the **Steel Rigg to Sewingshields Crags** GCR site together with evidence that transgression is commonly fault-controlled. The contacts of the sill are commonly reasonably sharp, implying that the host rocks were lithified prior to intrusion. In places in the Northumberland Basin, rafts of sedimentary rock detached from the host strata may be found within the body of the sill (e.g. at the **Cullernose Point to Castle Point** GCR site). At the **Budle Point to Harkess Rocks** GCR site the relationship between the sill and the sedimentary country rock is extraordinarily complex with numerous fragments and blocks of sandstone occurring within the sill. Here, the sedimentary rocks were probably disrupted prior to intrusion. Similar rafts of sedimentary rock can be observed at the **Longhoughton Quarry** GCR site and this site also provides evidence that the sill is unaffected by the major E–W-trending

Longhoughton Fault. Elsewhere, such large inclusions are rare, although there is a notable example at Wynch Bridge in the **Upper Teesdale** GCR site.

The alteration of country rock, both above and below the Great Whin Sill, was recognized by Sedgwick (1827) as evidence of an intrusive origin and a very detailed study of local effects of the metamorphism was made by Hutchings (1895, 1898). More recent studies, again of restricted areas (Randall, 1959; Robinson, 1971), have been summarized by Robinson (1970), Randall (1995b) and K.C. Dunham (1990), but there have been no studies as yet of the metamorphic effects of the sill-complex across its entire outcrop. The maximum effect is observed where the sill is thickest and emplaced at the lowest stratigraphical level, in Upper Teesdale. Here limestones are recrystallized for over 30 m from the contact and mudstones are spotted for almost 40 m (e.g. in the Rookhope Borehole). Where the sill is thinner, as along the Pennine escarpment, only the beds very close to the contact are affected.

Relatively pure limestones, such as the Melmerby Scar Limestone in Upper Teesdale, exhibit extensive recrystallization to give a saccharoidal texture and readily disaggregate on weathering. This 'sugar limestone' gives rise to a distinctive suite of soils that supports the renowned alpine flora on Cronkley and Widdybank fells. Impure limestones are converted into calc-silicate rocks containing a wide variety of minerals including garnet, idocrase, wollastonite, diopside, feldspar, chlorite and epidote. The usually dark mudstones become light-coloured, hard porcellanous rocks ('whetstones') close to the contact, and farther away they develop spots, normally of chlorite, quartz and illite, but andalusite and cordierite have been recorded. In several places, layers of pyrite nodules within country rocks close to the margins of sills and dykes have been altered to pyrrhotite (e.g. at Wynch Bridge, **Upper Teesdale** GCR site). The presence of wollastonite and idocrase in particular indicate very high temperatures in the contact zone and in rafts of sedimentary rock within the sill. Robinson (1970) calculated a temperature of 720°C, well within the hornblende-hornfels or K-feldspar-cordierite-hornfels facies, grading outwards into the albite-epidote-hornfels facies. Both Hutchings and Robinson have also recorded petrographical and geochemical evidence for soda-metasomatism close to the contact in mudstones, which show a marked increase in Na₂O and the development of abundant albite. In places the adjacent dolerite has been converted to 'white whin' and Wager (1928, 1929b) suggested that at these localities the metasomatism of both dolerite and host rock was caused by late-magmatic hydrothermal fluids.

More distant effects of heat from both the sills and the associated dykes are seen in coal seams (Jones and Cooper, 1970); the metamorphic effect of three leaves of the Whin Sill-complex in the Harton Borehole can be detected at distances of 425 m above and 180 m below the sills (Figure 6.7). As with the various Midland Valley sills (see also Chapter 5), the rank of the coal is increased dramatically towards an intrusion, vitrinite reflectance increases, the texture changes and ultimately the coal becomes a natural coke (Jones and Creany, 1977; Creany, 1980). Around upper Weardale, vitrinite reflectance and textures suggest multiple episodes of

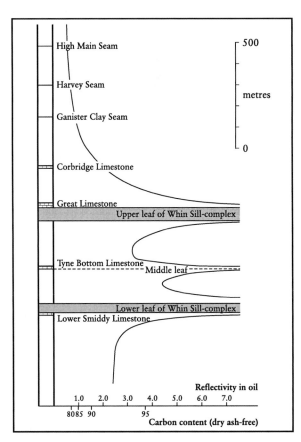

Figure 6.7 Variation in the rank of coals close to three leaves of the Whin Sill-complex in the Harton Borehole, Durham. After Jones and Cooper (1970).

metamorphism, and Johnson and K.C. Dunham (2001) have suggested that these may be due to injection of the Little Whin Sill and Great Whin Sill magmas at separate times.

In the Alston Block, the Whin sills and dykes are cut by mineral veins of the Northern Pennine Orefield (see **Upper Teesdale** GCR site report). The dolerite acts as a brittle wall-rock, like the limestones and the more massive sandstones, and hence is a favourable host for mineralization. In the Blackdene and Cambokeels mines of Weardale, the sill was a major host for fluorite ore-bodies, and at Settlingstones near Hexham, a wide vein of witherite was worked mainly in the Great Whin Sill and associated wall-rocks. At Closehouse Mine, a quartz-dolerite dyke within the Lunedale Fault that forms the southern boundary of the Alston Block, has been intensely mineralized. In this instance, earlier alteration to carbonate-rich 'white whin' has enabled subsequent extensive replacement by baryte to form an ore-body over 30 m wide in places (Hill and K.C. Dunham, 1968). K.C. Dunham (1990) has suggested that further good exploration targets exist where known veins may pass into dolerite wall-rock. The veins were deposited from hot aqueous solutions that appear to have come from depth and were channelled through the Weardale granitic pluton (K.C. Dunham *et al.*, 1965). The nature of these solutions has been the subject of great debate (Smith, 1995). Although there is some evidence from trace elements of a magmatic component (Ineson, 1969; Smith, 1974), most recent models invoke the deep circulation of connate brines or meteoric water that leached metals from various source rocks (K.C. Dunham, 1990). Evidence suggests that the primary mineralization occurred soon after the emplacement and cooling of the Whin Sill-complex (c. 284 Ma; K.C. Dunham *et al.*, 1968). For example, Young *et al.* (1985) have suggested that an unusual skarn assemblage containing magnetite, niccolite, galena and sphalerite, associated with the Teesdale Fault in Upper Teesdale, is evidence of mineralization during the final cooling of the sill, while metamorphism was still under-way. Hence it is possible that the deep magma chamber that supplied the sill-complex also provided the heat source to drive the convection system, even if it did not contribute directly to the mineralizing solutions. However, where mineral veins cut the sills and dykes, the dolerite has been altered to 'white whin' and it appears that metasomatism of the dolerite may have supplied Mg, Fe and Si to the circulating fluids (Wager, 1929b; A.C. Dunham and Kaye, 1965; Ineson, 1968; K.C. Dunham, 1990).

NORTH QUEENSFERRY (A90) ROAD CUTTINGS, FIFE (NT 126 807– NT 124 835)

S.C. Loughlin

Introduction

One of the most prominent and best-known features of the Carboniferous to Early Permian igneous activity in central Scotland is the Midland Valley Sill-complex. This quartz-dolerite sill-complex may be contemporaneous with the Whin Sill-complex of northern England and represents a brief period in Late Carboniferous times when magmas of tholeiitic affinity were generated (during much of Carboniferous and Permian times, transitional to alkaline volcanism predominated). The spectacular North Queensferry (A90) Road Cuttings GCR site comprises a 2.5 km-long road section along the A90 north of the Forth Road Bridge, together with several quarries to the east of the road (Figure 6.8). There are extensive fresh exposures of quartz-dolerite showing fine examples of chilled upper and lower margins, internal variations in rock-type and petrography, and late-stage segregation veins. No other site in the Midland Valley shows all these features of a quartz-dolerite sill in one continuous section.

The petrography of quartz-dolerite sills in the Edinburgh district has been described by numerous authors including Allport (1874), Geikie (1880), Teall (1888) and Falconer (1906). It was at North Queensferry that Allport described the presence of quartz in the dolerite, although he was of the opinion that it was a secondary mineral, and recognized pseudomorphs after olivine in the chilled margin. Peach *et al.* (1910) produced a thorough account of the petrography and field relationships of sills in the Edinburgh area in their Geological Survey memoir. This was a revision of the first edition (Howell and Geikie, 1861) that described the first published sheet of the Geological Survey of Scotland (Edinburgh, Sheet 32). Further geochemical study of the quartz-dolerites and segregation veins was carried out by Day (1928b). Walker (1935) provided the

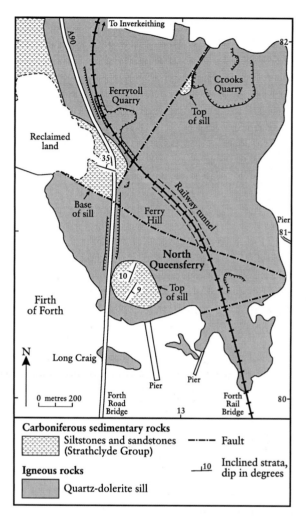

Figure 6.8 Map of the area around the North Queensferry Road Cuttings GCR site. Based on Geological Survey 1:10 560 Sheet NT 18 SW (1966).

first comprehensive account of the whole quartz-dolerite suite of the Midland Valley, and subsequent works on the regional and tectonic significance of the sill-complex include Walker (1965) and Francis (1978a). The emplacement mechanism of both the Whin Sill-complex and the Midland Valley Sill-complex was discussed by Francis (1982). The site has been described as a field excursion by Upton (1969).

Description

The quartz-dolerite of the sill exhibits deep spheroidal weathering in most natural outcrops (Figure 6.9) and hence the quarries and road cuttings provide far better illustrations of intrusive and petrographical features. The chilled upper and lower contacts of the quartz-dolerite

Figure 6.9 Quartz-dolerite of the Midland Valley Sill-complex at North Queensferry, showing spheroidal weathering. The hammer shaft (bottom left) is about 35 cm long. (Photo: British Geological Survey, No. D2580, reproduced with the permission of the Director, British Geological Survey, © NERC.)

sill and thermal alteration of the sedimentary country rocks of the Strathclyde Group can be observed at several places within the North Queensferry Road Cuttings GCR site. In a road-side exposure about 300 m north of the Forth Road Bridge (NT 126 811) the base of the sill cuts across an earlier normal fault that juxtaposes mudstones against sandstones. The quartz-dolerite has sagged into the mudstones on one side of the fault, and apophyses of dolerite intrude the locally crumpled and distorted mudstones, but there is no sagging into the more competent sandstone on the other side of the fault.

Coarse pegmatitic rocks characterized by long feathery clusters of augite crystals commonly form much of the top third of the sill at this site and segregation veins can be seen in many exposures. These segregations vary in grain size, texture, orientation and composition, but fine-grained to medium-grained quartzo-feldspathic

types predominate. In the disused Ferrytoll Quarry (NT 127 816), by the railway line, there are some excellent examples. Here, the veins are pinkish-yellow and are very distinctive against the dark-blue-grey dolerite. One prominent vein is 12–20 cm wide and extends horizontally across a large part of the quarry walls before slanting upwards slightly. The vein divides at one point then rejoins, enclosing a lenticular mass of dolerite about 2 m long and 30 cm wide. There are also small discontinuous offshoots from the main vein. Other veins have different attitudes and some narrow veins are almost vertical. All veins are cut by the vertical cooling joints.

The petrography and geochemistry of the quartz-dolerite at this site is typical of the Midland Valley Sill-complex in general. It is medium grained to coarse grained and consists of mainly labradorite laths, sub-ophitic augite and Fe-Ti oxides. Intersertal quartz and alkali feldspar are commonly intergrown as micro-pegmatite. Pseudomorphs after olivine occur in the margins of the sill in the North Queensferry area (Allport, 1874).

The segregation veins typically comprise abundant small plagioclase laths, some ortho-clase aligned parallel to the vein margins, and quartz; in addition they are commonly rich in micropegmatite. They contain fewer ferro-magnesian minerals and Fe-Ti oxides than the dolerite, although primary biotite and horn-blende are slightly more abundant. Some of the smaller veins have rather diffuse contacts, but larger veins typically have sharp margins although they are not chilled. The dolerite tends to be slightly finer grained near the margins of the segregation veins.

Day (1928b) analysed samples of quartz-dolerite from Prestonhill Quarry, Inverkeithing and Ferrytoll Quarry in this GCR site. Typical dolerites contain 47–49% SiO_2 whereas the most evolved segregation veins have values of 69–71% SiO_2. He also showed that the emplacement of the segregation veins did not affect the chemical composition of adjacent dolerite.

Interpretation

The intrusive nature of the Midland Valley Sill-complex was a subject of much debate and con-troversy during the 19th century (see 'Introduc-tion' to this chapter) but the road cutting at this GCR site, which was unavailable to the early geologists, shows clearly that the sedimentary rocks overlying the quartz-dolerite are baked.

More recent investigations show that the Midland Valley Sill-complex is generally saucer-shaped with much of the intrusion following bedding planes down to the bottoms of basins where the intrusions are thickest (Francis, 1982). Francis proposed that sill emplacement was partly controlled by down-dip gravitational flow on gradients of up to 5°, from feeder dykes that extended to within 0.5 km and 1.0 km of the surface. Prior to this work, most authors (an exception being Robertson in Robertson and Haldane, 1937) had assumed that magma only flowed either upwards or laterally. Francis (1982) described the apophyses of dolerite extending from the sill down into the distorted shales at this GCR site and used this as an example of the downward (gravitational) com-ponent to magma movement.

The coarse-grained pegmatitic upper part of the sill that is seen so well at this GCR site is a feature of many large sills worldwide. This common profile shows that the sill is a single cooling unit that was totally molten at the time of emplacement (Francis, 1982). It is clear that the segregation veins, commonly with diffuse contacts, are related to the same parent magma as the dolerite and also that they were intruded while the sill was still cooling (features that were first recognized by Peach *et al.*, 1910).

Conclusions

The extensive A90 road cuttings at North Queensferry expose a typical representative of the Midland Valley Sill-complex. The GCR site is significant because of the abundance and easy accessibility of complex features that characterize large sills in general. Much early work on the Midland Valley Sill-complex was carried out in this district but this relatively recently exposed site is the only location where all the critical features may be observed. The upper and lower margins of the sill are chilled to a dark glassy rock and are clearly seen to bake the surrounding sedimentary rock. This is particularly significant at the upper contact as this unequivocally demonstrates that the body is an intrusion and not a lava. Irregular veins of quartz-dolerite can be seen penetrating the underlying sedimentary rocks. Within the sill, grain-size variations are clearly visible, from finer-grained margins to a medium-grained interior, with patches and veins of coarse-grained pegmatitic material in the upper third of the sill. Pale-coloured segregation veins are the most silicic part of the intrusion and form sheet-like bodies within the sill.

WALLSTALE, STIRLING (NS 763 900–NS 776 923)

S.C. Loughlin

Introduction

The Wallstale GCR site shows an exceptional example of the abrupt step-like transgression of the Midland Valley Sill-complex along a pre-existing fault-line. The transgressive nature of the sill-complex in relation to the Carboniferous strata it intrudes has long been recognized on the basis of borehole and mining data, but this important structural feature is rarely seen at outcrop. Three examples of such a structure are exposed in the Stirling area but this is the best exposed and the most representative. A fault plane containing a dyke-like body (a 'fault riser') links two quartz-dolerite sills that are at the same stratigraphical level but different structural levels. These field relationships prove that the magma was emplaced *after* movement on the fault but, despite the name 'riser', magma probably moved down the fault plane rather than up it.

The site is located about 4 km south-west of Stirling on a segment of the Midland Valley Sill-complex commonly known as the 'Stirling Sill' (Figure 6.1). The sill crops out along the western limb of the Clackmannan Syncline and forms a striking west-facing scarp extending south from Abbey Craig and Stirling Castle. As a result of transgression it is intruded at various stratigraphical levels within the Limestone Coal Formation.

The Stirling Sill is similar petrographically to other outcrops of the quartz-dolerite sill-complex except that it has pegmatitic patches a few centimetres wide, fringing quartzo-feldspathic veins in its lower part. Petrographical accounts include those by Goodchild (in Monckton, 1892), Monckton (1895) and Dinham (1927), and a detailed account of differentiation in the southern part of the sill was given by Walker (1952). General accounts, including the field relationships, were produced by Dinham and Haldane (1932), Robertson and Haldane (1937), Francis (1956), Read and Wilson (1959) and Francis *et al.* (1970). There are several aggregate quarries within the area of the site.

Description

The Stirling Sill is up to 100 m thick and dips at 5°–15° to the east. There are a number of significant E–W-trending faults in the area that pre-date the sill, one of which is known as the 'Wallstale Fault'. South of the Wallstale Fault the sill forms a continuous west-facing escarpment that runs from North Third Reservoir (NS 757 895) along the east banks of the Bannock Burn (Figure 6.10). In this area the sill is intruded near the base of the Lower Limestone Formation. The disused Touchadam limestone quarry lies at the foot of the escarpment just south of the Wallstale Fault. The

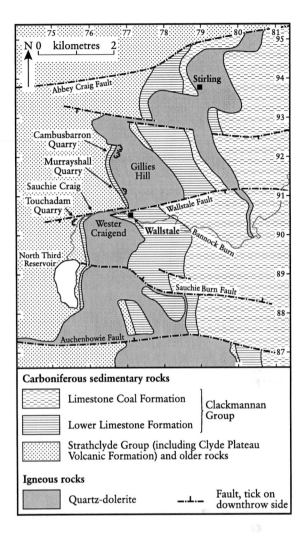

Figure 6.10 Map of the Midland Valley Sill-complex in the area around the Wallstale GCR site. After Read and Wilson (1959).

dolerite escarpment swings abruptly to the east in the vicinity of the fault and forms an E–W-orientated line of crags (Sauchie Craig) that follow the southern banks of the Bannock Burn almost as far as Wester Craigend. Along the top of Sauchie Craig is a prominent ridge of quartz-dolerite that rises well above the upper surface of the sill. The sill dips down to the east beneath sedimentary rocks of the Lower Limestone Formation but the ridge continues beyond the eastern end of the crags (NS 769 906) as a dyke-like body 30–60 m wide. It extends for almost 400 m and then merges with the sill that forms Gillies Hill (NS 772 916) and the west-facing escarpment, north of the Wallstale Fault. The dyke-like ridge coincides almost exactly with the line of the Wallstale Fault. The fault has a downthrow to the south of 130–150 m (Dinham and Haldane, 1932) and yet the sill is intruded at the same stratigraphical level (lower part of the Lower Limestone Formation) on both sides, apparently linked by the dyke in the fault plane.

The quartz-dolerite has been quarried extensively to the north of the Wallstale Fault at the Murrayshall Quarry (NS 771 913), where the chilled base of the sill is in contact with baked coals, ironstones and mudstones. About 200 m ESE of the quarry, the base of the sill has been thrown down 13 m to the south by a late ESE-trending fault; this is one of the only places in the region where a quartz-dolerite sill is clearly seen to be affected by later faulting. Farther north, on the southern edge of Cambusbarron Quarry (NS 770 920) (Figure 6.11), there is a 4 m-thick sheet of dolerite separated from the base of the main sill by just over 1 m of indurated mudstone.

Below Cambusbarron Quarry is the site of a mine from which the Murrayshall Limestone was recovered. The sill outcrop ends abruptly just north of Cambusbarron Quarry and borehole records show that farther to the north the sill is intruded into a horizon below the Murrayshall

Limestone. East of the GCR site, boreholes reveal that the sill divides into a number of distinct intrusive sheets; for example the Polmaise No. 5 shaft (NS 837 914) intersects at least three.

In general, the quartz-dolerite of the Stirling Sill is petrographically identical to that described elsewhere in the Midland Valley. Particularly good examples of hornblende and biotite, commonly mantling the augite and oxides, can be found in samples from Cambusbarron Quarry (Francis *et al.*, 1970). Samples showing skeletal patterns of iron oxide in the interstitial glass can also be found at this locality. As in many parts of the Midland Valley Sill-complex and the Whin Sill-complex, a pegmatitic zone occurs one-third of the way down from the top of the sill (Robertson and Haldane, 1937). However, an unusual feature of this sill is that there are additional quartzo-feldspathic veins in its lower part (Figure 6.12). These are fringed by a pegmatitic zone a few centimetres wide, comprising distinctive long feathery clusters of augite in a pink quartzo-feldspathic matrix (Walker, 1952; Francis *et al.*, 1970). The dolerite of the dyke-like 'riser' is a deeply weathered quartz-dolerite identical to that of the main sill.

Figure 6.11 Quartz-dolerite of the Midland Valley Sill-complex with strong vertical joints in Cambusbarron Quarry, Wallstale GCR site. The quarry face is 25–27 m high. (Photo: K.M. Goodenough.)

Figure 6.12 Pale-coloured felsic segregation vein cutting quartz-dolerite in Murrayshall Quarry, Wallstale GCR site. The lens cap is 50 mm in diameter. (Photo: K.M. Goodenough.)

Interpretation

The Midland Valley Sill-complex has been shown to be remarkably transgressive in relation to the sedimentary rocks into which it is intruded. Across the Midland Valley, sills are intruded into such widely differing stratigraphical levels that for many years the sill-complex was thought to represent numerous separate intrusions of different ages. In the coalfields adjacent to the Wallstale GCR site, borehole data and mine plans show that transgressions typically involve abrupt, step-like changes in horizon along dyke-like bodies known as 'risers'. Many of the risers exploit pre-existing fault planes but in some places the sill directly crosses a fault plane to a different stratigraphical level. Transgression is an important structural feature throughout the sill-complex but it is rarely seen at outcrop. The dyke-like body of quartz-dolerite at this site has been interpreted as a 'fault riser' and the site is unusual in that the transgressive dyke can clearly be seen to link the two sill outcrops. As a consequence of the transgression, the sills intrude the same stratigraphical horizon on both sides of the fault, despite a considerable offset on the fault prior to intrusion. The Wallstale Fault is one of three major E–W-trending faults in this area along which it is believed that transgressions have taken place, the others being the Auchenbowie and Abbey Craig faults. At the Abbey Craig Fault the sill does change stratigraphical horizon, but this was only confirmed by sub-surface evidence and hence Wallstale is certainly the clearest and most instructive example.

The quartz-dolerite sill is younger than most faulting in the Stirling area, the small fault near Murrayshall Quarry being the only proven example of a later fault. Immediately north of Cambusbarron Quarry, where the sill outcrop comes to an abrupt end, old mine plans show a small fault that was once considered to have thrown down the sill to the north. However, Dinham and Haldane (1932) and Read and Wilson (1959) considered it more likely that the abrupt drop of the base of the sill to the north is due to transgression of the dolerite into a lower level, possibly along an earlier fault. The dip-slope of the Stirling Sill in this area is dissected by many erosive channels, which appear to follow prominent joint planes. Read (1956) attributed this preferential erosion to hydro-thermal alteration of the dolerite along the joints and was unable to detect any evidence of fault movement.

Francis (1982) showed that the shapes of the Midland Valley Sill-complex and the Whin Sill-complex approximate to a series of saucers, with the lowest, thickest parts coinciding with the centres of synsedimentary Carboniferous basins. The magma was probably introduced into the basins via marginal dykes and then flowed gravitationally from higher levels down bedding planes to the centre of the basins (Francis, 1982; see 'Introduction' to this chapter). The transgressive steps, such as the one observed at this site, are therefore believed to have occurred in a downward sense even though the old name 'risers' implies the opposite sense of movement. At Wallstale, the Midland Valley Sill-complex is at one of its lowest stratigraphical levels and is also very thick (explaining the fine development of in-situ differentiation features).

Conclusions

The Midland Valley Sill-complex has been shown to be remarkably transgressive, changing horizons within the Carboniferous succession both gradually and in a series of abrupt step-like jumps along fault planes. This behaviour, which results in complex surface and sub-surface relationships, is rarely observed at outcrop. At the Wallstale GCR site the relationships between the quartz-dolerite intrusion and a fault are clearly evident. The pre-existing E–W-trending fault let down the Carboniferous strata vertically by 130–150 m to the south. North of the fault, magma was intruded into the lower part of the Lower Limestone Formation and moved gravitationally down the gently inclined bedding of the strata towards the fault. It then flowed *down* the fault plane and intruded the same stratigraphical level on the south side of the fault.

The sill is relatively thick at this site and shows good examples of very coarse-grained pegmatitic dolerite and veins rich in pale quartzo-feldspathic minerals, both formed during the final stages of crystallization of the magma.

LOMOND HILLS, FIFE (NO 178 043–NO 248 068)

S.C. Loughlin

Introduction

The Midland Valley quartz-dolerite sill-complex is the most extensive and arguably the most important single intrusion in central Scotland. Detailed mapping and data from various mines in the adjacent coalfields have shown that it crops out around the margins of a large area (see 'Introduction' to this chapter, and Figure 6.1). It may remain at a constant level in the stratigraphical succession for long distances but it may also change horizon, often abruptly via fault-controlled dyke-like bodies or 'risers' (Dinham and Haldane, 1932) and often in a step-like manner (Knox, 1954; see **Wallstale** GCR site report). The somewhat undulatory nature of the sill in areas not generally affected by such structures is an important feature and is shown very clearly in the scarp face of the Lomond Hills in central Fife. This exends westward from East Lomond above the village of Falkland, towards West Lomond, then south via Bishop Hill to Kinneston Craigs above Scotlandwell (Figure 6.13). Throughout this outcrop the sill is intruded mainly into rocks of the Lower Limestone Formation of the (Upper Visean) Clackmannan Group. Small details of the contact phenomena associated with the sill are also of merit, providing evidence of partial melting of the intruded strata (Walker, 1958).

The site is also of considerable interest because it includes two sub-volcanic necks, with plugs of alkali dolerite and basanite, at the summits of East Lomond and West Lomond, and a basanite plug at the summit of Green Hill. Their respective age relations to the sill are of critical importance in any consideration of the evolution of igneous activity in the Midland Valley and consequently have been the subject of much debate (e.g. Irving, 1924; Walker and Irving, 1928; Macgregor and MacGregor, 1948; Francis, 1965; Browne and Woodhall, 2000).

The first published geological map of this area (Sheet 40) was released by the Geological Survey in 1867. The second edition of the map was published in 1898 and was

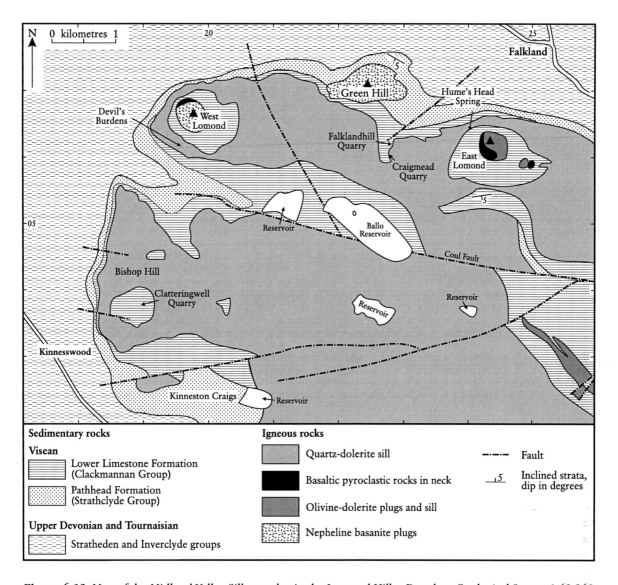

Figure 6.13 Map of the Midland Valley Sill-complex in the Lomond Hills. Based on Geological Survey 1:63 360 Sheet 40, Kinross (1971); and British Geological Survey 1:50 000 Sheet 40E, Kirkaldy (1999).

accompanied by two memoirs (Geikie, 1900, 1902). Since then the area has undergone a number of revisions and re-surveys and the latest edition was published in 1999 with accompanying sheet explanation and sheet description (Browne and Woodhall, 1999, 2000). Two field excursions, to the East Lomond and Bishop Hill areas of the site, have been described by MacGregor (1996).

The petrography and geochemistry of the quartz-dolerite at this GCR site is typical of the Midland Valley Sill-complex (Walker and Irving, 1928; see 'Introduction' to this chapter).

Description

The Midland Valley Sill-complex is here largely confined to the Lower Limestone Formation except at a few localities where it transgresses up as far as the Limestone Coal Formation or down into the Pathhead Formation (Strathclyde Group). Its total vertical range is in the order of 225 m and in thickness it varies from c. 50 m to c. 95 m. From East Lomond hill (NO 244 062) to Kinneston Craigs (NO 193 023), a distance of about 12 km, the sill forms a distinctive scarp (Figure 6.14) and is mostly intruded between two prominent limestones – the Hurlet

Figure 6.14 The escarpment formed by the Midland Valley Sill-complex on the north-west side of the Lomond Hills, with the basanitic plugs of West Lomond (nearest) and East Lomond (in the distance) protruding above the level of the sill. (Photo: P. Macdonald.)

Limestone (formerly the Charlestown Station Limestone) and the Blackhall Limestone (formerly the Charlestown Main Limestone). The Hurlet Limestone marks the base of the Lower Limestone Formation while the latter occurs some way above.

At Hume's Head spring (NO 2395 0630) on the north-western side of East Lomond hill, baked fossiliferous mudstones of the Lower Limestone Formation can be observed and, just a metre or so below, the top of the sill is also exposed. The position of the Blackhall Lime-stone is marked by a line of old workings which extend from just above the spring southwards to East Lomond Quarry. The limestone exposed in some of the workings is recrystallized but the top of the sill is not exposed in any. The rolling heather-covered slopes between East Lomond hill and West Lomond hill (NO 197 065) are composed of quartz-dolerite.

The lower part of the sill is clearly exposed at Craigmead Quarry (NO 228 061) (and also in Falklandhill Quarry (NO 228 062), but not as clearly), where it is spheroidally weathered, red-brown and columnar jointed (Figure 6.15). The base of the sill is chilled to a fine-grained, dense, black basaltic rock a few millimetres thick. The basal contact with underlying horizontally bedded sandstone is clearly transgressive and irregular, with tongues of dolerite extending into the baked sandstones.

The transgressive nature of the sill can also be seen clearly on the northern side of West Lomond hill in the vicinity of Longcraig Quarries (NO 202 072), where the undulose base cuts down through the sandstones and mudstones of the Lower Limestone Formation, through the Hurlet Limestone and into mud-stones of the underlying Pathhead Formation. On the western slopes of West Lomond hill the sill rises back up through the sedimentary sequence to its original stratigraphical level just above the Hurlet Limestone in the Lower Limestone Formation. The quartz-dolerite in the area known as the 'Devil's Burdens' (NO 193 061) is deeply altered to a distinctive orange-brown coloured sandy gravel. The sill stays at this level along most of the western scarp of the Lomond Hills and the position of the underlying Hurlet limestone is marked by a line of small quarry workings. North of Bishop Hill (NO 1830 0440) a combination of columnar jointing and weathering of the sill has formed an impressive needle of rock which is popular with climbers.

Figure 6.15 The base of the Lomond Hills quartz-dolerite sill in Craigmead Quarry. The contact, the underlying sedimentary rocks and a further thin sheet of dolerite are exposed in the shaded area to the right of the figure. (Photo: K.M. Goodenough.)

A succession through the Pathhead Formation, the Lower Limestone Formation and up to the base of the quartz-dolerite sill is exposed at the head of Kinnesswood Row, a steep gully 500 m north-east of Kinnesswood and the type locality for the Kinnesswood Formation. The top metre or so of sandstone has been recrystallized by the sill, and the highest mudstone bed is bleached and hardened. The basal margin of the sill is chilled, and above, the characteristic crude columnar joints and spheroidal weathering of the sill can be observed.

Around the summit of Bishop Hill, the Blackhall Limestone above the sill has been quarried extensively; in this area it is relatively thick due to microbial bioherm build-ups. The limestone is typically bedded and very rich in crinoids; in addition, two distinct reef mounds can be identified at Clatteringwell Quarry (NO 1875 0375). Just south of White Craigs, above Kinnesswood village (NO 184 032), the sill changes horizon abruptly to a level above the Blackhall Limestone so that on the southern side of Bishop Hill, several metres of fossiliferous sandstones and mudstones above the limestone

are recrystallized by the overlying sill. A line of small quarries marks the position of the Blackhall Limestone below the sill.

Three prominent summits rise above the general land surface of the Lomond Hills.

East Lomond (442 m) is a steep-sided, rounded hill with a distinct 'shoulder' on its western side. It stands above the scarp formed by the sill just south of Falkland. The gentle lower slopes of the hill are underlain by the Lower Limestone Formation, which directly overlies the sill. The summit of the hill is composed of a dark-green to black analcime-bearing olivine-dolerite. In hand specimen olivine phenocrysts are conspicuous and alter to a reddish colour on weathered surfaces. Crude joints radiate outwards from the centre of this intrusive body suggesting that it is probably a plug (Irving, 1924). Vesicles with an infilling of green serpentine occur widely but the rock generally has a 'fresh' appearance in contrast to the deeply weathered quartz-dolerite sill. The shoulder of the hill is composed of a friable pale-olive-green volcaniclastic breccia containing angular fragments of altered basaltic rock. Just to the east of East Lomond is a smaller, poorly exposed outcrop of olivine-dolerite, also with a basaltic breccia at its eastern margin. The olivine-dolerite of the main plug comprises mainly large olivine phenocrysts, laths of labradorite and intersertal (rather than ophitic) mauve-pink titaniferous augite. Accessory minerals include titaniferous magnetite, apatite and analcime with some devitrified glass.

West Lomond (522 m) is a cone-shaped hill also standing above the scarp of the sill. The hill is composed of nepheline basanite with a thin sliver of breccia on its northern margin, and is interpreted as a sub-volcanic neck and plug. The lower slopes are composed of sedimentary rocks of the Lower Limestone Formation which overlie the sill. Two smaller plugs occur just east of West Lomond (Browne and Woodhall, 2000).

Between East and West Lomond is the rounded summit of Green Hill (305 m), which lies below the scarp of the sill. It is composed of black, fine-grained nepheline basanite, slightly finer grained than that of West Lomond. The contacts with the surrounding sedimentary rocks are not exposed but it is assumed to be a plug (M.A.E. Browne, pers. comm., 2000).

Interpretation

Geikie (1900) recognized the intrusive nature of the Midland Valley Sill-complex and described the transgressive contacts and chilled margins in this area. He cited the undulose nature of the sill in the Lomond Hills as a particularly good example of transgression. The recrystallized limestones and baked mudstones above the sill at East Lomond provide clear evidence of the intrusive nature, and the sharp contacts with host sedimentary rocks observed throughout the GCR site indicate that the sediments were compacted and lithified prior to intrusion.

Walker (1958) investigated the contact between the sill and the sandstones and mudstones of the Lower Limestone Formation at East Lomond and found petrographical evidence for remobilization of the sedimentary host rocks. He observed a zone of alkali-feldspar-rich material, 1–3 mm thick, along the contacts; in places, thin veins of this material actually cut through the adjacent sedimentary layers but they do not cut the sill. The source of this remobilized material was thought to be the thin mudstone laminae intercalated with the sandstones.

The age relationships between the alkaline basic plugs and the tholeiitic sill at this site are equivocal, but historically they were regarded as fundamental to determining the overall sequence of Carboniferous–Permian igneous events. Geikie (1900) interpreted the outcrops that form the summits of East and West Lomond as erosional outliers of sills intruded above the main sill. However, Irving (1924) and Walker and Irving (1928) concluded that they are irregular plugs marking the sites of Late Carboniferous necks that penetrated the sill, and this interpretation was re-asserted by Macgregor and MacGregor (1948). Francis (1965), whilst accepting the interpretation of plugs, pointed out that there is no satisfactory field evidence for their age relationship with the sill. No contacts are exposed, no xenoliths of quartz-dolerite have been found in the plugs or associated breccias and, in addition, the East Lomond olivine-dolerite is petrographically similar to olivine-dolerite sills demonstrably older than the Midland Valley Sill-complex. The petrography and geochemistry of the plugs reveals that they are related to a separate period of alkaline volcanism, but this could be either before or after emplacement of the tholeiitic sill-complex. There is no doubt that olivine-dolerite sills, plugs and contemporaneous volcanic rocks were emplaced throughout Fife during a period of multiphase alkali magmatism throughout mid- to late Carboniferous and Early Permian times (see 'Introduction' to Chapter 4; and 'Introduction' to Chapter 5). The more highly silica-undersaturated alkaline basic rocks, such as nepheline basanites, are generally assigned to the later phases of igneous activity in the Midland Valley, but Browne and Woodhall (2000) consider that the alkaline basic plugs in the Lomond Hills area were intruded during late Visean or Namurian times, when the sediments were still unlithified and contained pore water. The volcaniclastic breccias exposed at East Lomond and West Lomond are therefore assumed to be the products of explosive volcanism, which occurred as a result of magma–water interaction.

Conclusions

The Lomond Hills GCR site is representative of the Midland Valley Sill-complex, a geological feature that has a profound effect on the topography of eastern central Scotland. At this site the quartz-dolerite sill and underlying sedimentary rocks form a steep escarpment that extends for a total distance of about 12 km. The margins of the sill are gently undulating and in several places the basal contact can be seen to transgress through several levels of the under-lying strata. There is also evidence that the thermal effects of sill emplacement have partly melted the sedimentary rocks immediately adja-cent to the sill. Baking and recrystallization of sedimentary rocks above the quartz-dolerite pro-vides evidence that it is an intrusive sill and not an extrusive lava. Sub-volcanic necks with plugs of alkaline basic rock occur above the escarp-ment and provide evidence of explosive volcanic activity in the region. The composition of the plugs suggests that this volcanism was unrelated to the sill, but the exposed field evidence cannot resolve whether it was earlier or later. The age relationships at this site were once regarded as crucial to determining the sequence of igneous events in the Midland Valley and consequently have been the subject of much debate.

GLOOM HILL, DOLLAR, CLACKMANNAN (NS 964 990)

S.C. Loughlin

Introduction

The geological relationships exposed in the quarry, on the southern margin of Gloom Hill, 0.5 km north of Dollar, are of considerable importance in understanding the relationships between magmatism and tectonism in the Midland Valley during Late Carboniferous to Early Permian times. The Ochil Fault, one of the most important faults in the Midland Valley, is exposed in the quarry along with a quartz-dolerite intrusion that was emplaced along the fault plane. Geochemical evidence (e.g. Macdonald *et al.*, 1981) suggests that this intrusion, and others intruded into the fault zone nearby, are associated with the Midland Valley Sill-complex.

The E–W-trending Ochil Fault is a long-lived structure that is responsible for the impressive escarpment of the Ochil Hills, east of Stirling (Figure 6.4). The tectonic significance of the fault was known long ago and the impressive vertical displacement (up to 4 km) was also recognized (e.g. Geikie, 1900). Nevertheless the tectonic evolution of the region and the sub-

surface structure of the fault have proved to be intriguing problems up to the present day (e.g. Haldane, 1927; Francis *et al.*, 1970; Gibbs, 1987; Coward and Gibbs, 1988; Rippon *et al.*, 1996). To the north of the fault the Ochil Hills are composed of late Silurian to Early Devonian lavas and volcaniclastic rocks. These are juxta-posed against Westphalian Coal Measures that form the low-lying undulating topography to the south. Although the fault may have been initiated in Early Devonian times, the main movement is believed to have occurred in Late Carboniferous times during a period of north–south extension that was accompanied by intrusion of quartz-dolerite magma along the fault plane (Rippon *et al.*, 1996). Dating of the fault-intrusions at *c.* 303 Ma therefore provides an age for this phase of extension (Forster and Warrington, 1985).

Five quartz-dolerite intrusions occur along the main part of the Ochil Fault near Dollar (termed the West Ochil Fault by Rippon *et al.*, 1996) and these are exposed in the burns running down the southern scarp of the Ochil Hills (Figure 6.16). The Gloom Hill GCR site reveals part of the largest intrusive body, which is over 3 km long and up to 300 m wide. Two other quartz-dolerite intrusions occur in the Arndean Fault which branches south-eastwards off the Ochil Fault to the east of Dollar and probably takes up a large part of the throw.

The area around the Ochil Fault has experi-enced recent seismic activity and this has been described by a number of authors (e.g. Davison, 1924; McQuillan in Francis *et al.*, 1970).

Description

The quartz-dolerite intrusion in the quarry at Gloom Hill is at least 40 m wide and the north-ern margin is chilled against scoriaceous, vesicu-lar, purple- and green-tinged andesitic lavas and volcaniclastic rocks of the Ochil Volcanic Forma-tion (Haldane, 1927; Francis *et al.*, 1970). This northern contact of the intrusion hades at 63° to the south (Figure 6.17). The southern contact is not visible but a southerly hade of 72° is revealed at the southern margin of a quartz-dolerite intru-sion at Castle Craig Quarry, Tillicoultry, 4 km to the west, where the exposed chilled contact lies against deformed Westphalian strata (Haldane, 1927). There, the contact is undulose and shows how intrusion of the dolerite has distor-ted the fault plane (Francis *et al.*, 1970).

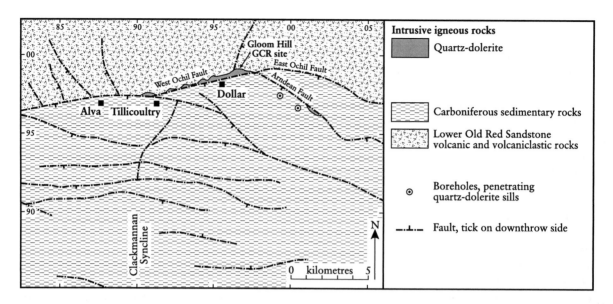

Figure 6.16 Map of the area around the Gloom Hill GCR site. After Rippon *et al.* (1996).

The quartz-dolerite in the quarry at Gloom Hill is of very similar composition and petrography to those of the Midland Valley Sill-complex, with abundant quartz and micropegmatite (Francis *et al.*, 1970; Macdonald *et al.*, 1981). The grain size clearly increases inwards from the northern margin towards the central part of the intrusion but overall it is finer grained than the usual sub-ophitic variety of the sill-complex. Some leucocratic segregation veins up to 2 cm thick can be seen on the quarry face but they are not a conspicuous feature.

Figure 6.17 View towards the east of the exposures of the Ochil Fault-intrusion in the quarry at Gloom Hill, with Siluro–Devonian lavas on the left, quartz-dolerite of the fault-intrusion on the right, and the contact parallel to the quarry face. (Photo: I.T. Williamson.)

Gloom Hill

Interpretation

The Ochil Fault plane is seen to be inclined to the south in three separate outcrops, including the quarry at Gloom Hill. However, early seismic evidence, based partly on the location of earthquake epicentres, suggested that the hade is to the north and the fault was therefore interpreted as a reverse fault by Davison (1924). Haldane (1927) discussed the contradictory seismic and geological evidence and suggested a number of solutions: (a) that that the seismic effects may have been caused by simultaneous movements along a series of NNW-trending faults on the north side of the Ochil Fault; (b) that they were caused by movement on a small subsidiary fault; or (c) that the hade of the fault is only to the south near the surface and is to the north at depth. MacQuillen (in Francis *et al.*, 1970) re-emphasized the strong seismic evidence for a northerly hade and proposed that the southerly dip of the fault exhibited at the surface is not a feature in the deeper part of the fracture zone (Haldane's option (c)). Since then, a number of contrasting tectonic models have been proposed. For example, Gibbs (1987) developed a complex tectonic model for the Kincardine Basin and suggested that the Ochil Fault is a reverse fault, dipping to the north, whereas Dentith (1988) proposed that the fault dips steeply to the south. The matter is clearly unresolved, though more recent seismic reflection studies reveal a southerly dipping fault plane to at least a depth of 2.5 km (Rippon *et al.*, 1996).

Estimates of the maximum total displacement on the West Ochil Fault are of the order of 4 km (Geikie, 1900; Francis *et al.*, 1970; Rippon *et al.*, 1996). The fault probably originated in Devonian time, prior to deposition of the Upper Red Sandstone, and acted as a control on subsidence and deposition throughout the Carboniferous Period. However, the main movement on the fault must have been late or post Westphalian in age, since Westphalian strata are juxtaposed against Lower Devonian volcanic rocks. The contact relationships exposed at Gloom Hill and Castle Craig Quarry indicate that the intrusive magma exploited the pre-existing fault plane as suggested by Haldane (1927), but Rippon *et al.* (1996) suggested that the presence of magma could also have facilitated later movement on the West Ochil and Arndean faults.

The quartz-dolerite intrusion at Gloom Hill, its margins and an aplitic vein were analysed by Macdonald *et al.* (1981), who confirmed that they are part of the large tholeiitic suite of sills and dykes emplaced during Late Carboniferous times in the Midland Valley of Scotland. Francis (1982) suggested that the Ochil Fault-intrusions may be feeders to the Midland Valley Sill-complex. However, the Ochil Fault only hosts intrusions in its central part and hence does not appear to be the location of a major feeder dyke system. On a more local scale, boreholes have revealed the presence of quartz-dolerite sills at about the level of the Castlecary Limestone (at the top of the Upper Limestone Formation) close to the Arndean Fault on the southern (downthrown) side (Rippon *et al.*, 1996). It seems quite likely that these may be linked to the Ochil Fault-intrusions.

Westphalian coals at Dollar show enhanced ranking which has been interpreted as a localized thermal effect of the Ochil Fault-intrusions (Rippon *et al.*, 1996) and the intrusions have a radiometric age of 303 ± 5 Ma (Forster and Warrington, 1985). It is therefore assumed that emplacement of the quartz-dolerite intrusions throughout the Midland Valley was in response to a brief but important phase of north–south extension in latest Carboniferous times (Rippon *et al.*, 1996).

Conclusions

At the Gloom Hill GCR site the Ochil Fault plane is clearly exposed and is intruded by a 40 m-wide quartz-dolerite body associated with the Midland Valley Sill-complex. The E–W-trending Ochil Fault played a critical role in the tectonic evolution of the Midland Valley in Late Carboniferous and Early Permian times and has had a major effect on the topography of the district. The fault is steeply inclined to the south at present surface levels, but studies of local minor earthquakes suggest that this may not be the case at depth. The maximum vertical displacement of 4 km juxtaposes Siluro–Devonian volcanic rocks against Westphalian coal measures, so the main movement on the fault probably occurred in Late Carboniferous times. At least some of this movement may have been contemporaneous with the intrusion of magma along the fault plane, which may have eased movement along the fault. A radiometric age of *c.* 303 Ma for this fault-intrusion is therefore believed to date the latest extensional movement on the Ochil Fault that coincided with a brief period of regional north–south extension.

MOLLINSBURN CUTTINGS (A80), NORTH LANARKSHIRE (NS 716 718)

S.C. Loughlin

Introduction

The E–W-trending dyke-swarm associated with the Midland Valley Sill-complex contains tholeiitic basalt and quartz-dolerite dykes between 3 m and 75 m wide, discontinuous outcrops of which may be traced for up to 300 km. The Mollinsburn Cuttings GCR site on the A80 Glasgow to Stirling road reveals an excellent section through the Lenzie–Torphichen Dyke, a typical quartz-dolerite dyke that can be traced for over 40 km. It forms a conspicuous feature along much of its length and partially coincides with pre-existing E–W-trending faults.

The first Geological Survey map of this area (Sheet 31, Airdrie) was published in 1875. It was re-surveyed and re-published in 1924 and again in 1992 as Sheet 31W, the latter with an accompanying memoir (Forsyth *et al.*, 1996). Based on the field relationships exposed at this site and nearby, early workers suggested that the dykes of the E–W-trending swarm acted as feeders for the Midland Valley Sill-complex (Tyrrell, 1909b; Clough *et al.*, 1925). More recently, geochemical studies have confirmed that the dykes and sills are comagmatic (Macdonald *et al.*, 1981; Howard, 1999), and their emplacement mechanism has been discussed in great detail by Francis (1982). The Lenzie–Torphichen Dyke is one of a few in the Midland Valley that can be demonstrated to have acted as a 'fault riser', facilitating the transgression of sills between different stratigraphical levels (see also **Wallstale** GCR site report).

Description

The Lenzie–Torphichen Dyke, which is exposed intermittently from north of Bishopbriggs (NS 573 714) in the west to Cairnpapple Hill (NS 990 720) in the east, has an overall length of over 40 km and an average breadth of 40 m. The dyke is resistant to weathering in comparison to the host sedimentary rocks and therefore forms a distinctive topographical feature that is seen particularly well over a distance of 5 km, between Millersneuk, Lenzie (NS 665 718) and Mollinsburn (NS 720 717).

At Mollinsburn there are two parallel branches of the dyke that cut the Upper Limestone Formation (Figure 6.18). The northern branch is seen in road cuttings and as a gorse-covered ridge, Mollin Craig, to the west of the road, where horizontal columnar joints perpendicular to the dyke margins are conspicuous (Figure 6.19). The central part of the dyke is medium grained, becoming finer grained towards the chilled margins which are commonly glassy. In common with other quartz-dolerites of the Midland Valley Sill-complex and dykes, the central part contains feldspar laths (bytownite or labradorite mantled by oligoclase), ophitic to sub-ophitic pale-brown augite, and a mesostasis of micropegmatitic quartz and feldspar.

To the west of Mollinsburn, two offshoots of quartz-dolerite extend north-westwards from the main, northern dyke, one between the Lyoncross and Orchard limestones just west of Mollin Craig (NS 711 718) and one 2 km farther west (NS 695 717). The dolerite was not encountered in workings below these outcrops, suggesting that they are portions of sills (Clough *et al.*, 1925). To the east of Mollinsburn, at North Medrox (NS 726 716), the dyke appears to be continuous with a sill on its south side, above the Calmy Limestone.

Evidence of the relationship between the intrusions and faulting is seen in other sectors of the Lenzie–Torphichen Dyke. Between Millersneuk (NS 665 718) and NS 695 717, just to the west of the GCR site, the dyke coincides with a major E–W-trending fault (the Annathill Fault). There, dark mudstones, thin coals and sandstones of the Lower Coal Measures are tilted up vertically against the northern wall of the dyke, whereas horizontal beds of indurated sandstone of the Passage Formation abut the southern margin. The dyke has been altered to 'white trap' up to 3 m inwards from both contacts. Some 25 km farther to the east, in the Torphichen district (around NS 970 720), the dyke is also emplaced along fault planes. The main sill in this area occurs in the Upper Limestone Formation on the north side of the fault but the only sill to the south of the fault occurs at much higher stratigraphical levels, in the Lower Coal Measures. Unfortunately the sill

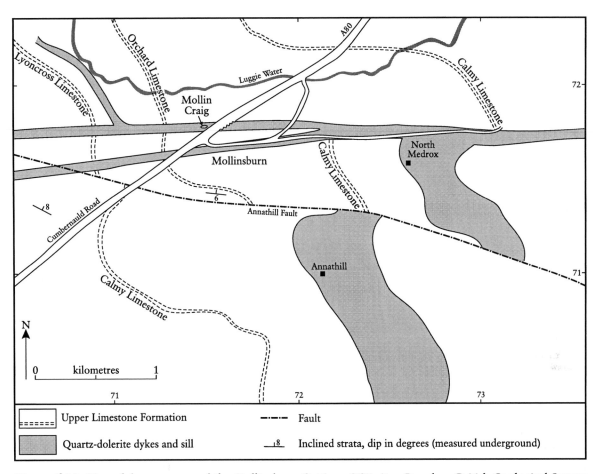

Figure 6.18 Map of the area around the Mollinsburn Cuttings GCR site. Based on British Geological Survey 1:10 000 Sheet NS 77 SW (1987).

Figure 6.19 E–W-trending quartz-dolerite dyke exhibiting good horizontal columnar jointing at Mollin Craig, Mollinsburn Cuttings GCR site. (Photo: C. MacFadyen.)

outcrops in that area are several kilometres apart so that the exact location and nature of the transgression cannot be determined.

Interpretation

The Late Carboniferous dyke-swarm of southern Scotland was emplaced partially along recently formed E–W-trending fractures. The petrological and geochemical similarities between the dykes and the Midland Valley Sill-complex were recognized long ago and have been confirmed recently by more detailed studies (see 'Introduction' to this chapter).

In the Kilsyth–Croy district, about 5 km north of Mollinsburn, east–west dykes are intimately associated with a lens-shaped body of quartz-dolerite termed a 'laccolite' by Tyrrell (1909b) (meaning that it was fed by vertical dykes and has slightly transgressive upper and lower contacts). He recognized from field evidence and mine plans that two dykes terminate in the intrusion. The 'laccolite' is thickest between the two dykes and thins away rapidly to the north and south, i.e. at right angles to the dykes. In addition, Tyrrell compiled isopachs (lines joining parts of the intrusion of equal thickness) and found that it is an ellipsoid elongated east–west, parallel to the dykes. Based on this evidence he suggested that the dykes were feeders to the intrusion. Evidence that the Lenzie–Torphichen Dyke is also a feeder to the sill-complex was revealed by Clough *et al.* (1925) when they described one of the offshoots of quartz-dolerite in the Mollinsburn district.

Peach *et al.* (1910) were the first to recognize the transgression of the sill-complex in the Torphichen district. In this area the Lenzie–Torphichen Dyke was described as a 'fault riser', meaning that emplacement was along a pre-existing fault plane. This provided a means for the sill-complex to transgress to different stratigraphical levels on either side of the fault along which it is emplaced. Similar relationships were interpreted by Clough *et al.* (1925) around Mollinsburn, and particularly good examples of transgression were described subsequently from the Stirling district (Dinham and Haldane, 1932; Francis *et al.*, 1970; see **Wallstale** GCR site report).

Early observations, such as these, all contributed to the overall model for the emplacement of the tholeiitic intrusions proposed by Francis (1982). In this model, magma rose along E–W-trending fault planes on the flanks of sedimentary basins (forming dykes) and then flowed down-dip into the centre of the basin (forming sills), transgressing down the succession whenever it met further fault planes (forming 'fault risers') (see 'Introduction' to this chapter).

Conclusions

The Lenzie–Torphichen Dyke, a typical and representative example of an E–W-trending quartz-dolerite dyke, is a well-known feature of the tholeiitic dyke-swarm of the Midland Valley. It is very well exposed in the road cuttings and along a ridge feature at the Mollinsburn Cuttings GCR site. The dyke is up to 40 m wide, over 40 km long and is one of the longest near-continuous lengths of dyke in the whole swarm. Dykes such as this are believed to have been feeders to the Midland Valley Sill-complex or to be 'fault risers', by which the magma transgressed from one stratigraphical level to another. Some of the earliest lines of evidence for such relationships were described from the area around this site and from other sectors of the same dyke.

CORSIEHILL QUARRY, PERTH AND KINROSS (NO 135 235)

D. Stephenson

Introduction

The extensive swarm of Late Carboniferous east- to ENE-trending tholeiitic basic dykes that crosses the Midland Valley and southern Highlands of Scotland is well represented in the area around Perth. The dykes have featured in several detailed accounts of the swarm and many have been used as type examples and are well known by name. One such dyke is the Corsiehill Dyke, which crops out on the northern slopes of Kinnoull Hill, 2 km to the east of Perth city centre. A complete cross-section of the dyke is well exposed in a disused quarry that has been converted into a car park for a local nature trail and is frequently visited for both educational and recreational purposes. The quarry is at the northern end of a larger SSSI that has been notified for its flora.

The dyke was shown on the first edition of the Geological Survey one-inch Sheet 48 (1883). At this time, all the E–W-trending dykes were considered to be of Tertiary age (e.g. Geikie, 1897). It was described, with an analysis, in definitive works on the swarm by Walker (1934, 1935), who included a comprehensive list of previous work in his 1935 paper. The geochemistry of the whole swarm was reviewed by Walker (1965) and subsequently by Macdonald *et al.* (1981), who included three analyses of the Corsiehill Dyke. A general description of the dykes in this area was also included in the Geological Survey district memoir (Armstrong *et al.*, 1985).

The tholeiitic dykes were divided petrographically by Walker (1930, 1934, 1935) on the basis of their texture. Those with an overall coarser grain-size but with microcrystalline areas of intergrown quartz and alkali feldspar (micropegmatite) were classed as quartz-dolerites. Dykes with a finer grain-size commonly have an interstitial groundmass that is either cryptocrystalline or consists of glass in various states of devitrification. These were termed 'tholeiites', as had become common practice in central Scotland, and the term persisted on Geological Survey maps, including Sheet 48W (Perth), until the early 1980s. It has now been abandoned as unnecessary ('basalt' or 'glass-bearing basalt' are sufficiently descriptive terms) and because of confusion with the term 'tholeiitic', which is now applied to magmas or suites of rocks defined by specific geochemical and mineralogical characteristics.

Walker further divided the 'tholeiites' into several named types, based mainly on the proportion and nature of the glassy groundmass. His 'Corsiehill' type is relatively coarse grained with only small areas of interstitial glass and grades into quartz-dolerite; other 'tholeiite' types are much more distinctive, with up to 20% of interstitial microlitic glass. However, more recent investigations (Stephenson in Armstrong *et al.*, 1985) have concluded that a spectrum of textures exists, from quartz-dolerite through the various types of 'tholeiite', and it is difficult to fit many individual rocks precisely into Walker's classification. All types share a common mineralogy in which similarities in mineral relationships outnumber the subtle differences, and Macdonald *et al.* (1981) identified no significant differences in geochemistry. Several dykes exhibit changes along their length through various 'tholeiite' types to quartz-dolerite and this close spatial relationship supports a genetic connection. Hence, although

the textural variations provide valuable information on the crystallization and cooling histories of the dykes (see 'Interpretation', below), their classification has little practical value and is mainly of historical interest.

Basalt ('tholeiite') dykes are particularly abundant in the northern sector of the swarm that passes through the Perth area, but apart from this there is no geographical distribution pattern to any of the various textural varieties. Both quartz-dolerite and basalt can occur as long persistent dykes, though, as would be expected, there is a tendency for basalt to occur as thinner dykes and also as a marginal facies of thicker quartz-dolerite intrusions (Walker, 1935; Francis *et al.*, 1970; Armstrong *et al.*, 1985).

Description

Corsiehill Quarry (also known as Kinnoullhill Quarry) was in existence in 1855 and was probably worked until 1925. The basalt dyke cuts lavas within a Lower Old Red Sandstone succession and both the dyke and the more massive parts of the lavas were worked, presumably for road metal. The dyke has been quarried away completely over a length of about 150 m, but complete cross-sections are exposed at both the east and west ends of the quarry. The northern and southern quarry walls expose only lavas, apart from a thin skin of basalt at one point on the northern wall (Figure 6.20).

The lavas comprise the upper part of the Ochil Volcanic Formation on the northern limb of the Sidlaw Anticline, and form the dip-slope of Kinnoull Hill. They dip generally at about 10° to the north-west. They have a greyish-purple to greenish hue, contain conspicuous feldspar phenocrysts, with pyroxene, hornblende and biotite in the groundmass, and are probably basaltic andesites. They are amygdaloidal and commonly scoriaceous with large flattened vesicles, particularly on the northern side of the quarry. Collections of amygdaloidal material from the quarry in Perth Museum and Art Gallery include quartz, agate, amethyst, calcite, aragonite and chlorite. Acicular and hemispherical forms of goethite within quartz are particularly notable. Although visible contact effects due to the dyke are limited to minor baking, Shand (1908) noted the development of grossular garnet in lava adjacent to the dyke

The dyke trends east–west, like most others of the same swarm in the immediate area around

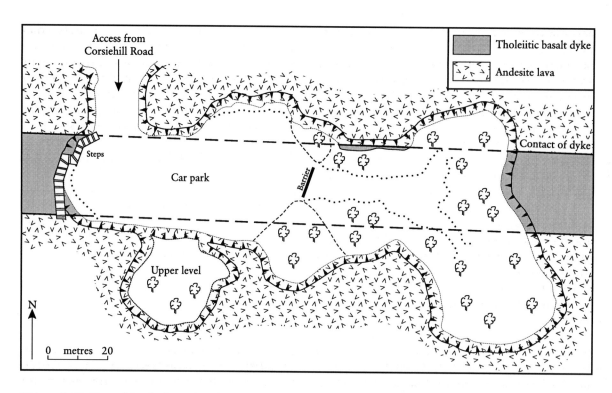

Figure 6.20 Map of the tholeiitic basalt dyke exposed in the Corsiehill Quarry GCR site. Adapted from an interpretive handout prepared by the Countryside Ranger Service, Perth and Kinross District Council (1990).

Perth, and can be traced for about 500 m. The contacts are vertical and the dyke is 20 m wide in the quarry. Both contacts can be observed at both ends of the quarry, where the dyke is seen to be chilled against baked lavas, and a thin skin of glassy basalt is preserved at one point on the northern quarry face. Joints perpendicular to the contact form crude hexagonal columns across the whole width of the dyke and these are the focus for well-developed spheroidal weathering that dominates the end walls of the quarry. The dyke is traversed by thin quartzo-feldspathic veins.

Despite the brown-weathering outer crust, the basalt is very fresh, particularly at the east end of the quarry. The rock varies from glassy to fine grained to medium grained, with plagioclase laths up to 2 mm long; the central part could be termed a dolerite. It comprises plagioclase (50%); subhedral to euhedral serpentine-carbonate pseudomorphs after early orthopyroxene and olivine (8%); sub-ophitic augite (30%); skeletal iron-titanium oxides (6%); and small amounts of interstitial microlitic glass (6%). Analyses show that it is quartz-hypersthene-normative with about 2% normative quartz.

Interpretation

The similarity of the basalts and quartz-dolerites of the dyke-swarm to the Midland Valley Sill-complex in all main aspects of geochemistry and petrography, and their close spatial relationships leave no doubt that they are comagmatic. The mantle origin and subsequent evolution of the high-Fe-Ti tholeiitic magmas was discussed by Macdonald *et al.* (1981) and is summarized in the 'Introduction' to this chapter. Individual dykes reveal only slight geochemical variation along their length, despite changes in texture, although fractionation is recorded between the margin and core of some thicker dykes and is noticeable in the three analyses from Corsiehill. Trace-element variation within individual dykes is much less than that observed between dykes so geochemical 'fingerprinting' is possible in some cases; however the Corsiehill Dyke is not particularly distinctive in this respect.

The basalt dykes of the swarm provide much useful petrological information that is not available from the coarser-grained quartz-dolerites. For instance, the early crystallizing phases such as olivine are preserved only in the finer-grained rocks, particularly in dyke margins, and the interstitial glass is a 'frozen' sample of the residuum that remains after the main phases have crystallized. The presence of residual Fe and Ti in this late liquid, a feature of tholeiitic magmas, is indicated by the abundance of ilmenite needles in the glass of many of the dykes. An analysis of glassy groundmass separated from a dyke near Kirkintilloch (Walker, 1935) demonstrates the high concentrations of SiO_2, K_2O and volatiles in the residuum. A few dykes have a tholeiitic andesite composition, but more evolved compositions occur only as aplitic veins and patches. These occur mainly in the associated sills but also in some of the thicker dykes and the Corsiehill Dyke is one of few where these can be observed.

The textural variations within the dyke-swarm that occur particularly in the area around Perth, were most likely induced by variations in the conditions of late-stage crystallization and cooling. Thus the glassy, quenched textures of many of the basalts ('tholeiites') contrast strongly with the interstitial crystalline intergrowths of the quartz-dolerites, which suggest slower cooling in the generally larger intrusions, possibly under the influence of trapped volatiles (see various GCR site reports describing the associated sills).

Conclusions

The Stephanian tholeiitic dyke-swarm that traverses central Scotland is dominated by medium-grained quartz-dolerites, but it also includes finer-grained basalts that are particularly abundant in the Perth area. At the Corsiehill Quarry GCR site one of these basalt dykes is particularly well displayed in a landscaped car park that serves a local nature trail. The 20 m-wide, E–W-trending dyke is intruded into lavas of Siluro–Devonian age that have yielded museum specimens of various minerals from infilled gas bubbles (amygdales). The chilled contacts of the dyke are well seen, as are horizontal columnar joints and spheroidal weathering, all in an ideal setting for demonstration to educational parties.

The basalt at Corsiehill Quarry is very fresh and consequently has been used in many microscopic and geochemical studies; it was the type example for a textural variety that formed part of a local classification of some historical interest. Like most of the basalt dykes in this swarm, it contains small areas of glass between the component crystals. These represent the liquid that

remained after the magma had almost completely crystallized. It was 'frozen' as glass when the dyke rose rapidly through the Earth's crust and cooled very quickly. A study of this glassy material can yield much information about the nature of the original magma and its potential to evolve other, more fractionated magmas.

WHIN SILL EXPOSURES IN UPPER TEESDALE, COUNTY DURHAM
High Force (NY 880 285–NY 885 286), Low Force (NY 903 281–NY 912 273), Falcon Clints (NY 815 285–NY 829 283), Cauldron Snout (NY 814 286), Cronkley Fell (NY 831 282–NY 854 282)

S.C. Loughlin

Introduction

Upper Teesdale contains a number of classic exposures of the Great Whin Sill, which combine textbook examples of features associated with sill intrusion with spectacular landscapes. The abundant features include the presence of baked sedimentary rocks at the upper and lower contacts of the sill, rafts of baked sedimentary rock within the sill, variations in grain size relating to cooling history, and transgressions where the sill changes level within the country-rock succession. Bands of very coarse-grained pegmatitic facies and felsic veins representing the final products of crystallization are well exposed. In places, joint and fracture surfaces are covered with the zeolite pectolite, which crystallized at a late stage in the cooling of the sill. There are also good examples of the bleached and altered sill-rock known as 'white whin', which is caused by the circulation of mineralizing fluids. The alteration of the sill by these fluids suggests that it pre-dates the northern Pennine mineralization. The Great Whin Sill is at its thickest (73 m) and occurs at its lowest stratigraphical level in Upper Teesdale. From here, the sill thins and rises in stratigraphical level in every direction, forming a 'saucer-shaped' intrusion (A.C. Dunham, 1970; Francis, 1982).

Upper Teesdale is a popular area for students and amateur geologists, which is reflected in the number of field guides and popular accounts of the area (e.g. A.C. Dunham, 1970; Johnson and K.C. Dunham in Johnson, 1973; Skipsey, 1992; Senior in Scrutton, 1995).

Description

The Teesdale Fault, which trends north-west–south-east along the upper part of Teesdale, has a downthrow to the north-east. Hence, to the south-west of the fault are the lowest Visean strata exposed in Teesdale, whereas to the north-east are strata that extend up through the Yoredale Series into the Namurian succession. The Great Whin Sill is here intruded into low stratigraphical levels, around the Melmerby Scar Limestone, and hence its outcrop is mostly restricted to the south-west side of the Teesdale Fault, where the valley sides are dominated by long crags of dolerite (Figure 6.21).

The margins of the Great Whin Sill are commonly fine grained and chilled, with a thin black skin that has commonly been described as glassy, although true glass may not be present. Moving away from the margins, the grain size increases to 2 mm (K.C. Dunham, 1948). Grain-size analyses have shown that the percentage of microphenocrysts increases towards the centre of the sill (Strasser-King, 1973; A.C. Dunham and Strasser-King, 1982). The quartz-dolerite of the main part of the sill is composed typically of 48% plagioclase, 29% clinopyroxene, 7% iron-titanium oxides with small amounts of orthopyroxene, pseudomorphs after olivine, chlorite, amphibole, carbonates, sulphides and apatite.

High Force

The spectacular waterfall of High Force (NY 880 284) cuts a classic section through the lower 7.3 m of the Great Whin Sill and the underlying sedimentary rocks. The waterfall lies at the head of a 300 m-long gorge in which the sill and associated sedimentary rocks are well exposed in the walls (Figure 6.22). The sill has strong vertical jointing giving a pseudo-columnar appearance to the rock. At the water-fall a sheet of dolerite is separated from the main sill by a thin raft of baked mudstone. The sill overlies baked sandstone and indurated mudstone and dark recrystallized fossiliferous carbonates of the Tyne Bottom Limestone; a good example of the contact with baked mudstone is exposed along the side of the path leading to the waterfall from the main road at High Force Hotel (NY 884 287). The section at High Force is as follows (thicknesses based on Clough, 1876):

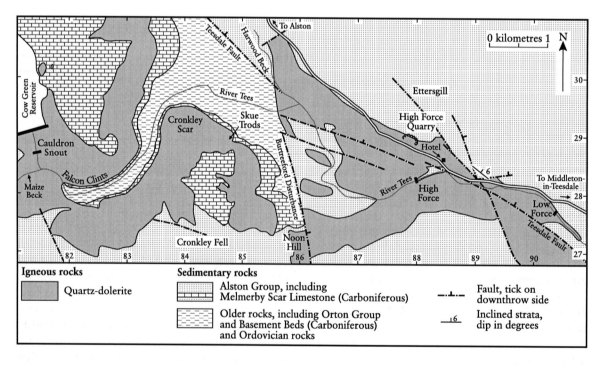

Figure 6.21 Map of the outcrops of the Great Whin Sill in the Upper Teesdale area. Based on Geological Survey 1:50 000 sheets 25, Alston (1965); and 31, Brough-under-Stainmore (1974).

Figure 6.22 Quartz-dolerite of the Great Whin Sill (upper half of the cliff) at High Force, Upper Teesdale. The two highest layers of massive rock are dolerite, separated by a thin raft of baked sedimentary rock forming a plane of weakness near the top of the waterfall. Beneath is a thick bed of baked sandstone, resting upon well-bedded mudstones and limestones of the Tyne Bottom Limestone in the lower half of the cliff. (Photo: British Geological Survey, No. LFP00382, reproduced with the permission of the Director, British Geological Survey, © NERC.)

Dolerite (Great Whin Sill)	7.31 m
Altered mudstone	0.45 m
Dolerite sill	1.82 m
Baked sandstone	3.65 m
Mudstones and limestones (Tyne Bottom Limestone)	9.75 m

High Force Quarry (NY 879 290) (also known as 'Hargreaves Quarry') lies 400 m WNW of the High Force Hotel and provides an excellent section through the central and upper part of the Great Whin Sill. Based on evidence from borings around Ettersgill (NY 882 299), the sill is about 70 m thick at this locality (K.C. Dunham, 1948). The quarry faces reveal considerable variations in grain size and excellent examples of coarsely pegmatitic quartz-dolerite within the 'normal' dark-grey quartz-dolerite. The pegmatitic facies occurs as flat-lying sheets up to 30 cm thick and is characterized by elongate, bladed crystals of black augite up to 50 mm long and smaller laths of plagioclase. Radiometric determinations on grains of baddelyite (ZrO_2) from the pegmatites at this quarry have yielded a weighted mean $^{206}Pb/^{238}U$ age of 297.04 ± 0.4 Ma (M.A. Hamilton and D.G. Pearson, pers. comm., 2002), the most precise date yet obtained from the Whin Sill-complex. Intersertal micropegmatite also occurs with accessory hornblende, biotite and chlorite. Some of the strong vertical joint faces are coated with chlorite, calcite and white radiating crystals of pectolite (a zeolite) up to 5 cm in length.

Low Force

Between Scoberry Bridge (NY 910 273) and Low Force (NY 903 277), the River Tees cuts an excellent section through Carboniferous sedimentary rocks down to the upper contact of the Great Whin Sill. The strata and the sill dip to the east or south-east at an angle just greater than the gradient of the river and hence a traverse upstream, to the north-west, is down the section. The Cockle Shell Limestone overlies sandstone, mudstone and then the Single Post Limestone, which has been baked and recrystallized to a soft, white, crystalline marble. Sandstones and mudstones beneath this limestone are also extensively altered and indurated. The upper contact of the sill is extremely sharp and it is well exposed along the north bank of the river.

Near the south-eastern end of the sill outcrop the dolerite has a bleached appearance where it has been altered to 'white whin' (see 'Introduction' to this chapter). The alteration has occurred around a series of thin anastomosing mineral veins, which, though barren within the sill, may be followed up through the succession and into an area of mineralization within the Single Post Limestone. The mineral veins and replacement deposits found here contain sphalerite, siderite and pyrite.

Farther upstream, just below Wynch Bridge (NY 904 279), a 74 m-long 'raft' of baked siltstone lies within the upper part of the sill, dipping at an angle of c. 20°. It is in sharp contact with the surrounding chilled dolerite. Low Force is a series of rapids where the river flows over columnar-jointed dolerite, just upstream from Wynch Bridge.

Cronkley Fell

On the south bank of the River Tees in Upper Teesdale, the Great Whin Sill forms a 3 km-long line of cliffs known as Cronkley Scar (NY 834 280–NY 852 285). At this location the sill is intruded in an irregular manner into the recrystallized Melmerby Scar Limestone near the base of the Carboniferous sequence, and a steeply inclined raft of saccharoidal limestone crops out within the dolerite at Skue Trods (NY 848 289). The upper contact of the sill is clearly exposed on the hill-top, where it transgresses from the Melmerby Scar Limestone up into the overlying Robinson Limestone, which

is also thermally metamorphosed (NY 842 285). This excellent example of the transgressive nature of the sill contrasts with the very constant level of the sill a short distance to the east at Noon Hill (NY 861 271). At Noon Hill the sill passes almost unaffected through the Burtreeford Disturbance, an east-facing faulted monocline. Hence, to the east of the monocline it is above the Tynebottom Limestone, whereas to the west it intrudes much lower beds (i.e. the Melmerby Scar Limestone).

Falcon Clints and Cauldron Snout

Cow Green Reservoir covers the site of Cow Green Mine which worked extensive veins of galena and baryte. Small mineral veins occur throughout this area and many were worked until the 1950s. At Cauldron Snout (NY 814 286), just 300 m south-east of the reservoir dam, the River Tees cascades spectacularly down columnar-jointed crags formed from the main body of the Great Whin Sill (Figure 6.23). In addition to typical dolerite, layers of coarse pegmatitic dolerite may be observed and radiating aggregates of pectolite occur as coatings on joint surfaces.

The sill also forms a cliff known as 'Falcon Clints' (NY 816 284–NY 827 281), which extends for over 1 km along the north side of the Tees valley, to the east of Cauldron Snout. The basal contact of the sill with the recrystallized (sugary textured) limestone of the Melmerby Scar Limestone and the altered upper part of the Orton Group is clearly exposed close to the foot of the crags. The thermal alteration of the sedimentary rocks is pronounced in this area both above and below the sill and, on weathering, it generates a thin soil that supports the relict arctic alpine flora (e.g. *Gentiana verna*) for which the area is well known (Johnson *et al.*, 1971).

Interpretation

The earliest debate about the origins of the Whin Sill focused on the sections in Upper Teesdale, where it was widely believed that the sill is conformable with the surrounding sedimentary rocks (hence the term 'Whin Sill', see 'Introduction' to this chapter). Sedgwick (1827) provided very good evidence for the intrusive nature of the sill in Upper Teesdale but, because it appeared to follow almost the same stratigraphical

Figure 6.23 The Great Whin Sill exhibiting large-scale columnar jointing at Cauldron Snout, Upper Teesdale. (Photo: D. Stephenson.)

horizon throughout the area, there were those, especially within the mining community, who continued to doubt the evidence (e.g. Hutton, 1838). Phillips (1836) described the sill as a conformable bed, citing the High Force section as an example, but detailed work by the Geological Survey conclusively demonstrated the intrusive nature of the sill in Teesdale (Clough, 1876). Clough presented evidence that the sill is not conformable with underlying sedimentary rocks in the High Force section and also drew attention to the irregular nature of the basal contact, where apophyses of dolerite branch off from the main sill.

The field relationships revealed at this GCR site are now regarded as type examples of the features required to prove the intrusive character of a sheet of igneous rock. For example, thermally metamorphosed sedimentary rocks at both the lower and upper contacts are clearly demonstrated at High Force, Low Force and at Cronkley Scar. The fine-grained nature of the sill close to *both* contacts is evidence for rapid chilling of the intruded magma against a cooler host rock (columnar jointing is also an expression of cooling between two surfaces although it also commonly develops in lava flows). At a glance the Great Whin Sill does look conformable with the sedimentary rocks at several places in Upper Teesdale but closer inspection shows that most contacts are in fact transgressive; this is demonstrated extremely well at Cronkley Scar but also on a smaller scale at High Force. Both the upper and lower contacts are transgressive and the occurrence of blocks or rafts of sedimentary rock within the dolerite that have clearly detached from the overlying host rock provide further evidence for intrusion.

The Great Whin Sill attains its greatest known thickness of over 70 m in Upper Teesdale. Hence cooling was slow, possibly having taken about 60 years, according to A.C. Dunham and Kaye (1965). Several features can be attributed to the later stages of this slow cooling, such as the sheets of pegmatitic dolerite and felsic veins that are best seen in this area. The radiating growths of pectolite on joints are also considered to have formed during the late stages of cooling, as hydrothermal fluids circulated through the jointed rock (Wager, 1929a,b; Smythe, 1930a). The mineral veins that cut the sill near Low Force, altering it to 'white whin', are particularly significant because they prove that the sill was emplaced prior to the local mineralization event, which is part of the regional northern Pennine mineralization.

Conclusions

The Upper Teesdale GCR site provides a number of classic and scenic exposures of the Great Whin Sill, which demonstrate clearly most features associated with sill intrusion. The sill represents an extensive magma body intruded between layers of Lower Carboniferous sedimentary rocks. Outcrops reveal superb examples of chilled margins, thermally metamorphosed sedimentary rocks at upper and lower contacts, transgressive upper and lower contacts, rafts of baked roof material incorporated in the sill, and columnar jointing. This is the thickest part of the Great Whin Sill and excellent examples of very coarse-grained pegmatitic dolerite, formed during slow cooling, are exposed. A very precise radiometric date of 297.4 Ma has been obtained from this pegmatitic facies. During the late-stage cooling of the sill, hydrothermal fluids deposited the hydrous zeolite mineral pectolite on joint surfaces, and in places the fluids associated with mineral veins have altered the quartz-dolerite to 'white whin'. The latter relationship suggests that the widespread northern Pennine mineralization post-dated emplacement of the sill, which therefore provides a maximum age for this major ore-field.

STEEL RIGG TO SEWINGSHIELDS CRAGS, NORTHUMBERLAND (NY 751 676–NY 813 704)

S.C. Loughlin

Introduction

In the Roman Wall region, between Newcastle-upon-Tyne and Carlisle, the Great Whin Sill forms a spectacular north-facing scarp that extends for over 25 km to the north of the River South Tyne. The scarp forms a natural barrier that provided an ideal site for the construction of a substantial length of Hadrian's Wall and several important Roman forts (Figure 6.6). The area is one of outstanding natural beauty, is popular with walkers and rock-climbers and has been used as a major film location. It has been a recommended site for geological conservation since 1945 and is also included in the GCR for its Quaternary geology (Huddart and Glasser, 2002).

The Steel Rigg to Sewingshields Crags GCR site extends from the car park at Steel Rigg (NY 751 677), ENE for about 7 km to Sewingshields Crags (NY 810 703) (Figure 6.24). The quartz-dolerite sill is beautifully exposed in a series of crags over 30 m high and exhibits several fault-controlled transgressions between stratigraphical levels within the Visean sequence, well seen at Sewingshields Crags and Housesteads. At Sewingshields Crags there are good exposures of the chilled base and of the contact between the top of the sill and metamorphosed sedimentary rocks. There is also a large raft of baked limestone near the base of the sill.

The geology of the area was described briefly by Wallis (1769), Winch (1817) and Tate (1867, 1868) in their accounts of the geology of Northumberland. Baked sedimentary rocks above the sill in the Roman Wall area were important features in the summary of evidence by Topley and Lebour (1877) that finally established the intrusive origin of the sill. The Geological Survey mapped central and south Northumberland in the 1870s and six-inch sheets 106NE and 106SE were published in 1881. Smythe (1930a) described the transgression of the sill at this site in his extensive study of the geochemistry of the Whin Sill-complex. Further descriptions of the site and a detailed account of the Carboniferous rocks into which the sill is intruded were produced by Johnson (1959). A revision survey was completed by the

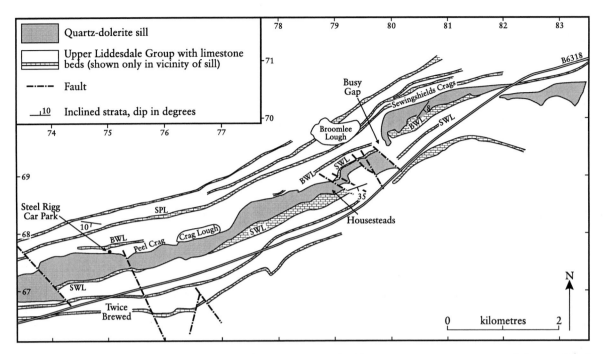

Figure 6.24 Map of the area around the Steel Rigg to Sewingshields Crags GCR site. (BWL = Bath-house Wood Limestone, SPL = Single Post Limestone, SWL = Shotto Wood Limestone.) After Johnson (1959).

Geological Survey in 1975 and 1:50 000 Sheet 13 (Bellingham) was published in 1980, together with a memoir (Frost and Holliday, 1980). The results of detailed ground magnetic surveys that clarify the structure of the sill at depth were described by Cornwell and Evans (1986). Descriptions are included in field guides of the area, including those by Jones (in Scrutton, 1995) and Johnson (1997).

Description

The north-facing scarp formed by the sill in this area is arguably the most impressive landscape feature of the whole Whin Sill-complex (Figure 6.25). At this site, and in adjacent areas, the scarp exhibits several offsets, which are caused by transgression of the sill between different levels within the Visean (Liddesdale Group) succession. In general, it is intruded at successively higher stratigraphical levels from east to west. Between the River North Tyne and Sharpley the sill is in the Oxford Limestone; between Carrowborough and Winshields (including this GCR site) it is among the Bath-house Wood and Shotto Wood limestones (it transgresses both up and down between them); and between Winshields and Greenhead the sill lies just below the Five Yard Limestone. The

sedimentary rocks comprise repeated sequences of limestone, mudstone, siltstone, sandstone and coal deposited as Yoredale cycles.

Several transgressions occur close together within this GCR site. They appear to take place along small faults, which are visible in places as truncations in the sedimentary rock outcrops above the sill (Johnson, 1959), but are commonly hidden beneath thick drift deposits. In the western part of the site the sill is intruded into the Shotto Wood Limestone (Scar Limestone of Johnson, 1959). The sill and limestone form a composite dip-slope for several kilometres, along which vegetation on the differing rock-types contrasts sharply in colour and variety (Tate, 1868; Frost and Holliday, 1980). The sill escarpment is heavily indented, probably as a result of small faults that have fractured and shattered the dolerite. The most westerly indentation (NY 753 675) is quite deep and well defined. Several small transgressions take place around Housesteads (NY 790 688), where the sill moves to the top of the Shotto Wood Limestone. Farther east, at Busy Gap (NY 800 695), the sill abruptly changes horizon to the Bath-house Wood Limestone (Cockleshell Limestone of Johnson, 1959) and is offset several hundred metres to the north.

255

Figure 6.25 View of the north-facing crags of the Great Whin Sill from Steel Rigg. Peel Crag (nearest to camera), Crag Lough and Sewingshields Crags in the distance, are all topped by Hadrian's Wall. (Photo: British Geological Survey, No. L1555, reproduced with the permission of the Director, British Geological Survey, © NERC.)

The sill at this site is composed of homogenous quartz-dolerite with thin chilled margins at the top and base (less than 0.5 m). The thickness of the sill varies from 20 m to 50 m. It shows well-developed columnar jointing, particularly at Sewingshields Crags (NY 800 700) where isolated trapezoid pinnacles have been weathered out at the top of the crag. At Crag Lough and Peel Crag, the columns provide some of the most popular rock climbs in Northumberland. The upper and lower contacts of the sill are very well exposed at several locations within the site; for example, the Bath-house Wood Limestone rests directly on the sill at Sewingshields Crags, forming a composite dip-slope for several kilometres to the east. The contact metamorphism of the overlying sedimentary rocks is also particularly clear at Sewingshields Crags and a 2 m-thick raft of baked Bath-house Wood Limestone is exposed near the base of the sill at Sewingshields Castle (NY 8114 7041).

Alteration of the sill typically includes chloritization along joint planes and there are also some good examples of pectolitization. Pectolite (a zeolite) occurs at several places in the Whin Sill-complex but is particularly abundant in the vicinity of the Roman Wall. It generally takes the form of thin veins associated with calcite and also occurs in amygdales (Smythe, 1930a). These are surrounded by an aureole up to 1.5 cm wide of light-green altered dolerite in which further clusters of pectolite crystals can be observed. In other places amygdales comprise quartz and calcite.

Interpretation

The origin of the Whin Sill-complex was debated at length early in the 19th century. Early workers considered that it represented lava flows (e.g. Phillips, 1836; Hutton, 1838) but Tate (1867, 1868) recognized the evidence for intrusion in the vicinity of the Roman Wall, based on the metamorphism of the overlying strata. In their definitive discussion on the intrusive nature of the Whin Sill-complex, Topley and Lebour (1877) cited Sewingshields Crags as one of the better places to see evidence of contact metamorphism at the upper contact.

Since drift deposits at this site commonly cover areas crucial to the understanding of the sill transgression and its relationship to faulting, magnetic surveys have been used to work out the structure of the sill at depth. Strong magnetic anomalies occur along outcrops of the sill and also down-dip, where the intrusions can be detected at depths of up to several hundred metres below the surface. The Roman Wall area reveals numerous complicated anomalies which have been investigated by several groups (e.g. Summers *et al.*, 1982; Cornwell and Evans, 1986). These studies reveal clearly the segmented nature of the sill and, in a study of the Hexham area, Cornwell and Evans identified many magnetic lineaments, interpreted as faults or joints that are not necessarily visible at the surface. Based on magnetic evidence within this GCR site, the main offset at Busy Gap is seen to coincide with a NW-trending lineament that swings to the ESE about 4 km south of the outcrop. A major offset in the sill at Limestone Corner, 10 km to the east of the site, is controlled by a similar structure (Cornwell and Evans, 1986).

The relationship of the sill to faulting in the region has been of interest to many authors. In the adjacent area east of the River North Tyne, Randall (1959) observed transgressions and faulting but was unable to ascertain the exact age relationship, although he considered that the faults could not be younger than the intrusion. Johnson (1959) considered the transgressive steps at this GCR site to be fault-controlled. The predominant fault trend in the region is ENE, with a secondary ESE trend. These have been interpreted as conjugate shears formed during a period of E–W-trending compression, after the main north–south Variscan compression, but before intrusion of the Whin Sill-complex (Frost and Holliday, 1980). However, Frost and Holliday also suggested that the faulting and intrusion could be contemporaneous. Cornwell and Evans (1986) interpreted the segmented nature of the sill in this region as evidence of fault and/or joint control on the form of the intrusion. They were unable to determine the age of faulting from magnetic evidence but considered it probable that a major component was in existence at the time of intrusion. The minor indentations in the scarp suggest some faulting after emplacement of the sill and the largest indentation acted as a water channel which drained a lake to the north of the sill at the end of the last glaciation. Crag Lough is a remnant of this glacial lake, which formed in an ice-scoured basin (Johnson, 1997).

The St Oswald's Chapel Dyke, a member of the dyke-swarm associated with the sill-complex (Figure 6.2), crops out over a distance of several tens of kilometres, sub-parallel to the outcrop of the sill and about 5–7 km to the south. It has a continuous magnetic anomaly showing no fault displacement or *en échelon* structures and appears to be emplaced partly along a pre-existing WNW-trending structure (Cornwell and Evans, 1986).

Conclusions

The Steel Rigg to Sewingshields Crags GCR site demonstrates very well the dramatic effect that the Great Whin Sill has on the landscape, here forming a substantial north-facing scarp upon which Hadrian's Wall and several Roman forts were built. The scarp is offset at several places as a result of transgression of the sill between different levels within the sedimentary succession of the Visean Liddesdale Group. These transgressions have been the subject of much discussion, as the role of faulting is not always clear. Geophysical methods tend to suggest that some of the transgressions are fault-controlled and that magma moved along pre-existing fault zones. Small later faults cut the sill forming minor indentations in the outcrop; one of these acted as a channel when water drained from a glacial lake on the north side of the scarp at the end of the last glaciation.

The site was important during the early debate on the origins of the Whin Sill as it provides abundant evidence of the contact metamorphism of overlying sedimentary rocks, thus proving that it is an intrusion and not a lava flow. Other features of this site, typical of sills in general, include a large raft of baked limestone near the base of the sill and well-developed columnar jointing.

LONGHOUGHTON QUARRY, NORTHUMBERLAND (NU 231 153)

S.C. Loughlin

Introduction

Longhoughton Quarry, 4 km north-east of Alnwick in Northumberland, is located at the western end of a number of quarries collectively known as 'Howlet Hill Quarry', which were formerly worked for sets and road metal (Figure 6.26). It provides an excellent example of the thermal metamorphism of sedimentary rocks overlying the Great Whin Sill. The chilled upper surface of the sill is clearly exposed in the quarry and baked rafts of sedimentary rock can be seen

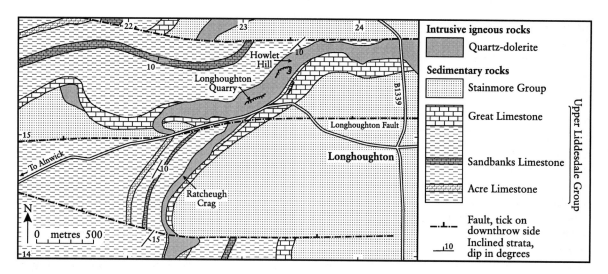

Figure 6.26 Map of the area around the Longhoughton Quarry GCR site. Based on Geological Survey 1:10 560 Sheet Northumberland 29SE (1926).

within the quartz-dolerite. The sill is intruded just below the (basal Namurian) Great Limestone at this site and nearby it cuts across two E–W-trending faults with no offset. This cross-cutting relationship provides evidence that the sill was intruded after the main movement on E–W-trending fractures in this area. However, shearing and slickensides within the dolerite imply that strike-slip movement also occurred after emplacement of the sill.

The area was first surveyed between 1860 and 1864 by the Geological Survey and, following revision of the six-inch maps in the 1920s, was published at the one-inch scale in 1930 as Sheet 6 (Alnwick). The quarries were described by Carruthers *et al.* (1930) in the memoir that accompanied the published map, and the timing of faulting and intrusion in this area was discussed by Jones *et al.* (1980), Turner *et al.* (1995) and Chadwick *et al.* (1995).

Description

A 20 m-high face at the north end of Longhoughton Quarry exposes the Great Whin Sill, which is intruded into sandstones and mudstones just below the Great Limestone. The overlying strata are thermally metamorphosed, and rafts of the overlying sandstones and mudstones, incorporated into the upper parts of the sill and prominent in this quarry, have been recrystallized. The chilled, fine-grained to glassy upper margin of the sill is exposed all along the eastern side of the workings. Just below the

upper margin is a zone in which bands of small amygdales occur. The main part of the sill at this site is typical of the Great Whin Sill and has well-developed columnar jointing. It comprises homogeneous quartz-dolerite containing plagioclase, clinopyroxene, magnetite-ilmenite, quartz, orthopyroxene and small amounts of biotite, hornblende and carbonate. There is no evidence of a pegmatitic zone or segregation veins. A small fault at the western side of the quarry has exposed the basal margin and under-lying indurated sandy mudstones. The basal contact can also be seen 300 m north-east of the summit of Howlet Hill, where thermally meta-morphosed sandstones and mudstones are exposed at the base of a quartz-dolerite crag.

Just 0.5 km to the west of this GCR site the sill transgresses upwards through sandstones and mudstones and is intruded fully into the Great Limestone. A further 1 km to the west is an isolated outcrop of quartz-dolerite that was intruded above the Great Limestone.

Immediately to the south of the site, the sill cuts across the E–W-trending Longhoughton Fault with no apparent offset. The fault has undergone over 1.5 km of lateral movement (Carruthers *et al.*, 1930) although the Great Limestone outcrops on either side of the fault happen to coincide (Figure 6.26). Farther to the south, the sill crosses another E–W-trending fault, also with no offset, but to the south of this fault it intrudes the Acre Limestone, over 60 m lower in the succession. Horizontal slicken-siding can be seen on some vertical surfaces of dolerite at Longhoughton Quarry and at nearby Ratcheugh Quarry. There is also evidence that the dolerite has been sheared.

Interpretation

Tate (1868) studied many outcrops of the Great Whin Sill throughout Northumberland and although Longhoughton Quarry was not so extensive at that time, he described the dolerite at nearby Ratcheugh Quarry as 'porphyritic' with large feldspar crystals scattered through the outcrop. His studies provided abundant evidence for the intrusive nature of the Great Whin Sill and led to a general acceptance. In particular, chilling of the upper margin of the sill, incorporation of rafts of the overlying sedimentary rock and thermal metamorphism of the overlying strata, all evidence of intrusion, are demonstrated in spectacular fashion at this GCR site.

The relationship of the Great Whin Sill to the Longhoughton Fault here shows that the sill postdates the main fault movement. The sill cuts directly across the fault plane with no offset. Nevertheless, horizontal slickensides and shearing on some vertical faces in the quarries imply that there was also some late-stage strike-slip movement along related fractures *after* emplacement of the sill (Jones *et al.*, 1980). This is valuable evidence to add to that from elsewhere that E–W-trending faulting occurred before intrusion, such as quartz-dolerite dykes intruded locally along faults (see **Wydon** GCR site report) and transgression of the sill along fault planes (see **Steel Rigg to Sewingshields Crags** GCR site report).

Conclusions

The Longhoughton Quarry GCR site shows abundant features that prove the intrusive origin of the Great Whin Sill, such as the metamorphism of overlying strata, chilling of the upper margin and rafts incorporated from the overlying sedimentary strata. In addition, the relationship of the sill to the nearby Longhoughton Fault provides evidence relating to the sequence of events in northern England in Late Carboniferous times. The intrusion of the sill clearly post-dates the main movement on the E–W-trending fault, but shearing of the quartz-dolerite and the presence of horizontal slickensides on vertical rock faces show that there was also some strike-slip (lateral) movement after emplacement of the sill.

CULLERNOSE POINT TO CASTLE POINT, NORTHUMBERLAND (NU 260 187–NU 259 221)

S.C. Loughlin

Introduction

The Cullernose Point to Castle Point GCR site extends for 3.5 km along the Northumberland coast from the promontory of Castle Point south to Cullernose Point (Figure 6.27). The Great Whin Sill has a striking influence on the scenery in this area. The rocky promontory of Castle Point is the spectacular setting for Dunstanburgh Castle, and inland, 300–700 m from the coast, the sill crops out again to form a distinctive west-facing scarp that has been extensively quarried. A fault that cuts the sill forms the 'haven' of Craster and provides a natural harbour which was used to ship out the quarried stone. The picturesque Craster village is an excellent place to see the quartz-dolerite of the sill used as a building stone.

The sill is intruded immediately below the Great Limestone at the base of the Namurian Series, and both sedimentary rocks and sill dip gently eastwards. Cross-dip sections are well exposed at both the southern and northern margins of the GCR site, and along the intervening coastline the upper dip-slope is well exposed on the shore between tide marks. The excellent coastal exposures at Cullernose Point and at Castle Point clearly reveal the contact metamorphosed sedimentary rocks above and below the sill (Figures 6.28 and 6.29). Columnar jointing is well developed and there are blocks of baked sedimentary rock incorporated into the quartz-dolerite. Veins and pods of distinctive pink felsic material are particularly abundant near Cushat Shiel and this is perhaps the best site to observe such features in the Whin Sill-complex. It is also one of the best localities to observe evidence for later injections of basaltic magma into the sill.

A number of general papers on the geology of Northumberland with references to the Whin Sill at this GCR site were published in the 19th century (e.g. Winch, 1817; Tate, 1868). The most significant early paper was that of Tate (1871), which provided many illustrations of the intrusive nature of the sill in Northumberland. The intrusive nature was debated for several

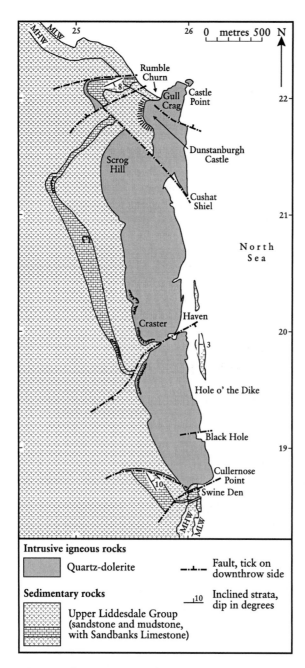

Figure 6.27 Map of the area around the Cullernose Point to Castle Point GCR site. Based on Geological Survey 1:63 360 Sheet 6, Alnwick (1930).

one-inch Sheet 6 (Alnwick) and an accompanying memoir (Carruthers *et al.*, 1930). The later basaltic intrusions and felsic veins and pods at this site were described and analysed by Smythe (1930a) in his paper on the geochemistry of the Whin Sill-complex.

Description

The Great Whin Sill is intruded below the Great Limestone into a sequence of mudstones, sandstones and limestones. Immediately to the north of Dunstanburgh Castle (NU 257 219), the sill and the underlying sedimentary rocks form the spectacular Gull Crag which comprises 16 m of columnar-jointed quartz-dolerite overlying 12 m of sandy mudstone and 2 m of grey and reddish-brown coarse sandstone. The latter is known as the Dunstanburgh Sandstone, which is distinctive because of the presence of abundant rounded clasts of quartz up to 3 mm in diameter. Contact metamorphism at the sill margins is confined to a narrow zone less than 0.5 m wide in which sandstones and limestones are recrystallized. The recrystallized limestones commonly contain pyrite, and mudstones typically become porcellanous. The main walls of Dunstanburgh Castle are made of the coarse, gritty Dunstanburgh Sandstone with a packing of quartz-dolerite boulders. The sill forms crags along the coastline for about 0.5 km south of the castle as far as Cushat Shiel (NW 259 213), a distinctive NW-trending slack that is the site of the Cushat Shiel Fault. The fault offsets the sill by almost 500 m to the west.

South of Cushat Shiel a number of faults intersect the coast, most of which have a trend of east–west or north-east–south-west. The upper surface of the sill is extremely well exposed on the shoreline between tide marks and shows the distinctive pattern of columnar joints perpendicular to the sill margins. At Craster (NW 259 200) a NE-trending fault cuts the sill, forming a natural harbour on the coast and a steep cleft in the escarpment west of the village. There has been very little movement on this structure since emplacement of the sill as the escarpment is not visibly offset. Between Scrog Hill (NW 254 214) and Craster the sill forms a steep west-facing escarpment cropping out 300–700 m inland and rising to a height of 35 m. This escarpment has been quarried extensively for both quartz-dolerite and the underlying Dunstanburgh Sandstone.

years until the abundant evidence was collated and presented by Topley and Lebour (1877). E.J. Garwood (in Bateson, 1895) presented a detailed account of the geology of this GCR site. The original geological survey of the Alnwick area was completed between 1871 and 1878 and the six-inch maps were revised between 1921 and 1925, leading to publication of the revised

Figure 6.28 Columnar-jointed quartz-dolerite of the Great Whin Sill overlying sandstone at Castle Point. (Photo: British Geological Survey, No. A3077, reproduced with the permission of the Director, British Geological Survey, © NERC.)

Figure 6.29 Columnar-jointed quartz-dolerite of the Great Whin Sill at Cullernose Point. The sill, like the underlying sedimentary rocks in the foreground, is gently folded, as is well illustrated by the columns perpendicular to its margin. (Photo: British Geological Survey, No. A3079, reproduced with the permission of the Director, British Geological Survey, © NERC.)

261

Immediately south of Craster is another zone of weakness in the sill known as 'Hole o' the Dike' which trends north-east–south-west. The dolerite within this zone is heavily jointed and there is some calcite veining. A few hundred metres farther south is another recessed feature known as 'Black Hole' (NW 261 191), which has a similar ENE–WSW orientation and is associated with fault-brecciated dolerite and extensive calcite veining. At the southern limit of the site is Cullernose Point (NW 261 187), a promontory rising to 20 m in height and composed entirely of columnar-jointed quartz-dolerite (Figure 6.29). This is a fine example of columnar jointing, with well-developed columns that are clearly perpendicular to the upper and lower margins of the sill. Just west of Cullernose Point at Swine Den, there are some spectacular xenoliths of Dunstanburgh Sandstone and mudstone within the sill (Smythe, 1931) and a few metres south of the main sill outcrop is a vertical quartz-dolerite dyke intruded into a fault. Xenoliths of fault-breccia can be observed within the dyke.

Xenoliths of country rock are also common in the sill in the vicinity of Dunstanburgh Castle and just north of the castle at Rumble Churn (Garwood in Bateson, 1895). The xenoliths of sandstone, mudstone and limestone are strongly affected by contact metamorphism. Mudstones have been converted to biotite-andalusite hornfels with a distinctive spotted appearance; sandstones have commonly undergone recrystallization to quartzite and impure limestones have become calc-silicate hornfels with garnet, wollastonite and idocrase (Westoll *et al.*, 1955). Impure limestones tend to show more alteration than pure limestones, as recognized by Randall (1959). Vesicles in the sill that are close to xenoliths commonly contain radiating crystals of quartz (in places amethysts), which are known locally as 'Dunstanburgh diamonds'.

Veins and pods of pink felsic material are particularly abundant around Cushat Shiel. The veins are up to 5 cm in width and the roundish pods are about 2 cm thick and several centimetres across. This felsic material varies in grain size from pegmatitic to cryptocrystalline in which the major components of quartz and feldspar cannot be distinguished. Smythe (1930a), in his extensive study of the Whin Sill-complex, believed this location to have the greatest concentration of felsic material. He also described intrusions of fine-grained basaltic rock at Cullernose Point and Scrog Hill, the latter being heavily altered. The intrusions are just a few centimetres thick and have chilled margins against the normal quartz-dolerite. The intrusion at Cullernose Point contains rare microphenocrysts of augite but is otherwise non-porphyritic. Smythe's analyses showed that these basic intrusions have broadly the same chemical composition as the sill.

Interpretation

Garwood (in Bateson, 1895) produced a field sketch showing the Cullernose Dyke at Swine Den feeding the sill, but Carruthers *et al.* (1930) were unable to find sufficient field evidence connecting the sill and the dyke. Westoll *et al.* (1955) discussed the emplacement of the Great Whin Sill in this area and described how it crosses pre-existing faults with little displacement but locally turns up or down a pre-existing fault zone to form transgressive connecting dykes between different stratigraphical or structural levels. They suggested that the Cullernose Dyke is an example of this process and the incorporation of inclusions of fault-breccia within the dyke proves the pre-existence of the fault. Magnetic evidence appears to support this hypothesis since the Cullernose Dyke has magnetic properties that are very similar to the Great Whin Sill (El-Harathi and Tarling, 1988) but different to the nearby Holy Island dyke system. This suggests that the Cullernose Dyke and the sill had a similar cooling history and may therefore have been emplaced contemporaneously.

The felsic pods in the vicinity of Cushat Shiel were described and analysed by Smythe (1930a). He concluded that as crystallization of the sill progressed, the remaining magma became progressively more acidic. The composition of this late-stage assemblage typically comprises small feldspar laths, some orthoclase and quartz. This assemblage forms either a relatively coarse-grained pegmatitic facies, an indeterminate fine-grained assemblage or, when concentrated, 'a crypto-pegmatite in spherulitic form'. Such segregation veins and pods are now recognized in the upper parts of many thick sills as the final product of differentiation.

The fine-grained basaltic intrusions, with chilled margins, are similar in composition to the sill and are therefore not differentiates. Smythe (1930a) argued that they must have been intruded later, 'at a time when the sill had become consolidated and cold'. This observation has potential significance in current debates concerning the relative ages of the sill-complex and the accompanying dyke-swarms.

Conclusions

At the Cullernose Point to Castle Point GCR site, excellent exposures reveal classic features relating to the intrusion and late-stage crystallization of a sill. In addition this site provides a spectacular example of the influence of the Great Whin Sill on the scenery of Northumberland, such as the high sea cliffs that were used as the foundations for Dunstanburgh Castle. The cliffs show well-developed columnar jointing and also contain large rafts of sedimentary rock incorporated during emplacement of the sill. These fragments of country rock are baked by the hot magma to form different metamorphic rocks depending on the composition of the original sedimentary rocks. Vesicles in the dolerite close to sandstone inclusions commonly contain radiating quartz crystals or amethyst and are known locally as 'Dunstanburgh diamonds'. In addition, the sill has abundant examples of quartz and feldspar-rich veins, which formed during the final stages of crystallization of the magma, and of later injections of basaltic magma.

BUDLE POINT TO HARKESS ROCKS, NORTHUMBERLAND (NU 163 361– NU 177 355)

S.C. Loughlin and D. Stephenson

Introduction

Coastal exposures to the west of Bamburgh village, Northumberland show the Great Whin Sill in extremely complicated contact with the host Carboniferous sedimentary rocks. At the Budle Point to Harkess Rocks GCR site, the sill encloses a variety of large rafts and blocks of sedimentary rock that dip in various directions and show varying degrees of contact metamorphism. It seems probable that the sedimentary

beds were disrupted, perhaps by faulting, prior to intrusion of the sill. The basal and upper contacts of the sill are irregular and cut up and down the sedimentary succession throughout the site. At Budle Point the upper part of the sill is vesicular, with sinuous flow structures, suggesting that it was intruded at quite a shallow depth. Hydrothermal alteration has occurred close to ENE-trending veins that carry baryte and pyrite, and carbonate-filled fractures may indicate post-emplacement faulting.

This is the most complex of the GCR sites that represent the Whin Sill-complex. The extreme complexity has provoked much interest and many authors have attempted to describe and explain the relationships (e.g. Tate, 1868; Lebour and Fryer, 1877; Lebour, 1886; Carruthers *et al.*, 1927; Smythe, 1930b). Tate (1868) and other early authors described the outcrops but their field sketches were commonly stylized. Short descriptions of the exposures by Randall and Senior can be found in an excusion guide (Scrutton, 1995).

Description

Some 500 m north-west of Bamburgh Castle (NW 184 350) the Great Whin Sill is exposed on the foreshore for about 2 km between Harkess Rocks and Budle Point (Figure 6.30). The sill and the Carboniferous sedimentary rocks into which it is intruded generally dip gently towards the east but there is some minor folding. The sill lies above the Brigantian Oxford Limestone near Bamburgh Castle (outside the GCR site) where it can be seen cutting transgressively through cross-bedded red sandstones, but it lies close to the Budle Limestone at Budle Point (NW 163 361).

The shoreline is devoid of exposures for several hundred metres between Bamburgh Castle and Harkess Rocks, suggesting that the south-eastern margin of the rocks may be fault-controlled. At Harkess Rocks (NW 177 356) the sill is sub-horizontal and the upper chilled surface is exposed on the foreshore, the overlying sedimentary rocks having been completely removed by erosion (Figure 6.31). Close to the chilled surface is a zone of elongate and flattened vesicles, generally up to about 30 cm long by 20 cm wide and little more than 10 mm deep, although some have been recorded that are several metres long. Some are filled with

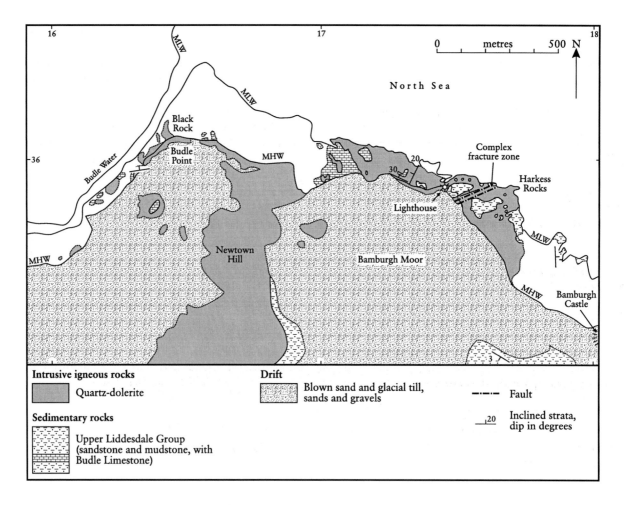

Figure 6.30 Map of the area around the Budle Point to Harkess Rocks GCR site. Based on Geological Survey 1:10 560 Sheet Northumberland, Old Series 16NE (1899).

quartz and a little calcite. Scattered about the sub-horizontal surfaces are areas of concentric curving ridges reminiscent of the surface patterns on pahoehoe lavas, but in miniature. These have been termed 'ropy flow structures' (Lebour and Fryer, 1877; Smythe, 1930b) and have been interpreted as having formed on the lower inside surfaces of the flattened vesicles. They have been exposed as the upper parts of the vesicles have been eroded away. Similar flow structures have been observed near to sub-horizontal contacts of the Holy Island intrusion (Randall and Farmer, 1970; see **Holy Island GCR site** report).

Large inclusions of sedimentary host rock occur within the quartz-dolerite throughout the Harkess Rocks area. Near the south-eastern edge of Harkess Rocks an inclusion of sandstone 11 m long dips steeply to the NNE. Farther to the north at the low-tide mark is a large mass of

indurated mudstone, which extends for about 150 m and contains a dyke-like intrusion of quartz-dolerite, 16 m long. This mass of mudstone is surrounded by quartz-dolerite, but farther to the north and west small, thin skins of indurated mudstone lie directly on the fine-grained upper surface of the dolerite. The sill transgresses up through mudstone towards the north and numerous small mudstone inclusions may be observed within the quartz-dolerite along the shoreline.

Two ENE-trending fracture zones, about 25 m apart and with several splays, contain thin veins with baryte and pyrite in places. Between the two fracture zones is a chaotic zone of large blocks of sedimentary rock and irregular intrusions of dolerite. One block of white, rippled, fine-grained sandstone dips south-west at about 10° and just to the east of this, another mass of coarser sandstone dips east at about 60°. These

Budle Point to Harkess Rocks

Figure 6.31 Bamburgh Castle, sited on a crag of quartz-dolerite of the Great Whin Sill, viewed from Harkess Rocks. The flat rocks in the foreground are close to the top surface of the sill; overlying sedimentary rocks have been removed completely, but the chilled margin of the sill is preserved as a thin skin in places. (Photo: D. Stephenson.)

sandstone bodies are clearly enclosed by quartz-dolerite. On the north side of the fracture zones, a thin bed of blue-grey recrystallized limestone dips NNW at about 30° and this is overlain by sandstone that crops out over a distance of about 30 m to the north to where it is overlain by the dolerite sill. The basal contact of the sill is magnificently exposed at the long low cliff extending to the ENE from the lighthouse and known as the Stag Rock (NW 175 359). The rocks here dip north-west at 10°–15° but curve around to dip just east of north at low-water mark. The contact transgresses the Budle Limestone and the immediately underlying and overlying mudstones and sandstones, cutting both up and down, usually in steps of 1–2 m along vertical joint or fault planes.

Near the lighthouse, the sill contains several rafts of varying size, up to 25 m long and 1 m thick, of blue-grey recrystallized limestone. In the vicinity of the larger rafts, the quartz-dolerite is cut by numerous thin carbonate-filled fractures. Further inclusions occur in the near-continuous exposures of dolerite that extend to

the west of the lighthouse for at least 350 m. Most are irregular-shaped bodies of limestone and/or mudstone, with sharp angular outlines and varying in size from several centimetres to several metres. The dips of the bodies vary in direction and degree although there is a tendency towards northerly dips.

Near Budle Point the lower 1.5 m of the sill is amygdaloidal; the amygdales are typically calcite-filled. The sill overlies altered sandy mudstone, and west of Budle Point it terminates sharply against a NW-trending lineament, which is probably the line of a fault. West of this fault, irregular apophyses of dolerite can be seen protruding into almost flat-lying limestone, which extends for a further 200 m along the shoreline.

Some of the beach sands at Budle Bay are pinkish or purple in colour due to a high content of garnet (up to 45%). The garnets are thought to have been derived from Carboniferous age sandstones, where they are present as detrital grains (Hawkes and Smythe, 1931); they have no association with the sill.

Interpretation

The relationship between the sill and the host sedimentary rocks at the Budle Point to Harkess Rocks GCR site is extremely complicated, which is unusual for the Whin Sill-complex. This site and some locations on the Farne Islands are the only places where so many inclusions are observed, although rafts of sedimentary rock are also well exposed at the **Longhoughton Quarry** GCR site. The inclusions tend to be angular, with distinct, sharp margins, and show evidence of baking and alteration. This implies that they were fully lithified and disrupted before thermal metamorphism took place (e.g. Raymond and Murchison, 1988).

The large blocks of sedimentary rock between the ENE-trending fracture zones are enclosed within and intruded by dolerite, and it seems likely that these were broken up and disrupted by faulting prior to emplacement of the sill. To the immediate south of the fracture zones, the top surface of the exposure seems to be the top surface of the sill, as patches of chilled margin are preserved. However, to the north, a basal contact is exposed. Hence it appears that either the sill changed horizon along the pre-existing fracture zones or there has been a post-emplacement downthrow to the south on the bounding faults to the fracture zones. The total displacement must be of the order of several tens of metres (i.e. the full thickness of the sill) and it is possible that this is due to a combination of both mechanisms. Elsewhere, the sill is known to use pre-existing fault zones as 'risers' along which it transgressed to different stratigraphical levels (e.g. Smythe, 1930b; see **Cullernose Point to Castle Point** GCR site report) but there is also evidence that some faulting took place after emplacement.

The zones of elongate vesicles are also unusual in the Whin Sill-complex and the internal ropy flow surfaces are highly unusual, if not unique, worldwide. Lebour and Fryer (1877) considered them to be 'shrinkage or cooling marks in the shape of concentric ridges' but Smythe (1930b) suggested that they are 'the result of the slow flow of highly viscous liquid with a free surface'. Smythe considered that these structures are developed at four separate levels within the sill. He almost certainly got this

impression as a result of the irregular upper surface of the sill, and Randall and Farmer (1970) pointed out that there is but a single zone, very close to the top. The structures are similar to those observed in short sill-like steps in a dyke at the **Holy Island** GCR site where Randall and Farmer (1970) suggested that emplacement occurred at shallow levels in the sedimentary pile, where vesicles formed as a result of rapid decompression and exsolution of volatiles from the magma. The vesicles then became flattened parallel to the contact and elongated in the flow direction. The linings of the vesicles began to cool before movement of the magma body had ceased and remained plastic long enough for flow structures to develop in them. Smythe (1930b) measured the elongation direction of the vesicles and the curvature of the ridges and deduced that the final movement of magma in the sill at Budle Point was from east to west, which is the opposite direction to that deduced for final movement in the Holy Island Dyke. Despite the fact that these are only local flow directions at the time of crystallization of the intrusive bodies, Randall and Farmer (1970) suggested that they cast doubt on the idea that the dykes and the Whin Sill were contemporaneous and that the dykes acted as feeders to the sill.

Conclusions

The Budle Point to Harkess Rocks GCR site is unique in the Whin Sill-complex because of the complexity of the relationship between the intrusion and the host sedimentary rocks. The rafts of sedimentary rock found within the intrusion are so numerous and of such diverse shape, size and orientation that it seems likely that the host rock was disrupted prior to intrusion. The angular, sharp margins of the inclusions show that the host rock was lithified prior to sill emplacement. Other features at this site include evidence of transgression of the sill and evidence of faulting after emplacement. Ropy flow surfaces on the inside of large elongate vesicles (gas cavities) near the top of the intrusion are an extremely rare, if not unique, feature worldwide and have been taken to imply emplacement at shallow depths. They suggest a magma flow direction from east to west.

GREENFOOT QUARRY, COUNTY DURHAM (NY 984 392)

S.C. Loughlin

Introduction

The abandoned Greenfoot Quarry, near Stanhope in Weardale, reveals the best available exposures of the distinctive Little Whin Sill, an important member of the Whin Sill-complex. This sill is intruded at a higher stratigraphical level than the Great Whin Sill, into the Upper Visean Three Yard Limestone, which has been slightly metasomatized at the contacts. Both the Little Whin Sill and the Great Whin Sill were intersected by the Rookhope Borehole, some 6 km north-west of the quarry; there the sills are about 130 m apart.

The Little Whin Sill was first described by Trevelyan as early as 1831. Clough (1880) suggested that the dolerite of the sill had assimilated the country rocks, and Egglestone (1910) described the field relationships in some detail. Principal descriptions of the petrography include those by Teall (1884a,b, 1888), Holmes

and Smith (1921), Holmes and Harwood (1928), Tomkeieff (1929) and K.C. Dunham (1948). Geochemical studies by Smythe (1930a), A.C. Dunham and Kaye (1965) and Harrison (1968) have shown that the sill is similar to, but geochemically and mineralogically distinct from, other members of the Whin Sill-complex. It is the only intrusion in which fresh olivine phenocrysts have been found and may represent a more primitive parental magma to the complex (A.C. Dunham and Kaye, 1965; A.C. Dunham and Wilkinson, 1992).

Description

Greenfoot Quarry is situated 1 km west of Stanhope (Figure 6.32). The eastern end of the quarry is partially flooded obscuring the basal contact of the sill, but the upper contact is exposed all along the upper part of the south-facing quarry wall and is clearly visible from the Stanhope–Wearhead Road (A689). The sill is intruded into the Upper Visean Three Yard Limestone, which is about 2.5 m thick throughout Weardale. The west end of the quarry face reveals a complete section through the sill, with

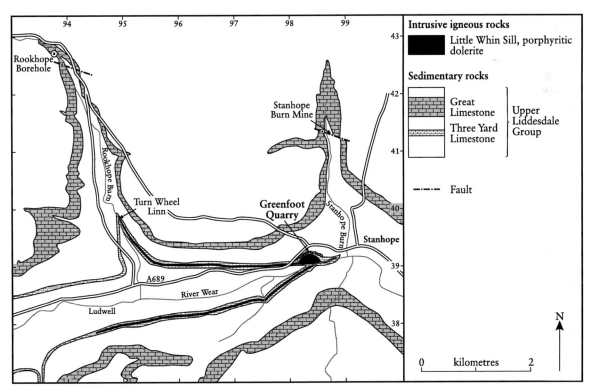

Figure 6.32 Map of the area around the Greenfoot Quarry GCR site. After A.C. Dunham and Kaye (1965).

metasomatized limestone above and below. The sill is 13 m thick and takes the form of a flat-lying sheet, with columnar jointing. This is the maximum known thickness of the Little Whin Sill, which thins westwards along the banks of the River Wear until it dies out in the vicinity of Ludwell (Figure 6.32). To the north, in the Rookhope Borehole (NY 937 427), the Little Whin Sill is about 2 m thick but it dies out rapidly to the west of Rookhope Burn. The sill has also been encountered to the north of the River Wear in Stotfield Burn Mine (NY 943 424) and Stanhope Burn Mine (NY 987 413). However, the absolute northern extent of the sill is unknown because mine workings and boreholes are too shallow to reach the northerly dipping Three Yard Limestone into which it is intruded. In the Woodland Borehole (NZ 091 277), some 15 km to the south-east of Stanhope, the Little Whin Sill is encountered 20 m above the Three Yard Limestone (Mills and Hull, 1968), but it is not present in outcrops in Upper Teesdale or in boreholes drilled to this level around Crook to the east.

The Little Whin Sill is a very fine- to fine-grained porphyritic dolerite. The grain size increases rapidly away from the chilled margins. Lath-shaped phenocrysts of plagioclase up to 2 mm long have labradorite cores (An_{70-68}) and may show normal, oscillatory and reversed zoning. The overall compositional range is from An_{70} to An_{35} and individual grains may show a great variation as a result of the zoning. This range increases away from the margins of the sill. Rare phenocrysts of calcic plagioclase (bytownite) with resorption textures have been observed. Clinopyroxene phenocrysts up to 2 mm long are granular and also show zoning. Sparse orthopyroxene phenocrysts are elongate and commonly embayed. Phenocrysts of fresh olivine, up to 1.5 mm in length, have been observed at the base of the Little Whin Sill in the Rookhope Borehole and at Turn Wheel Linn, but only pseudomorphs after olivine occur elsewhere, and even these are rare. Opaque minerals make up about 10% of the rock, with magnetite and ilmenite the dominant phases. Groundmass minerals include plagioclase, clinopyroxene, magnetite and ilmenite, and intersertal areas are filled by a mixture of quartz and alkali feldspar. Hornblende, biotite and apatite occur as accessory minerals, and pyrite and chalcopyrite have also been found at Greenfoot Quarry.

In the central parts of the sill irregular vugs occur, containing quartz rimmed by carbonate (ankerite and calcite). In places, granular pyrite is associated with these vugs.

The Little Whin Sill has a relatively high total iron content but, in comparison to the Great Whin Sill, contains less silica (47%) and potassium. There is a detectable increase in the FeO/Fe_2O_3 ratio towards the centre of the sill, but other major elements and trace elements show little variation (A.C. Dunham and Kaye, 1965).

Interpretation

The first paper to concentrate on the Little Whin Sill described it as a basaltic lava (Trevelyan, 1831). At that time the Great Whin Sill was also considered by many to be a lava flow, despite the compelling evidence of intrusion presented by Sedgwick (1827), but the intrusive nature of the Whin Sill-complex as a whole was eventually recognized (Topley and Lebour, 1877). Topley and Lebour considered the two sills to be branches of one large intrusive sheet and Teall (1884a,b) showed that they are petrologically almost identical. Egglestone (1910) also proposed that they are contemporaneous.

Based on the lack of disruption to, and varying thickness of, the Three Yard Limestone, Clough (1880) suggested that substantial quantities of the limestone must have been assimilated by the sill during emplacement. However, Smythe (1930a) found no evidence of assimilation in his abundant analyses of the Little Whin Sill, and A.C. Dunham and Kaye (1965) also discounted the assimilation hypothesis, pointing out the constant thickness of the Three Yard Limestone where it is intruded by the sill. They suggested that variations in the thickness of the limestone to the north-west and south of the Alston Block are structural and sedimentological features unrelated to the Little Whin Sill.

In contrast to the Great Whin Sill, the Little Whin Sill is lacking Ca-poor pyroxene in the groundmass. A.C. Dunham and Kaye (1965) suggested that this is partly due to the presence of olivine, which would have removed Mg and Fe from the system. In addition, a reduction of water vapour pressure on emplacement of the sill would have increased the solidus temperature of the magma and therefore inhibited orthopyroxene crystallization. A.C.

Dunham and Kaye (1965) also investigated the apparent lack of crystal settling. They calculated that the Little Whin Sill in Greenfoot Quarry would have cooled in one and a half to two years (compared to 75 years for the Great Whin Sill at its thickest point) and they went on to suggest that rapid crystallization of microlytes impeded the settling of the phenocrysts. This process would also have inhibited circulation of the magma, thus explaining the zoning of the phenocrysts. The phenocrysts would have rapidly depleted their surrounding magma in Ca and Mg and hence the plagioclase crystallized with relatively Na-rich rims and the mafic minerals with Fe-rich rims. The centre of the Little Whin Sill, with its quartz-carbonate-filled vugs, was interpreted by A.C. Dunham and Kaye (1965) as the last zone to crystallize.

Geochemical analyses of all of the Whin Sill-complex samples plot between the alkaline and tholeiite fields on a silica–total alkali discrimination diagram and so may be described as transitional. Nevertheless the petrographical affinities are dominantly tholeiitic (A.C. Dunham and Kaye, 1965). When plotted on an AFM diagram, (Na_2O+K_2O)–FeO–MgO, the Little Whin Sill analyses form a tight cluster, in contrast to the Great Whin Sill analyses, which show a very slight trend towards iron enrichment. Chemical and mineralogical evidence therefore suggests that the Little Whin Sill may represent the initial composition of the magma responsible for the whole sill-complex (A.C. Dunham and Kaye, 1965; Harrison, 1968). However, the iron-rich nature of the Little Whin Sill and the presence of some resorbed bytownite crystals suggest that it had already undergone some differentiation prior to its emplacement (A.C. Dunham and Kaye, 1965).

Conclusions

The Greenfoot Quarry GCR site provides the best available exposures of the distinctive Little Whin Sill, which was intruded into the Visean Three Yard Limestone, above the local stratigraphical level of the Great Whin Sill. The site clearly shows the fine-grained, chilled upper contact of the sill, columnar jointing and quartz-carbonate-filled vugs in the centre of the sill, the final part of the sill to crystallize.

The Little Whin Sill has a slightly lower silica content than the Great Whin Sill and contains rare olivine phenocrysts. It is of great importance in understanding the origin of the Whin Sill-complex as a whole because it is thought to be close to the composition of the initial magma from which the complex evolved. However, a relatively high iron content and a rare occurrence of feldspar crystals that show signs of having reacted with the magma after they crystallized, suggest that the magma had already undergone some modification prior to emplacement.

HOLY ISLAND, NORTHUMBERLAND (NU 123 416–NU 149 419)

S.C. Loughlin and D. Stephenson

Introduction

The Holy Island coastal GCR site exhibits excellent exposures of a dyke system, related to the Whin Sill-complex, extending for over 30 km from Coldstream in the west to reefs off the east coast of Northumberland (Figure 6.2). Outcrops of quartz-dolerite extend for 2 km along the south coast of Holy Island between St Cuthbert's Isle and Scar Jockey rocks (Figure 6.33). These outcrops were formerly regarded as *en échelon* sectors of a simple dyke, but are now thought to represent sill-like transgressions within a dyke (Figure 6.34). They provide excellent accessible exposures that reveal both steeply inclined side margins and gently sloping upper surfaces. Flattened, elongate amygdales with unusual ropy flow textures on their lower inner surfaces are a particularly striking feature. The 'dyke' intrudes sedimentary rocks of the Brigantian Liddesdale Group and stands proud from the low-lying island, providing a series of rocky ridges and promontories upon which Lindisfarne Castle and other buildings of historical and archaeological interest have been constructed (Figure 6.35).

The field relationships of the 'dyke' have been described by several authors (Winch, 1822; Trevelyan, 1823; Tate, 1868, 1871; Gunn, 1900; Carruthers *et al.*, 1927). Holmes and Harwood (1928) included it in their petrographical study of the Whin Sill-complex and Holmes and Mockler (1931) produced a general summary. The most definitive account of the field relationships is that by Randall and Farmer (1970), who described the internal structure and the unusual flow textures in some detail. The

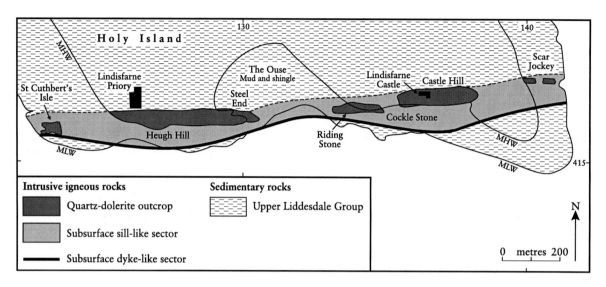

Figure 6.33 Map of the Holy Island GCR site. After Goulty *et al.* (2000).

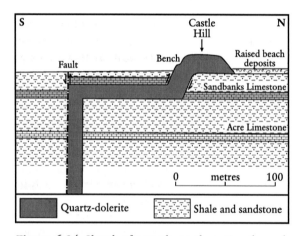

Figure 6.34 Sketch of a south–north section through the centre of Castle Hill, Holy Island, showing the alternating dyke-like and sill-like sectors of the intrusion. After Goulty *et al.* (2000).

intrusion was the subject of a palaeomagnetic study by Giddings *et al.* (1971) and a detailed magnetic survey of the mainland part of the dyke system was conducted by El-Harathi and Tarling (1988). However, it was the magnetic survey of Goulty *et al.* (2000) that revealed the most about the structure of the intrusion and resulted in a radical re-appraisal of its form. A weighted mean Ar-Ar age of 294 ± 2 Ma has recently been obtained from groundmass plagioclase in this intrusion (M. Timmerman, pers. comm., 2002). The 'dyke' is included in a field itinerary for Holy Island, described by Randall and Senior in the excursion guide of Scrutton (1995).

Description

The Holy Island Subswarm is the most northerly of the major dyke subswarms associated with the Great Whin Sill and is close to its northern limit (see **Budle Point to Harkess Rocks** GCR site report). In general, the mineralogy of the component dykes is the same as the sill, but the Holy Island 'Dyke' is porphyritic with phenocrysts of plagioclase, clinopyroxene and iron oxides in a fine-grained groundmass (Holmes and Harwood, 1928; Holmes and Mockler, 1931). On Holy Island itself there are five discrete *en échelon* outcrops, each of which has an east–west trend (Randall and Farmer, 1970). The outcrops reach a maximum width of *c*. 60 m but there is no northern contact exposed. The southern contact is undulating in places, but generally dips steeply to the south. The upper surface of each outcrop is generally irregular but in places it appears to be a planar margin to the intrusion, with a gentle dip to the east.

St Cuthbert's Isle

St Cuthbert's Isle (NW 123 416) is composed entirely of quartz-dolerite, having dominant sub-horizontal joints, and was interpreted by Goulty *et al.* (2000) as a sill-like body. Only the upper contact of the intrusion is exposed: in the eastern part of the isle the planar chilled surface dips gently to the east and the grain size of the rock increases downwards from this surface. The chilled margin contains a few microscopic

270

Figure 6.35 The south coast of Holy Island, clearly showing the overall apparent dyke-like nature of the quartz-dolerite intrusion, which provides the site for the castle in the far distance and shelters the priory in the middle distance. St Cuthbert's Isle, in the foreground, is formed from a sill-like step in the intrusion. (Photo: P. MacDonald.)

amygdales, but several centimetres lower there is a marked amygdaloidal zone, 15–23 cm thick, containing numerous flattened and elongate amygdales. The largest amygdales are several tens of centimetres across; they are flattened parallel to the chilled surface and are elongated towards the NNE. The amygdales comprise calcite, purple-tinted quartz and small amounts of chlorite. Where the filling has been removed by erosion the inner surfaces of the original vesicles can be seen. These are glassy, with tachylitic margins up to 2 mm thick. The lower inner surface of each vesicle has a ropy flow structure, similar (in miniature) to the ropy flow lobes on the surface of pahoehoe lava (Figure 6.36). The curvature on the flow lobes shows a fairly consistent flow direction to the east. These highly unusual features can also be seen near

Figure 6.36 Ropy flow structure on the lower inner surface of a large flattened amygdaloidal cavity (the amygdaloidal 'fill' having been eroded away), St Cuthbert's Isle, Holy Island GCR site. The lens cap is 50 mm in diameter. (Photo: D. Stephenson.)

the top of the Great Whin Sill in the **Budle Point to Harkess Rocks** GCR site, 7 km to the south-east of here.

Immediately below this zone is a further amygdaloidal layer, about 0.8 m thick, in which the amygdales are small and spherical. This layer can be traced across much of the isle, suggesting that the upper surface of the intrusion was nowhere more than a metre or so above the current erosion surface.

Immediately to the south-east of the isle, a south-facing dolerite scarp, less than 1 m high and trending east–west, is exposed at low tide. This has been interpreted by Goulty *et al.* (2000) as the southern margin of a dyke, in continuity with the flat-lying sill that forms the main outcrop of St Cuthbert's Isle.

Heugh Hill

The Heugh Hill outcrop is up to 30 m across and extends some 500 m from the coast opposite St Cuthbert's Isle to the slipway at Steel End (NU 130 417). The sharp, steeply inclined southern contact is magnificently exposed almost continuously along the full length of the outcrop, but the northern contact is not exposed. The dominant cooling joints are almost vertical and perpendicular to the southern margin, but a strong joint set also occurs parallel to the margin. Marginal parts of the intrusion generally contain small spherical amygdales. Adjacent to the contact the Acre Limestone and overlying mudstones are both thermally metamorphosed. The limestone is recrystallized to a white marble, but in places fossils (corals, brachiopods and orthoceratids) are remarkably well preserved very close to the contact. The mudstone is baked and altered, with prominent dark 'spots' up to 2 cm in diameter, over a distance of about 5 m from the contact. Thin mineral veins and disseminated pyrite occur in this area. Xenoliths are common in the marginal part of the dolerite. Of particular note are three small rafts of saccharoidal limestone in the southern margin of the intrusion about 60 m from the western end of the outcrop, and a xenolith of baked mudstone just to the east of where the path across Heugh Hill emerges at the coast. Farther east, where the country-rock sandstone contains ferruginous nodules, some nodules seem to have been incorporated in the dyke margin. In the eastern parts of the outcrop, the southern contact is undulating and in places forms almost horizontal benches, below which flattened amygdales may be observed similar to those at St Cuthbert's Isle. The bench surfaces and the steeper contacts are coated with patchy 'skins' of sedimentary rock. At Steel End (NU 130 416), a smooth chilled surface is exposed at low tide that dips gently to the east. This surface reveals numerous clustered and elongated amygdales; abundant ropy flow structures are seen and the original quartz-calcite infills are better preserved than at St Cuthbert's Isle.

Castle Hill

The outcrop of dolerite at Castle Hill is almost 60 m wide. The undulating southern margin is exposed above the beach, where sub-horizontal sections form a series of benches, some up to 3 m wide. The most obvious bench, at Cockle Stone (NU 134 417), has the appearance of a man-made quay and has in fact been used as such. Thin skins of sedimentary rock coat the margin in places and flattened vesicles with ropy textured bases may be found on the benches. Curving cooling joints are parallel to the undulating contact. Near the castle a small offshoot from the main intrusion extends for 11.5 m into the surrounding mudstones. This apophysis is composed of 'white whin', dolerite altered by circulating mineral-rich fluids. The rock exposed below and to the east of the castle is vesicular and fine grained, with pervasive horizontal jointing.

Scar Jockey

At Scar Jockey dolerite crops out on the shoreline but no contacts are exposed. Prominent joints dip at 20° to the south-east and are typical of those along the northern margin of the other outcrops (Randall and Farmer, 1970).

Plough Rock and Goldstone Rock

The Plough Rock, 1 km from shore, is composed entirely of dolerite and marks the edge of a reef known as Plough Seat, which is partially visible at very low tides. Dolerite is further exposed 3.5 km offshore on the Goldstone Rock.

Interpretation

The igneous and intrusive nature of the 'dyke' at Holy Island was recognized by early authors (Winch, 1822; Trevelyan, 1823). On early one-inch-scale geological maps of the 1870s all the outcrops on Holy Island and further *en échelon* segments on the mainland were joined as one long sinuous dyke. Gunn (1900) recognized the discontinuous nature of the dyke and a revision of the six-inch maps took place during the 1920s (Carruthers *et al.*, 1927).

Holmes and Harwood (1928) suggested that the Holy Island 'Dyke' and its mainland equivalents were intruded into pre-existing tension cracks developed during a period of Late Carboniferous east–west compression, which was also responsible for the Holburn and Lemmington anticlines. This theory was accepted by many authors (e.g. Robson, 1954, 1977; Westoll *et al.*, 1955; Shiells, 1964; Wilson, 1970). However, Carruthers *et al.* (1927) noted field relationships suggesting that the dykes post-dated the compression event, and Jones *et al.* (1980) pointed out that the tension gashes occur between shear faults that offset the axis of the Holburn Anticline. The magnetic survey of El-Harathi and Tarling (1988) showed that there are four distinct sub-parallel ENE-trending dykes in the mainland part of the subswarm, rather than numerous small offset segments, and they interpreted this as proof that dyke emplacement was not related to an east–west compressional event. They suggested that the dykes represent the infilling of tensional fractures formed after the compressional event, perhaps during isostatic adjustment between the Cheviot Massif and the Northumberland Trough.

Giddings *et al.* (1971) proposed that at the time of crystallization of the Holy Island 'Dyke', the magnetic pole was at latitude 38° N and longitude 177° E. This is consistent with its formation close to the equator in latest Carboniferous or Early Permian times when the ancient geomagnetic field was reversed. This location is statistically indistinguishable from that determined for the Great Whin Sill by Creer *et al.* (1959). However, the recently obtained Ar-Ar date of 294 ± 2 Ma is significantly younger than the even more precise 297.4 ± 0.4 Ma U-Pb date from the Great Whin Sill (see **Upper Teesdale** GCR site report) and may re-inforce views that the sills and dykes are not quite coeval.

The steeply inclined, chilled southern contacts to the intrusion on Holy Island imply a dyke-like body, but several of the outcrops also exhibit planar chilled upper surfaces that dip gently to the east. Sub-horizontal jointing is dominant close to these contacts, increasing in intensity towards them, and parallel zones of flattened elongate amygdales also occur. The sub-horizontal contacts were originally interpreted as the upper termination of a dyke within the Carboniferous sedimentary pile (Randall and Farmer, 1970). Such a blunt termination is most unusual in dykes, which normally taper and pinch-out upwards, yet this interpretation persisted until a detailed magnetic survey by Goulty *et al.* (2000) suggested a form that fits the field observations much more convincingly (Figure 6.34). The magnetic survey suggests that most of the outcrops (Heugh Hill, Castle Hill and Scar Jockey) are formed from a sill that 'turns down' to the south to become a steeply inclined dyke. (The northern margin has been removed by erosion, so it is not known whether the sill continued farther to the north or whether it turned up within a short distance to continue as a dyke.) To the south of these outcrops, the intrusion levels out to form another sill-like sector, seen only on St Cuthbert's Isle. This then turns down to the south into a dyke, seen only in the small scarp south-east of the isle, but traced by its magnetic anomaly to the south of all of the outcrops (Figure 6.33). Although the sill-like sectors have a slight dip to the east, they must also step up to the east, as they transgress up through the stratigraphy of the host rocks in this direction. Hence the intrusion has the form of a step-and-stair transgression that steps upwards both to the north and to the east, though probably as part of an overall dyke-like body with only minor sill-like sectors. The overall form is in fact hinted at by the bench-like 'steps' that have long been recognized in the steep contacts on the southern margin of the main outcrops.

The sill-like parts of the intrusion are characterized by amygdaloidal zones in much the same way as a lava flow. The amygdales are infills of vesicles that formed by the exsolution of volatiles from the magma, probably following rapid decompression as a result of injection into the near-surface sedimentary pile. The rapid release of volatiles causes undercooling, which leads to rapid crystallization of the magma, hence explaining the fine-grained linings around the vesicles (Randall and Farmer, 1970). The quenched linings must have remained plastic for long enough to allow flattening, elongation and the development of flow structures by the still-molten magma moving through the intrusion. The flow structures at the base of the vesicles resemble pahoehoe ropy flow structures on the surface of lava flows and can be used to infer local flow directions (Figure 6.36). Randall and Farmer (1970) constructed rose diagrams from their field data to deduce the modal flow directions at three different localities. All three sites showed evidence that the final, local horizontal component of the flow direction was from west to east. The appearance of the flow structures is very similar to ropy flow structures described by Smythe (1930b) towards the top of the sub-horizontal Great Whin Sill at Harkess Rocks west of Bamburgh. There, the flow direction indicated by these structures suggests that final movement of magma in the Great Whin Sill was from east to west (see **Budle Point to Harkess Rocks** GCR site report).

Conclusions

The Holy Island 'Dyke' is an extremely well exposed component of an E–W-trending dyke system at the northern margin of, and related to, the Whin Sill-complex. The upstanding rocky ridge is a significant landscape feature that has clearly influenced the defensive and monastic settlements of Lindisfarne, one of the prime historical sites in Britain.

The exposures comprise several outcrops of quartz-dolerite that show a confusing variety of contact-related features, some steeply inclined and some near horizontal. Originally these were attributed to several *en échelon* segments of a dyke that terminated close to the present land surface at a broad, gently sloping, near-planar upper surface. However, a geophysical survey has shown that the features are better explained by a series of step-and-stair transgressions that result in alternating dyke-like and sill-like sectors of the intrusion. This re-interpretation has in no way detracted from the potential international importance of the site, which preserves a wide variety of interesting features associated with such structural perturbations in an otherwise regionally persistent major dyke.

Of particular interest are near-horizontal joints and zones of large flattened and elongate amygdales that are prominent close to the upper contacts of the sill-like sectors. The original inner surfaces of the gas bubbles are revealed where the infilling material has been removed by later erosion and these show miniature 'ropey' flow structures. Such structures, which are very rare or possibly unique worldwide, have been used to determine the final flow direction of magma in the dyke.

WYDON, NORTHUMBERLAND (NY 695 629)

S.C. Loughlin

Introduction

The Wydon GCR site, on the north bank of the River South Tyne, 1.5 km south-west of Haltwhistle station, is an excellent natural exposure of the Haltwhistle Dyke, a tholeiitic basalt associated with the Whin Sill-complex (Figure 6.37). The dyke is orientated ENE–WSW and is part of the St Oswald's Chapel Subswarm that extends discontinuously between Haltwhistle and Druridge Bay and has also been proved beneath the North Sea (Randall, 1995b). Natural inland exposures of dykes associated with the Whin Sill-complex are rare and, although many

dykes have been quarried, most of the quarries have been infilled or have become overgrown. In coalfield areas, natural exposures and quarries have been lost through opencast working of coal from the surrounding strata. This rare exposure is therefore of considerable national significance.

The general geology of the site is also of interest. The dyke is intruded into flat-lying Namurian sandstones with thin intercalations of mudstone, and is overlain by Quaternary till containing a wide variety of igneous and sedimentary clasts.

The general geology of the nearby Roman Wall district has been described by Wallis (1769), Winch (1817), Tate (1868) and Johnson (1959). The Geological Survey mapped central and southern Northumberland in the 1870s and six-inch sheets 106NE and 106SE were published in 1881. A revision survey was completed in 1975 and 1:50 000 Sheet 13 (Bellingham), with an accompanying memoir, was published in 1980 (Frost and Holliday, 1980). It was Holmes and Harwood (1928) who first suggested that the dykes were comagmatic with the Whin Sill-

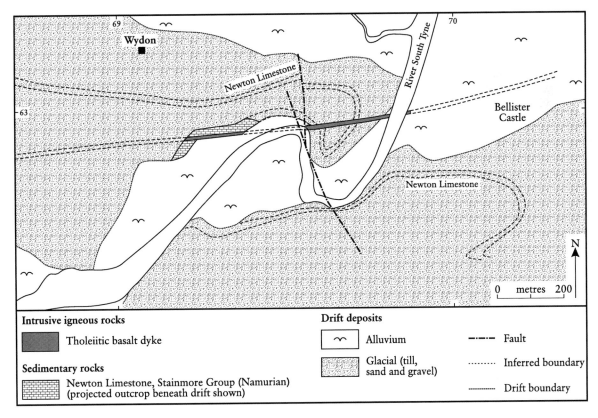

Figure 6.37 Map of the area around the Wydon GCR site. Based on Geological Survey 1:10 560 Sheet Northumberland, New Series 89SW (1926).

complex, and Thorpe and Macdonald (1985) included analyses of the dykes in their geochemical study of the complex. Popular field guides of the area include those by Scrutton (1995) and Johnson (1997).

Description

The sense of the *en échelon* offsets in the St Oswald's Chapel Subswarm is sinistral, like that of the High Green Subswarm to the north, but the offsets are not as well developed. Near Haltwhistle the subswarm trends ENE, almost parallel to the Roman Wall outcrops of the Great

Whin Sill, and following closely the line of the River South Tyne. Near Hexham, it swings to a more north-easterly trend, converging on the High Green Subswarm. Dykes regarded as part of the St Oswald's Chapel Subswarm also include the Erring Burn Dyke, the Bavington Dyke and the Causey Park Dyke, which has been traced for some distance offshore (Randall, 1995b).

At the Wydon GCR site the dyke forms a significant feature, over 10 m in height and *c.* 6 m in width (Figure 6.38). Contacts with the surrounding sedimentary rocks are obscured by slumped and fallen rock debris but flat-lying sedimentary rocks crop out in low cliffs along

Figure 6.38 The Haltwhistle Dyke, cutting sandstones and overlain by till, on the bank of the River South Tyne near Wydon. (Photo: British Geological Survey, No. A4129, reproduced with the permission of the Director, British Geological Survey, © NERC.)

the river to the east and in parts of the scarp to the west. These rocks comprise sandstones with thin intercalated layers of carbonaceous mudstone. The basalt of the dyke is uniformly fine grained and it is petrologically and geochemically very similar to rocks of the Whin Sill-complex (Frost and Holliday, 1980; Thorpe and Macdonald, 1985). Plagioclase feldspar is normally zoned, accessory olivine is replaced mainly by talc, augite is partially altered to smectite and there are abundant fresh opaque oxides. The segment of this subswarm farther to the east, known as the Erring Burn Dyke, is petrologically slightly different, containing ragged hypersthene crystals and rare large xenocrysts of labradorite.

Interpretation

The rocks of the Whin Sill-complex and dyke-swarm produce notable magnetic anomalies. Whereas anomalies over the sills are relatively low, those associated with the dykes are pronounced, enabling them to be traced where there is no surface exposure and enabling their sub-surface form to be ascertained. Frost and Holliday (1980) traced the dykes of the St Oswald's Chapel Subswarm across the Bellingham district and found that several of the *en échelon* segments coincide with faults. However, overall the subswarm follows an ENE trend, which is similar to the fabric of the Lower Palaeozoic basement.

Holmes and Harwood (1928) suggested that the two most northerly subswarms (the Holy Island and High Green subswarms) were emplaced along *en échelon* fractures during a period of east–west compression, and further work by Shiells (1961) and Wilson (1970) tended to support this. However, Anderson (1951) preferred to consider the dykes as sub-parallel and emplaced during regional tension. The more southerly St Oswald's Chapel and Hett subswarms were considered to have been affected by the edges of the Alston Block (Randall, 1995b) because they are more linear and the *en échelon* structure is not as well developed.

Conclusions

The Wydon GCR site provides one of the best natural exposures of a Late Carboniferous tholeiitic dyke in northern England. The dyke is only 6 m wide but it forms a positive topographical feature that runs for a considerable distance along the banks of the River South Tyne. The dyke cooled rapidly because it is thin and it is therefore a uniformly fine-grained basalt, rather than a medium-grained dolerite. The dyke is part of the St Oswald's Chapel Subswarm, segments of which were emplaced along pre-existing fractures. However, overall it follows a curving path and the *en échelon* structure is not as well developed as in some of the other subswarms.

Chapter 7

Carboniferous and Permian igneous rocks of central England and the Welsh Borderland

Introduction

INTRODUCTION

C.N. *Waters*

Carboniferous intrusive and extrusive rocks crop out in a number of relatively small and isolated centres in the Derbyshire Peak District, the Black Country of the West Midlands, the Welsh Borderlands and the Bristol area (Figure 7.1). Boreholes for oil and coal exploration in the East Midlands, Oxfordshire and Berkshire have proved additional Carboniferous igneous rocks at depth, showing a more extensive distribution than the surface exposures. Igneous rocks of Carboniferous and Permian age, south of the Variscan Front, are described fully in the *Igneous Rocks of South-West England* GCR Volume (Floyd *et al.*, 1993). These include Dinantian and Early Permian alkaline lavas and pyroclastic rocks, and the calc-alkaline granite batholith that was intruded during Late Carboniferous to Early Permian times.

The igneous rocks of central England were of importance in the early development of the understanding of geological processes when Hutton (1788) recognized that the 'ragstones' of south Staffordshire and 'toadstones' of Derbyshire are comparable to lavas erupted from active volcanoes and that these areas had formerly seen volcanic activity. Subsequent research has provided information on field relations and petrography, and more recently work on the geochemistry has contributed to the development of understanding of the tectonic evolution of the UK during the Carboniferous Period.

Carboniferous igneous activity in this area is all considered to have occurred in a within-plate environment on the Laurussian continent (see Chapter 1). There is no evidence of direct input from the subduction-related magmatism prevalent in south-west England at the time (Upton, 1982; Macdonald *et al.*, 1984). The nature of the igneous activity in this region evolved in response to changes in tectonic processes and can be broadly sub-divided into events of Dinantian and Silesian age (Figure 7.2). The products of all these events show a typical lack of differentiation in comparison with their Scottish equivalents, probably because only small volumes of magma were produced and the eruptive activity was short-lived (Francis, 1970a).

Dinantian igneous activity

The main control on development of Dinantian volcanicity throughout England and Wales was north–south lithospheric stretching and thinning associated with the formation of blocks and basins (Leeder, 1982). Much of the activity occurred along lines of pre-existing basement lineaments which commonly bound the main blocks and basins (Francis, 1970a). The main centre of igneous activity at this time was in the Derbyshire Dome, with minor volcanism in the Bristol and Wenlock areas and in the East Midlands.

In Derbyshire, basaltic lavas, pyroclastic rocks and sills occur within a Dinantian carbonate succession. The extrusive rocks are associated with Visean sedimentary rocks, which can be determined biostratigraphically to be late Holkerian to late Brigantian in age, although the majority of activity occurred during early Brigantian times (Walters and Ineson, 1981). The sills appear to be genetically related to the extrusive rocks and are probably also of late Dinantian age, although whole-rock K-Ar and Ar-Ar dates on the sills suggest they are considerably younger than the lavas (Fitch *et al.*, 1970; M. Timmerman, pers. comm., 2002); the discrepancy may be a function of hydrothermal alteration.

In general, the igneous bodies are poorly exposed, with active or former quarrying operations providing most of the important exposures. Arnold-Bemrose (1894, 1907) identified two major centres of igneous activity at Matlock and Miller's Dale, covering areas of about 200 km^2 and 145 km^2 respectively (Francis, 1970a). The GCR sites of **Litton Mill**, **Water Swallows Quarry**, **Tideswell Dale** and **Calton Hill** are all located in the more northerly Miller's Dale Centre (Figure 7.3). Francis (1970a) identified at least 14 agglomerate vents, and Walters and Ineson (1981) recognized 30 distinct lavas and beds of pyroclastic rock. Stevenson and Gaunt (1971) noted a lack of any relationship between the flows and the vents and suggested an origin through fissure eruptions. However, Walters and Ineson (1981) suggested that the volcanic rocks were the product of small, short-lived central vent volcanoes and proposed some correlations based on the more laterally extensive pyroclastic rocks. Aitkenhead *et al.* (1985) identified two further local eruptive centres, largely from subsurface occurrences, and renamed the Matlock and Miller's Dale centres 'Bonsall' and 'Tunstead' respectively. They noted that the eruptions from the four centres were not contemporaneous and that lavas cannot be correlated from one centre to another. Wilkinson (in Neves and Downie, 1967) has proposed that intrusions and volcanic vents

Carboniferous and Permian igneous rocks of England and Wales

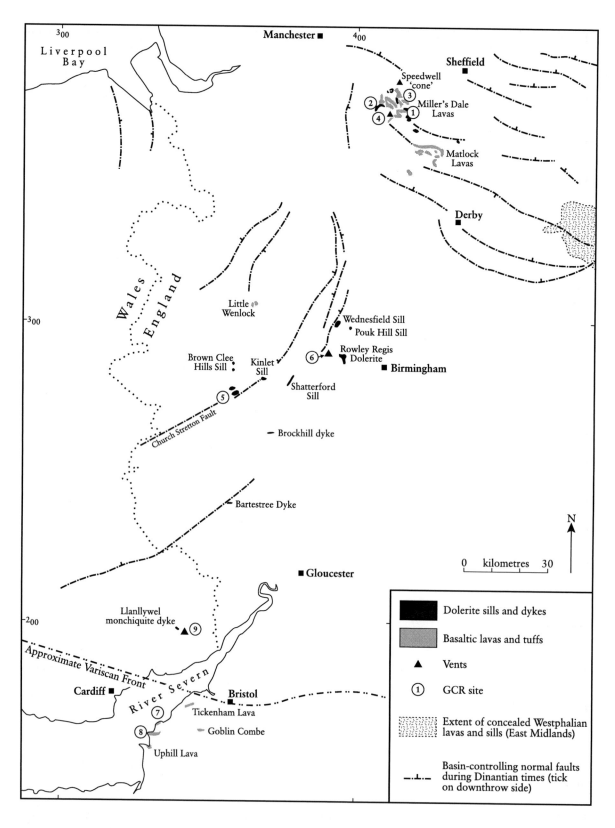

Figure 7.1 Map of central England and the Welsh Borderlands showing locations of Carboniferous igneous rocks and the GCR sites. GCR sites: 1 = Litton Mill Railway Cutting; 2 = Water Swallows Quarry; 3 = Tideswell Dale; 4 = Calton Hill; 5 = Clee Hill Quarries 6 = Barrow Hill; 7 = Middle Hope; 8 = Spring Cove; 9 = Golden Hill Quarry. Based on Geological Survey 1:625 000 Geological map of the UK South (1979).

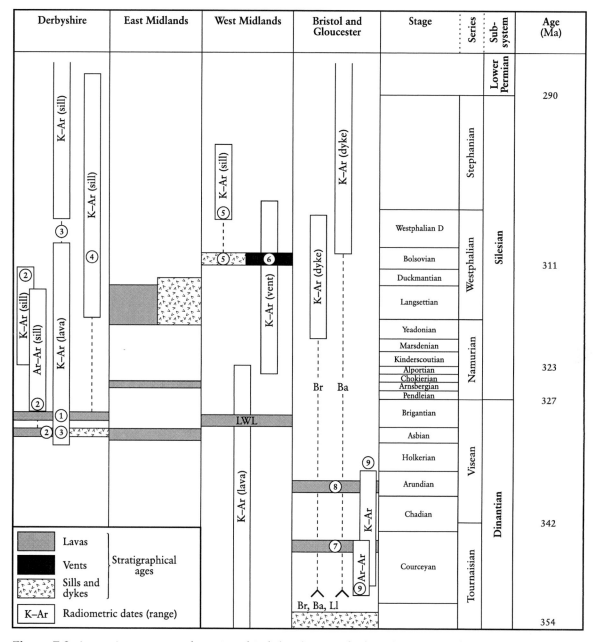

Figure 7.2 Approximate ages and stratigraphical distribution of selected igneous rocks from central England and the Welsh Borderlands. The GCR sites are numbered as for Figure 7.1. (Ba = Bartestree Dyke; Br = Brockhill Dyke; Ll = Llanllywel Monchiquite Dyke; LWL = Little Wenlock Lavas.) After Francis (1970a); and Kirton (1984). The timescale is that of Gradstein and Ogg (1996).

tend to coincide with WNW-trending anticlinal axes or occur along the margins of structural blocks.

The lavas are typically only a few tens of metres in thickness, but with some discrete flows up to 42 m thick (Francis, 1970a) and composite or compound flows in places (Walters and Ineson, 1981; Ineson and Walters, 1983; Macdonald *et al.*, 1984). The two main lava units exposed at

GCR sites in Derbyshire are the Upper Miller's Dale Lava and the Lower Miller's Dale Lava (note that the lithostratigraphical name refers to them in the singular despite the common presence of multiple lava flows). They are usually highly altered, fine-grained, olivine-phyric and aphyric basalts. The lavas are commonly vesicular with amygdales of carbonate, chlorite, chalcedony or albite (Macdonald *et al.*, 1984). Many of the lavas

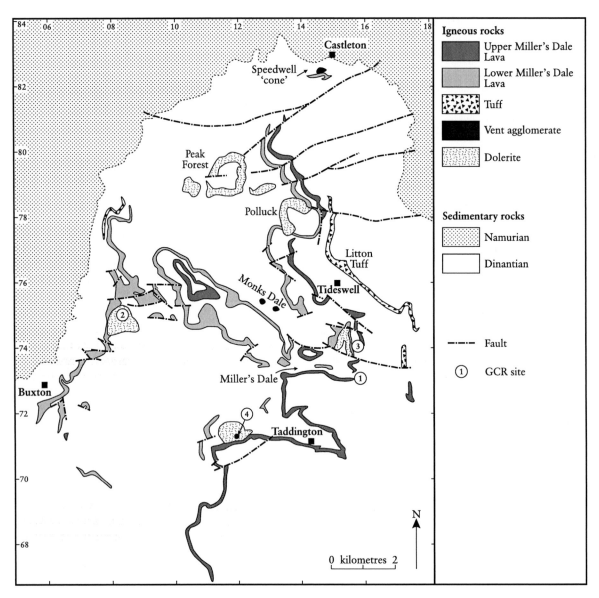

Figure 7.3 Map of the Buxton–Tideswell area, Derbyshire, showing the outcrops of Carboniferous igneous rocks and the positions of the GCR sites (numbered as in Figure 7.1). Based on Geological Survey 1:50 000 sheets 99, Chapel en le Frith (1975); and 111, Buxton (1978).

are thought to have been subaerial eruptions upon an emergent platform, and interdigitated breccias are characteristic of subaerial autobrecciation, formed in response to friction or internal disruption of flows (Ineson and Walters, 1983). However, it has been suggested that some lavas flowed across wet sediments, terminating locally in shallow water (Cheshire and Bell, 1977; Walkden, 1977; Macdonald *et al.*, 1984), and pillow lavas are recorded in marine basinal facies marginal to the platform. Tuffs are typically subordinate to the lavas, commonly preceding and/ or following lava eruption (Ineson and Walters,

1983). However, K-bentonites are widespread, most notably in the Bee Low Limestones of Asbian age, which contain 30–40 beds, generally less than 3 cm thick, though locally up to 1.25 m thick (Walkden, 1972, 1977; Aitkenhead *et al.*, 1985). Tuff-cones have been inferred or recognized at numerous localities and typically contain vitric and devitrified lapilli-tuffs, interpreted as the products of phreatomagmatic activity due to the interaction of magma and groundwater in the vent (Ineson and Walters, 1983).

The sills are dominantly medium- to coarse-grained olivine-dolerites, distinguished by the presence of altered olivine phenocrysts, ophitic intergrowths of clinopyroxene and plagioclase, and the absence or rarity of vesicles and amygdales (Macdonald *et al.*, 1984). The majority of these dolerite intrusions were emplaced along planes of weakness between lavas and limestones.

Small outcrops of volcanic rocks of late Tournaisian to early Visean age occur in the Bristol area, close to the final position of the Variscan Front (Figure 7.1). However, at the time of their eruption this area was within the extensional back-arc basin to the north of the front. The olivine basalt lavas and tuffs, some of which were submarine, are represented by the GCR sites at **Spring Cove** and **Middle Hope**. The Little Wenlock Lava of the Welsh Border-lands is a vesicular, microporphyritic, olivine basalt, up to 30 m thick, of Brigantian age (Francis, 1970a). Three minor dykes in the Welsh Borderlands cut strata of Devonian age, and are considered to have been intruded during Carboniferous time (Francis, 1970a). These are the Brockhill Dyke of analcime-gabbro (formerly 'teschenite'), the olivine-dolerite Bartestree Dyke and the monchiquitic Llanllywel Dyke, the last of these being associated lithologically and geographically with the monchiquite intrusion and volcanic pipe at the **Golden Hill Quarry** GCR site.

Silesian igneous rocks

During Namurian and early Westphalian times, north–south tectonic extension was largely replaced by a period of thermal crustal sagging caused by cooling of the asthenosphere beneath the thinned lithosphere. This process is not normally associated with the generation of igneous activity (Leeder, 1982). However, volcanic activity continued, although less abundantly and with relatively few lavas. Volcanicity became more explosive with production of tuffs and thin ash-fall clays, referred to as bentonites or tonsteins, typically a few millimetres to centimetres thick (Trewin, 1968; Francis, 1969; Price and Duff, 1969; Spears, 1970). Acidic ash-fall deposits generally cover very large areas and have been associated with Variscan volcanic activity at a destructive plate margin present to the south of Britain (Spears and Kanaris-Sotiriou, 1979). Basic bentonites are more locally developed and may relate to the alkaline igneous activity that produced the dolerite sills and lavas of the East

Midlands and sills of the West Midlands during Langsettian (Westphalian A) and Bolsovian (Westphalian C) times, respectively.

In the East Midlands, evidence of igneous activity during Carboniferous time is limited to the sub-surface, as revealed by coal and oil exploration activities (Harrison, 1977; Burgess, 1982; Kirton, 1984). Pyroclastic rocks of Namurian age have been proved, though the majority of information pertains to olivine basalt lavas and olivine-dolerite sills present within the Langsettian Coal Measures. Igneous activity appears to have terminated abruptly at the end of Langsettian time. The sills and lavas vary in composition from tholeiitic to alkaline basanite and basalt, basaltic hawaiite and hawaiite.

The Carboniferous igneous rocks of the West Midlands are predominantly alkaline olivine-dolerite sills (Kirton, 1984). The sills, exposed at the **Clee Hill Quarries** GCR site for example, are believed in many cases to have been emplaced into still-wet sediment of Bolsovian age. Because of the absence of any further geological clues to their age, they were selected by Urry and Holmes (1941) as a subject for early attempts at radiometric dating. Fitch *et al.* (1970) provided K-Ar radiometric dates for the sills, giving apparent minimum ages for intrusion of 295 ± 5 Ma to 265 ± 5 Ma (*c.* 301–271 Ma with new constants) (Stephanian–Permian). The sills are more limited in composition than those in the East Midlands, ranging from basaltic hawaiites to hawaiites. The Bolsovian Barrow Hill Complex, exposed at the **Barrow Hill** GCR site, is notably distinct from the other West Midlands intrusions as it comprises a vent agglomerate and dolerite, with associated volcaniclastic rocks (Marshall, 1946; Glover *et al.*, 1993).

LITTON MILL RAILWAY CUTTING, DERBYSHIRE (SK 158 729)

C.N. Waters

Introduction

The Litton Mill Railway Cutting, in the Wye Valley of Derbyshire, represents the Brigantian Upper Miller's Dale Lava. Here, the lava occurs within a limestone sequence and appears to have flowed across an eroded surface into a lagoonal embayment. The flow-front is well exposed and is shattered and brecciated as a consequence of contact with water. Numerous publications have referred to this section and the significance of the dramatic thinning and termination of the Upper Miller's Dale Lava (Green *et al.*, 1887; Arnold-Bemrose, 1907; Cope, 1933, 1937; Walkden, 1977).

The Upper Miller's Dale Lava, which is also present at the **Calton Hill** GCR site, commonly consists of several lava flows. The lavas are of Brigantian age and are younger than the Asbian Lower Miller's Dale Lava seen at the **Water Swallows Quarry** and **Tideswell Dale** GCR sites (Figure 7.3).

Description

The GCR site comprises a disused railway cutting, extending about 550 m to the west of the Litton Tunnel (SK 162 729) (Figure 7.4). The succession detailed below is a composite stratigraphical section (shown in descending order) from the former railway cutting and the cliffs below the cutting on the south bank of the River Wye. It is derived from descriptions by Cope (1937), R.A. Eden (unpublished Geological Survey field notes, 1954) and Walkden (1977).

Thickness (m)

Monsal Dale Limestones: 'Priestcliffe Beds' of Cope (1937)

Limestone, dark grey, thinly bedded, very fine-grained with chert nodules; a marked discontinuity is present in the lower part of the section (Figure 7.5) — 17.95

Limestone, grey, dark grey towards top, fine grained, irregular bedded with rounded fragments of decomposed lava near base — 1.37

Upper Miller's Dale Lava

Basalt, brown-weathered, upper 1.52 m poorly exposed, rough flow-banding, rounded masses of harder material up to 0.61 m diameter — up to 5.18

Monsal Dale Limestones: including 'Station Quarry Beds' of Cope (1937)

Limestone, dark grey, thinly bedded, fine grained, locally crinoidal, cherty in places especially in the upper part, 10 cm-thick K-bentonite 4 m above base; irregular base (unconformity) with pot-holes in underlying Bee Low Limestone filled with impersistent K-bentonite, up to 50 cm thick, overlying conglomerate with pale- and dark-grey limestone clasts — up to *c.* 10.00

Bee Low Limestones: Miller's Dale Beds of Cope (1937)

Limestone, pale grey, thickly bedded, very fine-grained, but with some slightly crinoidal or shelly beds — *c.* 15.00

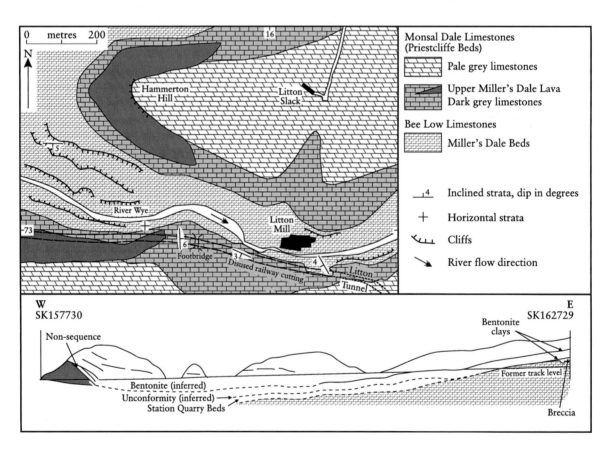

Figure 7.4 Map of the area around the Litton Mill Railway Cutting GCR site and horizontal section. After Walkden (1977).

The Upper Miller's Dale Lava is present only in the western part of the section (SK 157 730) (Figure 7.4). Here, the lava shows a rough flow-banding which dips at 40° to the east. The irregular upper surface of the lava is obscured by a small retaining wall (Figure 7.5), but was formerly seen by Cope (1933, fig. 5) with a dip toward the east of about 25°. A thin, irregular laminated tuff occurs locally beneath the lava (Cope, 1937).

At the eastern end of the cutting, at the western portal of Litton Tunnel (SK 1617 7289), the top of the Bee Low Limestones is described by Walkden (1977) as having a karstic hollow filled with limestone breccia, overlain by an impersistent K-bentonite up to 50 cm thick. A further K-bentonite band, 10 cm thick, occurs 4 m above the top of the Bee Low Limestones. This bentonite displays a relict vitroclastic texture, with rock fragments and glass shards up to 0.5 mm in diameter and bioclastic debris in a calcite matrix (Walkden, 1977).

Interpretation

The Upper Miller's Dale Lava has a typical thickness of about 30 m in Miller's Dale, but decreases markedly in thickness toward the Litton Mill Railway Cutting in the east. This GCR site provides a rare example in England of such a lateral termination of a lava flow, which is both well exposed and easily accessible.

Green *et al.* (1887) were first to recognize the lateral thinning and dying out of the lava flow. Arnold-Bemrose (1907) suggested that the absence of the flow along part of the railway cutting resulted from the presence of a fault with a downthrow of some 60 m to the east. However, in a detailed description of the cutting and adjacent area, Cope (1933, 1937) discounted the fault model and proposed that the lava died out as a flow-front about 550 m to the west of the Litton Tunnel. Walkden (1977) confirmed the presence of a flow-front and identified bentonites present laterally to the east of the

Figure 7.5 Litton Mill Railway Cutting viewed towards the south-east and showing the Upper Miller's Dale Lava (bottom right), overlain by well-bedded limestones of the Monsal Dale Limestones (above the inclined grassy ledge and re-inforcing wall). The cutting is here about 18 m deep; see hammer, bottom right. A sketch of this view, with annotation, was presented by Cope (1933, fig. 5). (Photo: British Geological Survey, No. L2270, reproduced with the permission of the Director, British Geological Survey, © NERC.)

lava. He also identified an intra-Brigantian unconformity beneath the flow and provided an interpretation of the environment of formation of the lava and of the events necessary to produce the succession seen at this site. This is summarized as follows:

1. Regional uplift at the end of Asbian time produced a karstic surface at the top of the Bee Low Limestones. Alternatively, this could have been caused by a sea-level fall (Aitkenhead *et al.*, 1985).
2. Resumed sedimentation with deposition of the Station Quarry Beds, of early Brigantian age.
3. Folding and development of a broad, low-amplitude anticline with a WNW-trending axis, referred to as the Taddington Anticline by Cope (1937), located to the south of the GCR site. The folding is associated with uplift and erosion, with localized removal of the Station Quarry Beds in the hinge of the anticline, re-exposure of the karstic surface on the top of the Bee Low Limestones and filling of pot-holes with limestone breccia, as seen at the Litton Tunnel portal (Figure 7.4). The broad syncline described by Walkden (1977) in the Bee Low Limestones beneath the railway cutting is a product of this folding event.
4. Eruption of earlier flows of the Upper Miller's Dale Lava to the west, with these flows not reaching the area of the Litton Mill Railway Cutting. Along the cutting this event is found as pyroclastic debris, evident as the lower K-bentonite present only in karstic hollows, such as at the portal of the Litton Tunnel.
5. Dormant phase associated with local subsidence and deposition of carbonates of the Monsal Dale Limestones, possibly in an embayment between inactive lava flows.
6. Resumption of extrusive activity with the earlier flows over-ridden by a lava that extends eastwards as far as the western end of the Litton Mill Railway Cutting. The tapered margin of this lava seen in the cutting is interpreted as an eastward-facing flow-front developed in a flooded embayment. The lava front displays a blocky and brecciated texture, interpreted by Walkden (1977) as a flow-foot breccia formed as a result of lava entering water and shattering. Palagonitization of the basalt is evident in places, in which devitrification of basaltic glass may have formed by rapid chill and hydration of lavas on entering

water. The rapid chilling was sufficient to halt the flow of the lava and cause the development of a steep flow-front. Separate inclined sheets of lava rubble would have developed under water, giving the rough flow-banding described by Cope (1937) and Aitkenhead *et al.* (1985). The upper 10 cm-thick K-bentonite present at the Litton Tunnel portal may represent a hyaloclastitic carpet of fine-grained volcanic detritus, which accumulated in the lagoon in front of, and was over-ridden by, the advancing lava (Walkden, 1977). The irregularly bedded limestones marginal to and overlapping the lava were interpreted by Cope (1937) as having being deposited at the time of the lava flow, and the angular discordance between two steeply dipping packages of limestone beds were interpreted as a fore-set by Walkden (1977).

Evidence for two distinct extrusive events is present at Lime Works Quarry (SK 140 730) in which a *c.* 30 m-thick, non-vesicular, holo-crystalline basalt is underlain by 5.2 m of tuffs with a thin amygdaloidal basalt (Walters and Ineson, 1981). The lava front observed at Litton Mill Railway Cutting is thought to equate to the thick upper flow.

Cope (1937) noted that the nearby Calton Hill Vent occurs in the core of the Taddington Anticline, with the inference that there may be a link between localized uplift and volcanic activity and that the Upper Miller's Dale Lava may have been sourced from the vent. However, the Calton Hill intrusion appears to be younger than the Upper Miller's Dale Lava and is of a different composition (see **Calton Hill** GCR site report).

Conclusions

The Litton Mill Railway Cutting GCR site shows a dominantly carbonate succession of Early Carboniferous age (*c.* 330–340 Ma), with evidence for a phase of broad folding, uplift and erosion interrupting deposition of the carbonate sediments. This folding event immediately predated the extrusion of several lavas, collectively known as the Upper Miller's Dale Lava, which crop out over a large area to the north-east of Buxton. The GCR site is representative of the upper part of this volcanic unit and is of great significance as it provides a rare opportunity in the Carboniferous rocks of England and Wales to study the lateral termination of a lava flow. This lava is interpreted as having flowed into a lagoonal embayment, becoming shattered and brecciated as it came into contact with the water. Explosive activity associated with rapid quenching of the lava may have produced a thin bed of fine volcanic detritus, which accumulated in the lagoon immediately in front of the lava flow and was subsequently partly over-ridden by the lava front.

WATER SWALLOWS QUARRY, DERBYSHIRE (SK 084 750)

C.N. Waters

Introduction

Water Swallows Quarry, now disused, about 3 km to the north-east of Buxton (Figure 7.3), has been selected as an excellent exposure of a thick olivine-dolerite sill, with spectacular examples of columnar cooling joints. The site is significant in that the Water Swallows Sill is seen to intrude the Lower Miller's Dale Lava, which is Visean in age, whereas the sill has been dated radiometrically to be around 10 Ma younger, of Namurian

age (Figure 7.2). Numerous descriptions of the site have been published, notably on the geometry, petrography, geochemistry and radiometric age of the sill (Moseley, 1966; Stevenson *et al.*, 1970; Stevenson and Gaunt, 1971; Ineson *et al.*, 1983). The latest published description, by Miller (1986), provides a review of previous literature and field descriptions from exposures revealed by quarrying operations from 1971 to 1985.

The Water Swallows Sill has been intruded at the same stratigraphical level as the sill at the **Tideswell Dale** GCR site and may be genetically related.

Description

The sill has an approximately semicircular outcrop about 800 m across (Figure 7.6) and with a thickness of up to at least 80 m in the west-central part of the intrusion (Ineson *et al.*, 1983). It is the thickest sill proved in the area. The upper contact has been removed by erosion and quarrying, though Stevenson and Gaunt (1971) recorded that the top of the sill is gently discordant and is overlain by basalt of the Lower Miller's Dale Lava. Ineson *et al.* (1983)

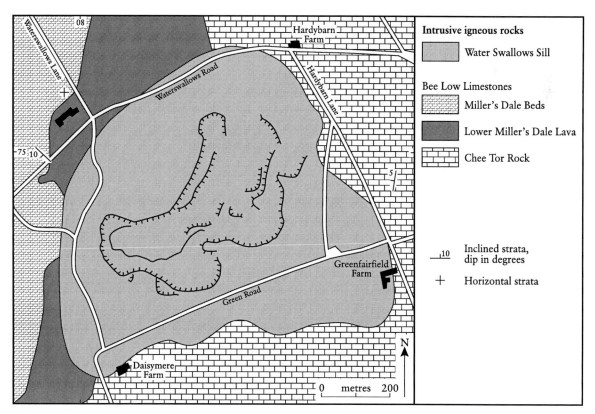

Figure 7.6 Map of Water Swallows Quarry. Based on Geological Survey 1:10 560 sheets SK 07 SE (1968); and SK 07 NE (1959).

established that the lower contact is saucer-shaped, broadly undulating, gently discordant to the east and strongly transgressive to the west. The succession shown below (from Moseley, 1966; Stevenson *et al.*, 1970; Stevenson and Gaunt, 1971) was taken from a drainage cut in the quarry, which is no longer exposed. It shows that the sill is also underlain by basalt of the Lower Miller's Dale Lava.

Thickness (m)

Water Swallows Sill
Dolerite, dark grey, commonly spheroidally weathered and with prominent columnar joints, typically medium grained; local presence of smectite-filled vesicles; sharp irregular base — 24.4 seen

Lower Miller's Dale Lava
Basalt, dark grey, locally hard and white where calcitized or soft and green where chloritized; the lower part commonly decomposed yellow-brown, amygdaloidal with chlorite- and calcite-filled vesicles; pyrite veins and pyrite amygdales present near to the top with euhedral crystals up to 2 mm; sharp base — 0–2.0

Bee Low Limestones
Limestone, pale grey, with slight marmorization — 0–3.0
Limestone breccia with clasts strongly altered — 0–0.8
Tuff, pale green, calcareous — 0–3.0

The sill comprises a coarse-grained, relatively altered, upper unit and a fine-grained, relatively unaltered, lower unit with columnar jointing. In the lower part of the quarry, where the base of the sill is approximately horizontal, columnar joints within the sill are vertical (Figure 7.7). Where the basal contact dips steeply below the deepest levels of the quarry the columnar jointing is horizontal with thin calcite veins along these joints (Moseley, 1966). The columnar joints were also described as horizontal in the north-east of the quarry, in the vicinity of a north-trending fault (Stevenson and Gaunt, 1971).

The rock of the sill is an olivine-dolerite, generally lacking the ophitic texture common in other intrusions of the area. Ineson *et al.* (1983) have shown that there is a systematic grain-size variation. The lower unit, 20–30 m thick, is fine grained and contains euhedral and partly rounded microphenocrysts of olivine, partly pseudomorphed by smectite, and labradorite feldspar. The groundmass, locally chloritized and carbonated, comprises pale-green to pale-brown anhedral augite and flow-aligned laths of labradorite. Anhedral grains of iron-titanium-manganese oxide are present and the interstitial

Figure 7.7 Columnar cooling joints developed in the dolerite of the Water Swallows Sill, taken in 1969. The section is probably about 20 m high, the base of the 24 m-thick sill being just below the quarry floor. Descriptions from this period indicate that the base of the sill is highly irregular and this may be the reason for the change in inclination of the joints from vertical in the lower tier, presumably above a horizontal base, to inclined away from the camera in the middle tier, where the base may be transgressing upwards. (Photo: British Geological Survey, No. L239, reproduced with the permission of the Director, British Geological Survey, © NERC.)

areas include apatite and partly devitrified glass. There is a gradation toward a middle unit, 40 m thick, slightly coarser and showing an increase in content of groundmass plagioclase and a reduction in augite content relative to the lower unit. Olivine microphenocrysts and interstitial areas have been completely replaced by smectite (Walters and Ineson, 1983). Towards the top of this unit there are spherical amygdales filled with smectite. The upper unit, of unknown thickness, is coarse grained with olivine phenocrysts, pseudomorphed by smectite, forming 25% of the rock. Miller (1986) has described the presence of rounded inclusions (5 mm to 50 cm diameter) of fine-grained basalt with some vesicles, comparable in appearance to the lower unit of the sill.

The underlying vesicular to non-vesicular lava is extensively albitized, chloritized and calcitized, and is considerably more altered than the sill. The top of the lava is irregular, commonly bulging upward into the overlying sill (Moseley, 1966).

The tuff seen at the base of the section was described by Ineson *et al.* (1983) as comprising a basal coarse tuff-breccia with rounded and iron-stained limestone clasts, on average 1 cm in diameter, overlain by lapilli-tuffs. The tuffs thicken up to 25 m beneath the north-western part of the sill, with graded beds dipping at 7°.

Mineralization is dominated by the presence of calcite amygdales and veins in the basalt; smectite and subordinate haematite, quartz and amethystine quartz veins in the sill; and pyrite in the tuffs (Miller, 1986). Moseley (1966) described the lowermost 0.6 m of the sill, containing narrow calcite veins that are parallel to its irregular basal contact. Marmorization (thermal alteration) of the limestone country rock of the sill is slight (Stevenson and Gaunt, 1971).

The olivine-dolerite sill is hypersthene-olivine-normative, with tholeiitic affinities. The lower and middle units of the sill show only minor geochemical variations, whereas the upper unit is depleted in Ca, Na, Si, Y, Zr and Sr and enhanced in Mg and total Fe (Ineson *et al.*, 1983).

Regionally, the Lower Miller's Dale Lava is underlain and overlain by beds of the Bee Low Limestones, which contain fauna indicative of late Lower *Dibunophyllum* (D$_1$) Zone (Stevenson and Gaunt, 1971). This shows the lavas to be Asbian in age (around 334–330 Ma on the timescale of Gradstein and Ogg, 1996). Whole-rock K-Ar age determinations of the sill gave an average date of 311 ± 6 Ma (*c.* 317 Ma with new constants) from three analyses (Stevenson *et al.*, 1970). Other, much younger dates from the same study and from a subsequent study by Ineson *et al.* (1983) were discounted as unreliable, probably due to argon loss. More recently, an Ar-Ar plateau age of *c.* 321 ± 8 Ma has been obtained from groundmass plagioclase of the sill (M. Timmerman, pers. comm., 2002), re-inforcing the suggestion of a Namurian age.

Interpretation

The presence of a sill at Water Swallows Quarry was first recognized by Arnold-Bemrose (1907) and it subsequently became well exposed through quarrying operations. Moseley (1966) provided a detailed description of the geometry of the igneous body, though he did not adequately distinguish between the sill and the underlying lavas, which he considered were both part of the same igneous event. The geological re-survey of the district established the distinct identities of the lava and sill and provided detailed petrographical and geochemical information (Stevenson and Gaunt, 1971). The discrepancy between the stratigraphical age of the Lower Miller's Dale Lava and the K-Ar radiometric age of the Water Swallows Sill led to the interpretation that the two are genetically unrelated (Stevenson *et al.*, 1970). Both the published K-Ar and the unpublished Ar-Ar radiometric dates for the sill suggest a Namurian or younger age. However, regionally the majority of dolerite sills only intrude at or below the level of the Upper Miller's Dale Lava and no intrusions are found in strata of Namurian or Westphalian age (Figure 7.3). It has been proposed that at Water Swallows Quarry the Lower Miller's Dale Lava acted as a barrier to upward migration of magma, so that the sill developed through the lateral migration of magma at or near the base of the lava (Stevenson *et al.*, 1970).

Ineson *et al.* (1983) concluded that the whole-rock K-Ar radiometric dates do not represent cooling ages, and have been reset to a younger age by argon loss, possibly during hydrothermal or deuteric alteration. They therefore proposed that the intrusions are no younger than Brigantian in age, thus re-opening the possibility that the eruption of the Lower Miller's Dale Lava and the intrusion of the sill were near-contemporaneous events.

However, the recent, unpublished Ar-Ar plateau age should not have been affected by any argon loss and would appear to confirm the time gap.

Moseley (1966) considered both the Lower Miller's Dale Lava and the sill to be lavas. He proposed that the geometry of the igneous body, in part determined from the orientation of the cooling joints, is indicative of formation within a vent, with the lava rising up a central pipe and spreading laterally as the extrusion of the Lower Miller's Dale Lava. The subsequent drilling of boreholes ascertained the saucer-shape geometry of the base of the intrusion, discounting the presence of a central pipe (Ineson *et al.*, 1983). However, Ineson *et al.* used the presence of the lapilli-tuff beneath the Lower Miller's Dale Lava, which shows a great thickening towards the north-west, to propose the presence of a tuff-cone associated with a nearby vent. This vent, as yet unlocated, was proposed to occur towards the north-west of the site. The association of the tuff-cone with the Lower Miller's Dale Lava and with the area of maximum discordance and thickness of the sill led Ineson *et al.* (1983) to suggest that this vent fed both the extrusive and intrusive igneous phases.

Arnold-Bemrose (1907) and Moseley (1966) recognized variations from fine grained to coarse grained within the sill. Ineson *et al.* (1983) determined that this grain-size variation is systematic, the lowest unit being finest and the uppermost unit being coarsest. Miller (1986) suggested that the relationship is more complex, with the coarse-grained gabbroic rocks not confined to the upper part of the sill. Geochemical variations in the sill have been attributed to the increase in proportion of olivine phenocrysts in the upper unit (Ineson *et al.*, 1983). This olivine-enriched unit cannot be a product of in-situ crystal settling as it occurs above the bulk of the intrusion. Ineson *et al.* (1983) proposed that the differentiation initially occurred in a magma chamber at depth. As the magma moved upwards, the upper olivine-poor magma was intruded first, forming the lower unit of the sill. Then, a final intrusion of the lower olivine-rich magma occurred into the top of the sill.

Although the sill lacks modal quartz, Stevenson and Gaunt (1971) indicated that it is quartz-normative, i.e. silica-saturated, and falls within the range of tholeiitic basalts. Ineson *et al.* (1983), however, suggested that these normative values do not take account of the deuteric alteration and calculated that the sill is hypersthene-olivine-normative, with tholeiitic affinities transitional to alkali basalt, and having geochemical affinities with the Lower Miller's Dale Lava.

The mineralization seen at Water Swallows Quarry has a mineral assemblage similar to that seen at the **Calton Hill** GCR site, lacking the phases more typical of hydrothermal mineralization in Derbyshire, e.g. galena, chalcopyrite and fluorite. As with **Calton Hill**, the mineralization is thought to be a late-stage, deuteric or low-temperature hydrothermal alteration (Walters and Ineson, 1983; Miller, 1986).

Conclusions

The Water Swallows Quarry GCR site is representative of the Carboniferous age dolerite sills of Derbyshire. It provides an excellent exposure of a thick dolerite sill, the Water Swallows Sill, which intrudes the Lower Miller's Dale Lava and limestones of late Visean age. Infilling of the quarry has greatly reduced the extent of section visible, though the site still provides the opportunity for future research to establish the likely relationships between the lava and the sill.

Spectacular examples of columnar joints are developed perpendicular to the sill margin in response to slow cooling of the magma. The orientation of these joints suggests that the base of the intrusion is saucer-shaped (concave-upwards). Variations in the amount of olivine at different levels in the sill have been attributed to pulses of magma from a compositionally zoned (layered) magma chamber at a deeper level.

It has been proposed that the Lower Miller's Dale Lava and the Water Swallows Sill were near contemporaneous, both having been fed from a nearby vent, which produced a tuff-cone at the surface. In contrast, radiometric dates suggest that the sill was intruded some 10 million years after the eruption of the lavas and hence that the sill and lavas are unconnected. Further study is clearly required in order to clarify the timing and the magmatic relationships, which have a wider significance for the understanding of magmatic evolution in the Carboniferous of Derbyshire.

TIDESWELL DALE, DERBYSHIRE (SK 154 740)

C.N. Waters

Introduction

The Tideswell Dale GCR site provides a good section through a dolerite sill, spatially associated with the Dinantian lavas of Derbyshire. It includes the contact with under-lying limestones, which have been affected by thermal metamorphism. The Tideswell Dale Sill, as is the case with the Water Swallows Sill (see **Water Swallows Quarry** GCR site report), was intruded at the level of the Lower Miller's Dale Lava, of Asbian age (Figure 7.2), but has yielded K-Ar radiometric dates significantly younger than the stratigraphical age of the lava.

The sill is slightly discordant, transgressing from below the lavas in the east to above the lavas in the west of the dale (Wilkinson in Neves and Downie, 1967) (Figure 7.8). The Lower

Miller's Dale Lava is thought in this area to occur as two distinct flows separated by a thin lime-stone parting (Stevenson and Gaunt, 1971). The northern and southern margins of the sill are truncated by WNW-trending faults. The site has been variously described by Arnold-Bemrose (1899, 1907), Sargent (1917), Wilkinson (in Neves and Downie, 1967), Macdonald *et al.* (1984) and Aitkenhead *et al.* (1985).

Description

The Tideswell Dale Sill was first described by Geikie (1897). Arnold-Bemrose (1899, 1907) provided the first petrographical details. He rec-ognized a broadly symmetrical succession, about 17 m thick. The central zone, 1.8 m thick, was referred to as ophitic olivine-dolerite in which augite predominates. Above and below this zone he described 3.4 m of coarse-grained olivine-dolerite in which feldspars predominate. A fine-grained olivine-dolerite, 4.3 m thick, was described by Arnold-Bemrose (1899, 1907) as

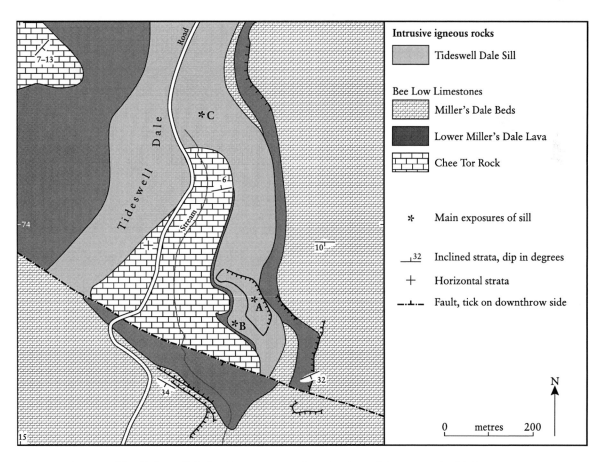

Figure 7.8 Map of the Tideswell Dale GCR site. Based on Geological Survey 1:10 560 Sheet SK 17 SE (1972).

occurring at the base and top of the intrusion. Aitkenhead *et al.* (1985) provided detailed descriptions of the petrography from the central part of the intrusion to the basal contact and were unable to identify dolerite with ophitic texture. They described the central part as medium grained, comprising phenocrysts and possible xenocrysts of olivine (12%) and augite (0.8%), set in a random intergrowth of plagioclase laths (49%), augite (20%) and opaque minerals (3.7%) with abundant interstitial devitrified glass (9%). The plagioclase is of approximate composition An_{70}. A progressive chilling is observed toward the base of the sill and at the basal contact there is extensive argillization of silicates and development of a slight flow foliation.

The Tideswell Dale GCR site comprises two former quarries located on the east side of Tideswell Dale (Figure 7.8). The main exposure (SK 155 738) (Location A; Figure 7.8) comprises about 25 m of spheroidally weathered dolerite, the upper 2.6 m containing scattered calcite amygdales. At the southern end of this quarry (SK 1547 7378), beneath the sill, there is a vesicular basalt, up to 1 m thick, which is probably a part of the Lower Miller's Dale Lava. This has been seen in temporary sections (e.g. Location B; Figure 7.8) to be underlain by at least a metre of red clay with well-developed columnar or prismatic structures, up to 6 cm in diameter (Arnold-Bemrose, 1899; Wilkinson in Neves and Downie, 1967; Aitkenhead *et al.*, 1985) (Figure 7.9). The clay has an extremely fine 'net-veined' fabric with veinlets of phyllosilicate a few microns across, in a microcrystalline matrix; the dominant mineral is an expanding-lattice mixed-layer clay (Aitkenhead *et al.*, 1985). Marmorized limestone of the Bee Low Limestones is evident below the sill on the western side of the dale (SK 1539 7410), although it is not exposed in direct contact with the sill (Wilkinson in Neves and Downie, 1967; Aitkenhead *et al.*, 1985). Arnold-Bemrose (1899) described this alteration as extending up to 3.9 m below the contact with the overlying clay and dolerite. Marmorized limestone is white, breaking with saccharoidal fracture.

Wilkinson (in Neves and Downie, 1967) described further sections in three roadside quarries at the entrance to the picnic site (SK 154 743) (Location C; Figure 7.8). These expose about 9 m of very spheroidally weathered, non-vesicular dolerite (referred to as lava by Wilkinson) with microphenocrysts of andesine and augite. This is in contact with a

Figure 7.9 Temporary exposure (July 2002) at the base of the Tideswell Dale Sill, on the east side of Tideswell Dale (Location B on Figure 7.8). The sill forms the massive natural exposures at the top of the picture and is underlain by altered basalt lava in the centre. Beneath this is a red clay with sigmoidal prismatic joints that is interpreted as a thoroughly altered lava. See text for further discussion. The cutting is 0.8 m deep. (Photo: M. Murphy.)

highly altered vesicular dolerite with pseudomorphs after olivine, flow-orientated feldspar laths and microlites of dominantly oligoclase composition. The vesicular dolerite is geochemically enriched in alkalis, especially sodium (Na_2O = 4%), in comparison with other Derbyshire lavas and sills.

The geochemical analysis of the Tideswell Dale Sill provided by Macdonald *et al.* (1984) is very similar to that of the Lower Miller's Dale Lava, with relatively high SiO_2 (51.2%) and low MgO (6.24%) in comparison with other Carboniferous lavas and sills from the region. The dolerite is quartz-hypersthene-normative.

The lava was extruded onto beds of the Bee Low Limestones, which have faunal assemblages indicative of late Lower *Dibunophyllum* (D₁) Zone of Asbian age (around 334–330 Ma on the timescale of Gradstein and Ogg, 1996) (Figure 7.2). The Lower Miller's Dale Lava, mistakenly referred to as Upper Miller's Dale Lava, has been radiometrically dated at this locality, with a whole-rock K-Ar age of 315 ± 12 Ma (*c.* 321 Ma with new constants) (Fitch *et al.*, 1970). Fitch *et al.* concluded that this age is a close approximation to the age of hydrothermal alteration. The sill yielded a whole-rock K-Ar age of 287 ± 13 Ma (*c.* 293 Ma with new constants), which Fitch *et al.* interpreted as a minimum age of hydrothermal alteration.

Veins of fibrous material present in the sill comprise chlorite, highly altered to amesite and montmorillonoids and intimately admixed with quartz (Sarjeant, 1967).

Interpretation

Macdonald *et al.* (1984) analysed 15 samples from the Tideswell Dale Sill and provided a single representative analysis. The analyses were presented on a Zr-Nb plot that is based upon stable incompatible trace elements less prone to mobility during secondary alteration. The plot showed the presence of internal chemical differentiation in the sill, although the range of Nb and Zr abundances for the sill is small in comparison with the full range of analyses of Derbyshire basalts. The plot also showed that, with respect to Nb and Zr, the Tideswell Dale Sill is compositionally similar to both the Upper and Lower Miller's Dale lavas.

Sargent (1917) interpreted the altered vesicular lava present beneath the sill as spilitic owing to the high alkali content (greater than 6%), though Walters and Ineson (1981) considered this to be more a reflection of deuteric and hydrothermal alteration, especially during the intrusion of the sill.

The Tideswell Dale GCR site shows the effects of thermal metamorphism on the country rock adjacent to the sill. Metamorphism of the limestones is seen only beneath the sill and only where the sill directly intrudes the limestone; no marmorization has been identified where the Lower Miller's Dale Lava intervenes between the sill and the limestone. The red clay with prismatic structures beneath the sill (Figure 7.9) was interpreted by Wilkinson (in Neves and Downie, 1967) as a volcanic ash, metamorphosed as a result of sill emplacement. However, this does not explain how the ash has been so thoroughly altered to clay, whereas the lava between the clay and the sill is relatively unaffected by thermal metamorphism. It is also unusual for the effects of baking at the margins of Carboniferous sills in central England to have developed more than a few centimetres into the country rock. The prismatic structures within the red clay resemble cooling joints developed within lavas or sills, and their sigmoidal nature suggests magma flow during cooling. The absence of joints from the upper and lower parts of the clay may indicate rapidly chilled margins, with the columnar joints forming only in the more slowly cooling core of the sheet. A possible explanation of this enigmatic section is that the red clay represents a basalt lava that was thoroughly altered by humid weathering during emergence and erosion, giving an irregular upper surface, which was subsequently buried by a further lava. The sill then intruded at the level of the Lower Miller's Dale Lava, exploiting the weak layer of weathered lava.

Conclusions

The Tideswell Dale GCR site provides exposures of the Tideswell Dale Sill, which intrudes Asbian (Visean) limestones and the Lower Miller's Dale Lava, erupted around 330 million years ago. The dolerite sill appears to have been intruded preferentially along or near to the planar contact between limestones and lavas, locally exploiting the relative weakness of deeply weathered lava. The site also demonstrates several features typical of intrusive bodies, namely a reduction in grain size towards the margins of the sill, chilled margins and thermal alteration of the adjacent country rocks.

Radiometric dates suggest that the sill was intruded well after the eruption of the lavas and hence that the sill and lavas are unconnected. However, as at the **Water Swallows Quarry** GCR site, the radiometric dates may have been affected by alteration of the rocks by circulating hot fluids, resulting in anomalously young dates. Further study into the relationship between the lava and sill is required, particularly to assess their relative ages.

Carboniferous and Permian igneous rocks of England and Wales

CALTON HILL, DERBYSHIRE (SK 119 715)

C.N. Waters

Introduction

The quarry at the Calton Hill GCR site, about 6 km east of Buxton (Figure 7.3), is noted for the presence of spinel lherzolite and harzburgite nodules within a basanite intrusion. These nodules, brought to the surface during Carboniferous volcanic activity, represent the only known examples in England of mantle-derived material, which provide insight into the petrology and geochemistry of the Earth's mantle. The **Golden Hill Quarry** GCR site in Wales is the only other location where ultramafic nodules have been found in Great Britain, outside of Scotland.

The intrusion shows a complex relationship with tuffs, agglomerates and lavas of the Upper Miller's Dale Lava, within which it has been intruded. The Upper Miller's Dale Lava is of Brigantian age, equivalent to the lava present at the **Litton Mill Railway Cutting** GCR site, and younger than the Asbian Lower Miller's Dale

Lava seen at the **Water Swallows Quarry** and **Tideswell Dale** GCR sites.

The Calton Hill GCR site has been described in detail in numerous publications (Arnold-Bemrose, 1894, 1907, 1910; Tomkeieff, 1928; Aitkenhead *et al.*, 1985), although many of the sections described are no longer exposed. Miller (1988) provided an update on the condition of the site following partial infilling. Recent publications have concentrated on description of the ultramafic nodules (Hamad, 1963; Donaldson, 1978) and mineralization (Ford in Neves and Downie, 1967; Sarjeant, 1967; Curtis, 1976; Walters and Ineson, 1981).

Description

The Calton Hill Volcanic Complex has a broadly circular outcrop with a maximum dimension of about 1000 m across (Figure 7.10). The complex comprises basanite intrusions within tuffs, agglomerates and lavas of the Upper Miller's Dale Lava. The basanite is typically hard, bluish-black and relatively unaltered, whereas the lava is soft, very weathered, brown or green, and highly vesicular with chlorite infills.

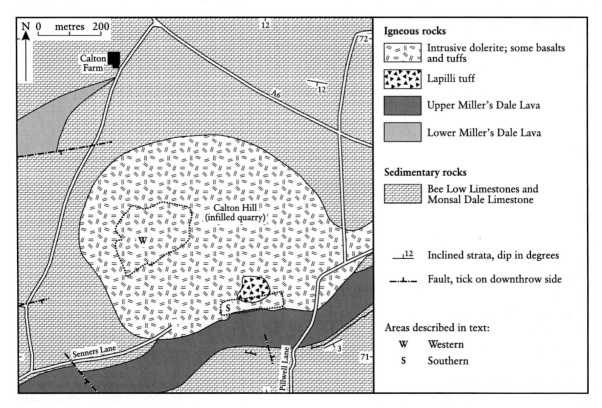

Figure 7.10 Map of the Calton Hill GCR Site. Based on Geological Survey 1:10 560 Sheet SK 17 SW (1972).

296

Calton Hill

The site has been extensively quarried and progressively infilled over a prolonged period, with only two small areas left unfilled. Therefore, all descriptions have been limited to partial exposures with no single comprehensive description of the entire site. The remaining exposures that form the GCR site can be sub-divided into western and southern areas, summarized below.

Western Area (SK 1157 7137)

The south side of this area shows tongues of massive basanite, locally with columnar joints, intruding vesicular and amygdaloidal basalt. Ultramafic nodules have been found in the basanite intrusion (Miller, 1988). On the north side there are dolerite dykes up to 3.2 m wide, with good columnar joints, intruded into basalt lava. The lava is soft weathered, highly chloritized, vesicular and amygdaloidal in part with some geodes of quartz, calcite and haematite present at the contact between the two lithologies (Aitkenhead *et al.*, 1985). Oval areas of buff to greenish-grey coarse tuffs and agglomerates, containing limestone fragments up to 13 cm in diameter and basalt bombs up to 10 cm in diameter, project upwards into the lavas (Miller, 1988). A grey, calcareous, lapilli-tuff, locally bedded and graded, has also been described (Miller, 1988).

Southern Area (SK 1198 7122)

Aitkenhead *et al.* (1985) and Miller (1988) provide descriptions from different phases of quarrying; their combined descriptions provide the succession shown below.

	Thickness (m)
Basalt, very vesicular with irregular and trangressive base	c. 6.0
Basanite, spheroidally weathered, crudely columnar jointed with ultramafic nodules (up to 0.11 m diameter) near the base; terminates abruptly to the west at an irregular vertical contact with weathered and mineralized basalt	10.5
Basalt, heavily jointed at base, vesicular in middle and massive with some calcite mineralization at top, intruded by a thin basanite sheet with irregular upper and lower contacts	2.0
Lapilli-tuff, olive-green, calcareous; in places cross-bedded with coarser beds with pumice fragments up to 5 mm and rare bombs up to 60 mm diameter; the coarser beds are more numerous and thicker towards the top	2.5+
Limestone, dome-shaped surface at bottom of excavation	

The intrusive rock is an analcime basanite, variously described as 'analcite-basalt' by Tomkeieff (1928), 'ankaramite lava' by Donaldson (1978), 'dolerite' by Aitkenhead *et al.* (1985) and 'basanite' by Miller (1988). It generally comprises subhedral phenocrysts of olivine (Fo_{80-85}) and augite ($Wo_{45}En_{45}Fs_{10}$) in a groundmass of granular augite, plagioclase laths (An_{64}) often showing flow orientation, iron-titanium oxide, analcime and calcite with ultramafic xenoliths and xenocrysts. A representative analysis of a clinopyroxene, identified as a salite, has relatively high contents of Al_2O_3 (>4%) and TiO_2 (>1.5%) in comparison with clinopyroxenes from the Lower Miller's Dale Lava (Macdonald *et al.*, 1984).

The peridotite xenoliths occur as coarse-grained, spinel-bearing nodules (Figure 7.11) in which marginal re-equilibration of minerals occurs adjacent to the basanite (Hamad, 1963; Donaldson, 1978). Typically, the nodules are dominated by the presence of olivine (64–85%), partially serpentinized and Mg-rich (Fo_{91-92}), with subordinate orthopyroxene (8–24%) ($Wo_1En_{91}Fs_8$), minor clinopyroxene (1–2%) ($Wo_{47}En_{49}Fs_4$) and spinel (less than 4%) (Donaldson, 1978). Some nodules have been identified as harzburgites, which contain enstatite (an orthopyroxene) as the second dominant mineral, whereas the majority are lherzolites in which both enstatite and chrome-diopside (a clinopyroxene) are abundant. The nodules show extreme depletion of Ca, Al, Ti and Na relative to undepleted mantle and a high Mg/(Mg + Fe) ratio (Donaldson, 1978).

The tuffs, agglomerates and lavas of the Upper Miller's Dale Lava appear to have been deposited upon an erosion surface on top of the Asbian (D_1) Bee Low Limestones. They are in turn overlain by the Monsal Dale Limestones with faunal assemblages of the Upper *Dibunophyllum* (D_2) Zone, indicative of a Brigantian age (George *et al.*, 1976). The age of the basanite intrusion is, in contrast, poorly constrained. Fitch and Miller (1964) provided a whole-rock K-Ar date of 295 ± 14 Ma (*c.* 301 Ma with new constants) indicative of a Stephanian age of intrusion, at least 26 million years after extrusion of the lavas. This date almost certainly relates to the age of hydrothermal alteration associated with mineralization and not to the age of intrusion.

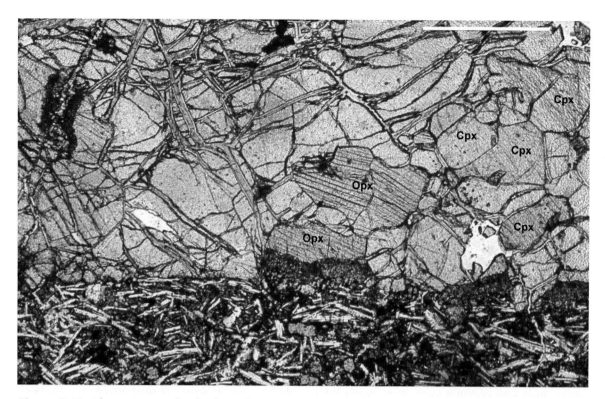

Figure 7.11 Photomicrograph of a lherzolite nodule from Calton Hill (BGS thin section No. E8340) with coarse-grained olivine, only serpentinized along fractures, subordinate orthopyroxene (Opx) and clino-pyroxene (Cpx). The contact with the host basalt (bottom) is very sharp with hardly any visible reaction. Plane-polarized light. The scale bar (top right) is 1 mm. (Photo: British Geological Survey, No. MN39854, reproduced with the permission of the Director, British Geological Survey, © NERC.)

The site shows extensive development of hydrothermal mineralization. The basanite contains analcime and spherulitic chlorite, commonly filling amygdales (Aitkenhead *et al.*, 1985). Veins, 1–5 cm wide, of a fibrous mineral described by Sarjeant (1967) as chlorite, weather to form a clay mineral identified by Curtis (1976) as the smectite saponite. Ford (in Neves and Downie, 1967) has identified a complex history of mineralization including calcite, chlorite, quartz, haematite, baryte and limonite.

Interpretation

The Calton Hill Volcanic Complex was first discovered by Arnold-Bemrose (1894, 1907, 1910), who recognized an olivine basalt containing ultramafic nodules, and an agglomerate. Quarrying operations gradually revealed further the nature of the north-east part of the complex, described in detail by Tomkeieff (1928). He recognized two distinct components to the basalts: amygdaloidal Upper Miller's Dale Lava and associated stratified tuff with fragments of

lava and limestone, intruded by a basanitic sill, with analcime, ultramafic nodules and showing a chilled margin against the lavas. Tomkeieff, and most subsequent workers, considered that the tuffs and amygdaloidal lavas at Calton Hill formed in a vent, which subsequently controlled the emplacement of the intrusion. The sections described by Arnold-Bemrose and Tomkeieff are no longer exposed. Aitkenhead *et al.* (1985) provided additional descriptions, broadly confirming the interpretations of previous workers.

Macdonald *et al.* (1984) provided a radically different interpretation, suggesting that the site displays five discrete lava flows in which the basanite forms the relatively unaltered centres of each flow, whilst the tops and bottoms of the flows have been extensively altered. They interpreted the Calton Hill Volcanic Complex as a phreatic tuff-ring comprising tuffs, agglomerates and flows of subaqueous lavas, which accumulated on the Bee Low Limestones, and which are separated from the overlying Upper Miller's Dale Lava by 15 m of limestone. The exposures used as evidence for this model are no longer visible. They also noted that the nodule-bearing 'lava' is silica-undersaturated, with clino-pyroxene compositions consistent with the rock being alkaline. This is distinct from the tholeiitic affinities of the Lower and Upper Miller's Dale lavas.

Miller (1988) provided an update on the condition of the site following partial infilling and stated the evidence for the intrusive nature of the basanites. This includes transgressive and in places vertical contacts, chilling of the basanite margins, restriction of analcime and ultramafic nodules to the basanite, and the mineralization of the lavas. From this evidence he concluded that the basalt lavas and the basanite intrusion are parts of two distinct igneous events. He was also unable to find supporting evidence for the limestone separating the complex from the Upper Miller's Dale Lava.

Numerous publications have concentrated on describing the ultramafic nodules (Hamad, 1963; Donaldson, 1978) and mineralization (Ford in Neves and Downie, 1967; Sarjeant, 1967; Curtis, 1976; Walters and Ineson, 1981). The depletion of certain major elements and high Mg/(Mg + Fe) ratios (Donaldson, 1978) suggest that the nodules represent residues from partial melting of the mantle at an approximate depth of 45 km.

Conclusions

The quarry at Calton Hill is of international importance as the only known locality in England at which material from the Earth's mantle can be found. The material, in the form of nodules composed exclusively of minerals rich in magnesium and iron (olivine, pyroxene and spinel), probably formed in the upper levels of the mantle. Subsequently, during Carboniferous volcanic activity, fragments of this mantle material were brought closer to the surface within basaltic magma.

Around Calton Hill, an early cone of consolidated volcanic ash (tuff) and lavas that were erupted through water-saturated sediments or shallow water, is overlain by more persistent basaltic lavas of tholeiitic geochemical affinities. These Early Carboniferous volcanic rocks are intruded by basaltic sills of alkaline geochemical affinities, which are hosts to the mantle nodules. There are clearly two separate igneous events but currently available radiometric dates suggest an unrealistic time gap between the volcanic

rocks and the sills. The site therefore provides opportunities for future research into the timing of these two magmatic phases, with important implications for the understanding of magmatic evolution in the Carboniferous rocks of Derbyshire.

CLEE HILL QUARRIES, SHROPSHIRE (SO 595 760)

W.J. Barclay

Introduction

The Clee Hill Quarries GCR site in Shropshire provides excellent exposures of an alkaline, olivine-dolerite sill intruded into Coal Measures strata at the Langsettian (Westphalian A)–Duckmantian (Westphalian B) boundary. The sill is variously termed the 'Clee Hills Sill' or the 'Titterstone Clee Sill'. The outcrops on Clee Hill and Titterstone Clee Hill are two of several outliers, representing remnants of a formerly extensive sheet; there are other outliers in the Brown Clee Hills. The Clee Hill Quarries GCR site is important in demonstrating the intrusive nature of the sill and its relationship with the Coal Measures strata that it intrudes. It also exhibits Pleistocene red weathering of the dolerite.

The sill is exposed in a complex of two quarries extending over an area of 1 km², Dhustone Quarry (SO 593 765) in the north-west and Incline Quarry (SO 596 757) in the south (Figure 7.12). A third quarry, Belfry Quarry (SO 598 765), is now back-filled with Coal Measures waste. Current workings for hard rock aggregate are in Dhustone Quarry in an area formerly covered by over 30 m of Coal Measures, the workings extending eastwards almost to Belfry Quarry. The outlier on Titterstone Clee Hill to the north was formerly worked extensively.

Field relationships indicate merely that the sill is Westphalian or later in age; it had been suggested that it may even be Tertiary until Urry and Holmes (1941) used it as a subject for early attempts at Pb-He dating and calculated an age of 135 Ma (see also **Dubh Loch** GCR site report). Subsequently Fitch and Miller (1964) determined a K-Ar whole-rock age of 295 ± 5 Ma (*c.* 301 Ma with new constants). Descriptions of the quarries were given by Pocock (1931), Marshall (1942), Toghill (1990), Turner and Spinner (1990) and Crump and Donnelly (1994).

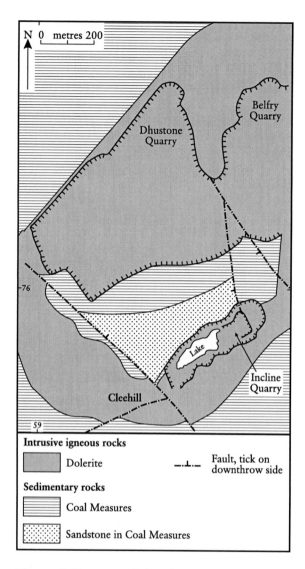

Figure 7.12 Map of the Clee Hill Quarries GCR Site. Based on British Geological Survey 1:10 000 mapping by W. Barclay (1997).

Description

The Clee Hill Quarries GCR site lies in the axial area of a NE-trending syncline occupied partly by Coal Measures strata (Dixon, 1917). The Coal Measures overlie a thin succession of unconformity-bound units, the Namurian Cornbrook Sandstone and the Dinantian Carboniferous Limestone. The sill intrudes the Coal Measures in the quarries and steps down to progressively lower levels to rest on Upper Old Red Sandstone on Titterstone Clee Hill. It is about 60 m thick, displays good columnar jointing locally and has a conchoidal fracture. Fitch and Miller (1964) noted that two sills are present, indicating

multiple intrusion. Lateral offshoots of the sill into the Coal Measures, and the presence of chilled margins confirm an intrusive origin and the contact of the sill with the overlying Coal Measures is well displayed at Incline Quarry (Figure 7.13). Crump and Donnelly (1994) noted that where the sill is unprotected by a cover of Coal Measures, it is deeply weathered to an orange-red regolith, probably the product of weathering during the warm, humid interglacial periods of the Pleistocene Epoch. A diamicton that overlies the solid rocks of Clee Hill has been interpreted variously as a solifluction/gelifluction deposit (Hains and Horton, 1969) and a glacial (?Anglian) till (Crump and Donnelly, 1994).

The rock is a very hard, fine-grained olivine-dolerite, typically dark blue-grey where fresh but weathering to greenish-grey. Based on descriptions by Urry and Holmes (1941), Sabine (unpublished Geological Survey report, 1953) and Crump and Donnelly (1994), the rock consists of olivine phenocrysts set in a groundmass of plagioclase laths (bytownite-labradorite with some zoning to oligoclase) and augite, with minor magnetite, pigeonite, apatite and rutile. Analcime occurs interstitially. Olivine shows complete to partial serpentinization and some plagioclase is albitized and replaced by carbonate. A major element oxide analysis of the sill was given by Kirton (1984), who noted that the sill is nepheline-normative. Fitch and Miller (1964) dated a fresh analcime-bearing olivine-dolerite, with only slight zeolitization and minor serpentinization, from the lower of two sills on Titterstone Clee Hill.

Interpretation

Early workers (Lapworth *et al.*, 1898; Watts, 1904) interpreted the dolerite as intrusive but it was later interpreted as extrusive by Pocock (1931). Pocock's conclusion was challenged by Marshall (1942), who presented convincing evidence, now universally accepted, of the intrusive nature of the sheet. This was supported by E.B. Bailey (in discussion of Marshall, 1942), who suggested that the sill was intruded into water-logged Coal Measures sediment, a suggestion later repeated by Francis (1970a) and Kirton (1984). Turner and Spinner (1990) provided confirmation of the intrusive nature of the dolerite, with the observation that spores in the Coal Measures overlying the sill are thermally blackened. The spores date the Coal Measures

Figure 7.13 Columnar-jointed dolerite in a quarry at Clee Hills (probably Incline Quarry), taken in 1933. The section is about 25 m high, including about 6 m of baked mudstones and sandstones of the Coal Measures over-lying the sill. (Photo: British Geological Survey, No. A6226, reproduced with the permission of the Director, British Geological Survey, © NERC.)

enclosing the sill as spanning the Langsettian (Westphalian A)–Duckmantian (Westphalian B) boundary, with the strata below the sill corre-lated with the Ra miospore biozone (equivalent to a Langsettian age) and those above with the NJ biozone (equivalent to a Duckmantian age). Given the Bolsovian (Westphalian C) age of the volcanic rocks of the West Midlands suite (see **Barrow Hill** GCR site report), the K-Ar whole-rock age of *c*. 301 Ma determined by Fitch and Miller (1964) is probably a minimum age, as suggested by Kirton (1984), and not the age of intrusion.

Conclusions

The Clee Hill Quarries GCR site provides exten-sive exposures of a fresh, Westphalian alkaline igneous intrusion and constitute a type locality for the West Midlands suite of sills. The sill appears to consist of more than one intrusion, and columnar jointing is well displayed in parts of the site. The intrusive relationship with the containing Coal Measures strata of Langsettian to Duckmantian (Westphalian A to B) age is demonstrable, with Coal Measures overlying the sill at Incline Quarry. As a result of temperate weathering in Pleistocene times, the sill is deeply weathered locally, with an overlying red-brown, ferruginous clay soil. The site also has historical importance as the sill was the subject of one of the earliest attempts at radiometric dating.

BARROW HILL, DUDLEY (SO 911 896)

C.N. Waters

Introduction

Barrow Hill, about 3 km west of Dudley, has been selected for its spectacular demonstration of complex inter-relationships between basalt and agglomerate of a volcanic vent, tuffs and volcaniclastic breccias deposited on the margins of the vent, and dykes of volcaniclastic material and basalt intruded into adjacent alluvial sedimentary rocks. The site is also of importance for the presence of the oldest anatomically preserved, conifer-like stems, which were buried by ash falls associated with eruptions from this volcanic centre.

The Barrow Hill Complex represents one of numerous small outcrops of igneous rocks of Westphalian age distributed widely across the West Midlands. The Barrow Hill GCR site is notable as it demonstrates explosive volcanic activity, whereas all the other outcrops, including the **Clee Hill Quarries** GCR site, are dolerite intrusions with no evidence of having reached the surface. The Barrow Hill GCR site occupies two disused quarries at Barrow Hill, described by Whitehead and Eastwood (1927) and Marshall (1942; 1946), and a clay pit located at Tansey Green, described by Galtier *et al.* (1992) and Glover *et al.* (1993).

Description

The Barrow Hill GCR site comprises a volcanic vent, located at Barrow Hill (SO 917 896), and volcaniclastic deposits at Tansey Green Clay Pit (SO 910 896) (Figure 7.14). The vent has a maximum dimension of about 400 m, broadly parallel to SW-trending faults, which mark the north-west and south-east margins of the vent. The volcaniclastic deposits occur interbedded with alluvial mudstones and sandstones of the Etruria Formation, which dip locally up to 30° to the south-west. These deposits are cut by several normal and reverse faults.

The Etruria Formation is of Bolsovian (Westphalian C) age (approximately 311 Ma according to Claoué-Long *et al.*, 1995) (Figure 7.2). The vent breccias and dolerite intrusions, which were emplaced in the lower part of the Etruria Formation, show such striking petro-

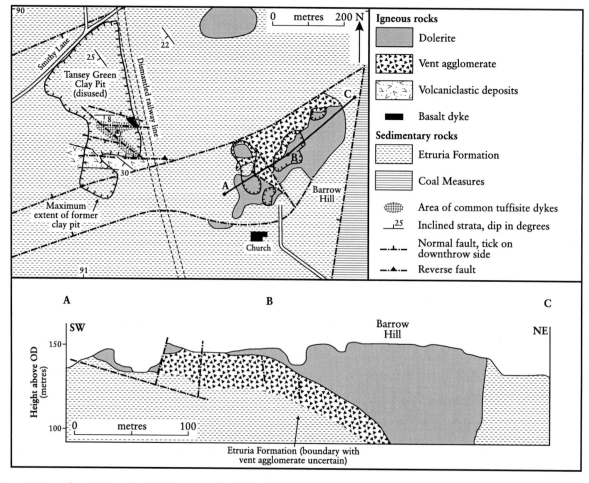

Figure 7.14 Map of the Barrow Hill GCR Site. After Glover *et al.* (1993); and British Geological Survey 1:10 000 Sheet SO 98 NE (1989). Cross-section from Marshall (1946).

graphical similarities to, and are so near to, the volcaniclastic deposits that the two are undoubtedly linked genetically and are of the same age. A K-Ar whole-rock date of 308 ± 10 Ma (*c.* 314 Ma using new constants) determined on a dolerite from Barrow Hill probably represents a close minimum for the true intrusive age (Fitch *et al.*, 1970).

Barrow Hill Vent

The quarries at Barrow Hill expose a fault-bound volcaniclastic breccia, very weathered and yellow-brown with large blocks of Etruria Formation and Coal Measures mudstones, coal clasts (up to 30 cm), rounded masses of basalt and rounded quartzite pebbles (up to 10 cm) in a tuffaceous matrix containing shards. Basalt forms pipe-like, markedly transgressive and commonly fault-bound intrusions within the vent agglomerates and the Etruria Formation country rock (Marshall, 1942, 1946). In the upper part of the main quarry (SO 9149 8958) a 1–2 m-thick sill extends from the basalt pipe and intrudes the adjacent vent agglomerate. The overall geometry of the intrusion has been complicated by post-intrusive faulting (Figure 7.14).

The basalt is typically fine grained and microporphyritic, containing abundant xenoliths. An example of an analcime-bearing olivine basalt was described in detail by Marshall (1946). Feldspar microphenocrysts, typically labradorite ($Ab_{35}An_{65}$) but with more sodic rims, are up to 0.5 mm in diameter. They commonly occur clustered around serpentinized olivine crystals up to 0.7 mm in diameter, or as single crystals showing flow alignment. The groundmass comprises small laths of labradorite-andesine ($Ab_{50}An_{50}$ to $Ab_{60}An_{40}$) showing flow alignment, granular and prismatic augite, granular magnetite and some interstitial analcime. A coarser-grained variation of this is characterized by the presence of relatively few xenoliths, a greater proportion of analcime, more prominent flow alignment of feldspar laths, and locally tends toward a sub-ophitic texture. Towards the contacts of the intrusion the basalt is generally finer grained with phenocrysts up to 0.3 mm in diameter, and markedly heterogeneous, in part due to the very abundant, minute xenoliths.

Coal Measures and Etruria Formation xenoliths up to 4.5 m in diameter are numerous. The smaller clasts (up to 0.4 m) are typically rounded and highly altered with a glassy appearance, whereas the larger blocks, which tend to be present in the lower part of the exposed mass, are rounded or irregular and show rims of alteration, 0.6 m to 0.9 m wide (Marshall, 1942, 1946).

Veins of calcite, chlorite, quartz, chalcedony and haematite are common, and calcite and chlorite infill vesicles in the dolerite at the margins of the intrusion (Marshall, 1946).

Tansey Green volcaniclastic deposits

A stratigraphical section from Tansey Green Clay Pit, recorded by Glover *et al.* (1993), is shown below.

	Thickness (m)
Volcaniclastic breccia, poorly sorted, faintly bedded in lower part; contains beds rich in bombs of amygdaloidal basalt (especially near the base) and beds with abundant lithic fragments of Coal Measures and Etruria Formation (up to 1.5 m long); tuffaceous matrix with scoriaceous textures and fresh glomeroporphyritic plagioclase, angular quartz grains, carbonate nodules, lithic fragments	*c.* 30.0
Tuffaceous mudstone and siltstone, green-grey, finely laminated with small-scale asymmetric folds; lacks in-situ conifer stems	0.4
Lapilli-tuff, scoriaceous, centimetre-scale parallel lamination, plagioclase laths commonly glomeroporphyritic, feldspar microlites and sub-angular grains of volcanic beta-quartz; sharp based with conifer stems in growth position	0.6

The conifer stems present in the lapilli-tuff are 5 mm to 15 mm in diameter and up to 250 mm in length, occurring with a vertical or near-vertical orientation (Galtier *et al.*, 1992). The stems are partly converted to coaly material (fusain) with the outer bark commonly absent.

Both the volcaniclastic deposits and the underlying Etruria Formation are cut by discordant tuffisite veins (Figure 7.15), ranging from millimetres to 0.2 m in thickness. The veins are generally orientated parallel to the dominant east–west and north-west–south-east fault trends. They are composed predominantly of fragments of probable Coal Measures origin, in particular quartz grains, coal, plant fragments, carbonaceous siltstone and sideritic nodules. Sparse, rounded clasts of altered basalt similar to those seen in the volcaniclastic breccia are also present. The veins may show alignment of clasts

Figure 7.15 Photomicrograph showing details of a tuffisite vein cutting through mudstones, from Tansey Green Clay Pit, Barrow Hill. Grain alignment occurs parallel with the vein and grain size decreases toward the vein margin. Plane-polarized light. (Photo: from Glover *et al.*, 1993.)

parallel with the dyke wall and a broad decrease in grain size from the centre to the margins. Associated with the tuffisite veins is a single agglomerate pipe, up to 10 m in diameter, and a NW-trending alkali basalt dyke, approximately 0.3 m wide. The agglomerate pipe contains rounded clasts similar in composition to the tuffisite veins, although with a greater abundance of basaltic clasts. The basalt dyke is extensively altered to chlorite and calcite, though it displays a relict ophitic texture. Amygdales of chlorite and calcite are common, being larger and more abundant towards the margins of the dyke.

Interpretation

The presence of igneous rocks at Barrow Hill was first recorded by Jukes (1859), though reference was made only to the presence of a mass of basalt. Whitehead and Eastwood (1927) suggested that the basalt has a laccolithic form, intrusive into the lower part of the Etruria Formation. The first detailed descriptions of the Barrow Hill intrusion were provided by Marshall (1942, 1946), in which the vent-like geometry was established and the presence of abundant country-rock xenoliths was recorded. The volcaniclastic rocks became well exposed as a consequence of excavations at Tansey Green Clay Pit. Galtier *et al.* (1992) described the volcaniclastic deposits in the context of their importance in preserving delicate conifer-like stems. A more thorough description of these deposits and associated volcaniclastic and basaltic intrusions was provided by Glover *et al.* (1993).

The complex of agglomerates and dolerite intrusions present at Barrow Hill are interpreted as a vent, with the igneous rocks in some cases intruding along pre-intrusion or penecontemporaneous faults (Marshall, 1942, 1946). The basalt pipes and vent agglomerates are thought to be near coeval. The country rock appears to have been relatively wet and unlithified at the time of intrusion, suggesting emplacement at or near the penecontemporaneous ground surface (Glover *et al.*, 1993). The surface expression of the vent is not preserved but is thought to have been a tuff-cone.

Glover *et al.* (1993) provided a complex history of evolution of the volcaniclastic deposits developed marginal to the vent. The lapilli-tuff, which formed the first volcanic material erupted from the vent, is interpreted as ash fall that accumulated rapidly in an alluvial floodplain environment, with each laminae representing a distinct pulse. Temperatures were sufficient to char the conifer stems, removing the outer cuticle (bark) layer (Galtier *et al.*, 1992). This charring can result from an initial hot, gaseous, base surge, which precedes the passive fall of lapilli-tuffs from a convective turbulent cloud. The tuffs were succeeded by tuffaceous mudstone and siltstone, in turn followed by highly explosive, gaseous, phreatomagmatic eruptions, which deposited the volcaniclastic breccia. The absence of impact craters beneath large clasts in the breccia may suggest that the deposit had undergone some reworking as debris flows, though the preservation of delicate euhedral plagioclase crystals and glomeroporphyritic texture suggest that the breccias could not have been transported far from the volcanic source.

The tuffisite dykes and the agglomerate pipe are interpreted as the product of phreatomagmatic activity. Interaction of hot, gaseous magma and groundwater resulted in the explosive vaporization of the water and the fragmentation of the country rock, with a rapid upward migration of gas, transporting fragments of Coal Measure material and injecting them into the overlying Etruria Formation. The tuffisite dykes, agglomerate pipe and basalt dyke probably represent lateral feeders from the main Barrow Hill Complex. The orientation of the tuffisite and basalt dykes parallel with the main faults in the area, suggest that emplacement of the complex occurred coeval with a phase of extensional faulting.

Conclusions

The Barrow Hill GCR site is nationally important for the spectacular demonstration of the relationship between a volcanic vent and adjacent volcanic deposits erupted from that vent around 307 million years ago. The vent comprises a breccia of igneous and sedimentary clasts intruded by basaltic rocks, which contain abundant fragments and blocks of Upper Carboniferous sedimentary rocks. The level of erosion seen in the vent at Barrow Hill appears to be at or near to what was the ground surface

at the time of eruption. Hot, gassy magma penetrated wet and largely unconsolidated sediments, and the interaction with groundwater resulted in explosive activity in which dykes of sedimentary and igneous material were forced underground for some distance marginal to the vent. The surface expression of the explosive activity is seen as ash-fall deposits, hot, gaseous lateral surge deposits and a thick breccia, similar in composition to that present in the vent.

The ash-fall deposits preserve the oldest anatomically preserved conifers found to date. The excellent preservation of the wood, pith and xylem make these stems of considerable importance in the understanding of the evolution of gymnosperms and provides constraints on the environment of growth of conifers during the Carboniferous Period.

MIDDLE HOPE, NORTH SOMERSET (ST 322 659–ST 350 670)

V.P. Wright and P.J. Cossey

Introduction

The Middle Hope GCR site, a large coastal site near Weston-super-Mare and about 4 km northeast of the **Spring Cove** GCR Site, provides a Courceyan to Chadian section extending from the Black Rock Limestone through to the Gully Oolite. The section includes an exceptional development of the Middle Hope Volcanic Beds with undersea lavas and pyroclastic deposits. The section has been described by Geikie and Strahan (1899), Morgan and Reynolds (1904), Sibly (1905), Reynolds (1908, 1917), and more recently by Matthews *et al.* (1973), Speedyman (in Savage, 1977), Jeffreys (1979), Whittaker and Green (1983) and Faulkner (1989b). The following account is based mainly on the work of Faulkner (1989b). Details of the lava geochemistry are to be found in Faulkner (1989a).

Description

The Lower Carboniferous succession on the Middle Hope peninsula (see Figure 7.16a) includes 97 m of the Black Rock Limestone, 30 m of the Black Rock Dolomite and 10 m of the Gully Oolite (Faulkner, 1989b). The principal feature of interest is the Tournaisian Middle Hope Volcanic Beds (also known as the Woodspring Lava and Tuff). These volcanic beds,

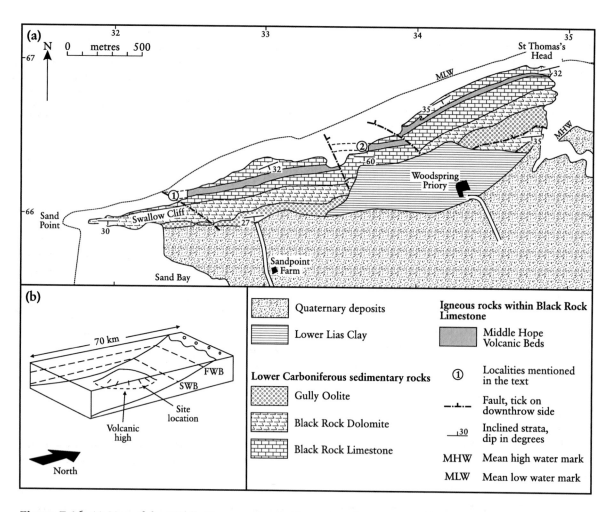

Figure 7.16 (a) Map of the Middle Hope peninsula illustrating the position of localities referred to in the text (1 = Swallow Cliff (ST 3245 6605); 2 = 700 m WNW of Woodspring Priory (ST 337 664)). (b) Schematic model of the volcanic high responsible for the formation of the Middle Hope Volcanic Beds (FWB = fair-weather wave base; SWB = storm-wave base). Modified after Faulkner (1989b).

4–37 m thick, occur within the Black Rock Limestone, lying entirely within the *Polygnathus communis carinata* biozone of Groessens (1976) and the *Caninophyllum patulum* assemblage biozone of Ramsbottom and Mitchell (1980). Additional biostratigraphical information relating to this part of the succession, including detail of the distribution of conodonts, corals and brachiopods, is given by Whittaker and Green (1983).

The Middle Hope Volcanic Beds crop out at several locations on the northern side of the Middle Hope peninsula (see Figure 7.16a). They are best examined in two small bays, one at the eastern end of Swallow Cliff (ST 3245 6605) and the other 700 m WNW of Woodspring Priory (ST 337 664) (localities 1 and 2 in Figure 7.16a). Details of the succession are illustrated in Figure 7.17.

The lower part of the Black Rock Limestone, below the volcanic rocks, consists of decimetre-scale, bioturbated wackestones and packstones, with fissile and marly layers. The fauna consists of crinoids, brachiopods, and rugose and tabulate corals. Trace fossils include *Zoophycos*, *Chondrites*, *Planolites* and *Thalassinoides*-like burrows. This is overlain by a unit of multi-coloured tuffs, which coarsens upwards. Lapilli-rich layers, 3–5 cm thick, within this unit also increase in grain size upwards. Bioclastic material of marine origin is present in these tuffs. Associated with the tuffs are thin-bedded limestones, some planar stratified or showing symmetrical ripples. The multi-coloured tuffs are in turn overlain by a unit of green, graded and ungraded lapilli-tuffs, with clasts of devitrified

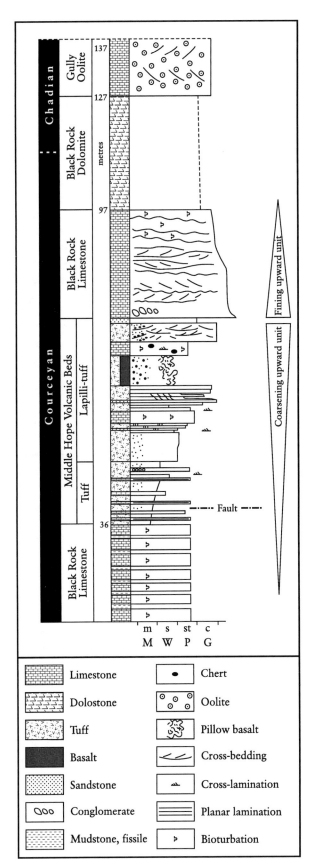

Figure 7.17 Generalized sedimentary log of the Lower Carboniferous succession at the Middle Hope GCR site. The vertical scale is non-linear; figures are metres above base of section. Horizontal scale indicates grain size: (m = mudstone; s = siltstone; st = sandstone; c = conglomerate; M = mudstone (calcareous); W = wackestone; P = packstone; G = grainstone). After Faulkner (1989b).

amygdaloidal basalt and unidentified chloritized rock, mixed with marine bioclastic material (Figure 7.18). Calcite vein networks are prominent locally. Within the ungraded lapilli-tuffs there are matrix- and clast-supported conglomerates, with clasts of chert nodules and limestones. Also associated with the lapilli-tuffs are bioclastic limestones and both cross-stratified and laminated sandstones (Figure 7.19). The latter have abundant small vertical burrows ('pipe rock') associated with the brachiopod *Lingula mytiloides* (Faulkner, 1989b). Within the lapilli-tuffs is a prominent, laterally impersistent basaltic pillow lava. At Swallow Cliff, the lava ranges in thickness from 3.5 m to 4.3 m. The basalt is very weathered with abundant calcite-filled amygdales up to 10 cm across. The upper surface is very irregular and highly amygdaloidal.

The Middle Hope Volcanic Beds thin laterally from 37 m at Swallow Cliff in the west, to 4 m in the east of the site (ST 348 669). They are overlain erosively by the upper part of the Black Rock Limestone, which comprises a fining-upwards, cross-stratified bioclastic grainstone unit (24 m thick) with a conglomerate at its base and a gradational top contact with the overlying Black Rock Dolomite. Faunal evidence presented by Whittaker and Green (1983) indicates the presence of a significant non-sequence at the top of the Black Rock Dolomite after which the Gully Oolite was deposited. The Gully Oolite is a massive cross-bedded oolite, fossiliferous and partly dolomitized in its lower part.

Interpretation

The lower matrix-rich limestones at the base of the Black Rock Limestone represent deposits formed in the outer part of a sloping, shallow marine shelf (Figure 7.16b), below storm-wave base (Faulkner, 1989b). The lower tuff unit records the onset of volcanic activity, which increased in intensity with time, producing the coarsening-up trend. The lapilli-rich layers in this unit indicate periods of more energetic eruptions. Associated limestones were probably

deposited by storm currents (Faulkner, 1989b). An upward-shallowing trend recognizable in these lower units is interpreted as a response to local updoming associated with the volcanicity.

The overlying lapilli-tuffs were also deposited in marine waters, and were emplaced either by sediment gravity flows related to the eruptions, or by marine currents. The pillow basalts indicate subaqueous igneous activity, and show that the site was close to the volcanic centre. The marine limestones associated with the lapilli-tuffs were current reworked. The style of the vertical burrows in the sandstones suggests rapid sedimentation and the cyclic repetition of thin rippled layers with drapes of fine tuff indicates fair-weather deposition above wave base (Faulkner, 1989b). This sequence is interpreted as representing deposition of the lapilli-tuffs in relatively shallow water as the volcanic cone built up to its maximum height. Progressive eastward thinning of the volcanic beds suggests that the source of this volcanic material lay to the west of the site.

The thick, cross-stratified grainstone unit at the top of the Black Rock Limestone represents part of a transgressive, high-energy offshore shoal, influenced by longshore or tidal currents that formed in progressively deeper water as the volcanic cone was eroded or as the regional sea level rose, drowning the shoal (Faulkner, 1989b).

Figure 7.18 Graded lapilli-tuffs in the Middle Hope Volcanic Beds. The hammer shaft is about 35 cm long. (Photo: P.J. Cossey.)

Figure 7.19 Graded and cross-bedded lapilli-tuffs, interbedded with limestones in the Middle Hope Volcanic Beds. The hammer shaft is about 35 cm long. (Photo: P.J. Cossey.)

Conclusions

The Middle Hope GCR site provides an exceptional section of Tournaisian (Courceyan) marine limestones and volcanic rocks, representing the growth and subsidence of a volcanic cone on the outer part of an Early Carboniferous shallow-sloping marine shelf. The repeated exposure of the Middle Hope Volcanic Beds along the northern shoreline of the site allows the anatomy of the volcanic pile to be reconstructed in detail. The combined association of sedimentological and palaeontological features indicates that although the volcanic high was initially below storm-wave base, it subsequently developed in progressively shallower water as a result of volcanic updoming and the formation of a volcanic cone, which came close to sea level before finally subsiding. Together these features make Middle Hope one of the most important sites for the understanding of Early Carboniferous volcanic processes in southern England.

SPRING COVE, NORTH SOMERSET (ST 310 625)

C.N. Waters

Introduction

The Spring Cove GCR site, a coastal section north of Weston-super-Mare, has been selected as a representative of Arundian (Dinantian) extrusive igneous rocks from southern England. Submarine pillow lavas display an intimate association with adjacent carbonate rocks and the section provides excellent exposures of the Dinantian succession from the top of the Gully Oolite, through the Caswell Bay Mudstone, to the Birnbeck Limestone, for which Spring Cove is the type locality (Figure 7.20).

The presence of igneous rocks in the Weston-super-Mare district has long been known, though uncertainty as to their intrusive or extrusive nature was not resolved until the descriptions of Geikie and Strahan (1899). Numerous publications provided descriptions of the lavas (Boulton, 1904; Strahan and Cantrill, 1912; Reynolds, 1917; Speedyman in Savage, 1977), culminating in the detailed lithological and petrographical descriptions in the Geological Survey memoir for the district (Whittaker and Green, 1983).

Sibly (1905) showed that the volcanic rocks of the Weston-super-Mare district occur at two distinct stratigraphical positions, estimated to be about 145 m apart (Whittaker and Green, 1983). The lower, Middle Hope Volcanic Beds, described in the **Middle Hope** GCR site report, have subsequently been shown to be Courceyan in age, and the higher volcanic rocks, which include the Spring Cove Lava, are Arundian (George *et al.*, 1976). Whittaker and Green (1983) have demonstrated that the Spring Cove Lava is approximately contemporaneous with lavas and tuffs from the Bristol district at Goblin Combe, Broadfield Down, Cadbury Camp and Tickenham, and that the volcanic activity occurred over a relatively wide area and included several small vents.

Description

The Spring Cove GCR site comprises a lava about 15 m thick with an exposed length along-strike of about 140 m (Figure 7.20). It occurs within the Birnbeck Limestone, which contains corals and brachiopods indicative of an early Arundian age (Whittaker and Green, 1983). The lava has a gently undulating contact with the underlying limestone and the strata dip at about 25° to 35° to the south.

The critical stratigraphical section at Spring Cove (see below) is derived from a composite section logged by G.W. Green (Geological Survey 1:10 560 map ST 36 SW, 1967) and reproduced by Whittaker and Green (1983).

Thickness (m)

Birnbeck Limestone
Limestone, reddish-fawn, dolomitized but with relict cross-bedding and corals; tuffaceous debris in lower 1.5 m, increasing towards the base   9.7

Spring Cove Lava
Olivine basalt, typically fine grained, chocolate-brown, massive and highly amygdaloidal with imperfect pillow structures and red oolitic limestone fragments in all stages of alteration and assimilation, which in places appear to occupy spaces between pillows (Figure 7.21). In the centre of the exposure, cindery lava is mixed with broken limestone fragments. Calcite veins are common throughout. The base is irregular and channelled up to 1.2 m into the underlying limestone   c. 15.0

Birnbeck Limestone
Limestone, red and grey, very massive, dolomitized, but with relict cross-bedding, ooliths, corals and crinoid debris   up to 12.0

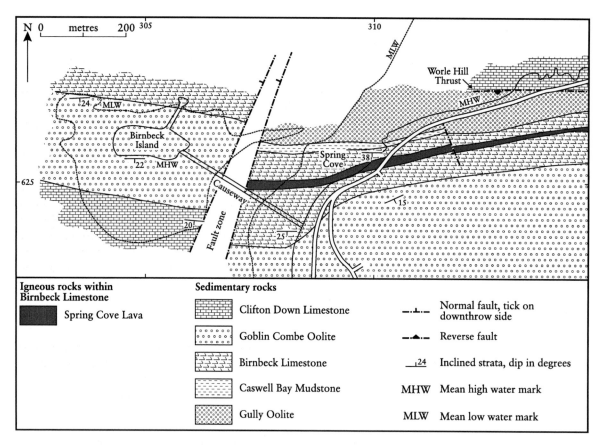

Figure 7.20 Map of the Spring Cove GCR Site. After Whittaker and Green (1983).

Boulton (1904) described a progressive variation in the lava. To the north-east a 27 m section was described as a relatively uniform 'pillowy' basalt, brecciated and amygdaloidal with large masses of limestone. The pillows are best developed at the base of the lava, where they have a diameter of 1 m or more. To the south-west of this an 18 m-long exposure was described by Boulton as tuff or agglomerate with masses of highly slaggy basalt, 1.5–1.8 m long, and lumps of limestone, often very fractured, up to 3.7 m in length. Speedyman (in Savage, 1977) described one 'agglomeratic tuff' cutting obliquely across the lava. In this body, the larger blocks of limestone and rounded pillows of basalt are commonly closely spaced and are elongate parallel to the margins. The matrix comprises densely packed angular fragments of basalt and has a planar fabric that is deformed around the blocks. The 'agglomeratic tuff' is overlain locally by basaltic pillow lavas with rare irregular 'agglomeratic' zones. The remaining approximately 100 m of section was described as hard, massive, purplish-brown, slightly amygdaloidal olivine basalt with pseudomorphs after olivine (Boulton, 1904; Speedyman in Savage, 1977). Pillows and rare blocks of limestone up to 0.3 m across occur in this basalt.

Petrographical details for the lava and adjacent sedimentary rocks were provided by Whittaker and Green (1983). The basalt contains olivine and possibly augite phenocrysts, up to 3 mm in length, showing slightly corroded euhedral outlines, though totally pseudomorphed by calcite and a clay mineral. The groundmass comprises microlitic feldpars, forming laths rarely longer than 0.8 mm, which are highly altered and show a swirling flow alignment. The groundmass is deeply stained by ferric oxide. Morgan and Reynolds (1904) and Reynolds (1917) described a 'variolitic', or spherulitic glassy basalt, but Whittaker and Green (1983) described this as a finely mottled pale-red and dark-reddish-brown scoriaceous rock and were unable to identify any evidence of spherules (varioles). They did, however, describe ovoid vesicles filled with iron-stained calcite and vermicular clay aggregates.

Figure 7.21 Basaltic pillow lava at the Spring Cove GCR site with clasts of altered limestone and numerous calcite veins (ST 309 625). The hammer shaft is about 35 cm long. (Photo: British Geological Survey, No. A11792, reproduced with the permission of the Director, British Geological Survey, © NERC.)

The section is notable for the presence of reddened oolitic limestone for 12 m below the lava, which is not observed in this part of the succession elsewhere in the district. The limestone contains iron-stained, sub-angular to rounded pumice fragments, which are generally devitrified and replaced by a clay mineral or carbonate. Some pumice fragments and other clastic fragments display oolitic coatings. An unusual feature of the limestone is the presence of authigenic orthoclase, which has developed in micrite pellets and ooliths in the tuffaceous limestones. Ashy particles have also been noted up to 2.4 m above the lava (Morgan and Reynolds, 1904). These have been described by Whittaker and Green (1983) as comprising sub-rounded argillized fragments of fine-grained basalt in a matrix of sparry calcite.

Reynolds (1917) published two chemical analyses for the 'variolitic' basalts at Spring Cove, noting low Na_2O (0.72 and 1.10%) and very high K_2O (5.01 and 4.93%) contents.

Interpretation

The internal structure of lenticular sheets of lava, tuff and agglomerate, sloping to the south, as described by Boulton (1904), was used by him to suggest the presence of a vent to the north.

The complex relationships between pillow lavas, tuffs and agglomerates suggest that the section shows more than one lava. The pillow structures, for which this site is of importance, are indicative of subaqueous eruption, and hence Reynolds (1917) interpreted the lavas as spilites, but he did note the low sodium and very high potassium contents, which are atypical of spilites. In a review of Carboniferous basalts in the Bristol district, Dearnley (1960) observed that the more highly vesicular and altered the rock, the higher the total alkali content and the lower the Na:K ratio. He concluded that the petrographical and geochemical characteristics are indicative of late-stage autometasomatism by alkali-rich residual fluids rather than as a result of interaction of magma with seawater to produce spilites, as proposed by Reynolds, and this interpretation was accepted by Whittaker and Green (1983).

The irregular shape of limestone fragments present within the lava in various stages of alteration and assimilation (Figure 7.21) and the slightly undulating and cross-cutting relationship of the lava with underlying limestones, led Boulton (1904) and Whittaker and Green (1983) to suggest that the lava was extruded onto sediments that were not fully consolidated. The 'tuffs and agglomerates' were interpreted by Speedyman (in Savage, 1977) as an autobreccia, possibly formed as a result of a submarine slide of pillow lavas with included clasts of limestone. These deposits were subsequently over-ridden by further pillow lavas.

Red-stained limestones present above the lava contain highly altered basalt fragments, which are interpreted as the erosion products of the underlying lava. The limestones immediately beneath the lava contain pumaceous material, which is interpreted not as primary ash-fall material but as the product of reworking and re-sedimentation. Oolitic coatings to some pumice fragments suggest that the pumice had undergone some marine transport and the growth of authigenic orthoclase before the final development of the oolitic coating suggests that high concentrations of potassium were present in the environment of limestone deposition (Whittaker and Green, 1983). The red iron staining of the limestone is generally considered to be due to the weathering of the tuffaceous material present (Geikie and Strahan, 1899; Whittaker and Green, 1983), though Morgan and Reynolds (1904), Boulton (1904) and Reynolds (1917) had disputed this interpretation. Both the iron and the potassium were probably derived from fragments of lava and volcanic glass as a product of leaching following re-sedimentation in an enclosed basin where concentrations of the leached material could occur (Whittaker and Green, 1983).

Conclusions

The Spring Cove GCR site represents Lower Carboniferous (Visean) volcanic rocks of south-west England, in a well-exposed and easily accessible section. It demonstrates fine examples of pillow lavas and brecciated lavas, formed when magma is erupted under water, in this case probably on the seabed.

The complex lava flow was extruded during a period of dominantly marine carbonate deposition. The lava was preceded by limestone containing reworked fragments of earlier pumice. The weathering of this volcanic material during and soon after deposition produced a distinctive red colouration to the limestone. This carbonate deposit was not fully consolidated when it became buried by the lava. As a result the lava has an undulating base and contains an abundance of irregularly shaped limestone blocks. The subsequent return to carbonate deposition is marked by the presence of further limestones above the lava. These limestones are also reddened due to the presence of fragments of basalt eroded from the underlying lava flow.

GOLDEN HILL QUARRY, MONMOUTHSHIRE (ST 4308 9709)

R.E. Bevins

Introduction

An understanding of the mineralogy and chemistry of the Earth's lower crust and upper mantle is provided mainly by the study of xenoliths brought to the surface by magmas. The nature of the lithosphere in southern Britain is poorly understood, owing to the dearth of mantle and lower-crustal xenolith occurrences, in contrast to the area to the north of the Iapetus Suture (see chapters 2, 4 and 5). The supposed volcanic diatreme pipe at Golden Hill Quarry, in the county of Monmouthshire, along with a nearby associated dyke at Glen Court (ST 4036 9824), is of national importance as it represents one of only two occurrences of mantle-derived xenoliths in southern Britain, the other being at **Calton Hill**, Derbyshire (see GCR site report).

The first account of the Golden Hill Quarry diatreme pipe was by Boulton (1911), who provided a petrographic account of the igneous rocks, and described the presence of a dyke or plug, containing augite and biotite megacrysts and probable ultramafic nodules, all contained in a monchiquitic groundmass. This study was based on the rather poor exposures available at that time. Subsequent quarrying in the late 1940s and early 1950s provided much better exposures, particularly of the contacts, precipitating the report by Cox (1954).

A more complete description of these more extensive exposures was provided by Eyles and Blundell (1957) who reported that in fact the majority of the igneous material at the quarry is agglomeratic, and that this was the site of a volcanic vent, cut by a monchiquite dyke. Eyles and Blundell also provided critical evidence for the age of the volcanic activity. Welch and Trotter (1961) gave a further account of the petrography of the monchiquite, while Upton *et al.* (1983) referred to the presence at Golden Hill Quarry of carbonated and/or hydrated biotite-rich ultramafic xenoliths (probably biotite pyroxenites), biotite megacrysts and tectonized quartz-plagioclase xenoliths. Finally, Haslett (1992) compared the petrography of the Golden Hill Quarry monchiquite with a similar rock exposed at Glen Court, 3 km to the WNW.

On the basis of stratigraphical evidence, combined with the age of blocks contained in the diatreme pipe at Golden Hill Quarry, the magmatism is thought to be Early Carboniferous in age (Eyles and Blundell, 1957). There is scattered evidence for Carboniferous igneous activity across a wide area in southern Britain, and the Golden Hill Quarry GCR site provides important regional information concerning the character and extent of this episode in south Wales.

Golden Hill Quarry

Description

The Golden Hill Quarry GCR site is located to the north-east of Great House Farm (Figure 7.22), some 7 km south-east of Usk. The quarry, now disused, is some 100 m in diameter and up to 15 m deep. It contains an agglomeratic facies and a NW-orientated dyke, cutting through sandstones (Brownstones) of Devonian age (Figure 7.23). Aeromagnetic data suggest that the overall form of the intrusion is pipe-like, with a total surface area of no more than 900 m². The host rock is a monchiquite.

The most complete description of the Golden Hill Quarry agglomerates and the monchiquite intrusion, however, lies in the unpublished work of D.T. Moffat, which is included in part in the account below.

The dyke is exposed only at the southern margin of the quarry (c. 10% of the outcrop area). It consists of a melanocratic, dark-grey, fine-grained, xenolithic, amygdaloidal monchiquite. In thin section this rock is seen to possess a groundmass comprising laths of plagioclase and pyroxene, rare biotite and minor ?analcime and magnetite, along with euhedral microphenocrysts of olivine and clinopyroxene (now replaced by chlorite-like phases, carbonate or serpentine) all set in abundant, partially devitrified glass. Included xenoliths, which make up 5–15% of the rock, comprise

sedimentary wall-rock, tectonized quartz-plagioclase rocks, and ultramafic lithologies, in addition to mafic megacrysts (Figure 7.24), typically in the range 0.4–4 cm. All are of similar character to those present in the agglomeratic facies (see below).

The agglomerate comprises fragments of the monchiquitic dyke (70–80%) along with sedimentary wall-rock, tectonized quartz-plagioclase rocks, ultramafic xenoliths (10–25%) and mafic megacrysts (3–15%), contained in a clay- and carbonate-rich ochreous matrix with scattered quartz crystals. The clasts are rounded, oblate ellipsoid to spherical in shape, and range in size from 0.5 cm to 15 cm. Within the pipe, Moffat (unpublished manuscript) noted a number of petrographically distinct subunits, although each is massive, unstratified and lacking obvious sorting.

The monchiquitic fragments (up to 5 cm across) are virtually identical to the monchiquite of the dyke (see above). The wall-rock fragments comprise chiefly sub-angular to rounded, red to green, fine- to medium-grained sandstones, red-brown mudstones and micaceous sandstones, reaching a maximum size of 150 cm. In addition, however, Eyles and Blundell (1957) reported the presence of various lithologies of Visean and Tournaisian age.

The quartz-plagioclase xenoliths are small (0.5–2 cm) in size and rare (less than 1% of all xenoliths). They comprise medium-grained

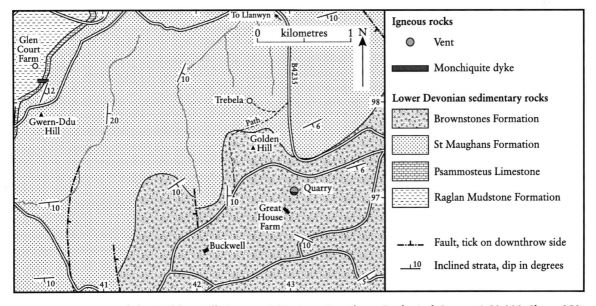

Figure 7.22 Map of the Golden Hill Quarry GCR site. Based on Geological Survey 1:50 000 Sheet 250, Chepstow (1972).

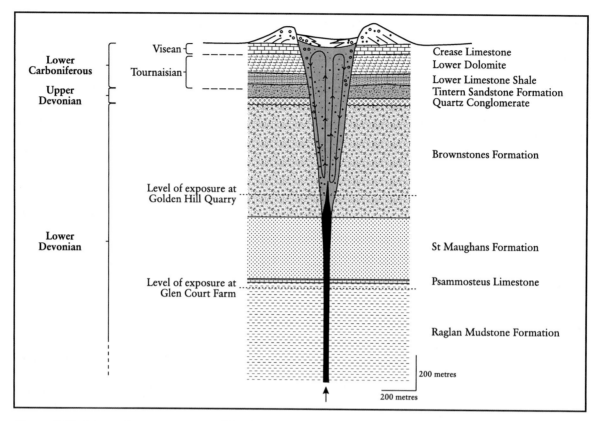

Figure 7.23 Schematic representation of the diatreme pipe, sub-diatreme monchiquite dyke and stratigraphical relationships at the Golden Hill Quarry GCR site. After D.T. Moffat (unpublished manuscript).

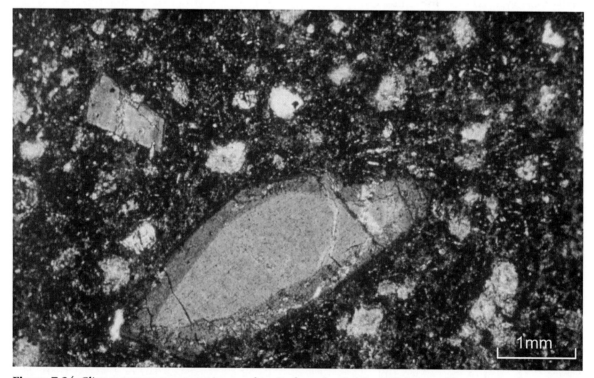

Figure 7.24 Clinopyroxene megacryst in monchiquite from the Golden Hill Quarry. The crystal is 4 mm across. Crossed polars. (Photo: R.E. Bevins.)

plagioclase porphyroclasts contained within a granular mosaic of strained quartz crystals. They are broadly tonalitic in composition.

Ultramafic xenoliths are typically rounded and are in the size range 0.5–15 cm. Investigation of the primary mineralogy of these nodules is extremely difficult due to the intense nature of alteration, with almost all the mafic phases being replaced by carbonate, serpentine and chlorite-like minerals. Originally, they appear to have been peridotites (lherzolites and harzburgites), with 62–85% olivine, 10–25% orthopyroxene, 2–12% clinopyroxene, and less than 3% chrome-spinel and minor glass (D.T. Moffat, unpublished manuscript). Original clinopyroxenes (chrome-rich diopsides) are the most common mineral to show at least partial preservation. Texturally, the majority of the ultramafic xenoliths are coarse grained (grain size in the range 0.4–1.0 cm) and show little evidence of deformation. Some xenoliths, however, show evidence of deformation, recrystallization and annealing.

Mafic megacrysts in the agglomerate, as in the dyke, comprise clinopyroxene and biotite. Clinopyroxene megacrysts typically have diameters of 1–5 cm and are subhedral to anhedral. Most are pale- to emerald-green chrome-rich diopsides, although a small proportion are black in colour and of augitic composition, the latter typically possessing lamellar intergrowths of ilmenite. Biotite megacrysts are euhedral to subhedral, dark-brown single crystals ranging between 0.5 cm and 5 cm in size. They are phlogopitic in composition.

The age of magmatic activity at Golden Hill Quarry is constrained in three ways. First, the agglomerate and dyke cut through strata of early Devonian age. Secondly, Ramsbottom (in Eyles and Blundell, 1957) identified various fossils of Carboniferous age in carbonate blocks from the agglomerate. In particular, he recorded Visean age fossils in a block of crinoidal limestone, with no post-Visean age fossils being identified, suggesting that magmatism may have occurred during Visean times. However, a K-Ar date of 336 ± 7 Ma (*c.* 342 Ma using new constants) (Fitch *et al.*, 1969) and an Ar-Ar plateau age of 347 ± 3.2 Ma (M. Timmerman, pers. comm., 2002), both on biotite megacrysts, suggest a Tournaisian or very early Visean age.

Interpretation

The earliest account by Boulton (1911) interpreted the Golden Hill Quarry igneous rocks as forming either a wide, irregular dyke or a plug, although it is clear that interpretation was hampered by poor exposure. Better exposures, resulting from more extensive quarrying, allowed Cox (1954) to propose that the intrusion has a plug-like form, and to compare it to the kimberlite pipes of the Kimberley area of South Africa. Eyles and Blundell (1957) argued that it does indeed have a pipe-like form, but is in fact a volcanic vent, comparing it with the volcanic vents exposed on the Ayrshire coast of Scotland, rather than the Kimberley-type pipes.

D.T. Moffat (unpublished manuscript) has provided the most recent interpretation, arguing that a transition from monchiquite through to agglomerate can be observed and that therefore the two facies are coeval. He took this gradation to reflect the transition from a liquid–solid dyke system to a gas–solid diatreme system. In the gas–solid system, ultramafic mantle and lower-crustal xenoliths were transported rapidly to the near surface where they were mixed with blocks from the highest crustal levels. A circulatory flow was established, witnessed by some of the incorporated blocks being preserved at up to 1000 m below their original stratigraphical position. In this circulatory system, the ultramafic xenoliths were altered by carbonitization and hydrothermal fluids.

The ultramafic xenoliths appear to represent samples derived from the upper mantle (spinel-bearing lherzolites and harzburgites), while the tectonized quartz-plagioclase lithologies are possibly from lower-crustal levels.

On the basis of stratigraphical evidence, the age of included blocks, and K-Ar and Ar-Ar dates on biotite separates, the magmatic activity appears to be Early Carboniferous, most likely Tournaisian or earliest Visean, in age. Boulton (1911) correlated the Golden Hill Quarry monchiquite with the basic intrusion cutting Devonian strata at Bartestree, near Hereford (Reynolds, 1908). Farther to the south, Carboniferous age lavas and tuffs are exposed at a number of localities to the west of Bristol (see Whittaker and Green, 1983), as at the **Spring Cove** and **Middle Hope** GCR sites. Evidence for Carboniferous volcanism in Wales is scant, however. The Mathry quartz-dolerite dyke (Cave *et*

Carboniferous and Permian igneous rocks of England and Wales

al., 1989), of probable Carboniferous age, can be traced for some 40 km across south-west Wales and interestingly is approximately in-line with the Golden Hill Quarry and Glen Court occurrences. A thin dyke was also exposed in a temporary road cut at Castleton, north-east of Cardiff, cutting strata of Devonian age and presumed to be of Carboniferous age (Lawrence *et al.*, 1981), while R.A. Waters (in Institute of Geological Sciences, 1978) reported the presence of thin tuffaceous siltstones and a bentonite in the Cwrt-yr-Ala borehole a short distance to the west of Cardiff. What makes correlation difficult, however, is that none of these sites contain lamprophyric rocks of the type seen at Golden Hill Quarry and Glen Court.

Conclusions

The Golden Hill Quarry GCR site exposes a volcanic pipe and an associated dyke-like intrusion of probable Early Carboniferous age. The intrusion is of an unusual rock-type termed 'monchiquite', and the pipe is infilled with a coarse deposit, which contains a variety of exotic blocks as well as large individual crystals of magmatic origin. The exotic blocks derived from the wall-rock, along with stratigraphical relationships between the pipe and surrounding country rocks, provide age constraints for the igneous activity. The site is most important, however, because of the presence of a variety of ultramafic rocks that originated in the Earth's mantle and quartz-plagioclase rocks that probably came from the lower part of the Earth's crust. These have been carried to higher crustal levels by rising magma and occur as blocks and fragments (xenoliths) in both the pipe and the intrusion. This is one of only two sites in southern Britain where mantle-derived xenoliths are known to occur, and hence is of national importance in providing an insight into the character of the mantle beneath this area.

References

In this reference list the arrangement is alphabetical by author surname for works by sole authors and dual authors. Where there are references that include the first-named author with others, the sole-author works are listed chronologically first, followed by the dual author references (alphabetically) followed by the references with three or more authors listed *chronologically*. Chronological order is used within each group of identical authors.

Adams, A.E. and Wadsworth, W.J. (1993) The Humphrey Head Borehole: evidence for Carboniferous vulcanicity and Permian dolomitization in the southern Lake District. *Geological Journal*, **28**, 159–69.

Aitkenhead, N., Chisholm, J.I. and Stevenson, I.P. (1985) *Geology of the Country around Buxton, Leek and Bakewell*, Memoir of the British Geological Survey, Sheet 111 (England and Wales), HMSO, London, 168 pp.

Alexander, R.W.S., Dawson, J.B., Patterson, E.M. and Hervig, R.L. (1986) The megacryst and inclusion assemblage from the Black Rock vent, Ayrshire. *Scottish Journal of Geology*, **22**, 203–12.

Allan, D.A. (1924) The igneous geology of the Burntisland district. *Transactions of the Royal Society of Edinburgh*, **53**, 479–501.

Allan, D.A. (1931) A nepheline-basanite sill at Fordell, Fife. *Proceedings of the Liverpool Geological Society*, **15**, 309–17.

Allan, T. (1812) On the rocks in the vicinity of Edinburgh. *Transactions of the Royal Society of Edinburgh*, **6**, 405–33.

Allport, S. (1874) On the microscopic structure and composition of British Carboniferous dolerites. *Quarterly Journal of the Geological Society of London*, **30**, 529–67.

Anderson, E.M. (1951) *The Dynamics of Faulting and Dyke Formation, with Applications to Britain*, 2nd edn, Oliver and Boyd, Edinburgh.

Anderson, F.W. (1963) The Geological Survey bore at Rashiehill, Stirlingshire (1951). *Bulletin of the Geological Survey of Great Britain*, **20**, 43–106.

Anderson, T.B., Parnell, J. and Ruffell, A.H. (1995) Influence of basement on the geometry of Permo–Triassic basins in the northwest British Isles. In *Permian and Triassic Rifting in Northwest Europe* (ed. S.A.R. Boldy), *Geological Society Special Publication*, No. **91**, The Geological Society, London, pp. 103–22.

Armstrong, D. (1957) Dating of some minor intrusions of Ayrshire. *Nature*, **180**, 1277.

Armstrong, M., Paterson, I.B and Browne, M.A.E. (1985) *Geology of the Perth and Dundee District*, Memoir of the British Geological Survey, sheets 48W, 48E and 49 (Scotland), HMSO, London, 108 pp.

Arnold-Bemrose, H.H. (1894) On the microscopical structure of the Carboniferous dolerites and tuffs of Derbyshire. *Quarterly Journal of the Geological Society of London*, **50**, 603–44.

References

Arnold-Bemrose, H.H. (1899) On a sill and faulted inlier in Tideswell Dale (Derbyshire). *Quarterly Journal of the Geological Society of London*, **55**, 239–50.

Arnold-Bemrose, H.H. (1907) The toadstones of Derbyshire; their field relations and petrography. *Quarterly Journal of the Geological Society of London*, **63**, 241–81.

Arnold-Bemrose, H.H. (1910) On olivine nodules in the basalt of Calton Hill, Derbyshire. *Geological Magazine*, **57**, 1–8.

Aspen, P., Upton, B.G.J. and Dickin, A.P. (1990) Anorthoclase, sanidine and associated megacrysts in Scottish alkali basalts: high-pressure syenitic debris from upper mantle sources? *European Journal of Mineralogy*, **2**, 503–17.

Avison, M.M. (1976) The stratigraphy and petrology of the tract of Carboniferous lavas covering the Black Hill region of southern Kintyre. Unpublished BSc thesis, University of Lancaster.

Ayles, H.M. (1977) A stratigraphical, petrological and geochemical study of the aphyric basal succession of the Carboniferous lavas, southern Kintyre, Scotland. Unpublished BSc thesis, University of Lancaster.

Bailey, E.B. (1923) Volcanic vent parasitic on St Leonard's sill. *Transactions of the Edinburgh Geological Society*, **11**, 223–9.

Bailey, E.B. and Maufe, H.B. (1960) *The Geology of Ben Nevis and Glencoe and the Surrounding Country*, 2nd edn, Memoir of the Geological Survey of Great Britain, Sheet 53 (Scotland), HMSO, Edinburgh, 307 pp.

Balsillie, D. (1920a) Description of some volcanic vents near St Andrews. *Transactions of the Edinburgh Geological Society*, **11**, 69–80.

Balsillie, D. (1920b) Descriptions of some new volcanic vents in East Fife. *Transactions of the Edinburgh Geological Society*, **11**, 81–5.

Balsillie, D. (1922) Notes on the dolerite intrusions of East Fife. *Geological Magazine*, **59**, 442–52.

Balsillie, D. (1923) Further observations on the volcanic geology of East Fife. *Geological Magazine*, **60**, 530–42.

Balsillie, D. (1927) Contemporaneous volcanic activity in East Fife. *Geological Magazine*, **64**, 481–94.

Balsillie, D. (1936) Leucite-basanite in East Lothian. *Geological Magazine*, **73**, 16–18.

Bamford, D. (1979) Seismic constraints on the deep geology of the Caledonides of northern Britain. In *The Caledonides of the British Isles, Reviewed* (eds A.L. Harris, C.H. Holland and B.E. Leake), *Geological Society of London Special Publication*, No. 8, Scottish Academic Press, Edinburgh, for The Geological Society of London, pp. 93–6.

Barnett, J.A.M. (1985) Fracture patterns related to volcanic necks and pipes in an Upper Limestone Group (Namurian) coal seam in the Kincardine Basin, West Fife, Scotland. *Proceedings of the Yorkshire Geological Society*, **45**, 249–59.

Barrett, B.H. and Richey, J.E. (1945) *Economic Geology of Canonbie Coalfield (Dumfries and Cumberland)*, Wartime Pamphlet of the Geological Survey of Great Britain, No. **42**, Geological Survey and Museum, London, 51 pp.

Bateman, R.M. and Scott, A.C. (1990) A reappraisal of the Dinantian floras at Oxroad Bay, East Lothian, Scotland. 2. Volcanicity, palaeoenvironments and palaeoecology. *Transactions of the Royal Society of Edinburgh: Earth Sciences*, **81**, 161–94.

Bateman, R.M., Rothwell, G.W. and Cleal, C.J. (1995) Oxroad Bay. In *Palaeozoic Palaeobotany of Great Britain* (eds C.J. Cleal and B.A. Thomas), Geological Conservation Review Series, No. 9, Chapman and Hall, London, pp. 127–39.

Bateson, E. (1895) A *History of Northumberland, Volume 2: The parishes of Embleton, Ellingham, Howick, Long Houghton and Lesbury*, A. Reid, Newcastle-upon-Tyne, for Northumberland County History Committee.

Batty, M.H. and Moss, A.A. (1962) Powellite from Traprain Law, Haddington, Scotland. *Mineralogical Magazine*, **33**, 158–67.

Baxter, A.N. (1987) Petrochemistry of late Palaeozoic alkali lamprophyre dykes from N. Scotland. *Transactions of the Royal Society of Edinburgh: Earth Sciences*, **77**, 267–77.

Baxter, A.N. and Mitchell, J.G. (1984) Camptonite–monchiquite dyke swarms of northern Scotland; age relationships and their implications. *Scottish Journal of Geology*, **20**, 297–308.

Beckinsale, R.D. and Obradovich, J.D. (1973) Potassium-argon ages for minerals from the Ross of Mull, Argyllshire, Scotland. *Scottish Journal of Geology*, **9**, 147–56.

Bénard, F., Mascle, A., Le Gall, B., Doligez, B. and Rossi, T. (1990) Palaeo-stress fields in the Variscan foreland during the Carboniferous from microstructural analysis in the British Isles. *Tectonophysics*, **117**, 1–13.

References

Bennett, J.A.E. (1945) Some occurrences of leucite in East Lothian. *Transactions of the Edinburgh Geological Society*, **14**, 34–52.

Bentley, M.R. (1988) The Colonsay Group. In *Later Proterozoic Stratigraphy of the Northern Atlantic Regions* (ed. J.A. Winchester), Blackie and Son, Glasgow, pp. 119–30.

Benton, M.J., Cook, E. and Turner, P. (2002) *Permian and Triassic Red Beds and the Penarth Group of Great Britain*, Geological Conservation Review Series, No. 24, Joint Nature Conservation Committee, Peterborough, 337 pp.

Besly, B.M. (1998) Carboniferous. In *Petroleum Geology of the North Sea: Basic Concepts and Recent Advances*, 4th edn (ed. K.W. Glennie), Blackwell Scientific Publications, Oxford, pp. 104–36.

Black, G.P. (1966) *Arthur's Seat: A History of Edinburgh's Volcano*, Oliver and Boyd, Edinburgh, 226 pp.

Blackburn, E.L., Wilson, L. and Sparks, R.S.J. (1976) Mechanisms and dynamics of strombolian activity. *Journal of the Geological Society of London*, **132**, 429–40.

Bluck, B.J. (ed.) (1973) *Excursion Guide to the Geology of the Glasgow District*, Geological Society of Glasgow, Glasgow, 181 pp.

Bonney, T.G. (1878) Note on the relations of the igneous rocks of Arthur's Seat. *Proceedings of the Geologists' Association*, **5**, 1–12.

Bott, M.H.P. (1964) Formation of sedimentary basins by ductile flow of isostatic origin in the upper mantle. *Nature*, **201**, 1082–4.

Boué, A. (1820) *Essai Géologique sur l'Écosse*, Ve Courcier, Paris, 519 pp.

Boulton, W.S. (1904) On the igneous rocks at Spring Cove, near Weston-super-Mare. *Quarterly Journal of the Geological Society of London*, **67**, 158–69.

Boulton, W.S. (1911) On a monchiquite intrusion in the Old Red Sandstone of Monmouth. *Quarterly Journal of the Geological Society of London*, **67**, 460–76.

Boyd, W.W. (1974) Geochemical investigation of composite bodies involving intermediate members of the alkali basalt–trachyte suite. Unpublished PhD thesis, University of Edinburgh.

Boyle, R. (1908) The occurrence of ultra-basic rocks in the igneous intrusions of the Lugar and Cumnock district. *Transactions of the Geological Society of Glasgow*, **13**, 202–23.

Bridgwater, D. and Harry, W.T. (1968) Anorthosite xenoliths and plagioclase megacrysts in Precambrian intrusions of South Greenland. *Grønlands Geologiske Undersøgelse Bulletin*, **77** (also *Meddelelser om Grønland*, **185**,2), 243 pp.

Brindley, S. and Spinner, E. (1987) Spores from Lower Carboniferous deposits at Burntisland, Fife, Scotland. *Pollen et Spores*, **28**, 435–50.

Brindley, S. and Spinner, E. (1989) Palynological assemblages from Lower Carboniferous deposits, Burntisland district, Fife, Scotland. *Proceedings of the Yorkshire Geological Society*, **47**, 215–31.

Brookfield, M.E. (1978) Revision of the stratigraphy of Permian and supposed Permian rocks of southern Scotland. *Geologische Rundschau*, **67**, 110–49.

Brookfield, M.E. (1980) Permian intermontane basin sedimentation in southern Scotland. *Sedimentary Geology*, **27**, 167–94.

Brookfield, M.E. (1981) Field guide to the Permian rocks of the Thornhill and Moffat basins. *Transactions of the Dumfries and Galloway Natural History and Antiquarian Society*, **56**, 1–9.

Brooks, C.K. and Jakobsson, S.P. (1974) Petrochemistry of the volcanic rocks of the North Atlantic ridge system. In *Geodynamics of Iceland and the North Atlantic Area* (ed. L. Kristjansson), *NATO Advanced Study Institutes Series, Series C: Mathematical and Physical Sciences*, No. 11, Reidel, Dordrecht, pp. 139–54.

Brown, J.F. (1975) Potassium-argon evidence of a Permian age for the camptonite dykes: Orkney. *Scottish Journal of Geology*, **11**, 259–62.

Browne, M.A.E. and Thirlwall, M.F. (1981) An occurrence of Lower Carboniferous lavas at Monksgrave (Powmill) near Dollar. *Scottish Journal of Geology*, **17**, 275–9.

Browne, M.A.E. and Woodhall, D.G. (1999) *Geology of the Kirkcaldy District – a brief explanation of the Geological Map*, Sheet Explanation of the British Geological Survey, 1:50 000 Sheet 40E (Scotland), British Geological Survey, Keyworth, 30 pp.

Browne, M.A.E. and Woodhall, D.G. (2000) *Geology of the Kirkcaldy District*, Sheet Description of the British Geological Survey, 1:50 000 Series Sheet 40E (Scotland), British Geological Survey, Keyworth, 50 pp.

References

Browne, M.A.E., Dean, M.T., Hall, I.H.S., McAdam, A.D., Monro, S.K. and Chisholm, J.I. (1996) A lithostratigraphical framework for the Carboniferous rocks of the Midland Valley of Scotland. *British Geological Survey, Onshore Geology Series, Technical Report*, **WA/96/29**.

Burgess, I.C. (1982) The stratigraphical distribution of Westphalian volcanic rocks in the area east and south of Nottingham, England. *Proceedings of the Yorkshire Geological Society*, **44**, 29–44.

Burgess, P.M. and Gayer, R.A. (2000) Late Carboniferous tectonic subsidence in South Wales: implications for Variscan basin evolution and tectonic history in SW Britain. *Journal of the Geological Society, London*, **157**, 93–104.

Cadell, H.M. (1925) *The Rocks of West Lothian: an Account of the Geological and Mining History of the West Lothian District*, Oliver and Boyd, Edinburgh, 390 pp.

Cameron, I.B. and Stephenson, D. (1985) *British Regional Geology: The Midland Valley of Scotland*, 3rd edn, HMSO, London, 172 pp.

Cameron, I.B., Aitken, A.M., Browne, M.A.E. and Stephenson, D. (1998) *Geology of the Falkirk District*, Memoir of the British Geological Survey, Sheet 31E (Scotland), The Stationery Office, London, for the British Geological Survey, 106 pp.

Campbell, R. (1914) On the occurrence of petrified plant remains in the Lion's Head Vent, Arthur's Seat. *Transactions of the Edinburgh Geological Society*, **13**, 148–73.

Campbell, R. and Lunn, J.W. (1925) Chlorophaeite in the dolerites (tholeiites) of Dalmahoy and Kaimes Hill, Edinburgh. *Mineralogical Magazine*, **20**, 435–40.

Campbell, R. and Lunn, J.W. (1927) The tholeiites and dolerites of the Dalmahoy Syncline. *Transactions of the Royal Society of Edinburgh*, **15**, 489–505.

Campbell, R. and Stenhouse, A.G. (1908) The geology of Inchcolm. *Transactions of the Edinburgh Geological Society*, **9**, 121–34.

Campbell, R. and Stenhouse, A.G. (1933) The occurrence of nepheline and fayalite in the phonolitic trachyte of the Bass Rock. *Transactions of the Edinburgh Geological Society*, **13**, 126–32.

Campbell, R., Day, T.C. and Stenhouse, A.G. (1932) The Braefoot Outer Sill, Fife: Part I. *Transactions of the Edinburgh Geological Society*, **12**, 342–75.

Campbell, R., Day, T.C. and Stenhouse, A.G. (1934) The Braefoot Outer Sill, Fife: Part II. *Transactions of the Edinburgh Geological Society*, **13**, 148–73.

Capewell, J.G. (1954) The basic intrusions and an associated vent near Little Mell Fell, Cumberland. *Transactions of the Leeds Geological Association*, **6**, 243–8.

Capewell, J.G. (1955) The post-Silurian, premarine Carboniferous sedimentary rocks of the eastern side of the English Lake District. *Quarterly Journal of the Geological Society of London*, **111**, 23–46.

Carr, M.K. (1976) The petrography and stratigraphy of the Old Red Sandstone and volcanic rocks of southern Kintyre, Scotland. Unpublished BSc thesis, University of Lancaster.

Carruthers, R.G., Dinham, C.H., Burnett, G.A. and Maden, J. (1927) *The Geology of Belford, Holy Island, and the Farne Islands*, 2nd edn, Memoir of the Geological Survey of Great Britain, Sheet 4 (England and Wales), HMSO, London, 195 pp.

Carruthers, R.G., Burnett, G.A. and Anderson, W. (1930) *The Geology of the Alnwick District*, Memoir of the Geological Survey of Great Britain, Sheet 6 (England and Wales), HMSO, London, 138 pp.

Cas, R.A.F. and Wright, J.V. (1987) *Volcanic Successions: Modern and Ancient: a Geological Approach to Processes, Products and Successions*, Allen and Unwin, London, 528 pp.

Cave, R., Cornwell, J.D. and Evans, A.D. (1989) The Mathry Dyke, a quartz-dolerite intrusion of probable Carboniferous age in southwest Wales. *Geological Magazine*, **126**, 715–21.

Chadwick, R.A. and Holliday, D.W. (1991) Deep crustal structure and Carboniferous basin development within the Iapetus convergence zone, northern England. *Journal of the Geological Society, London*, **148**, 41–53.

Chadwick, R.A., Holliday, D.W., Holloway, S. and Hulbert, A.G. (1995) *The Structure and Evolution of the Northumberland–Solway Basin and Adjacent Areas*, Subsurface Memoir of the British Geological Survey, HMSO, London, 90 pp.

Chapman, N.A. (1974) Ultrabasic inclusions from the Coalyard Hill Vent, Fife. *Scottish Journal of Geology*, **10**, 223–7.

References

Chapman, N.A. (1975) An experimental study of spinel-clinopyroxenite xenoliths from the Duncansby Ness Vent, Caithness, Scotland. *Contributions to Mineralogy and Petrology,* **51**, 223–30.

Chapman, N.A. (1976) Inclusions and megacrysts from undersaturated tuffs and basanites, East Fife, Scotland. *Journal of Petrology,* **16**, 29–35.

Chapman, N.A. and Powell, R. (1976) Origin of anorthoclase megacrysts in alkali basalts. *Contributions to Mineralogy and Petrology,* **58**, 29–35.

Cheshire, S.G. and Bell, J.D. (1977) The Speedwell vent, Castleton, Derbyshire; a Carboniferous littoral cone. *Proceedings of the Yorkshire Geological Society,* **41**, 173–84.

Chough, S.K. and Sohn, Y.K. (1990) Depositional mechanics and sequences of base-surges, Songaksan tuff ring, Cheju Island, Korea. *Sedimentology,* **37**, 1115–35.

Claoué-Long, J.C., Compston, W., Roberts, J. and Fanning, C.M. (1995) Two Carboniferous ages: a comparison of Shrimp zircon dating with conventional zircon ages and $^{40}Ar/^{39}Ar$ analysis. In *Geochronology, Time Scales and Global Stratigraphic Correlation* (ed. W.A. Berggren), *Society of Economic Palaeontologists and Mineralogists Special Publication,* No. **54**, Society of Economic Palaeontologists and Mineralogists (SEPM), Tulsa, pp. 3–21.

Clark, R.H. (1956) A petrological study of the Arthur's Seat volcano. *Philosophical Transactions of the Royal Society of Edinburgh,* **63**, 37–70.

Cleal, C.J. and Thomas, B.A. (1995) *Palaeozoic Palaeobotany of Great Britain,* Geological Conservation Review Series, No. 9, Chapman and Hall, London, 295 pp.

Cleal, C.J. and Thomas, B.A. (1996) *British Upper Carboniferous Stratigraphy,* Geological Conservation Review Series, No. 11, Chapman and Hall, London, 339 pp.

Clough, C.T. (1876) The section at the High Force, Teesdale. *Quarterly Journal of the Geological Society of London,* **32**, 466–71.

Clough, C.T. (1880) The Whin Sill of Teesdale as an assimilator of the surrounding beds. *Geological Magazine,* **7**, 433–47.

Clough, C.T., Barrow, G., Crampton, C.B., Maufe, H.B., Bailey, E.B. and Anderson, E.M. (1910) *The Geology of East Lothian, including parts of the counties of Edinburgh and Berwick,* 2nd edn, Memoir of the Geological Survey of Great Britain, Sheet 33 and parts of 34 and 41 (Scotland), HMSO, Edinburgh, 226 pp.

Clough, C.T., Hinxman, L.W., Wilson, J.S.G., Crampton, C.B., Wright, W.B., Bailey, E.B., Anderson, E.M. and Carruthers, R.G. (1911) *The Geology of the Glasgow District,* Memoir of the Geological Survey of Great Britain, parts of sheets 30, 31, 22 and 23 (Scotland), HMSO, Edinburgh, 270 pp.

Clough, C.T., Hinxman, L.W., Wilson, J.S.G., Crampton, C.B., Wright, W.B., Bailey, E.B., Anderson, E.M. and Carruthers, R.G. (1925) *The Geology of the Glasgow District,* 2nd edn, Memoir of the Geological Survey of Great Britain, parts of sheets 30, 31, 22 and 23 (Scotland), HMSO, Edinburgh, 299 pp.

Colvine, R.J.L. (1968) Pyrope from Elie, Fife. *Scottish Journal of Geology,* **4**, 283–6.

Coombs, D.S. and Wilkinson, J.F.G. (1969) Lineages and fractionation trends in undersaturated volcanic rocks from the East Otago Volcanic Province (New Zealand) and related rocks. *Journal of Petrology,* **10**, 440–501.

Cooper, A.H., Millward, D., Johnson, E.W. and Soper, N.J. (1993) The early Palaeozoic evolution of northwest England. *Geological Magazine,* **130**, 711–24.

Cooper, D.C., Lee, M.K., Fortey, N.J., Cooper, A.H., Rundle, C.C., Webb, B.C. and Allen, P.M. (1988) The Crummock Water aureole: a zone of metasomatism and source of ore metals in the English Lake District. *Journal of the Geological Society, London,* **145**, 523–40.

Cope, F.W. (1933) The Lower Carboniferous succession in the Wye Valley region of North Derbyshire. *Journal of the Manchester Geological Association,* **1**, 125–45.

Cope, F.W. (1937) Some features in the D_1–D_2 limestones of the Miller's Dale region, Derbyshire. *Proceedings of the Yorkshire Geological Society,* **23**, 178–95.

Corfield, S.M., Gawthorpe, R.L., Gage, M., Fraser, A.L. and Besty, B.M. (1996) Inversion tectonics of the Variscan foreland of the British Isles. *Journal of the Geological Society, London,* **153**, 17–32.

Cornwell, J.D. and Evans, A.D. (1986) Magnetic surveys and structures in the Whin Sill, northern England. In *Geology in the Real World: the Kingsley Dunham Volume* (eds R.W. Nesbitt and I. Nichol), The Institution of Mining and Metallurgy, London, pp. 65–74.

References

Cossey, P., Adams, A.E., Wright, V.P., Whiteley, M.J., Whyte, M. and Purnell, M. (in press) *British Lower Carboniferous Stratigraphy*, Geological Conservation Review Series, Joint Nature Conservation Committee, Peterborough.

Cotton, W.R. (1968) A geological survey of the Campsie and Kirkpatrick Hills. Unpublished PhD thesis, University of Glasgow.

Coward, M.P. (1990) The Precambrian, Caledonian and Variscan framework to NW Europe. In *Tectonic Events Responsible for Britain's Oil and Gas Reserves* (eds R.F.P. Hardman and J. Brooks), *Geological Society Special Publication*, No. 55, The Geological Society, London, pp. 1–34.

Coward, M.P. (1993) The effect of Late Caledonian and Variscan continental escape tectonics on basement structure, Palaeozoic basin kinematics and subsequent Mesozoic basin development in NW Europe. In *Petroleum Geology of Northwest Europe, Proceedings of the 4th Conference held at the Barbican Centre*, London, 29 March–1 April, 1992 (ed. J.R. Parker), The Geological Society, London, pp. 1095–108.

Coward, M.P. (1995) Structural and tectonic setting of the Permo–Triassic basins of northwest Europe. In *Permian and Triassic Rifting in Northwest Europe* (ed. S.A.R. Boldy), *Geological Society Special Publication*, No. 91, The Geological Society, London, pp. 7–39.

Coward, M.P. and Gibbs, A.D. (1988) *Structural Interpretation with Emphasis on Extensional Tectonics, Joint Association for Petroleum Exploration Courses (UK) Course Notes*, No. 75, The Geological Society, London.

Cox, A.H. (1954) The Usk monchiquite – a 'pipe intrusion'. *Geological Magazine*, 91, 519.

Craig, G.Y. (1991) *Geology of Scotland*, 3rd edn, The Geological Society, London, 612 pp.

Craig, P.M. (1980) The volcanic geology of the Campsie Fells area, Stirlingshire. Unpublished PhD thesis, University of Lancaster.

Craig, P.M. and Hall, I.H.S. (1975) The Lower Carboniferous rocks of the Campsie–Kilpatrick area. *Scottish Journal of Geology*, 11, 171–4.

Creaney, S. (1980) Petrographic texture and vitrinite reflectance variation on the Alston Block, north-east England. *Proceedings of the Yorkshire Geological Society*, 42, 553–80.

Creer, K.M., Irving, E. and Nairn, A.E.M. (1959) Palaeomagnetism of the Great Whin Sill. *Geophysical Journal of the Royal Astronomical Society*, 2, 306–23.

Crump, L.A. and Donnelly, R. (1994) Opencast coal mining: a unique opportunity for Clee Hill Quarry. In *Mineral Resource Evaluation II: Methods and Case Histories* (eds M.K.G. Whateley and P.K. Harvey), *Geological Society Special Publication*, No. 79, The Geological Society, London, pp. 219–32.

Cumming, G.A. (1928) The lower limestones and associated volcanic rocks of a section of the Fifeshire coast. *Transactions of the Edinburgh Geological Society*, 12, 124–40.

Cumming, G.A. (1936) The structural and volcanic geology of the Elie–St Monance district, Fife. *Transactions of the Edinburgh Geological Society*, 13, 340–65.

Cunningham, R.J.H. (1838) On the geology of the Lothians. *Memoir of the Wernerian Natural History Society*, 7, 3–160.

Cunningham Craig, E.H., Wright, W.B. and Bailey, E.B. (1911) *The Geology of Colonsay and Oronsay with Part of the Ross of Mull*, Memoir of the Geological Survey of Great Britain, Sheet 35 and part of 27 (Scotland), HMSO, Edinburgh, 109 pp.

Curtis, C.D. (1976) 'Unmixed' Ca^{2+}/Mg^{2+} saponite at Calton Hill, Derbyshire. *Clay Minerals*, 11, 85–9.

Dakyns, J.R., Tiddeman, R.H. and Goodchild, J.G. (1897) *The Geology of the Country between Appleby, Ullswater and Haweswater*, Memoir of the Geological Survey of Great Britain, Sheet 30 (England and Wales), HMSO, London, 102 pp.

Dalrymple, G.B. (1979) Critical tables for conversion of K-Ar ages from old to new constants. *Geology*, 7, 558–60.

Davidson, K.A.S., Sola, M., Powell, D.W. and Hall, J. (1984) Geophysical model for the Midland Valley of Scotland. *Transactions of the Royal Society of Edinburgh: Earth Sciences*, 75, 175–81.

Davies, A. (1974) The Lower Carboniferous (Dinantian) sequence at Spilmersford, East Lothian, Scotland. *Bulletin of the Geological Survey of Great Britain*, 45, 1–38.

Davies, A., McAdam, A.D. and Cameron, I.B. (1986) *Geology of the Dunbar District*, Memoir of the British Geological Survey, Sheet 33E and part of 41 (Scotland), HMSO, London, 69 pp.

References

Davison, C. (1924) *A History of British Earthquakes*, Cambridge University Press, Cambridge, 416 pp.

Day, J.B.W. (1970) *Geology of the Country around Bewcastle*, Memoir of the Geological Survey of Great Britain, Sheet 12 (England and Wales), HMSO, London, 357 pp.

Day, T.C. (1912) Some observations on the Long Row and the Dasses, Arthur's Seat. *Transactions of the Edinburgh Geological Society*, **10**, 40–8.

Day, T.C. (1914) Notes on the Hummell Rocks, Gullane. *Transactions of the Edinburgh Geological Society*, **10**, 114–19.

Day, T.C. (1923) Note on the exposure of St Leonard's Craig, at No. 39 St Leonard's Hill. *Transactions of the Edinburgh Geological Society*, **11**, 266–7.

Day, T.C. (1925) Two unrecorded volcanic vents on the shore east of North Berwick. *Transactions of the Edinburgh Geological Society*, **11**, 338–45.

Day, T.C. (1928a) The volcanic vents on the shore between North Berwick and Tantallon Castle. *Transactions of the Edinburgh Geological Society*, **12**, 41–52.

Day, T.C. (1928b) Chemical analyses of quartz-dolerites and segregation veins at Hound Point, North Queensferry and Inverkeithing. *Transactions of the Edinburgh Geological Society*, **12**, 80–6.

Day, T.C. (1930a) Chemical analyses of white trap from Dalmeny, Granton, Weak Law, and North Berwick. *Transactions of the Edinburgh Geological Society*, **12**, 189–94.

Day, T.C. (1930b) Volcanic vents on the coast, from Tantallon Castle eastwards to Peffer Sands, and at Whitberry Point. *Transactions of the Edinburgh Geological Society*, **12**, 213–33.

Day, T.C. (1930c) Chemical analyses of phonolites from Traprain Law, the Bass Rock and North Berwick Law. *Transactions of the Edinburgh Geological Society*, **12**, 234–5.

Day, T.C. (1930d) Two large xenoliths within the phonolite of Traprain Law. *Transactions of the Edinburgh Geological Society*, **12**, 252–5.

Day, T.C. (1930e) An igneous dyke in the quartz-bankite of Bangly Quarry near Haddington. *Transactions of the Edinburgh Geological Society*, **12**, 256–9.

Day, T.C. (1930f) The intrusive rocks of Frances Craig, and the teschenite of Ravensheugh. *Transactions of the Edinburgh Geological Society*, **12**, 260–1.

Day, T.C. (1932a) The teschenite of Point Garry, North Berwick. *Transactions of the Edinburgh Geological Society*, **12**, 334–7.

Day, T.C. (1932b) Large sandstone xenolith within the phonolite of Traprain Law. *Transactions of the Edinburgh Geological Society*, **12**, 338–41.

Day, T.C. (1932c) Volcanic vents at Longskelly Rocks, and Yellow Craig Plantation, west of North Berwick. *Transactions of the Edinburgh Geological Society*, **12**, 376–81.

Day, T.C. (1933) *Arthur's Seat, a Ruined Volcano*, Oliver and Boyd, Edinburgh, 75 pp.

Day, T.C. and Bailey, E.B. (1928) Bombs of nepheline-basanite in the Partan Craig Vent, North Berwick. *Transactions of the Edinburgh Geological Society*, **12**, 87–9.

Dearnley, R. (1960) Petrology of the Carboniferous igneous rocks of the Bristol area. *Institute of Geological Sciences, Petrology Unit Internal Report*, No. **137**.

Dentith, M.C. (1988) Geophysical constraints on upper crustal structure in the Midland Valley of Scotland. Unpublished PhD thesis, University of Glasgow.

Dentith, M.C. and Hall, J. (1989) MAVIS – an upper crustal seismic refraction experiment in the Midland Valley of Scotland. *Geophysical Journal International*, **99**, 627–43.

De Souza, H.A.F. (1974) Potassium-argon ages of Carboniferous igneous rocks from East Lothian and the south of Scotland. Unpublished MSc thesis, University of Leeds.

De Souza, H.A.F. (1979) The geochronology of Scottish Carboniferous volcanism. Unpublished PhD thesis, University of Edinburgh.

De Souza, H.A.F. (1982) Age data from Scotland and the Carboniferous time scale. In *Numerical Dating in Stratigraphy* (ed. G.S. Odin), John Wiley and sons Ltd, Chichester, pp. 455–65.

Dewey, J.F. (1982) Plate tectonics and the evolution of the British Isles. *Journal of the Geological Society of London*, **139**, 371–412.

Dickson, J.A.D., Ford, T.D. and Swift, A. (1987) The stratigraphy of the Carboniferous rocks around Castletown, Isle of Man. *Proceedings of the Yorkshire Geological Society*, **46**, 203–29.

Dineley, D.L. and Metcalf, S.J. (1999) *Fossil Fishes of Great Britain*, Geological Conservation Review Series, No. **16**, Joint Nature Conservation Committee, Peterborough, 675 pp.

References

Dinham, C.H. (1927) The Stirling district. *Proceedings of the Geologists' Association*, **38**, 470–92.

Dinham, C.H. and Haldane, D. (1932) *The Economic Geology of the Stirling and Clackmannan Coalfield*, Memoir of the Geological Survey of Great Britain (Scotland), HMSO, Edinburgh, 242 pp.

Dixon, C.G. (1938) The geology of the Fintry, Gargunnock and Touch hills. *Geological Magazine*, **75**, 425–32.

Dixon, E.E.L. (1917) The geology of the Titterstone Clee Hill Coalfield. *Transactions of the Royal Society of Edinburgh*, **51**, 1064–71.

Dixon, J.E., Fitton, J.G. and Frost, R.T.C. (1981) The tectonic significance of post-Carboniferous igneous activity in the North Sea Basin. In *Petroleum Geology of the Continental Shelf of North-west Europe: Proceedings of the Second Conference on Petroleum Geology*, London, 4–6 March, 1980 (eds L.V. Illing and G.D. Hobson), Heyden and Son on behalf of the Institute of Petroleum, London, pp. 121–37.

Donaldson, C.H. (1978) Petrology of the uppermost upper mantle deduced from spinel-lherzolite and harzburgite nodules at Calton Hill, Derbyshire. *Contributions to Mineralogy and Petrology*, **65**, 363–77.

Donaldson, C.H. (1984) Kinematics of pyrope megacryst reactions in ascending basaltic magma – relevance to high-pressure magmatic crystallisation at Elie Ness, East Fife. *Geological Magazine*, **121**, 615–20.

Downes, H., Upton, B.G.J., Handisyde, E. and Thirlwall, M.F. (2001) Geochemistry of mafic and ultramafic xenoliths from Fidra (Southern Uplands, Scotland): implications for lithospheric processes in Permo–Carboniferous times. *Lithos*, **58**, 105–24.

Drever, H.I. and MacDonald, J.G. (1967) Some new data on "Kylitic" sills and associated picrites in Ayrshire, Scotland. *Proceedings of the Royal Society of Edinburgh*, **B70**, 31–48.

Dubey, V.S. and Holmes, A. (1929) Estimates of the ages of the Whin Sill and Cleveland Dyke by the helium method. *Nature*, **123**, 794–5.

Du Bois, P.M. (1957) Comparison of palaeomagnetic results for selected rocks for Great Britain and North America. *Advances in Physics*, **6**, 177–86.

Duckworth, S.P. (1977) Stratigraphy and petrography of the Carboniferous lava flows near Machrihanish, Kintyre. Unpublished BSc thesis, University of Lancaster.

Duff, P.McL.D. and Smith, A.J. (eds) (1992) *Geology of England and Wales*, The Geological Society, London, 671 pp.

Dunham, A.C. (1970) Whin sills and dykes. In *Geology of Durham County* (eds G.A.L. Johnson and G. Hickling), *Transactions of the Natural History Society of Northumberland, Durham and Newcastle-upon-Tyne*, **41**(1), Large and Sons Ltd, Newcastle-upon-Tyne, for the Natural History Society of Northumberland, Durham and Newcastle-upon-Tyne, pp. 92–100.

Dunham, A.C. and Kaye, M.J. (1965) The petrology of the Little Whin Sill, County Durham. *Proceedings of the Yorkshire Geological Society*, **35**, 229–76.

Dunham, A.C. and Strasser-King, V.E.H. (1981) Petrology of the Great Whin Sill in the Throckley Borehole, Northumberland. *Report of the Institute of Geological Sciences*, **81/4**.

Dunham, A.C. and Strasser-King, V.E.H. (1982) Late Carboniferous intrusions of northern Britain. In *Igneous Rocks of the British Isles* (ed. D.S. Sutherland), John Wiley and sons Ltd, Chichester, pp. 277–83.

Dunham, A.C. and Wilkinson, F. (1992) A note on the mineralogy of the chilled margin of the Little Whin Sill at Turn Wheel Linn, Weardale, Co. Durham. *Proceedings of the Yorkshire Geological Society*, **49**, 67–70.

Dunham, A.C., Copley, P.A. and Strasser-King, V.E.H. (1972) Submicroscopic exsolution lamellae in pyroxenes in the Whin Sill, northern England. *Contributions to Mineralogy and Petrology*, **37**, 211–20.

Dunham, K.C. (1932) Quartz-dolerite pebbles (Whin Sill) in the Upper Brockram. *Geological Magazine*, **69**, 425–7.

Dunham, K.C. (1948) *Geology of the Northern Pennine Orefield, Volume 1: Tyne to Stainmore*, Memoir of the Geological Survey of Great Britain (England and Wales), HMSO, London, 357 pp.

Dunham, K.C. (1990) *Geology of the Northern Pennine Orefield, Volume 1: Tyne to Stainmore*, 2nd edn, Memoir of the British Geological Survey, sheets 19 and 25 and parts of 13, 24, 26, 31, 32 (England and Wales), HMSO, London, 299 pp.

Dunham, K.C., Dunham, A.C., Hodge, B.L. and Johnson, G.A.L. (1965) Granite beneath Visean sediments and mineralization at Rookhope, northern Pennines. *Quarterly Journal of the Geological Society of London*, **121**, 383–417.

References

Dunham, K.C., Fitch, F.J., Ineson, P.R., Miller, J.A. and Mitchell, J.G. (1968) The geochronological significance of Argon-40/Argon-39 age determinations on White Whin from the northern Pennine orefield. *Proceedings of the Royal Society of London*, A307, 251–66.

Eastwood, T. (1928) The Cockermouth Lavas, Cumberland – a Carboniferous volcanic episode. *Summary of Progress of the Geological Survey of Great Britain*, for 1927, Part 2, 15–22.

Eastwood, T., Hollingworth, S.E., Rose, W.C.C. and Trotter, F.M. (1968) *Geology of the Country around Cockermouth and Caldbeck*, Memoir of the Geological Survey of Great Britain, Sheet 23 (England and Wales), HMSO, London, 298 pp.

Eckford, R.J.A. and Ritchie, M. (1939) The igneous rocks of the Kelso District. *Transactions of the Edinburgh Geological Society*, 13, 464–72.

Egglestone, W.M. (1910) The geology of the Little Whin Sill in Weardale. *Transactions of the Institution of Miners and Engineers*, 39, 18–51.

El-Harathi, R.M. and Tarling, D.H. (1988) A magnetic study of the Holy Island dyke system, Northumberland. *Transactions of the Natural History Society of Northumbria*, 55, 12–19.

Ellis, N.V. (ed.), Bowen, D.Q., Campbell, S., Knill, J.L., McKirdy, A.P., Prosser, C.D., Vincent, M.A. and Wilson, R.C.L. (1996) *An Introduction to the Geological Conservation Review*, Geological Conservation Review Series, No. 1, Joint Nature Conservation Committee, Peterborough, 131 pp.

Elliott, R.B. (1960) The Carboniferous volcanic rocks of the Langholm district. *Proceedings of the Geologists' Association*, 71, 1–24.

Emeleus, C.H. and Gyopari, M.C. (1992) *British Tertiary Volcanic Province*, Geological Conservation Review Series, No. 4, Chapman and Hall, London, 259 pp.

Ernst, R. and Buchan, K.L. (1997) Giant radiating dyke swarms; their use in identifying pre-Mesozoic large igneous provinces and mantle plumes. In *Large Igneous Provinces; Continental, Oceanic and Planetary Flood Volcanism* (eds J.J. Mahoney and M.F. Coffin), *Geophysical Monograph Series*, No. 100, American Geophysical Union, Washington DC, pp. 297–333.

Esang, C.B. and Piper, J.D.A. (1984) Palaeomagnetism of the Carboniferous E–W dyke swarm in Argyllshire. *Scottish Journal of Geology*, 20, 309–14.

Eyles, V.A. and Blundell, C.R.K. (1957) On a volcanic vent and associated monchiquite intrusions in Monmouthshire. *Geological Magazine*, 94, 54–7.

Eyles, V.A., Simpson, J.B. and MacGregor, A.G. (1929) The igneous geology of central Ayrshire. *Transactions of the Geological Society of Glasgow*, 18, 361–87.

Eyles, V.A., Simpson, J.B. and MacGregor, A.G. (1949) *Geology of Central Ayrshire*, 2nd edn, Memoir of the Geological Survey of Great Britain, Sheet 14 (Scotland), HMSO, Edinburgh, 160 pp.

Falconer, J.D. (1906) The igneous geology of the Bathgate and Linlithgow Hills. Part 2. Petrography. *Transactions of the Royal Society of Edinburgh*, 45, 133–50.

Falconer, J.D. (1907) The geology of Ardrossan. *Transactions of the Royal Society of Edinburgh*, 45, 601–10.

Faulkner, T.J. (1989a) Carbonate facies on a Lower Carboniferous storm-influenced ramp in South-West Britain. Unpublished PhD thesis, University of Bristol.

Faulkner, T.J. (1989b) The early Carboniferous (Courceyan) Middle Hope volcanics of Weston-super-Mare: development and demise of an offshore volcanic high. *Proceedings of the Geologists' Association*, 100, 93–106.

Fitch, F.J. and Miller, J.A. (1964) The age of the paroxysmal Variscan Orogeny in England. In *The Phanerozoic Time-Scale: a Symposium Dedicated to Professor Arthur Holmes* (eds W.B. Harland, A. Gilbert Smith and B. Wilcock), *Quarterly Journal of the Geological Society of London, Supplement*, 120S, The Geological Society of London, London, pp. 159–73.

Fitch, F.J. and Miller, J.A. (1967) The age of the Whin Sill. *Liverpool and Manchester Geological Journal*, 5, 233–50.

Fitch, F.J., Miller, J.A., Evans, A.L., Grasty, R.L. and Meneisy, M.Y. (1969) Isotopic age determinations on rocks from Wales and the Welsh Borders. In *The Precambrian and Lower Palaeozoic Rocks of Wales* (ed. A. Wood), University of Wales Press, Cardiff, pp. 23–45.

Fitch, F.J., Miller, J.A. and Williams, S.C. (1970) Isotopic ages of British Carboniferous rocks. In *Compte Rendu: Sixième Congrès International de Stratigraphie et de Géologie du Carbonifère*, Sheffield, 11–16 September, 1967 (ed. C.J. Stubblefield), van Aelst, Maastricht, Volume 2, pp. 771–90.

References

Flett, J.S. (1900) The trap dykes of the Orkneys. *Transactions of the Edinburgh Geological Society*, **39**, 865–908.

Flett, J.S. (1930) The teschenite of Easter Dalmeny. *Summary of Progress of the Geological Survey of Great Britain*, for **1929**, Part 3, 59–74.

Flett, J.S. (1931a) The Saline No. 1 teschenite. *Summary of Progress of the Geological Survey of Great Britain*, for **1930**, Part 2, 44–50.

Flett, J.S. (1931b) The Blackness teschenite. *Summary of Progress of the Geological Survey of Great Britain*, for **1930**, Part 3, 39–45.

Flett, J.S. (1932) The Stankards Sill. *Summary of Progress of the Geological Survey of Great Britain*, for **1931**, Part 2, 141–55.

Flett, J.S. (1934) A thomsonized inclusion from the Blackness Sill. *Summary of Progress of the Geological Survey of Great Britain*, for **1933**, Part 2, 85–90.

Floyd, J.D. (1994) The derivation and definition of the 'Southern Upland Fault': a review of the Midland Valley–Southern Uplands terrane boundary. *Scottish Journal of Geology*, **30**, 51–62.

Floyd, P.A., Exley, C.S. and Styles, M.T. (1993) *Igneous Rocks of South-west England*, Geological Conservation Review Series, No. **5**, Chapman and Hall, London, 256 pp.

Forster, S.C. and Warrington, G. (1985) Geochronology of the Carboniferous, Permian and Triassic. In *The Chronology of the Geological Record* (ed. N.J. Snelling), *Geological Society Memoir*, No. **10**, Blackwell Scientific Publications, Oxford, for The Geological Society, pp. 99–113.

Forsyth, I.H. and Chisholm, J.I. (1968) Geological Survey boreholes in the Carboniferous of East Fife. *Bulletin of the Geological Survey of Great Britain*, **28**, 61–101.

Forsyth, I.H. and Chisholm, J.I. (1977) *The Geology of East Fife*, Memoir of the Geological Survey of Great Britain, Sheet 41 and part of 49 (Scotland), HMSO, Edinburgh, 284 pp.

Forsyth, I.H. and Rundle, C.C. (1978) The age of the volcanic and hypabyssal rocks of East Fife. *Bulletin of the Geological Survey of Great Britain*, **60**, 23–9.

Forsyth, I.H., Hall, I.H.S. and McMillan, A.A. (1996) *Geology of the Airdrie District*, Memoir of the British Geological Survey,
Sheet 31 (Scotland), The Stationery Office, London, for the British Geological Survey, 94 pp.

Fowler, A. and MacGregor, A.G. (1938) Kelso district Sheet 25. *Summary of Progress of the Geological Survey of Great Britain*, for **1937**, 55–9.

Francis, E.H. (1956) *The Economic Geology of the Stirling and Clackmannan Coalfield, Scotland: Area North of the River Forth*, Coalfield Papers of the Geological Survey of Great Britain, No. **1**, HMSO, Edinburgh, 36 pp.

Francis, E.H. (1957) New evidence of volcanicity in West Fife. *Transactions of the Edinburgh Geological Society*, **17**, 71–80.

Francis, E.H. (1959) A volcanic vent in the Bogside mines, Fife. *Geological Magazine*, **96**, 457–69.

Francis, E.H. (1960) Intrusive tuffs related to the Firth of Forth volcanoes. *Transactions of the Edinburgh Geological Society*, **18**, 32–50.

Francis, E.H. (1961a) *The Economic Geology of the Fife Coalfields, Area 2: Cowdenbeath and Central Fife including Fordell, Lochgelly, Cadham and Kirkcaldy*, 2nd edn, Memoir of the Geological Survey, Scotland, HMSO, Edinburgh, 152 pp.

Francis, E.H. (1961b) Volcanism in relation to sedimentation in the Carboniferous rocks of the Saline district, Fife. *Bulletin of the Geological Survey of Great Britain*, **17**, 116–44.

Francis, E.H. (1961c) Thin beds of graded tuffs and tuffaceous siltstone in the Carboniferous of Fife. *Bulletin of the Geological Survey of Great Britain*, **17**, 191–215.

Francis, E.H. (1965) Carboniferous–Permian igneous rocks. In *Geology of Scotland*, 1st edn (ed. G.Y. Craig), Oliver and Boyd, Edinburgh, pp. 359–82.

Francis, E.H. (1967) Review of Carboniferous–Permian Volcanicity in Scotland. *Geologische Rundschau*, **57**, 219–46.

Francis, E.H. (1968a) Pyroclastic and related rocks of the Geological Survey boreholes in East Fife. *Bulletin of the Geological Survey of Great Britain*, **28**, 121–35.

Francis, E.H. (1968b) Effect of sedimentation on volcanic processes, including neck–sill relationships in the British Carboniferous. In *International Geological Congress, Prague, 1968: Report of the 23rd Session, Section 2: Volcanism and Tectogenesis* (ed. M. Kuthan), Academia, Prague, Volume 2, pp. 163–74.

References

Francis, E.H. (1969) Les tonstein du Royaume-Uni. *Annales de la Société Géologique du Nord*, **89**, 209–14.

Francis, E.H. (1970a) Review of Carboniferous volcanism in England and Wales. *Journal of Earth Sciences, Leeds Geological Association*, **8**, 41–56.

Francis, E.H. (1970b) Bedding in Scottish (Fifeshire) tuff-pipes and its relevance to maars and calderas. *Bulletin Volcanologique*, **34**, 697–712.

Francis, E.H. (1978a) Igneous activity in a fractured craton: Carboniferous volcanism in northern Britain. In *Crustal Evolution in Northwestern Britain and Adjacent Regions: Proceedings of an International Conference held in Glasgow University, 5–8 April, 1977* (eds D.R. Bowes and B.E. Leake), *Geological Journal Special Issue*, No. **10**, Seel House Press, Liverpool, pp. 279–96.

Francis, E.H. (1978b) The Midland Valley as a rift, seen in connection with the late Palaeozoic European Rift system. In *Tectonics and Geophysics of Continental Rifts* (eds I.B. Ramberg and E.-R. Neumann), *NATO Advanced Study Institutes Series, Series C: Mathematics and Physical Sciences*, No. **37**, Reidel, Dordrecht, pp. 133–47.

Francis, E.H. (1982) Magma and sediment – 1. Emplacement mechanism of late Carboniferous tholeiite sills in northern Britain. *Journal of the Geological Society of London*, **139**, 1–20.

Francis, E.H. (1983) Carboniferous–Permian igneous rocks. In *Geology of Scotland*, 2nd edn (ed. G.Y. Craig), Scottish Academic Press, Edinburgh, pp. 297–324.

Francis, E.H. (1985) Recent ash-fall: a guide to tonstein distribution. In *Compte Rendu: Dixième Congrès International de Stratigraphie et de Géologie du Carbonifère*, Madrid, 12–17 September, 1983 (eds J.L. Escobedo *et al.*), Ministerio de Industria y Energia, Madrid, pp. 189–95.

Francis, E.H. (1988) Mid-Devonian to early Permian volcanism: Old World. In *The Caledonian–Appalachian Orogen* (eds A.L. Harris and D.J. Fettes), *Geological Society Special Publication*, No. **38**, Blackwell Scientific Publications, Oxford, for The Geological Society, pp. 573–84.

Francis, E.H. (1991) Carboniferous–Permian igneous rocks. In *Geology of Scotland*, 3rd edn (ed. G.Y. Craig), The Geological Society, London, pp. 393–420.

Francis, E.H. (1992) Upper Palaeozoic volcanism of the craton. In *Geology of England and Wales* (eds P.McL.D. Duff and A.J. Smith), The Geological Society, London, pp. 502–5.

Francis, E.H. and Ewing, C.J.C. (1961) Coal Measures and volcanism off the Fife coast. *Geological Magazine*, **98**, 501–10.

Francis, E.H. and Hopgood, A.M. (1970) Volcanism and the Ardross Fault, Fife, Scotland. *Scottish Journal of Geology*, **6**, 162–85.

Francis, E.H. and Walker, B.H. (1987) Emplacement of alkali-dolerite sills relative to extrusive volcanism and sedimentary basins in the Carboniferous of Fife, Scotland. *Transactions of the Royal Society of Edinburgh: Earth Sciences*, **77**, 309–23.

Francis, E.H., Sabine, P.A. and Young, B.R. (1961) Thin beds of graded kaolinized tuff and tuffaceous siltstone in the Carboniferous of Fife. *Bulletin of the Geological Survey of Great Britain*, **17**, 191–214.

Francis, E.H., Forsyth, I.H., Read, W.A. and Armstrong, M. (1970) *The Geology of the Stirling District*, Memoir of the Geological Survey of Great Britain, Sheet 39 (Scotland), HMSO, Edinburgh, 357 pp.

Fraser, A.J. and Gawthorpe, R.L. (1990) Tectono-stratigraphic development and hydrocarbon habitat of the Carboniferous in northern England. In *Tectonic Events Responsible for Britain's Oil and Gas Reserves* (eds R.F.P. Hardman and J. Brooks), *Geological Society Special Publication*, No. **55**, The Geological Society, London, pp. 49–86.

Frost, D.V. and Holliday, D.W. (1980) *Geology of the Country around Bellingham*, Memoir of the Geological Survey of Great Britain, Sheet 13 (England and Wales), HMSO, London, 112 pp.

Furnes, H. and Sturt, B.A. (1976) Beach/shallow marine hyaloclastite deposits and their geological significance – an example from Gran Canaria. *Journal of Geology*, **84**, 439–53.

Fyfe, J.A., Long, D. and Evans, D. (1993) *United Kingdom Offshore Regional Report: Geology of the Malin–Hebrides Sea Areas*, HMSO, London, for the British Geological Survey, 91 pp.

Gallagher, M.J. (1963) Lamprophyre dykes from Argyll. *Mineralogical Magazine*, **33**, 415–30.

Galtier, J., Scott, A.C., Powell, J.H., Glover, B.W. and Waters, C.N. (1992) Anatomically preserved conifer-like stems from the Upper Carboniferous of England. *Proceedings of the Royal Society of London*, **B247**, 211–14.

References

Garwood, E.J. (1931) The Tuedian Beds of northern Cumberland and Roxburghshire, east of the Liddel Water. *Quarterly Journal of the Geological Society of London*, **87**, 97–159.

Gawthorpe, R.L., Gutteridge, P. and Leeder, M.R. (1989) Late Devonian and Dinantian basin evolution in northern England and North Wales. In *The Role of Tectonics in Devonian and Carboniferous Sedimentation in the British Isles* (eds R.S. Arthurton, P. Gutteridge and S.C. Nolan), *Yorkshire Geological Society Occasional Publication*, No. 6, Yorkshire Geological Society, Leeds, pp. 1–24.

Geikie, A. (1866) Traces of a group of Permian volcanoes in the south-west of Scotland. *Geological Magazine*, **3**, 243–8.

Geikie, A. (1880) On the Carboniferous volcanic rocks of the basin of the Firth of Forth – their structure in the field and under the microscope. *Transactions of the Royal Society of Edinburgh*, **29**, 437–518.

Geikie, A. (1897) *The Ancient Volcanoes of Great Britain*, 2 volumes, McMillan, London.

Geikie, A. (1900) *The Geology of Central and Western Fife and Kinross*, Memoir of the Geological Survey of Great Britain, Sheet 40 (Scotland), HMSO, Edinburgh, 284 pp.

Geikie, A. (1902) *The Geology of Eastern Fife*, Memoir of the Geological Survey of Great Britain, Sheet 41 and parts of 40, 48 and 49 (Scotland), HMSO, Edinburgh, 421 pp.

Geikie, A. and Strahan, A. (1899) Volcanic group in the Carboniferous Limestone of North Somerset. *Summary of Progress of the Geological Survey of the United Kingdom*, for **1898**, 104–11.

Geikie, A., Geikie, J. and Peach, B.N. (1869) *Ayrshire: Southern District*, Sheet Explanation of the Geological Survey of Great Britain, Sheet 14 (Scotland), HMSO, Edinburgh, 27 pp.

Geikie, J. (1893) *Fragments of Earth Lore*, Bartholomew and Co., Edinburgh, 428 pp.

George, T.N. (1960) The stratigraphic evolution of the Midland Valley. *Transactions of the Geological Society of Glasgow*, **24**, 32–107.

George, T.N., Johnson, G.A.L., Prentice, J.E., Sevastopulo, G.D., Mitchell, M., Ramsbottom, W.H.C. and Wilson, R.B. (1976) *A Correlation of Dinantian Rocks in the British Isles*, *Geological Society of London Special Report*, No. 7, Scottish Academic Press, Edinburgh, for The Geological Society of London, 87 pp.

Gibbs, A. (1987) Development of extension and mixed-mode sedimentary basins. In *Continental Extensional Tectonics* (eds M.P. Coward, J.F. Dewey and P.L. Hancock), *Geological Society Special Publication*, No. **28**, Blackwell Scientific Publications, Oxford, for The Geological Society, pp. 19–33.

Giddings, J.W., Randall, B.A.O. and Farmer, N. (1971) The palaeomagnetism of the Holy Island Dyke. *Transactions of the Natural History Society of Northumberland, Durham and Newcastle-upon-Tyne*, **17**, 177–82.

Gillespie, M.R. and Styles, M.T. (1999) BGS rock classification scheme, Volume 1: Classification of igneous rocks, 2nd edn. *British Geological Survey Research Report*, **RR/99/6**.

Glover, B.W., Powell, J.H. and Waters, C.N. (1993) Etruria Formation (Westphalian C) palaeoenvironments and volcanicity on the southern margins of the Pennine Basin, south Staffordshire, England. *Journal of the Geological Society, London*, **150**, 737–50.

Godchaux, M.M., Bonnischsen, W. and Jenks, M.D. (1992) Types of phreatomagmatic volcanoes in the western Snake River Plain, Idaho, USA. *Journal of Volcanology and Geothermal Research*, **52**, 1–25.

Goodchild, J.G. (1904) The geological history of Lower Tweedside. *Proceedings of the Geologists' Association*, **18**, 105–42.

Gordon, W.T. (1909) On the nature of occurrence of the plant-bearing rocks at Pettycur, Fife. *Transactions of the Edinburgh Geological Society*, **9**, 353–60.

Gordon, W.T. (1935) The genus *Pitys*, Witham, emend. *Transactions of the Royal Society of Edinburgh*, **58**, 279–311.

Goswami, G. (1968) A magnetic and chemical study of the titanium-bearing ore minerals of Carboniferous igneous rocks of the Midland Valley of Scotland. Unpublished PhD thesis, University of Glasgow.

Goulty, N.R., Pierce, C., Flatman, T.D., Home, M. and Richardson, J.H. (2000) Magnetic survey of the Holy Island Dyke on Holy Island, Northumberland. *Proceedings of the Yorkshire Geological Society*, **53**, 111–18.

Gradstein, F.M. and Ogg, J.G. (1996) A Phanerozoic time scale. *Episodes*, **19**, 3–5.

Graham, A.M. and Upton, B.G.J. (1978) Gneisses in diatremes, Scottish Midland Valley: petrology and tectonic implications. *Journal of the Geological Society of London*, **135**, 219–28.

References

Green, A.H., Le Neve Foster, C. and Dakyns, J.R. (1887) *The Geology of the Carboniferous Limestone, Yoredale Rocks and Millstone Grit of North Derbyshire*, 2nd edn, Memoir of the Geological Survey of Great Britain, parts of sheets 88SE, 81NE, 81SE, 72NE, 82NW, 82SW and 71NW (England and Wales), HMSO, London, 212 pp.

Green, J.F.N. (1918) The Mell Fell Conglomerate. *Proceedings of the Geologists' Association*, **29**, 117–25.

Greig, D.C. (1971) *British Regional Geology: The South of Scotland*, 3rd edn, HMSO, Edinburgh, 125 pp.

Groessens, E. (1976) Preliminary range chart of conodont biozonation in the Belgian Dinantian. In *International Symposium on Belgian Micropalaeontological Limits from Emsian to Visean*, Namur, 1–10 September, 1974 (eds J. Bouckaert and M. Streel), Publication No. **17**, Ministry of Economic Affairs, Brussels.

Guion, P.D., Gutteridge, P. and Davies, S.J. (2000) Carboniferous sedimentation and volcanism on the Laurussian margin. In *Geological History of Britain and Ireland* (eds N.H. Woodcock and R.A. Strachan), Blackwell Scientific Publications, Oxford, pp. 227–70.

Gunn, W. (1900) *The Geology of Belford, Holy Island and the Farne Islands Northumberland*, Memoir of the Geological Survey of Great Britain, Sheet 110SE (England and Wales), HMSO, London, 155 pp.

Hains, B.A. and Horton, A. (1969) *British Regional Geology: Central England*, 3rd edn, HMSO, London, 142 pp.

Haldane, D. (1927) The Ochil Fault and its dolerite intrusion. *Summary of Progress of the Geological Survey of Great Britain*, for **1926**, 147–53.

Hall, I.H.S., Gallagher, M.J., Skilton, B.R.H. and Johnson, C.E. (1982) Investigation of polymetallic mineralisation in Lower Devonian volcanics near Alva, central Scotland. *Institute of Geological Sciences, Mineral Reconnaissance Programme Report*, No. **53**.

Hall, I.H.S., Browne, M.A.E. and Forsyth, I.H. (1998) *Geology of the Glasgow District*, Memoir of the British Geological Survey, Sheet 30E (Scotland), The Stationery Office, London, for the British Geological Survey, 117 pp.

Hall, J. (1805) Experiments on whinstone and lava. *Transactions of the Royal Society of Edinburgh*, **5**, 43–75.

Hall, J. (1971) A preliminary seismic survey adjacent to the Rashiehill borehole near Slamannan, Stirlingshire. *Scottish Journal of Geology*, **7**, 170–4.

Hall, J. (1974) A seismic reflection survey of the Clyde Plateau Lavas in North Ayrshire and Renfrewshire. *Scottish Journal of Geology*, **9**, 253–79.

Halliday, A.N., Aftalion, M., Upton, B.G.J., Aspen, P. and Jocelyn, J. (1984) U-Pb isotopic ages from a granulite-facies xenolith from Partan Craig in the Midland Valley of Scotland. *Transactions of the Royal Society of Edinburgh: Earth Sciences*, **75**, 71–4.

Halliday, A.N., Dickin, A.P., Hunter, R.N., Davies, G.R., Dempster, T.J., Hamilton, P.J. and Upton, B.G.J. (1993) Formation and composition of the lower continental crust: evidence from Scottish xenolith suites. *Journal of Geophysical Research*, **98**, 581–607.

Halliday, A.N., McAlpine, A. and Mitchell, J.G. (1977) The age of the Hoy Lavas, Orkney. *Scottish Journal of Geology*, **13**, 43–52.

Hamad, S. el D. (1963) The chemistry and mineralogy of the olivine nodules of Calton Hill, Derbyshire. *Mineralogical Magazine*, **33**, 483–97.

Harcombe-Smee, B.J., Piper, J.D.A., Rolph, T.C. and Thomas, D.N. (1996) A palaeomagnetic and palaeointensity study of the Mauchline lavas, south-west Scotland. *Physics of the Earth and Planetary Interiors*, **94**, 63–74.

Harker, A. (1895) *Petrology for Students: an Introduction to the Study of Rocks under the Microscope*, Cambridge University Press, Cambridge, 306 pp.

Harrison, R.K. (1968) Petrology of the Little and Great Whin sills in the Woodland Borehole, County Durham. *Bulletin of the Geological Survey of Great Britain*, **28**, 38–54.

Harrison, R.K. (1977) Petrology of the intrusive rocks in the Duffield Borehole, Derbyshire. *Bulletin of the Geological Survey of Great Britain*, **59**, 41–59.

Hartley, J. and Leedal, G.P. (1951) A monchiquite vent, Stob a'Ghrianain, Inverness-shire. *Geological Magazine*, **88**, 140–4.

Haslett, S.K. (1992) Petrology of a monchiquite from the Welsh Borderlands. *Mercian Geologist*, **13**, 43–6.

Haszeldine, R.S. (1984) Carboniferous North Atlantic palaeogeography: stratigraphic evidence for rifting, not megashear or subduction. *Geological Magazine*, **121**, 443–63.

References

Haszeldine, R.S. (1988) Crustal lineaments in the British Isles: their relationship to Carboniferous basins. In *Sedimentation in a Synorogenic Basin Complex: the Upper Carboniferous of Northwest Europe* (eds B.M. Besly and G. Kelling), Blackie and Son, Glasgow, pp. 53–68.

Hatch, F.H. (1891) *An Introduction to the Study of Petrology: the Igneous Rocks*, Swan Sonnenschein, London, 128 pp.

Hatch, F.H. (1892) The Lower Carboniferous Volcanic Rocks of East Lothian (Garleton Hills). *Transactions of the Royal Society of Edinburgh*, **37**, 115–26.

Hatch, F.H., Wells, A.K. and Wells, M.K. (1961) *Petrology of the Igneous Rocks*, 12th edn, Thomas Murby and Co., London, 515 pp.

Hawkes, L. and Smythe, J.A. (1931) Garnet-bearing sands of the Northumberland coast. *Geological Magazine*, **68**, 345–61.

Henderson, C.M.B. and Gibb, F.G.F. (1983) Felsic mineral crystallization trends in differentiating alkaline basic magmas. *Contributions to Mineralogy and Petrology*, **84**, 355–64.

Henderson, C.M.B. and Gibb, F.G.F. (1987) The petrology of the Lugar Sill, SW Scotland. *Transactions of the Royal Society of Edinburgh: Earth Sciences*, **77**, 325–47.

Henderson, C.M.B., Foland, K.A. and Gibb, F.G.F. (1987) The age of the Lugar Sill and a discussion of the Late-Carboniferous/ Early Permian sill complex of SW Scotland. *Geological Magazine*, **22**, 43–52.

Henderson, J. (1880) On the structure and arrangement of the rocks of Arthur's Seat. *Transactions of the Edinburgh Geological Society*, **3**, 222–44.

Heslop, M.K. (1908) On some elementary forms of crystallization in the igneous dykes of Northumberland and Durham. *Proceedings of the University of Durham Philosophical Society*, **3**, 37–46.

Heslop, M.K. (1912) A preliminary note on the uniaxial augites of the north of England igneous dykes. *Proceedings of the University of Durham Philosophical Society*, **4**, 172–4.

Higazy, R.A. (1952) The distribution and significance of the trace elements in the Braefoot Outer Sill, Fife. *Transactions of the Edinburgh Geological Society*, **15**, 150–86.

Hill, J.A. and Dunham, K.C. (1968) The barites deposits of Closehouse, Lunedale, Yorkshire. *Proceedings of the Yorkshire Geological Society*, **36**, 351–72.

Hinton, R.W. and Upton, B.G.J. (1991) The chemistry of zircon; variations within and between large crystals from syenite and alkali basalt xenoliths. *Geochimica et Cosmochimica Acta*, **55**, 3287–302.

Hjelmqvist, S. (1939) Some post-Silurian dykes in Scania and problems suggested by them. *Sveriges Geologiske Undersokning Arsbok*, **33**(10), 1–32.

Holmes, A. and Harwood, H.F. (1928) The age and composition of the Whin Sill and the related dykes of the north of England. *Mineralogical Magazine*, **21**, 493–542.

Holmes, A. and Mockler, G.S. (1931) Late Carboniferous and Tertiary intrusions. *Proceedings of the Geologists' Association*, **42**, 261–71.

Holmes, A. and Smith, S. (1921) The Wackerfield Dyke, County Durham. *Geological Magazine*, **58**, 440–54.

House, M.R., Richardson, J.B., Chaloner, W.G., Allen, J.R.L., Holland, C.H. and Westoll, T.W. (1977) *A Correlation of Devonian Rocks in the British Isles*, Geological Society of London Special Report, No. 8, Scottish Academic Press, Edinburgh, 110 pp.

Howard, M. (1999) The geochemistry of Late-Palaeozoic quartz tholeiite intrusions in northern Britain. Unpublished MRes thesis, University of Edinburgh.

Howell, H.H. and Geikie, A. (1861) *The Geology of the Neighbourhood of Edinburgh (with Appendix and List of Fossils by J.W. Slater)*, Memoir of the Geological Survey of Great Britain, Sheet 32 and part of 31 (Scotland), HMSO, Edinburgh, 151 pp.

Howell, H.H., Geikie, A. and Young, J. (1866) *The Geology of East Lothian including parts of the counties of Edinburgh and Berwick*, Memoir of the Geological Survey of Great Britain, sheets 33, 34 and part of 41 (Scotland), HMSO, Edinburgh, 77 pp.

Howells, M.F. (1969) Cryptovents and allied structures in Carboniferous strata between Port Seton and Aberlady, East Lothian. *Scottish Journal of Geology*, **5**, 1–10.

Huddart, D. and Glasser, N.F. (2002) *Quaternary of Northern England*, Geological Conservation Review Series, No. **25**, Joint Nature Conservation Committee, Peterborough, 745 pp.

Hunter, R.H. and Upton, B.G.J. (1987) The British Isles – a Palaeozoic mantle sample. In *Mantle Xenoliths* (ed. P.H. Nixon), John Wiley and sons Ltd, Chichester, pp. 107–18.

References

Hunter, R.H., Upton, B.G.J. and Aspen, P. (1984) Meta-igneous granulite and ultramafic xenoliths from basalts of the Midland Valley of Scotland: petrology and mineralogy of the lower crust and upper mantle. *Transactions of the Royal Society of Edinburgh: Earth Sciences*, **75**, 75–84.

Hutchings, W.M. (1895) An interesting contact rock, with notes on contact-metamorphism. *Geological Magazine*, **2**, 122–31, 163–9.

Hutchings, W.M. (1898) The contact rocks of the Great Whin Sill. *Geological Magazine*, **5**, 69–82, 123–31.

Hutton, J. (1788) Theory of the Earth: or an investigation of the laws observable in the composition, dissolution, and restoration of the land upon the globe. *Transactions of the Royal Society of Edinburgh*, **1**, 209–304.

Hutton, W. (1838) On the stratiform basalt associated with the Carboniferous formation in the north of England. *Transactions of the Natural History Society of Northumbria*, **2**, 187–214.

Ineson, P.R. (1968) The petrology and geochemistry of altered quartz-dolerite in the Close House Mine area. *Proceedings of the Yorkshire Geological Society*, **36**, 373–84.

Ineson, P.R. (1969) Trace-element aureoles in limestone wallrocks adjacent to lead-zinc-barite-fluorite mineralization in the northern Pennine and Derbyshire ore fields. *Transactions of the Institute of Mining and Metallurgy, London*, **B78**, 29–40.

Ineson, P.R. and Walters, S.G. (1983) Dinantian extrusive activity in the south Pennines. *Mercian Geologist*, **9**, 88–98.

Ineson, P.R., Walters, S.G. and Simon, R.M. (1983) The petrography and geochemistry of the Waterswallows Sill, Buxton, Derbyshire. *Proceedings of the Yorkshire Geological Society*, **44**, 341–54.

Institute of Geological Sciences (1978) IGS Boreholes 1977. *Report of the Institute of Geological Sciences*, **78/21**.

Irving, E. (1977) Drift of the major continental blocks since the Devonian. *Nature*, **270**, 304–9.

Irving, J. (1924) The Carboniferous igneous intrusions of North-eastern Fifeshire. Unpublished PhD thesis, University of St Andrews.

Irving, J. (1930) Four 'Felstone' intrusions in central Berwickshire. *Geological Magazine*, **67**, 529–41.

Jackson, D.I., Jackson, A.A., Wingfield, R.T.R., Evans, D., Barnes, R.P. and Arthurs, M.P. (1995) *United Kingdom Offshore Regional Report: The Geology of the Irish Sea*, HMSO, London, for the British Geological Survey, 123 pp.

Jackson, D.I., Johnson, H. and Smith, N.J.P. (1997) Stratigraphical relationships and a revised lithostratigraphical nomenclature for the Carboniferous, Permian and Triassic rocks of the offshore East Irish Sea Basin. In *Petroleum Geology of the Irish Sea and Adjacent Areas* (eds N.S. Meadows, S.P. Trueblood, M. Hardman and G. Gowan), *Geological Society Special Publication*, No. **124**, The Geological Society, London, pp. 11–32.

Jameson, J. (1987) Carbonate sedimentation on a mid-basin high: the Petershill Formation, Midland Valley of Scotland. In *European Dinantian Environments* (eds J. Miller, A.E. Adams and V.P. Wright), *Geological Journal Special Issue*, No. **12**, John Wiley and sons Ltd, Chichester, pp. 309–27.

Jeffreys, D.H. (1979) Sedimentology of the Dinantian volcaniclastic and carbonate rocks of Middle Hope and Spring Cove, Weston-super-Mare. Unpublished MSc thesis, University of Reading.

Johnson, G.A.L. (1959) The Carboniferous stratigraphy of the Roman Wall district in western Northumberland. *Proceedings of the Yorkshire Geological Society*, **32**, 83–130.

Johnson, G.A.L. (ed.) (1973) *The Durham Area*, 2nd edn, Geologists' Association Guide, No. **15**, Benham and Co., Colchester, 32 pp.

Johnson, G.A.L. (1997) *Geology of Hadrian's Wall*, Geologists' Association Guide, No **59**, Geologists' Association, London, 89 pp.

Johnson, G.A.L. and Dunham, K.C. (2001) Emplacement of the Great Whin Dolerite Complex and the Little Whin Sill in relation to the structure of northern England. *Proceedings of the Yorkshire Geological Society*, **53**, 177–86.

Johnson, G.A.L., Robinson, D. and Hornung, M. (1971) Unique bedrock and soils associated with the Teesdale flora. *Nature*, **232**, 453.

Johnstone, G.S. (1965) The volcanic rocks of the Misty Law–Knockside Hills district, Renfrewshire. *Bulletin of the Geological Survey of Great Britain*, **22**, 53–64.

Jones, J.G. and Nelson, P.H.H. (1970) The flow of basalt lava from air into water – its structural expression and stratigraphic significance. *Geological Magazine*, **107**, 13–21.

References

Jones, J.M. and Cooper, B.S. (1970) Coal. In *Geology of Durham County* (eds G.A.L. Johnson and G. Hickling), *Transactions of the Natural History Society of Northumberland, Durham and Newcastle-upon-Tyne*, 41(1), Large and Sons Ltd, Newcastle-upon-Tyne, for the Natural History Society of Northumberland, Durham and Newcastle-upon-Tyne, pp. 43–65.

Jones, J.M. and Creany, S. (1977) Optical character of thermally metamorphosed coals of northern England. *Journal of Microscopy*, 109, 105–18.

Jones, J.M., Magraw, D., Robson, D.A. and Smith, F.W. (1980) Movements at the end of the Carboniferous Period. In *The Geology of North East England* (ed. D.A. Robson), *Natural History Society of Northumbria Special Publication*, No. 3, Natural History Society of Northumbria, Newcastle-upon-Tyne, pp. 79–85.

Judd, J.W. (1875) On the structure and age of Arthur's Seat, Edinburgh. *Quarterly Journal of the Geological Society of London*, 31, 131–48.

Jukes, J.B. (1859) *The South Staffordshire Coalfield*, 2nd edn, Memoir of the Geological Survey of Great Britain, sheets 54NW, 62, 72SW and 72SE (England and Wales), HMSO, London, 241 pp.

Kelling, G. (1988) Silesian sedimentation and tectonics in the South Wales Basin: a brief review. In *Sedimentation in a Synorogenic Basin Complex: the Upper Carboniferous of Northwest Europe* (eds B.M. Besly and G. Kelling), Blackie and Son, Glasgow, pp. 38–42.

Kennedy, W.Q. (1931) On composite lava flows. *Geological Magazine*, 68, 166–81.

Kennedy, W.Q. (1933) Composite auto-intrusion in a Carboniferous lava flow. *Summary of Progress of the Geological Survey of Great Britain*, for 1932, 83–93.

Kimbell, G.S., Chadwick, R.A., Holliday, D.W. and Werngren, O.C. (1989) The structure and evolution of the Northumberland Trough from new seismic reflection data and its bearing on modes of continental extension. *Journal of the Geological Society, London*, 146, 775–87.

Kirton, S.R. (1981) Petrogenesis and tectonic relationships of Carboniferous lavas of the English Midlands. Unpublished PhD thesis, University of Lancaster.

Kirton, S.R. (1984) Carboniferous volcanicity in England with special reference to the Westphalian and the east and west Midlands. *Journal of the Geological Society of London*, 141, 161–70.

Klingspor, I. (1976) Radiometric age-determination of basalts, dolerites and related syenite in Skåne, Southern Sweden. *Geologiska Föreningens i Stockholm Förhandlingar*, 98, 195–215.

Knox, J. (1954) *The Economic Geology of the Fife Coalfields, Area 3: Markinch, Dysart and Leven*, Memoir of the Geological Survey, Scotland, HMSO, Edinburgh, 134 pp.

Kokelaar, B.P. (1983) The mechanism of Surtseyan volcanism. *Journal of the Geological Society of London*, 140, 939–44.

Kokelaar, B.P. (1986) Magma–water interactions in subaqueous and emergent basaltic volcanism. *Bulletin of Volcanology*, 48, 275–89.

Land, D.H. and Cheeney, R.F. (2000) *Discovering Edinburgh's Volcano: a Geological Guide to Holyrood Park*, Edinburgh Geological Society, Edinburgh.

Lapworth, C., Watts, W.W. and Harrison, W.J. (1898) Sketch of the geology of the Birmingham district. *Proceedings of the Geologists' Association*, 15, 313–89.

Lawrence, D.J.D., Sanderson, R.W. and Waters, R.A. (1981) A Lower Carboniferous dyke from Castleton, Gwent, South Wales. *Proceedings of the Geologists' Association*, 92, 125–7.

Lawson, J.D. and Weedon, D.S. (eds) (1992) *Geological Excursions around Glasgow and Girvan*, Geological Society of Glasgow, Glasgow, 495 pp.

Le Maitre, R.W. (ed.) (2002) *Igneous Rocks: a Classification and Glossary of Terms; Recommendations of the International Union of Geological Sciences Subcommission on the Systematics of Igneous Rocks*, Cambridge University Press, Cambridge.

Leake, R.C., Cameron, D.G., Bland, D.J., Styles, M.T. and Fortey, N.J. (1997) The potential for gold mineralisation in the British Permian and Triassic red beds and their contacts with underlying rocks. *Mineral Reconnaissance Programme Report, British Geological Survey*, No. 144.

Lebour, G.A.L. (1886) *Outlines of the Geology of Northumberland and Durham*, 2nd edn, Lambert and Co., Newcastle-upon-Tyne, 219 pp.

References

Lebour, G.A.L. and Fryer, M. (1877) On the Harkess Rocks near Bamburgh. *Transactions of the North of England Institute of Mining and Mechanical Engineers*, **26**, 121–9.

Lee, D.-C., Halliday, A.N., Hunter, R.H., Holden, P. and Upton, B.G.J. (1993) Rb-Sr and Sm-Nd isotopic variations in dissected crustal xenoliths. *Geochimica et Cosmochimica Acta*, **57**, 219–30.

Leedal, G.P. (1951) Faulted Permian dykes in the Highlands. *Geological Magazine*, **88**, 60–4.

Leeder, M.R. (1971) Initiation of the Northumberland Basin. *Geological Magazine*, **108**, 511–16.

Leeder, M.R. (1974) The origin of the Northumberland Basin. *Scottish Journal of Geology*, **10**, 283–96.

Leeder, M.R. (1982) Upper Palaeozoic basins of the British Isles – Caledonian inheritance versus Hercynian plate marginal processes. *Journal of the Geological Society of London*, **139**, 479–91.

Leeder, M.R. and McMahon, A.H. (1988) Upper Carboniferous (Silesian) basin subsidence in northern Britain. In *Sedimentation in a Synorogenic Basin Complex: the Upper Carboniferous of Northwest Europe* (eds B.M. Besly and G. Kelling), Blackie and Son, Glasgow, pp. 43–52.

Leeder, M.R., Fairhead, D., Lee, A., Stuart, G., Clemmey, H., Al-Haddeh, B. and Green, C. (1989) Sedimentary and tectonic evolution of the Northumberland Basin. In *The Role of Tectonics in Devonian and Carboniferous Sedimentation in the British Isles* (eds R.S. Arthurton, P. Gutteridge and S.C. Nolan), *Yorkshire Geological Society Occasional Publication*, No. 6, Yorkshire Geological Society, Leeds, pp. 207–23.

Leitch, D. (1942) The Upper Carboniferous rocks of Arran. *Transactions of the Geological Society of Glasgow*, **20**, 141–54.

Lewis, C.L.E. (2001) Arthur Holmes' vision of a geological timescale. In *The Age of the Earth: from 4004BC to AD2002* (eds C.L.E. Lewis and S.J. Knell), *Geological Society, London, Special Publication*, No. **190**, The Geological Society, London, pp. 121–38.

Liss, D., Hutton, D.H.W. and Owen, W.H. (2001) Macroscopic and magnetic magma flow indicators from the Whin Sill, England (abstract). *Tectonic Studies Group Annual Meeting, University of Leeds, 3–6 January, 2001.*

Livingstone, A. and McKissock, G.M. (1974) The geochemistry of the igneous rocks in the Lower Carboniferous (Dinantian) sequence at Spilmersford, East Lothian, Scotland. *Bulletin of the Geological Survey of Great Britain*, **45**, 47–61.

Long, A.M., Menzies, M.A., Thirlwall, M.F., Upton, B.G.J. and Aspen, P. (1994) Carbonatite mantle interaction: a possible origin for megacryst/xenolithic suites in Scotland. In *Proceedings of the Fifth International Kimberlite Conference*, Araxá, Brazil, 1991 (eds H.O.A. Meyer and O.H. Leonardis), Conpanhia de Pesquisa de Recursos Minerais, Rio de Janeiro, Volume 1, pp. 467–77.

Lorenz, V. (1973) On the formation of maars. *Bulletin Volcanologique*, **37**, 183–204.

Lorenz, V. (1986) On the growth of maars and diatremes and its relevance to the formation of tuff rings. *Bulletin of Volcanology*, **48**, 265–74.

Loveland, P.J. and Bendelow, V.C. (1984) Celadonite–aluminous-glauconite: an example from the Lake District, UK. *Mineralogical Magazine*, **48**, 113–17.

Lumsden, G.I. (1967) Intrusive coal at Douglas in Scotland. *Scottish Journal of Geology*, **3**, 235–41.

Lumsden, G.I. and Wilson, R.B. (1961) The stratigraphy of the Archerbeck Borehole, Canonbie, Dumfriesshire. *Bulletin of the Geological Survey of Great Britain*, **18**, 1–89.

Lumsden, G.I., Tulloch, W., Howells, M.F. and Davies, A. (1967) *The Geology of the Neighbourhood of Langholm*, Memoir of the Geological Survey of Great Britain, Sheet 11 (Scotland), HMSO, Edinburgh, 255 pp.

Lunn, J.W. (1928) The intrusion of Binny Craig, West Lothian. *Transactions of the Edinburgh Geological Society*, **12**, 74–9.

McAdam, A.D. (1974) The petrography of the igneous rocks in the Lower Carboniferous (Dinantian) at Spilmersford, East Lothian, Scotland. *Bulletin of the Geological Survey of Great Britain*, **45**, 39–46.

McAdam, A.D. and Clarkson, E.N.K. (eds) (1986) *Lothian Geology – an Excursion Guide*, 3rd edn, Scottish Academic Press, Edinburgh, 221 pp.

McAdam, A.D. and Tulloch, W. (1985) *Geology of the Haddington District*, Memoir of the British Geological Survey, Sheet 33W and part of 41 (Scotland), HMSO, London, 99 pp.

References

McCallien, W.J. (1927) Preliminary account of the post-Dalradian geology of Kintyre. *Transactions of the Geological Society of Glasgow*, **18**, 40–126.

McCallien, W.J. and Anderson, R.B. (1930) The Carboniferous sediments of Kintyre. *Transactions of the Royal Society of Edinburgh*, **56**, 599–619.

MacCulloch, J. (1819) *A Description of the Western Isles of Scotland, including the Isle of Man: Comprising an Account of their Geological Structure; with Remarks on their Agriculture, Scenery and Antiquities*, Hurst, Robinson and Co., London.

MacCulloch, J. (1840) *Geological Map of Scotland, 1:253 440*, G.F. Cruchley, London.

MacDonald, J.G. (1965) The petrology of the Clyde Plateau Lavas of the Campsie and Kilpatrick hills. Unpublished PhD thesis, University of Glasgow.

MacDonald, J.G. (1967) Variations within a Scottish Lower Carboniferous lava flow. *Scottish Journal of Geology*, **3**, 34–45.

MacDonald, J.G. (1973) Carbon-dioxide metasomatism in the Campsie lavas. *Mineralogical Magazine*, **39**, 119–20.

MacDonald, J.G. and Whyte, F. (1981) Petrochemical evidence for the genesis of a Lower Carboniferous transitional basaltic suite in the Midland Valley of Scotland. *Transactions of the Royal Society of Edinburgh: Earth Sciences*, **72**, 75–88.

Macdonald, R. (1975) Petrochemistry of the early Carboniferous (Dinantian) lavas of Scotland. *Scottish Journal of Geology*, **11**, 269–314.

Macdonald, R. (1980) Trace element evidence for mantle heterogeneity beneath the Scottish Midland Valley in the Carboniferous and Permian. *Philosophical Transactions of the Royal Society of London*, **280**, 111–23.

Macdonald, R. and Walker, B.H. (1985) Geochemistry and tectonic significance of the Lower Carboniferous Cockermouth lavas, Cumbria. *Proceedings of the Yorkshire Geological Society*, **45**, 141–6.

Macdonald, R., Thomas, J.E. and Rizzello, S.A. (1977) Variations in basalt chemistry with time in the Midland Valley province during the Carboniferous and Permian. *Scottish Journal of Geology*, **13**, 11–22.

Macdonald, R., Gottfried, D., Farrington, M.J., Brown, F.W. and Skinner, N.G. (1981) The geochemistry of a continental tholeiitic suite: late Palaeozoic quartz-dolerite dykes of Scotland. *Transactions of the Royal Society of Edinburgh: Earth Sciences*, **72**, 57–74.

Macdonald, R., Gass, K.N., Thorpe, R.S. and Gass, I.G. (1984) Geochemistry and petrogenesis of the Derbyshire Carboniferous basalts. *Journal of the Geological Society of London*, **141**, 147–59.

McGill, R.A.R., Hall, A.J., Braithwaite, C.J.R., Fallick, A.E. and Rolfe, W.D.I. (1990) Petrography and geochemistry of a Lower Carboniferous lacustrine hot-spring deposit, East Kirkton, Bathgate, Scotland. In *Proceedings of the 12th New Zealand Geothermal Workshop* (eds C.C. Harvey, P.R.L. Browne, D.H. Freestone and G.L. Scott), Auckland University Press, Auckland, pp. 203–8.

McGill, R.A.R., Hall, A.J., Fallick, A.E. and Boyce, A.J. (1994) The palaeoenvironment of East Kirkton, West Lothian, Scotland: stable isotope evidence from silicates and sulphides. *Transactions of the Royal Society of Edinburgh: Earth Sciences*, **84**, 223–37.

MacGregor, A.G. (1928) The classification of Scottish Carboniferous olivine-basalts and mugearites. *Transactions of the Geological Society of Glasgow*, **18**, 324–60.

MacGregor, A.G. (1936) The composite sill of St Leonard's Craig and Heriot Mount, Edinburgh. *Transactions of the Edinburgh Geological Society*, **13**, 317–31.

MacGregor, A.G. (1937) The Carboniferous and Permian volcanoes of Scotland. *Bulletin Volcanologique, Serie 2*, **1**, 41–58.

MacGregor, A.G. (1948) Problems of Carboniferous–Permian volcanicity in Scotland. *Quarterly Journal of the Geological Society of London*, **108**, 133–53.

MacGregor, A.G. and Ennos, F.R. (1922) The Traprain Law phonolite. *Geological Magazine*, **59**, 514–23.

MacGregor, A.R. (1973) *Fife and Angus Geology: an Excursion Guide*, Scottish Academic Press, Edinburgh, 281 pp.

MacGregor, A.R. (1996) *Fife and Angus Geology: an Excursion Guide*, 3rd edn, The Pentland Press, Edinburgh, 291 pp.

Macgregor, M. and Haldane, D. (1933) *The Economic Geology of the Central Coalfield, Area 3: Bo'ness and Linlithgow*, Memoir of the Geological Survey, Scotland, HMSO, Edinburgh, 128 pp.

Macgregor, M. and MacGregor, A.G. (1948) *British Regional Geology: The Midland Valley of Scotland*, 2nd edn, HMSO, Edinburgh, 95 pp.

References

Macgregor, M., Lee, G.W. and Wilson, G.V. (1920) *The Iron Ores of Scotland*, Special Report on the Mineral Resources of Great Britain, Memoir of the Geological Survey of Great Britain, Vol. **11**, HMSO, London, 236 pp.

Macintyre, R.M., Cliff, R.A. and Chapman, N.A. (1981) Geochronological evidence for phased volcanic activity in Fife and Caithness necks, Scotland. *Transactions of the Royal Society of Edinburgh: Earth Sciences*, **72**, 1–7.

McKenzie, D.P. (1978) Some remarks on the development of sedimentary basins. *Earth and Planetary Science Letters*, **40**, 25–32.

McKerrow, W.S., MacNiocaill, C., Ahlberg, P.E., Clayton, G., Cleal, C.J. and Eagar, R.M.C. (2000) The late Palaeozoic relations between Gondwana and Laurussia. In *Orogenic Processes: Quantification and Modelling in the Variscan Belt* (eds W. Franke, V. Haak, O. Oncken and D. Tanner), *Geological Society, London, Special Publication*, No. **179**, The Geological Society, London, pp. 9–20.

Maclaren, C. (1834) On Arthur's Seat, the environs of Edinburgh and Calton Hill. *The Scotsman*, Five articles.

Maclaren, C. (1839) A *Sketch of the Geology of Fife and the Lothians: including Detailed Descriptions of Arthur's Seat and Pentland Hills*, A. and C. Black, Edinburgh.

Maclaren, C. (1866) A *Sketch of the Geology of Fife and the Lothians: including Detailed Descriptions of Arthur's Seat and Pentland Hills*, 2nd edn, A. and C. Black, Edinburgh.

McLean, A.C. (1966) A gravity survey in Ayrshire and its geological interpretation. *Transactions of the Royal Society of Edinburgh*, **66**, 239–65.

McLean, A.C. (1978) Evolution of fault-controlled ensialic basins in northwestern Britain. In *Crustal Evolution in Northwestern Britain and Adjacent Regions: Proceedings of an International Conference held in Glasgow University, 5–8 April, 1977* (eds D.R. Bowes and B.E. Leake), *Geological Journal Special Issue*, No. **10**, Seel House Press, Liverpool, pp. 325–46.

McLean, A.C. and Qureshi, I.R. (1966) Regional gravity anomalies in the western Midland Valley of Scotland. *Transactions of the Royal Society of Edinburgh*, **66**, 267–83.

McMillan, A.A. (2002) *Geology of the New Galloway and Thornhill District*, Memoir of the British Geological Survey, sheets 9W and 9E (Scotland), The Stationery Office, London, for the British Geological Survey, 126 pp.

McMillan, A.A. and Brand, P.J. (1995) Depositional setting of Permian and Upper Carboniferous strata of the Thornhill Basin, Dumfriesshire. *Scottish Journal of Geology*, **31**, 43–52.

MacPherson, K.A.T. and Phillips, E.R. (1998) A welded pyroclastic deposit within the Dinantian Clyde Plateau Volcanic Formation, near Eaglesham, in the east Renfrewshire Hills of the Midland Valley. *Scottish Journal of Geology*, **34**, 165–72.

MacPherson, K.A.T., Smith, R.A. and Akhurst, M.C. (2001) *Geology of the Kilmarnock District – a brief explanation of the Geological Map*, Sheet Explanation of the British Geological Survey, 1:50 000 Series Sheet 22E (Scotland), British Geological Survey, Keyworth, 30 pp.

McPhie, J., Doyle, M. and Allen, R. (1993) *Volcanic textures: a Guide to the Interpretation of Textures in Volcanic Rocks*, Centre for Ore Deposit and Exploration Studies, University of Tasmania, Tasmania, 198 pp.

McRobert, R.W. (1914) Acid and intermediate intrusions and associated ash-necks in the neighbourhood of Melrose (Roxburghshire). *Quarterly Journal of the Geological Society of London*, **70**, 303–14.

McRobert, R.W. (1920) Igneous rocks of Teviot and Liddesdale. *Transactions of the Edinburgh Geological Society*, **11**, 86–103.

Marshall, C.E. (1942) Field relations of certain of the basic igneous rocks associated with the Carboniferous strata of the Midland counties. *Quarterly Journal of the Geological Society of London*, **98**, 1–25.

Marshall, C.E. (1946) The Barrow Hill intrusion, South Staffordshire. *Quarterly Journal of the Geological Society of London*, **101**, 177–205.

Martin, N.R. (1955) Lower Carboniferous volcanism near North Berwick. *Bulletin of the Geological Survey of Great Britain*, **7**, 90–100.

Matthews, S.C., Butler, M. and Sadler, P.M. (1973) Lower Carboniferous successions in north Somerset: report by directors of field meeting. *Proceedings of the Geologists' Association*, **84**, 175–9.

Max, M.D. (1976) The pre-Palaeozoic basement in southeastern Scotland and the Southern Uplands Fault. *Nature*, **264**, 485–6.

Maynard, J.R., Hofman, W., Dunay, R.E., Bentham, P.N., Dean, K.P. and Watson, I. (1997) The Carboniferous of western Europe: the development of a petroleum system. *Petroleum Geoscience*, **3**, 97–115.

References

Menning, M., Weyer, D., Drozdzewski, G., van Amerom, H.W.J. and Wendt, I. (2000) A Carboniferous timescale 2000: discussion and use of geological parameters as time indicators from central and western Europe. *Geologisches Jahrbuch*, **A156**, 3–44.

Menzies, M.A. and Halliday, A.N. (1988) Lithospheric mantle domains beneath the Archaean and Proterozoic crust of Scotland. In *Oceanic and Continental Lithosphere: Similarities and Differences* (eds M.A. Menzies and K.G. Cox), *Journal of Petrology Special Lithosphere Issue*, Oxford University Press, Oxford, pp. 275–302.

Miller, G.D. (1986) The unveiling of a sill: Waterswallows 1900–1985. *The Amateur Geologist*, **12**, 13–24.

Miller, G.D. (1988) The Calton Hill S.S.S.I. – an update. *The Amateur Geologist*, **12**, 31–9.

Miller, H. (1887) *The Geology of the Country around Otterburn and Elsdon*, Memoir of the Geological Survey of Great Britain, Sheet 8 (England and Wales), HMSO, London, 147 pp.

Miller, J.A. and Mussett, A.E. (1963) Dating basic rocks by the potassium-argon method: the Whin Sill. *Geophysical Journal of the Royal Astronomical Society*, 7, 547–53.

Mills, D.A.C. and Hull, J.H. (1968) The Geological Survey borehole at Woodland, Co. Durham (1962). *Bulletin of the Geological Survey of Great Britain*, **28**, 1–37.

Millward, D., Carruthers, R.M., Marriner, G.F., Molyneux, S.G. and Beddoe-Stephens, B. (1999) The Eycott Volcanic Group. *British Geological Survey, Onshore Geology Series, Technical Report*, WA/99/68.

Milne, D. (1837) A geological survey of Berwickshire. *Prize Essays and Transactions of the Highland and Agricultural Society of Scotland*, **11**, 171–253.

Mitchell, G.H. and Mykura, W. (1962) *The Geology of the Neighbourhood of Edinburgh*, 3rd edn, Memoir of the Geological Survey of Great Britain, Sheet 32 (Scotland), HMSO, Edinburgh, 159 pp.

Mitchell, M., Taylor, B.J. and Ramsbottom, W.H.C. (1978) Carboniferous. In *The Geology of the Lake District* (ed. F. Moseley), *Yorkshire Geological Society Occasional Publication*, No. **3**, Yorkshire Geological Society, Leeds, pp. 168–77.

Monckton, H.W. (1892) The geology of the country around Stirling. *Proceedings of the Geologists' Association*, **12**, 242–53.

Monckton, H.W. (1895) The Stirling dolerite. *Quarterly Journal of the Geological Society of London*, **51**, 480–92.

Monro, S.K. (1982) Sedimentation, stratigraphy and tectonics in the Dalry Basin, Ayrshire. Unpublished PhD thesis, University of Edinburgh.

Monro, S.K. (1999) *Geology of the Irvine District*, Memoir of the British Geological Survey, Sheet 22 and part of 21 (Scotland), The Stationery Office, London, for the British Geological Survey, 140 pp.

Monro, S.K., Loughnan, F.C. and Walker, M.C. (1983) The Ayrshire Bauxitic Clay – an allochthonous deposit? In *Residual Deposits: Surface Related Weathering Processes and Materials* (ed. R.C.L. Wilson), *Geological Society Special Publication*, No. **11**, Blackwell Scientific Publications, Oxford, pp. 47–58.

Moore, J.G., Phillips, R.L., Grigg, R.W., Peterson, D.W. and Swanson, D.A. (1973) Flow of lava into the sea, 1969–71, Kilauea Volcano, Hawaii. *Bulletin of the Geological Society of America*, **84**, 537–46.

Morgan, C.L. and Reynolds, S.H. (1904) The igneous rocks associated with the Carboniferous Limestone of the Bristol district. *Quarterly Journal of the Geological Society of London*, **60**, 137–57.

Morrison, M.A., Hendry, G.L. and Leat, P.T. (1987) Regional and tectonic implications of parallel Caledonian and Permo–Carboniferous lamprophyre dyke swarms from Lismore, Ardgour. *Transactions of the Royal Society of Edinburgh: Earth Sciences*, 77, 279–88.

Moseley, F. (1966) The volcanic vents and pocket deposits of Derbyshire. *Mercian Geologist*, **1**, 283–5.

Murchison, D.G. and Raymond, A.C. (1989) Igneous activity and organic maturation in the Midland Valley of Scotland. *International Journal of Coal Geology*, **14**, 47–82.

Mykura, W. (1965) White trap in some Ayrshire coals. *Scottish Journal of Geology*, **1**, 176–84.

Mykura, W. (1967) The Upper Carboniferous rocks of south-west Ayrshire. *Bulletin of the Geological Survey of Great Britain*, **26**, 23–98.

Mykura, W. (1976) *British Regional Geology: Orkney and Shetland*, HMSO, Edinburgh, 149 pp.

Nairn, A.E.M. (1956) The Lower Carboniferous rocks between the Rivers Esk and Annan, Dumfriesshire. *Transactions of the Geological Society of Glasgow*, **22**, 80–93.

References

Nairn, A.E.M. (1958) Petrology of the Whita Sandstone, southern Scotland. *Journal of Sedimentary Petrology*, **28**, 57–64.

Neves, R. and Downie, C. (eds) (1967) *Geological Excursions in the Sheffield Region and the Peak District National Park*, University of Sheffield, Sheffield, 163 pp.

Neves, R., Gueinn, K.J., Clayton, G., Ioannides, N.S., Neville, R.S.W. and Kruszewska, K. (1973) Palynological correlations within the Lower Carboniferous of Scotland and northern England. *Transactions of the Royal Society of Edinburgh*, **69**, 23–70.

Nicol, J. (1847) On the geology of Roxburghshire. *Transactions of the Highland and Agricultural Society of Scotland*, **10**, 35–83.

Nicol, J. (1852) On the geology of the southern portion of the peninsula of Cantyre, Argyllshire. *Quarterly Journal of the Geological Society of London*, **8**, 406–25.

Oertel, G. (1952) A structural investigation of the porphyritic basalts of Arthur's Seat, Edinburgh. *Transactions of the Edinburgh Geological Society*, **14**, 360–78.

Pallister, J.W. (1952) The Birrenswark Lavas, Dumfriesshire. *Transactions of the Edinburgh Geological Society*, **14**, 336–48.

Parnell, J. (1984) Hydrocarbon minerals in the Midland Valley of Scotland with particular reference to the Oil-shale Group. *Proceedings of the Geologists' Association*, **95**, 275–85.

Parrish, J.T. (1993) Climate of the supercontinent Pangaea. *Journal of Geology*, **101**, 215–33.

Paterson, I.B. and Hall, I.H.S. (1986) Lithostratigraphy of the late Devonian and Early Carboniferous rocks in the Midland Valley of Scotland. *Report of the British Geological Survey*, **18/3**.

Paterson, I.B., Hall, I.H.S. and Stephenson, D. (1990) *Geology of the Greenock District*, Memoir of the British Geological Survey, Sheet 30 and part of 29E (Scotland), HMSO, London, 69 pp.

Paterson, I.B., McAdam, A.D. and MacPherson, K.A.T. (1998) *Geology of the Hamilton District*, Memoir of the British Geological Survey, Sheet 23W (Scotland), The Stationery Office, London, for the British Geological Survey, 94 pp.

Patterson, E.M. (1945) The distribution of trace-elements in a Scottish Permo–Carboniferous teschenite and its lugaritic differentiate. *Geological Magazine*, **82**, 230–4.

Patterson, E.M. (1946) The teschenite–picrite sill of Saltcoats, Ayrshire. *Transactions of the Geological Society of Glasgow*, **21**, 1–28.

Peach, B.N. (1911) *Description of Arthur's Seat Volcano*, Memoir of the Geological Survey, Scotland, HMSO, Edinburgh, 26 pp.

Peach, B.N. and Horne, J. (1903) The Canonbie Coalfield: its geological structure and relations to the Carboniferous rocks of the North of England and Central Scotland. *Transactions of the Royal Society of Edinburgh*, **40**, 835–77.

Peach, B.N., Clough, C.T., Hinxman, L.W., Wilson, J.S.G., Crampton, C.B., Maufe, H.B., Bailey, E.B. *et al.* (1910) *The Geology of the Neighbourhood of Edinburgh*, Memoir of the Geological Survey of Great Britain, Sheet 32 with part of 31 (Scotland), HMSO, Edinburgh, 445 pp.

Pederson, T. and van der Beek, P. (1994) Extension and magmatism in the Oslo rift, southeast Norway: no sign of a mantle plume. *Earth and Planetary Science Letters*, **123**, 342–3.

Penn, I.E., Holliday, D.W., Kirby, G.A., Kubala, M., Sobey, R.A. *et al.* (1983) The Larne No. 2 borehole: discovery of a new Permian volcanic centre. *Scottish Journal of Geology*, **19**, 333–46.

Phillips, J. (1836) *Illustrations of the Geology of Yorkshire Part 2: The Mountain Limestone District*, John Murray, London.

Phillips, W.J. (1968) The crystallisation of the teschenite from the Lugar Sill, Ayrshire. *Geological Magazine*, **105**, 23–34.

Pocock, R.W. (1931) The age of the Midland basalts. *Quarterly Journal of the Geological Society of London*, **87**, 1–12.

Praegel, N.-O. (1981) Origin of ultramafic inclusions and megacrysts in a monchiquite dyke at Streap, Inverness-shire, Scotland. *Lithos*, **14**, 305–22.

Price, N.R. and Duff, P.McL.D. (1969) Mineralogy and chemistry of tonsteins from Carboniferous sequences in Great Britain. *Sedimentology*, **13**, 45–69.

Pringle, J. and Bailey, E.B. (1944) The Carboniferous rocks of Glas Eilean, Sound of Islay, Argyllshire. *Transactions of the Geological Society of Glasgow*, **20**, 249–59.

Ramsay, J.G. (1955) A camptonitic dyke suite at Monar, Ross-shire and Inverness-shire. *Geological Magazine*, **92**, 297–308.

Ramsbottom, W.H.C. and Mitchell, M. (1980) The recognition and division of the Tournaisian Series in Britain. *Journal of the Geological Society of London*, **137**, 61–3.

References

Randall, B.A.O. (1959) Intrusive phenomena of the Whin Sill, east of the R. North Tyne. *Geological Magazine*, **96**, 385–92.

Randall, B.A.O. (1995a) Lower Carboniferous igneous rocks. In *Robson's Geology of North East England*, 2nd edn (ed. G.A.L. Johnson), *Transactions of the Natural History Society of Northumbria*, **56**(5), Natural History Society of Northumbria, Newcastle-upon-Tyne, pp. 317–18.

Randall, B.A.O. (1995b) The Great Whin Sill and its associated dyke suite. In *Robson's Geology of North East England*, 2nd edn (ed. G.A.L. Johnson), *Transactions of the Natural History Society of Northumbria*, **56**(5), Natural History Society of Northumbria, Newcastle-upon-Tyne, pp. 319–27.

Randall, B.A.O. and Farmer, N. (1970) The Holy Island Dyke. *Transactions of the Natural History Society of Northumberland, Durham and Newcastle-upon-Tyne*, **17**, 79–91.

Raymond, A.C. and Murchison, D.G. (1988) Development of organic maturation in the thermal aureoles of sills and its relation to sediment compaction. *Fuel*, **67**, 1599–608.

Read, W.A. (1956) Channelling on the dip-slope of the Stirling Sill. *Transactions of the Edinburgh Geological Society*, **16**, 299–306.

Read, W.A. (1988) Controls on Silesian sedimentation in the Midland Valley of Scotland. In *Sedimentation in a Synorogenic Basin Complex: the Upper Carboniferous of Northwest Europe* (eds B.M. Besly and G. Kelling), Blackie and Son, Glasgow, pp. 222–41.

Read, W.A. and Johnson, S.R.H. (1967) The sedimentology of sandstone formations within the Upper Old Red Sandstone and lowest Calciferous Sandstone Measures west of Stirling, Scotland. *Scottish Journal of Geology*, **3**, 242–67.

Read, W.A. and Wilson, R.B. (1959) *The Economic Geology of the Stirling and Clackmannan Coalfield, Scotland: Area South of the River Forth*, Coalfield Papers of the Geological Survey of Great Britain, No. 2, HMSO, Edinburgh, 73 pp.

Rex, G.M. and Scott, A.C. (1987) The sedimentology, palaeoecology and preservation of the Lower Carboniferous plant deposits at Pettycur, Fife, Scotland. *Geological Magazine*, **124**, 43–66.

Reynolds, S.H. (1908) The basic intrusion of Bartestree. *Quarterly Journal of the Geological Society of London*, **64**, 501–11.

Reynolds, S.H. (1917) Further work on the igneous rocks associated with the Carboniferous Limestone of the Bristol district. *Quarterly Journal of the Geological Society of London*, **72**, 23–42.

Rhind, W. (1836) *Excursions Illustrative of the Geology and Natural History of the Environs of Edinburgh*, 2nd edn, J. Anderson, Edinburgh, 146 pp.

Richey, J.E. (1939) The dykes of Scotland. *Transactions of the Edinburgh Geological Society*, **13**, 395–435.

Richey, J.E., Anderson, E.M. and MacGregor, A.G. (1930) *The Geology of North Ayrshire*, Memoir of the Geological Survey of Great Britain, Sheet 22 (Scotland), HMSO, Edinburgh, 417 pp.

Ridd, M.F., Walker, D.B. and Jones, J.M. (1970) A deep borehole at Harton on the margin of the Northumbrian trough. *Proceedings of the Yorkshire Geological Society*, **38**, 75–103.

Rippon, J., Read, W.A. and Park, R.G. (1996) The Ochil Fault and the Kincardine basin: key structures in the tectonic evolution of the Midland Valley of Scotland. *Journal of the Geological Society, London*, **153**, 573–87.

Robertson, T. and Haldane, D. (1937) *The Economic Geology of the Central Coalfield, Area I: Kilsyth and Kirkintilloch*, Memoir of the Geological Survey, Scotland, HMSO, Edinburgh, 169 pp.

Robinson, D. (1970) Metamorphic rocks. In *Geology of Durham County* (eds G.A.L. Johnson and G. Hickling), *Transactions of the Natural History Society of Northumberland, Durham and Newcastle-upon-Tyne*, **41**(1), Large and Sons Ltd, Newcastle-upon-Tyne, for the Natural History Society of Northumberland, Durham and Newcastle-upon-Tyne, pp. 119–123.

Robinson, D. (1971) Whin Sill metamorphism in Teesdale. Unpublished PhD thesis, University of Durham.

Robson, D.A. (1954) A preliminary account of the geological structure of north Northumberland and the Borders. *Proceedings of the University of Durham Philosophical Society*, **12**, 1–9.

Robson, D.A. (1977) The structural history of the Cheviot and adjacent regions. *Scottish Journal of Geology*, **13**, 255–62.

Rock, N.M.S. (1982) Petrography and age of agglomeratic vents near Toscaig, Applecross. *Proceedings of the Geologists' Association*, **93**, 305–8.

References

Rock, N.M.S. (1983) The Permo–Carboniferous camptonite–monchiquite dyke-suite of the Scottish Highlands and Islands: distribution, field and petrological aspects. *Report of the Institute of Geological Sciences*, **82/14**.

Rolfe, W.D.I., Durant, G.P., Baird, W.J., Chaplin, C., Paton, R.L. and Reekie, R.J. (1994) The East Kirkton Limestone, Viséan, of West Lothian, Scotland: introduction and stratigraphy. *Transactions of the Royal Society of Edinburgh: Earth Sciences*, **84**, 177–88.

Russell, D.G. (1984) Experimental and petrological studies of phenocryst assemblages in Scottish Permo–Carboniferous basaltic rocks. Unpublished PhD thesis, University of Edinburgh.

Russell, M.J. (1976) A possible Lower Permian age for the onset of ocean floor spreading in the northern North Atlantic. *Scottish Journal of Geology*, **12**, 315–23.

Russell, M.J. and Smythe, D.K. (1978) Evidence for an Early Permian oceanic rift in the northern North Atlantic. In *Petrology and Geochemistry of Continental Rifts* (eds E.-R. Neumann and I.B. Ramberg), *NATO Advanced Study Institutes Series, Series C: Mathematical and Physical Sciences*, No. **36**, Reidel, Dordrecht, pp. 173–9.

Russell, M.J. and Smythe, D.K. (1983) Origin of the Oslo Graben in relation to the Hercynian-Alleghenian Orogeny and lithosphere rifting in the North Atlantic. In *Processes of Continental Rifting: Selected Papers from the Lunar and Planetary Institute Topical Conference on the Processes of Planetary Rifting held in St Helena*, California, USA, 3–5 December, 1981 (eds P. Morgan and B.H. Barker), *Developments in Geotectonics*, No. **19**, Elsevier, Oxford, Amsterdam, pp. 457–72.

Rutledge, H. (1952) A petrological note on a composite sill, The Dasses, Arthur's Seat. *Transactions of the Edinburgh Geological Society*, **14**, 379–88.

Sabine, P.A. and Sutherland, D.S. (1982) Petrography of British igneous rocks. In *Igneous Rocks of the British Isles* (ed. D.S. Sutherland), John Wiley and sons Ltd, Chichester, pp. 479–544.

Sargent, H.C. (1917) On a spilitic facies of Lower Carboniferous lava-flows in Derbyshire. *Quarterly Journal of the Geological Society of London*, **73**, 11–25.

Sarjeant, W.A.S. (1967) Fibrous chlorites in the volcanic rocks of Derbyshire. *Mercian Geologist*, **2**, 85–95.

Savage, R.J.G. (ed.) (1977) *Geological Excursions in the Bristol District*, University of Bristol, Bristol, 196 pp.

Scott, A. (1915) The Crawfordjohn Essexite and associated rocks. *Geological Magazine, New Series*, **2**, 455–61, 513–19.

Scott, A.C. (1990) Preservation, evolution, and extinction of plants in Lower Carboniferous volcanic sequences in Scotland. In *Volcanism and Fossil Biotas* (eds M.G. Lockley and A. Rice), *Geological Society of America Special Paper*, No. **244**, Geological Society of America, Boulder, pp. 25–38.

Scott, A.C., Galtier, J. and Clayton, G. (1984) Distribution of anatomically preserved floras in the Lower Carboniferous in Western Europe. *Transactions of the Royal Society of Edinburgh: Earth Sciences*, **75**, 311–40.

Scott, A.C., Meyer-Berthaud, B., Galtier, J., Rex, G.M., Brindley, S.A. and Clayton, G. (1986) Studies on a new Lower Carboniferous flora from Kingswood, near Pettycur, Scotland. 1. Preliminary Report. *Review of Palaeobotany and Palynology*, **48**, 161–80.

Scrutton, C.T. (ed.) (1995) *Northumbrian Rocks and Landscape: a Field Guide*, Ellenbank Press, Maryport, for the Yorkshire Geological Society, 216 pp.

Sedgewick, A. (1827) On the association of trap rocks with the Mountain Limestone formation in High Teesdale. *Transactions of the Cambridge Philosophical Society*, **2**, 139–96.

Shand, S.J. (1908) Note upon crystals of grossularite from Corsiehill Quarry. *Transactions and Proceedings of the Perthshire Society of Natural Science*, **4**, 210–12.

Shiells, K.A.G. (1961) The geology of part of the limestone group of North Northumberland. Unpublished PhD thesis, University of Newcastle-upon-Tyne.

Shiells, K.A.G. (1964) The geological structure of north-east Northumberland. *Transactions of the Royal Society of Edinburgh: Earth Sciences*, **65**, 449–81.

Sibley, T.F. (1905) The Carboniferous limestones of the Weston-super-Mare district (Somerset). *Quarterly Journal of the Geological Society of London*, **61**, 548–63.

Simpson, J.B. and Richey, J.E. (1936) *The Geology of the Sanquhar Coalfield and Adjacent Basin of Thornhill*, Memoir of the Geological Survey, Scotland, HMSO, Edinburgh, 47 pp.

References

Skipsey, E. (1992) Upper Teesdale. *Proceedings of the Cumberland Geological Society*, **5**, 473–75.

Smedley, P.L. (1986a) Petrochemistry of Dinantian volcanism in northern Britain. Unpublished PhD thesis, University of Edinburgh.

Smedley, P.L. (1986b) The relationship between calc-alkaline volcanism and within-plate continental rift volcanism: evidence from Scottish Palaeozoic lavas. *Earth and Planetary Science Letters*, **77**, 113–28.

Smedley, P.L. (1988a) Trace element and isotope variations in Scottish and Irish Dinantian volcanism: evidence for an OIB-like mantle source. *Journal of Petrology*, **29**, 413–43.

Smedley, P.L. (1988b) The geochemistry of Dinantian volcanism in south Kintyre and the evidence for provincialism in the southern Scottish mantle. *Contributions to Mineralogy and Petrology*, **99**, 374–84.

Smellie, W.R. (1916) The igneous rocks of Bute. *Transactions of the Geological Society of Glasgow*, **15**, 334–73.

Smith, F.W. (1974) Factors governing the development of fluorspar orebodies in the north Pennine orefield. Unpublished PhD thesis, University of Durham.

Smith, F.W. (1995) The mineralization of the Alston Block. In *Robson's Geology of North East England*, 2nd edn (ed. G.A.L. Johnson), *Transactions of the Natural History Society of Northumbria*, **56**(5), Natural History Society of Northumbria, Newcastle-upon-Tyne, pp. 344–52.

Smith, K. (1992) Carboniferous magmatism in the Iapetus convergence zone: evidence from deep seismic reflection profiles. *Journal of the Geological Society, London*, **149**, 907–14.

Smith, R.A., Stephenson, D. and Monro, S. (1994) The geological setting of the southern Bathgate Hills, West Lothian, Scotland. *Transactions of the Royal Society of Edinburgh: Earth Sciences*, **84**, 189–96.

Smythe, D.K. (1987) Deep seismic reflection profiling of the Lewisian foreland. In *Evolution of the Lewisian and Comparable Precambrian High-grade Terrain* (eds R.G. Park and J. Tarney), *Geological Society Special Publication*, No. 27, Blackwell Scientific Publications, Oxford, for The Geological Society, pp. 193–203.

Smythe, D.K. (1994) Geophysical evidence for ultrawide dykes of the late Carboniferous quartz-dolerite swarm of northern Britain. *Geophysical Journal International*, **119**, 20–30.

Smythe, D.K., Russell, M.J. and Skuce, A.G. (1995) Intra-continental rifting inferred from the major late Carboniferous quartz-dolerite dyke swarm of NW Europe. *Scottish Journal of Geology*, **31**, 151–62.

Smythe, J.A. (1930a) A chemical study of the Whin Sill. *Transactions of the Natural History Society of Northumbria*, **7**, 16–150.

Smythe, J.A. (1930b) The Harkess Rocks. *Vasculum*, **16**, 9–15.

Smythe, J.A. (1931) Intrusion phenomena of the Whin Sill. *Proceedings of the Geologists' Association*, **42**, 272–3.

Soper, N.J., England, R.W., Snyder, D.B. and Ryan, P.D. (1992) The Iapetus suture zone in England, Scotland and eastern Ireland: a reconciliation of geological and deep seismic data. *Journal of the Geological Society, London*, **149**, 697–700.

Sowerbutts, A.A. (1999) Geology of the Dunure, Carrick Hills and Heads of Ayr area. *British Geological Survey, Onshore Geology Series, Technical Report*, **WA/99/102**.

Spears, D.A. (1970) A kaolinitic mudstone (tonstein) in the British Coal Measures. *Journal of Sedimentary Petrology*, **40**, 386–94.

Spears, D.A. and Kanaris-Sotiriou, R. (1979) A geochemical and mineralogical investigation of some British and other European tonsteins. *Sedimentology*, **26**, 407–25.

Speight, J.M. and Mitchell, J.G. (1979) The Permo–Carboniferous dyke-swarm of northern Argyll and its bearing on dextral displacement on the Great Glen Fault. *Journal of the Geological Society of London*, **136**, 3–12.

Stecher, E. (1888) Contacterscheinungen an Schottischen Olivindiabasen. *Tschermaks Mineralogische und Petrographische Mitteilungen*, **9**, 145–205.

Steiger, R.H. and Jäger, E. (1977) Subcommission on geochronology: convention on the use of decay constants in geo- and cosmochronology. *Earth and Planetary Science Letters*, **36**, 359–62.

Stephenson, D. (1983) Polymetallic mineralisation in Carboniferous rocks at Hilderston, near Bathgate, central Scotland. *Institute of Geological Sciences, Mineral Reconnaissance Programme Report*, No. **68**.

References

Stephenson, D. and Coats, J.S. (1983) Baryte and copper mineralisation in the Renfrewshire Hills, central Scotland. *Institute of Geological Sciences, Mineral Reconnaissance Programme Report*, No. **67**.

Stephenson, M.H. (2000) Report on palynology of samples from the Ballagan Formation, Doonfoot, Ayrshire. *British Geological Survey Technical Report*, **WH/00/14R**.

Stevenson, I.P. and Gaunt, G.D. (1971) *Geology of the Country around Chapel en le Frith*, Memoir of the Geological Survey of Great Britain, Sheet 99 (England and Wales), HMSO, London, 444 pp.

Stevenson, I.P., Harrison, R.K. and Snelling, N.J. (1970) Potassium-argon age determination of the Waterswallows Sill, Buxton, Derbyshire. *Proceedings of the Yorkshire Geological Society*, **37**, 445–7.

Stone, P. (ed.) (1996) *Geology in South-West Scotland: an Excursion Guide*, British Geological Survey, Keyworth, 214 pp.

Storetvedt, K.M. and Gidskehaung, A. (1969) The magnetisation of the Great Whin Sill, northern England. *Physics of the Earth and Planetary Interiors*, **2**, 105–14.

Strahan, A. and Cantrill, T.C. (1912) *The Geology of the South Wales Coalfield: Part 3 The Country around Cardiff*, 2nd edn, Memoir of the Geological Survey of Great Britain, Sheet 263 (England and Wales), HMSO, London, 157 pp.

Strasser-King, V. (1973) The petrology of the Whin Sill. Unpublished PhD thesis, University of Manchester.

Summers, T.P., Los, A.P. and Westbrook, G.K. (1982) Geophysical investigations of the Whin Sill in the Roman Wall district of Northumberland. *Proceedings of the Yorkshire Geological Society*, **44**, 109–18.

Sundvoll, B. and Larsen, B.T. (1993) Rb-Sr and Sm-Nd relationships in dyke and sill intrusions in the Oslo Rift and related areas. *Norges Geologiske Undersøkelse Bulletin*, **425**, 25–42.

Sutherland, D.S. (ed.) (1982) *Igneous Rocks of the British Isles*, John Wiley and sons Ltd, Chichester, 645 pp.

Tate, G. (1867) The geology of the district traversed by the Roman Wall. In *The Roman Wall: a Description of the Mural Barrier of the North of England*, 3rd edn (ed. J.C. Bruce), Longmans and Co., London, pp. 359–70.

Tate, G. (1868) Geology. In *A New Flora of Northumberland and Durham* (eds J.G. Baker and G.R. Tate), *Natural History Transactions of Northumberland and Durham*, No. **2**, Williams and Norgate, London, pp. 1–35.

Tate, G. (1871) On the basaltic rocks of Northumberland. *Proceedings of the Berwickshire Natural History Club*, 6, 197–217.

Taylor, B.J., Burgess, I.C., Land, D.H., Mills, D.A.C., Smith, D.B. and Warren, P.T. (1971) *British Regional Geology: Northern England*, 4th edn, HMSO, London, 121 pp.

Teall, J.J.H. (1884a) Petrological notes on some north of England dykes. *Quarterly Journal of the Geological Society of London*, **40**, 209–47.

Teall, J.J.H. (1884b) On the chemical and microscopical characters of the Whin Sill. *Quarterly Journal of the Geological Society of London*, **40**, 640–57.

Teall, J.J.H. (1888) *British Petrography; with Special Reference to the Igneous Rocks*, Dulau, London, 469 pp.

Thirlwall, M.F. (1982) Systematic variation in chemistry and Nd-Sr isotopes across a Caledonian calc-alkaline volcanic arc: implications for source materials. *Earth and Planetary Science Letters*, **58**, 27–50.

Thirlwall, M.F. (1986) Lead isotope evidence for the nature of the mantle beneath Caledonian Scotland. *Earth and Planetary Science Letters*, **80**, 55–70.

Thomas, D.N., Rolph, T.C. and Shaw, W. (1995) Palaeointensity results from the P-C (Kiaman) reversed superchron: the Great Whin and Midland Valley sills of the northern United Kingdom. *Geophysical Journal International*, **123**, 798–816.

Thompson, R.N. (1982) Magmatism of the British Tertiary Volcanic Province. *Scottish Journal of Geology*, **18**, 49–107.

Thomson, J. (1865) On the geology of the Campbeltown district. *Transactions of the Geological Society of Glasgow*, **2**, 76–89.

Thorarinsson, S. and Sigvaldason, G.E. (1972) The Hekla eruption of 1970. *Bulletin Volcanologique*, **36**, 269–88.

Thorpe, R.S. and Macdonald, R. (1985) Geochemical evidence for the emplacement of the Whin Sill complex of northern England. *Geological Magazine*, **122**, 389–96.

Toghill, P. (1990) *Geology in Shropshire*, Swan Hill Press, Shrewsbury, 188 pp.

Tomkeieff, S.I. (1928) The volcanic complex of Calton Hill, Derbyshire. *Quarterly Journal of the Geological Society of London*, **84**, 703–16.

References

Tomkeieff, S.I. (1929) A contribution to the petrology of the Whin Sill. *Mineralogical Magazine*, **22**, 100–20.

Tomkeieff, S.I. (1931) Lower Carboniferous igneous rocks. *Proceedings of the Geologists' Association*, **42**, 259–61.

Tomkeieff, S.I. (1937) Petrochemistry of the Scottish Carboniferous–Permian igneous rocks. *Bulletin Volcanologique, Serie 2*, **1**, 59–87.

Tomkeieff, S.I. (1945) Petrology of the Carboniferous igneous rocks of the Tweed Basin. *Transactions of the Edinburgh Geological Society*, **14**, 53–75.

Tomkeieff, S.I. (1952) Analcite-trachybasalt in the phonolite of Traprain Law. *Transactions of the Edinburgh Geological Society*, **15**, 360–73.

Tomkeieff, S.I. (1953) The Carboniferous igneous rocks of the Kelso district. *Proceedings of the University of Durham Philosophical Society*, **11**, 95–101.

Topley, W. and Lebour, G.A. (1877) On the intrusive character of the Whin Sill in Northumberland. *Quarterly Journal of the Geological Society of London*, **33**, 406–21.

Torsvik, T.H., Lyse, O., Atteras, G. and Bluck, B.J. (1989) Palaeozoic palaeomagnetic results from Scotland and their bearing on the British apparent polar wander path. *Physics of the Earth and Planetary Interiors*, **55**, 93–105.

Townson, R. (1799) *Tracts and Observations in Natural History and Physiology*, J. White, London, 232 pp.

Trevelyan, W.C. (1823) Sketch of the geognosy of part of the coast of Northumberland. *Memoir of the Wernerian Natural History Society*, **4**, 253–61.

Trevelyan, W.C. (1831) Notice of a bed of whin at Stanhope in Weardale. *Transactions of the Natural History Society of Northumberland*, **1**, 58–9.

Trewin, N.H. (1968) Potassium bentonites in the Namurian of Staffordshire and Derbyshire. *Proceedings of the Yorkshire Geological Society*, **37**, 73–91.

Trewin, N.H. (in press) *The Geology of Scotland*, 4th edn, The Geological Society, London.

Turner, B.R., Robson, D.A., Dearman, W.R., Jones, J.M., Magraw, D. and Smith, F.W. (1995) Structure. In *Robson's Geology of North East England*, 2nd edn (ed. G.A.L. Johnson), *Transactions of the Natural History Society of Northumbria*, **56**(5), Natural History Society of Northumbria, Newcastle-upon-Tyne, pp. 331–41.

Turner, N. (1994) Palynology of Devonian and Carboniferous rocks of the Cumnock and Doon Valley District, Strathclyde. *British Geological Survey, Biostratigraphy and Sedimentology Group Report*, **WH/94/294 R**.

Turner, N. and Spinner, E. (1990) Palynological evidence for the age of the Coal Measures of the Titterstone Clee Coalfield, Shropshire, England. *Proceedings of the Yorkshire Geological Society*, **48**, 81–98.

Tyrrell, G.W. (1909a) The classification of the post-Carboniferous intrusive igneous rocks of the west of Scotland. *Transactions of the Geological Society of Glasgow*, **13**, 298–317.

Tyrrell, G.W. (1909b) The geology and petrology of the intrusions of the Kilsyth–Croy district. *Geological Magazine*, **46**, 299–309.

Tyrrell, G.W. (1912) The late-Palaeozoic alkaline igneous rocks of the west of Scotland. *Geological Magazine*, **9**, 125–7.

Tyrrell, G.W. (1915) The bekinkinite of Barshaw. *Geological Magazine*, **2**, 304–11, 361–6.

Tyrrell, G.W. (1917a) The igneous geology of the Cumbrae Islands, Firth of Clyde. *Transactions of the Geological Society of Glasgow*, **16**, 244–74.

Tyrrell, G.W. (1917b) The picrite-teschenite sill of Lugar (Ayrshire). *Quarterly Journal of the Geological Society of London*, **74**, 84–131.

Tyrrell, G.W. (1920) The igneous geology of the Ayrshire coast from Doonfoot to the Heads of Ayr. *Transactions of the Geological Society of Glasgow*, **16**, 339–63.

Tyrrell, G.W. (1923) Classification and age of the analcite-bearing igneous rocks of Scotland. *Geological Magazine*, **60**, 249–60.

Tyrrell, G.W. (1928a) A further contribution to the petrography of the late-Palaeozoic igneous suite of the west of Scotland. *Transactions of the Geological Society of Glasgow*, **18**, 259–94.

Tyrrell, G.W. (1928b) On some dolerite sills containing analcite-syenite in central Ayrshire. *Quarterly Journal of the Geological Society of London*, **84**, 540–69.

Tyrrell, G.W. (1937) Flood basalts and fissure eruptions. *Bulletin Volcanologique, Serie 2*, **1**, 89–111.

Tyrrell, G.W. (1948) A boring through the Lugar Sill. *Transactions of the Geological Society of Glasgow*, **21**, 157–202.

Tyrrell, G.W. (1952) A second boring through the Lugar Sill. *Transactions of the Edinburgh Geological Society*, **15**, 374–392.

References

Upton, B.G.J. (1969) *Field Excursion Guide to the Carboniferous Volcanic Rocks of the Midland Valley of Scotland*, Edinburgh Geological Society, Edinburgh, 46 pp.

Upton, B.G.J. (1982) Carboniferous to Permian volcanism in the stable foreland. In *Igneous Rocks of the British Isles* (ed. D.S. Sutherland), John Wiley and sons Ltd, Chichester, pp. 255–75.

Upton, B.G.J. (1994) Regional setting of Carboniferous volcanism in the Midland Valley of Scotland. *Transactions of the Royal Society of Edinburgh: Earth Sciences*, **84**, 209–12.

Upton, B.G.J., Aspen, P., Graham, A.M. and Chapman, N.A. (1976) Pre-Palaeozoic basement of the Scottish Midland Valley. *Nature*, **260**, 517–18.

Upton, B.G.J., Aspen, P. and Chapman, N.A. (1983) The upper mantle and deep crust beneath the British Isles: evidence from inclusions in volcanic rocks. *Journal of the Geological Society of London*, **140**, 105–21.

Upton, B.G.J., Aspen, P. and Hunter, R.H. (1984) Xenoliths and their implications for the deep geology of the Midland Valley of Scotland and adjacent regions. *Transactions of the Royal Society of Edinburgh: Earth Sciences*, **75**, 65–70.

Upton, B.G.J., Fitton, J.G. and Macintyre, R.M. (1987) The Glas Eilean lavas: evidence of a Lower Permian volcano-tectonic basin between Islay and Jura, Inner Hebrides. *Transactions of the Royal Society of Edinburgh: Earth Sciences*, **77**, 289–93.

Upton, B.G.J., Mitchell, R.H., Long, A. and Aspen, P. (1992) Primitive olivine melanephelinite dykes from the Orkney Islands, Scotland. *Geological Magazine*, **129**, 319–24.

Upton, B.G.J., Aspen, P., Rex, D.C., Melcher, F. and Kinny, P. (1998) Lower crustal and possible shallow mantle samples from beneath the Hebrides: evidence from a xenolithic dyke at Gribun, western Mull. *Journal of the Geological Society, London*, **155**, 813–28.

Upton, B.G.J., Hinton, R.W., Aspen, P., Finch, A. and Valley, J.W. (1999) Megacrysts and associated xenoliths: evidence for migration of geochemically enriched melts in the upper mantle beneath Scotland. *Journal of Petrology*, **40**, 935–56.

Upton, B.G.J., Aspen, P. and Hinton, R.W. (2001) Pyroxenite and granulite xenoliths from beneath the Scottish Northern Highlands Terrane: evidence of lower-crust/upper-mantle relationships. *Contributions to Mineralogy and Petrology*, **142**, 178–97.

Urry, W.D. and Holmes, A. (1941) Age determinations of Carboniferous basic rocks from Shropshire and Colonsay. *Geological Magazine*, **78**, 45–61.

Van Breemen, O. and Hawkesworth, C.J. (1980) Sm-Nd isotopic study of garnets and their metamorphic host rocks. *Transactions of the Royal Society of Edinburgh: Earth Sciences*, **71**, 97–102.

Wadge, A.J. (1978) Devonian. In *The Geology of the Lake District* (ed. F. Moseley), *Yorkshire Geological Society Occasional Publication*, No. 3, Yorkshire Geological Society, Leeds, pp. 164–7.

Wadge, A.J., Harrison, R.K. and Snelling, N.J. (1972) Olivine-dolerite intrusions near Melmerby, Cumberland, and their age-determination by the potassium-argon method. *Proceedings of the Yorkshire Geological Society*, **39**, 59–70.

Wager, L.R. (1928) A metamorphosed nodular shale previously described as a 'spotted' metamorphic rock. *Geological Magazine*, **65**, 88–91.

Wager, L.R. (1929a) Metasomatism in the Whin Sill of the north of England. Part I: Metasomatism by lead vein solutions. *Geological Magazine*, **66**, 97–110.

Wager, L.R. (1929b) Metasomatism in the Whin Sill of the north of England. Part II: Hydrothermal alteration by juvenile solutions. *Geological Magazine*, **66**, 221–38.

Wagner, R.H. (1983) A Lower Rotliegend flora from Ayrshire. *Scottish Journal of Geology*, **19**, 135–55.

Walkden, G.M. (1972) The mineralogy and origin of interbedded clay wayboards in the Lower Carboniferous of the Derbyshire Dome. *Geological Journal*, **8**, 143–60.

Walkden, G.M. (1977) Volcanic and erosive events on an Upper Visean carbonate platform, north Derbyshire. *Proceedings of the Yorkshire Geological Society*, **41**, 347–67.

Walker, B.H. (1986) Emplacement mechanism of high-level dolerite sills and related eruptions in sedimentary basins, Fife, Scotland. Unpublished PhD thesis, University of Leeds.

Walker, B.H. and Francis, E.H. (1987) High-level emplacement of an olivine-dolerite sill into Namurian sediments near Cardenden, Fife. *Transactions of the Royal Society of Edinburgh: Earth Sciences*, **77**, 295–307.

References

Walker, F. (1923) The igneous geology of the Dalmeny district. *Transactions of the Royal Society of Edinburgh*, **53**, 361–75.

Walker, F. (1925) A monchiquite dyke in Lauderdale. *Transactions of the Edinburgh Geological Society*, **11**, 390–1.

Walker, F. (1930) A tholeiitic phase of the quartz-dolerite magma of central Scotland. *Mineralogical Magazine*, **22**, 368–76.

Walker, F. (1934) A preliminary account of the quartz-dolerite dykes of Perthshire. *Transactions and Proceedings of the Perthshire Society of Natural Science*, **9**, 109–17.

Walker, F. (1935) The late Palaeozoic quartz dolerites and tholeiites of Scotland. *Mineralogical Magazine*, **24**, 131–59.

Walker, F. (1936) Geology of the Isle of May. *Transactions of the Edinburgh Geological Society*, **13**, 275–85.

Walker, F. (1952) Differentiation in a quartz-dolerite sill at Northfield Quarry, Stirlingshire. *Transactions of the Edinburgh Geological Society*, **15**, 393–405.

Walker, F. (1958) Dolerite-sandstone contact phenomena on the East Lomond, Fife. *Transactions of the Edinburgh Geological Society*, **17**, 113–16.

Walker, F. (1965) The part played by tholeiitic magma in the Carbo–Permian volcanicity of central Scotland. *Mineralogical Magazine*, **34**, 498–516.

Walker, F. and Irving, J. (1928) The igneous intrusions between St Andrews and Loch Leven. *Transactions of the Royal Society of Edinburgh*, **56**, 1–17.

Walker, G.P.L. and Croasdale, R. (1972) Characteristics of some basaltic pyroclastics. *Bulletin Volcanologique*, **35**, 303–17.

Walker, G.P.L. and Ross, J.V. (1954) A xenolithic monchiquite dyke near Glenfinnan, Inverness-shire. *Geological Magazine*, **91**, 463–72.

Wallace, I.F. (1916) Notes on the petrology of agglomerates and hypabyssal intrusions between Largo and St. Monance. *Transactions of the Edinburgh Geological Society*, **10**, 348–62.

Wallis, J. (1769) *The Natural History and Antiquities of Northumberland; and so much of the County of Durham as lies between the Rivers Tyne and Tweed; Commonly Called North Bishoprick*, 2 volumes, S. Bladon, London.

Wallis, S.M. (1989) Petrology and geochemistry of Upper Carboniferous–Lower Permian volcanic rocks in Scotland. Unpublished PhD thesis, University of Edinburgh.

Walters, S.G. and Ineson, P.R. (1981) A review of the distribution and correlation of igneous rocks in Derbyshire, England. *Mercian Geologist*, **8**, 81–132.

Walters, S.G. and Ineson, P.R. (1983) Clay minerals in the basalts of the south Pennines. *Mineralogical Magazine*, **47**, 21–6.

Warn, C.R. (1975) *Rocks and Scenery from Tyne to Tweed*, Frank Graham, Newcastle-upon-Tyne.

Waters, C.N., Glover, B.W. and Powell, J.H. (1994) Structural synthesis of S. Staffordshire, UK: implications for the Variscan evolution of the Pennine Basin. *Journal of the Geological Society, London*, **151**, 697–713.

Watts, W.W. (1904) The long excursion to the Ludlow district. *Proceedings of the Geologists' Association*, **18**, 487–91.

Weigand, P.W. (1975) *Geochemistry of the Oslo Basaltic Rocks, Skrifter det Norske Videnskaps-Akademi i Oslo, I. Matematisk-Naturvidenskapelig Klasse, Ny Serie*, No. **34**, Universitetsforlaget, Oslo, 38 pp.

Welch, F.B.A. and Trotter, F.M. (1961) *Geology of the Country around Monmouth and Chepstow*, Memoir of the Geological Survey of Great Britain, sheets 233 and 250 (England and Wales), HMSO, London, 164 pp.

Westoll, T.S., Robson, D.A. and Green, R. (1955) A guide to the geology of the district around Alnwick, Northumberland. *Proceedings of the Yorkshire Geological Society*, **30**, 61–100.

White, J.D.L. and Houghton, B. (2000) Surtseyan and related phreatomagmatic eruptions. In *Encyclopedia of Volcanoes* (eds H. Sigurdsson *et al.*), Academic Press, San Diego, pp. 495–511.

Whitehead, T.H. and Eastwood, T. (1927) *The Geology of the Southern Part of the South Staffordshire Coalfield (South of the Bentley Faults)*, Memoir of the Geological Survey of Great Britain (England and Wales), HMSO, London, 218 pp.

Whittaker, A. and Green, G.W. (1983) *Geology of the Country around Weston-super-Mare*, Memoir of the Geological Survey of Great Britain, Sheet 279 and parts of sheets 263 and 295 (England and Wales), HMSO, London, 147 pp.

Whyte, F. (1963a) Volcanic vents of the Kilpatrick and Campsie hills. Unpublished PhD thesis, University of Glasgow.

Whyte, F. (1963b) The Heads of Ayr Vent. *Transactions of the Geological Society of Glasgow*, **25**, 72–97.

Whyte, F. (1966) Dumbarton Rock. *Scottish Journal of Geology*, **2**, 108–21.

Whyte, F. (1968) Lower Carboniferous volcanic vents in the west of Scotland. *Bulletin Volcanique*, **32**, 253–68.

Whyte, F. (1980) Trace element variation at the contact of the Dumbarton Rock basalt. *Scottish Journal of Geology*, **16**, 263–6.

Whyte, F. and MacDonald, J.G. (1974) Lower Carboniferous vulcanicity in the northern part of the Clyde plateau. *Scottish Journal of Geology*, **10**, 187–98.

Wilson, G. (1970) Wrench movements in the Aristarchus region of the Moon. *Proceedings of the Geologists' Association*, **81**, 595–608.

Wilson, G.V. (1922) *The Ayrshire Bauxitic Clay*, Memoir of the Geological Survey, Scotland, HMSO, Edinburgh, 28 pp.

Wilson, G.V., Edwards, W., Knox, J., Jones, J.C.B. and Stephens, J.V. (1935) *The Geology of the Orkneys*, Memoir of the Geological Survey of Great Britain, sheets 117–122 (Scotland), HMSO, Edinburgh, 205 pp.

Wilson, H.E. and Robbie, J.A. (1966) *The Geology of the Country around Ballycastle*, Memoir of the Geological Survey of Northern Ireland, Sheet 8, HMSO, Belfast, 370 pp.

Wilson, M., Timmerman, M. and Partners, P.N. (2000) Permo–Carboniferous magmatism in western and central Europe: plume impact versus plume incubation models, Unpublished conference abstract, Geoscience 2000, Manchester.

Winch, N.J. (1817) Observations on the geology of Northumberland and Durham. *Transactions of the Geological Society of London*, **4**, 1–101.

Winch, N.J. (1822) Remarks on the geology of Lindisfarne, or Holy Island. *Annals of Philosophy, New Series*, **20**, 426–34.

Woodhall, D.G. (1998) The volcanic and intrusive igneous rocks of the Burntisland and Kinghorn areas, Fife. *British Geological Survey, Onshore Geology Series, Technical Report*, **WA/98/34**.

Wyllie, P.J. (1999) Hot little crucibles are pressured to reveal and calibrate igneous processes. In *James Hutton – Present and Future* (eds G.Y. Craig and J.H. Hull), *Geological Society, London, Special Publication*, No. **150**, The Geological Society, London, pp. 37–57.

Young, B., Dyer, A., Hubbard, N. and Starkey, R.E. (1991) Apophyllite and other zeolite-type minerals from the Whin Sill in the northern Pennines. *Mineralogical Magazine*, **55**, 203–7.

Young, B., Styles, M.T. and Berridge, N.G. (1985) Niccolite-magnetite mineralization from Upper Teesdale, North Pennines. *Mineralogical Magazine*, **49**, 555–9.

Young, B.R. (1903) An analcite diabase and other rocks from Gullane. *Transactions of the Edinburgh Geological Society*, **8**, 326–35.

Young, J. (1860) The geology of the Campsie district. *Transactions of the Geological Society of Glasgow*, **1**, 1–45.

Yuill, M. (1963) Fossil tree stumps at Saltcoats. *Transactions of the Geological Society of Glasgow*, **25**, 1–3.

Zirkel, F. (1870) *Untersuchungen uber die Mikroskopische Zusammensetzung und Struktur der Basaltsteine*, Adolph Marcus, Bonn.

Glossary

This glossary aims to provide simple explanations of the geological terms used in Chapter 1 and in the 'Introduction' and 'Conclusions' sections of site descriptions. It also includes many of the more important terms encountered in other sections of the volume. *The explanations are not intended to be comprehensive definitions, but concentrate instead on the way in which the terms are used in this volume.* **Bold** typeface indicates a further glossary entry.

Chronostratigraphical names not listed in the glossary are given in Figure 1.2 (Chapter 1). For the names of minerals and non-igneous rock-types, the reader is referred to standard textbooks. The names of most common crystalline igneous rocks are better explained by means of classification diagrams (Figures G.1–G.6, all simplified after Le Maitre (2002) to include only rock names encountered in this volume). Names of igneous or igneous-related rocks that do not fit easily into these classification diagrams are included in the glossary, as are the names of most fragmental volcanic rocks, which require extended explanations commonly involving their mode of formation.

The classification and nomenclature of crystalline igneous rocks used in this volume follow the recommendations of the International Union of Geological Sciences (IUGS) Subcommission on the Systematics of Igneous Rocks (Le Maitre, 2002). Slight modifications follow the classification scheme of the British Geological Survey (BGS) (Gillespie and Styles, 1999), in which an attempt is made to distinguish 'root names' (i.e. largely those which figure on the main classification diagrams) from variants, mostly indicated by mineral qualifiers as prefixes to the root names. This is achieved through a strict use of hyphens:

- Compound root names, usually involving an *essential* mineral, are hyphenated (e.g. quartz-syenite, olivine-gabbro).
- Mineral qualifiers are hyphenated together (e.g. biotite-hypersthene andesite).
- Mineral qualifiers are *not* hyphenated to the root name, whether compound or not (e.g. biotite-hornblende trachyte, biotite quartz-trachyte, fayalite-augite nepheline-syenite).

Fragmental volcanic rocks are also classified and named according to the IUGS scheme, with minor modifications from the BGS scheme. Two points should be noted in particular: the term 'volcaniclastic' is applied to all fragmental rocks that occur in a volcanic setting, including *both* rocks that have been fragmented by volcanic processes (i.e. pyroclastic rocks) *and* sedimentary rocks that comprise reworked fragments of volcanic rocks. The terms 'volcanogenic' and 'epiclastic', which are commonly used elsewhere in an inconsistent and confusing manner, are not used in the BGS scheme or in this volume.

The Carboniferous and Permian basic lavas of Scotland are almost invariably porphyritic to varying degrees. This feature was utilized by MacGregor (1928) to devise a nomenclature based in part on phenocryst size (microporphyritic or macroporphyritic) and in part on the phenocryst assemblages (ol + cpx, ol + cpx + pl, pl ± ol). They were assigned type locality names (e.g.

Glossary

'Craiglockhart' type for macroporphyritic ol + cpx-phyric basalts, and 'Hillhouse' type for microporphyritic ol + cpx-phyric basalts). This scheme was widely used on Scottish maps for many years as a convenient 'shorthand' way of representing the wide range of petrographical types that are distinctive in the field and hence form mappable units. It also enabled lavas such as the feldspar-phyric 'Markle' and 'Jedburgh' types, which commonly range in composition from basalt to hawaiite, to be assigned a name without the need for an analysis. The scheme has now fallen into disuse in favour of less parochial descriptions, but the 'MacGregor' names are given in some places in this volume in addition, especially where they enable comparison with existing literature (Table G.1). Other local names for distinctive rock-types and obsolete names are explained where they occur in the main text.

Aa: **lava** with a rough, clinkery surface, broken into angular blocks.

Acid: descriptive of light-coloured igneous rocks relatively enriched in silica.

Aeolian: descriptive of sediments or landforms formed under the action of the wind.

Age: a geological time unit (cf. **chronostratigraphy**), usually taken to be the smallest standard division of geological time, of shorter duration than an **epoch**.

Agglomerate: a **pyroclastic** rock with predominantly rounded **clasts** greater than 64 mm in diameter.

Alkali basalt: a type of **basalt**, parental to a suite of **silica-saturated** to -**undersaturated** igneous rocks characterized by high alkalis relative to silica, formed dominantly in extensional within-plate settings (see Figures G.5 and G.6).

Alkaline: descriptive of igneous rocks that contain more sodium and/or potassium than is required to form feldspar and hence contain, or have the potential to contain (i.e. in the **norm**), other alkali-bearing minerals such as feldspathoids, alkali pyroxenes and alkali amphiboles.

Amygdale: a gas bubble cavity in an igneous rock that has been infilled later with minerals.

Andesite: a fine-grained, **mafic**, **intermediate** igneous rock (see Figures G.1 and G.5).

Aphyric (or **non-porphyritic**): a textural term, applied to igneous rocks that lack relatively large, conspicuous crystals (**phenocrysts**) compared with the grain size of the groundmass.

Aplitic: descriptive of relatively finer-grained areas, typically **veins**, within an igneous rock (contrast with **pegmatitic**).

Assimilation: the addition of solid material such as **country rock** to a **magma**, changing its composition.

Asthenosphere: a weak layer within the Earth's **mantle** and immediately below the **lithosphere**.

Back-arc basin: the region adjacent to a **subduction**-related volcanic arc, on the opposite side of the arc from the trench and subducting plate. Stresses in the back-arc region are typically extensional.

Basalt: a fine-grained, **mafic**, **basic** igneous rock (see Figures G.1, G.5 and G.6).

Basanite: a fine-grained, **mafic**, **basic** or **ultrabasic** igneous rock with the mineralogy of a **basalt** but with the addition of a feldspathoid mineral (see Figures G.1, G.5 and G.6).

Basement: the oldest rocks recognized in a given area; an assemblage of metamorphic and/or igneous rocks that underlies all the sedimentary formations.

Basic: descriptive of an igneous rock relatively rich in the 'bases' of early chemistry (MgO, FeO, CaO, Fe_2O_3); silica (SiO_2) is relatively low (nominally 45–52%).

Basin (i.e. sedimentary basin): a region of prolonged subsidence of the Earth's surface, typically formed either by stretching of the **lithosphere** under extensional forces, or by **flexural subsidence**.

Bed: in **lithostratigraphical** terms, a subdivision of either a **member** or a **formation**; the smallest unit within the scheme of formal **lithostratigraphical** classification. Also used informally to indicate a stratum within a sedimentary rock succession.

Bedding: a feature of sedimentary rocks, in which planar or near-planar surfaces known as 'bedding planes' indicate successive depositional surfaces formed as the sediments were laid down.

Benmoreite: a fine-grained, **mafic**, **intermediate** igneous rock, belonging to the **alkali basalt** suite (see Figures G.1, G.5 and G.6).

Glossary

Bentonite: a light coloured rock, mainly composed of clay minerals and colloidal silica, produced by **devitrification** and chemical alteration of glassy fine ash (see also **tonstein**).

Biostratigraphy: the stratigraphical subdivision and correlation of sedimentary rocks based on their fossil content.

Blastomylonite: an extremely sheared (mylonitic) rock in which some recrystallization and growth of new minerals has taken place during deformation.

Block: a **pyroclastic** rock fragment, more than 64 mm in diameter, with an angular to subangular shape, which indicates that it was formed by the breaking of solid rock.

Bole: a fine, earthy, compact red-brown clay formed by tropical weathering and leaching of a **lava** surface (see **laterite**).

Bomb: a **pyroclastic** rock fragment, more than 64 mm in diameter, which has a 'streamlined' shape or surface indicating that it was erupted as a mass of molten or partially molten **lava** that then cooled during flight.

Breccia: a rock composed of angular broken fragments greater than 2 mm in diameter; can be **pyroclastic**, sedimentary or fault-related.

Brockram: a term used in Cumbria for a sedimentary **breccia** of Permian age; commonly red or purple.

Caldera: a circular, basin-shaped depression, usually many times greater than the size of any individual volcanic **vent**, caused by collapse of the roof of an underlying **magma chamber** following an eruption; also refers to the underlying volcanic structure.

Caledonian Orogeny: a major period of **orogenesis** that took place during the **Palaeozoic Era**, associated with the closure of the ancient Iapetus Ocean that was situated between Scotland and the rest of present-day Britain.

Camptonite: an **alkaline** variety of **lamprophyre**, in which the **phenocrysts** are various combinations of olivine and titanium-bearing amphibole, augite and biotite. The groundmass consists of the same minerals (except olivine) together with plagioclase, and possibly subordinate alkali feldspar and/or feldspathoids.

Carbonatite: a magmatic carbonate rock.

Carboniferous Period: a geological time division (**period**; cf **chronostratigraphy**), ranging from 354 to 290 million years ago. It precedes the **Permian Period**.

Chilled margin: that part of an igneous rock adjacent to a contact with an older rock, where the **magma** has been cooled rapidly (chilled), forming a zone of fine-grained rock.

Chronostratigraphy: the correlation and subdivision of rock units on the basis of relative age – a hierarchy of sequential units to which the layers of sedimentary rocks are allocated, through the study and interpretation of their stratigraphy. The hierarchy of principal chronostratigraphical units is erathem, **system**, **series** and **stage**, which are related, respectively, to the geological time units of **era**, **period**, **epoch** and **age**.

Cinder cone: a small volcanic cone built almost entirely of loose volcanic fragments, ash and **pumice** (cinder/scoria).

Clast: a fragment in a **pyroclastic** or sedimentary rock.

Cleavage: a plane of incipient parting in a rock, produced by the alignment of platy crystals, such as mica, in response to confining pressure during deformation.

Columnar jointing: the division of an igneous rock body into columns by cracks (**joints**) produced through thermal contraction on cooling. The columns form perpendicular to the cooling surface.

Comagmatic: a term applied to igneous rocks that are considered to have been derived from the same parent **magma**, or at least from the same source region, at the same time and under identical physical and chemical conditions.

Complex: used herein to refer to a large-scale, spatially related assemblage of igneous rock units possibly, but not necessarily, with complicated igneous and/or **tectonic** relationships and of various ages and diverse origins.

Composite: used to refer to an igneous intrusion or **lava** flow that has formed from two or more different pulses of **magma**, each pulse differing slightly from the others in mineralogy, texture and/or chemistry.

Concretion: a hard, compact mass, usually rounded, in a sedimentary rock, formed by precipitation of a cementing mineral around a nucleus during or after deposition.

Conglomerate: a sedimentary rock, a significant proportion of which is composed of rounded pebbles and boulders, greater than 2 mm in diameter.

Glossary

Country rock: rock that has been intruded by an igneous rock.

Crust: the outermost layer or shell of the Earth, above the **Moho** and **mantle**. It consists of two parts: a **basic** layer, which forms the oceanic crust and underlies the continents at depth; and a layer of dominantly **acid** rocks, which forms the thickest, upper part of the continental crust.

Cryptocrystalline: very finely crystalline, such that individual crystals can only be distinguished under very powerful magnification (e.g. electron microscope).

Crystal fractionation: see **fractional crystallization**.

Cumulate: an igneous rock formed by crystals that precipitated early from a **magma** and accumulated due to gravitational settling, current activity or other magmatic processes, without modification by later crystallization.

Depleted mantle: **mantle** that has been depleted in **incompatible elements**, through **partial melting**.

Deuteric: descriptive of the reactions between primary minerals and the water-rich fluids that separate from the same body of **magma** at a late stage in its cooling history.

Devitrification: the conversion of glass, e.g. in the interstices of a volcanic or **hypabyssal** rock, to **cryptocrystalline** or crystalline material.

Diagenesis: the process of mineral growth and/or recrystallization leading to lithification of unconsolidated sediment to form rock.

Diapir: a dome-shaped body of **magma** or mobile rock that has risen through **country rocks** due to its lower density and/or greater plasticity.

Diatreme: a **breccia**-filled volcanic pipe formed by a gaseous explosion.

Dinantian sub-System: a **chronostratigraphical** division; equivalent to the Lower Carboniferous in Europe, dated at 354–327 Ma. It precedes the **Namurian Series**, and comprises the **Tournaisian** and **Visean series**.

Diorite: a coarse-grained, **mafic**, **intermediate** igneous rock (see Figure G.2).

Distal: far from the source.

Dolerite: used herein as a synonym of microgabbro (see Figure G.2).

Dyke: a tabular body of igneous rock, originally intruded as a vertical or steeply inclined sheet.

Dyke-swarm: a collection of **dykes**.

Effusive: descriptive of an eruption as **lava** rather than as **pyroclasts**.

Enclave: an inclusion (**xenolith**) within an igneous rock, usually of some other igneous rock that may or may not be related.

En échelon: descriptive of a series of linear features, such as **dykes** or **faults**, which follow roughly the same trend but are 'stepped'.

Enriched mantle: **mantle** that has been enriched in **incompatible elements**, through the introduction of partial melts and **metasomatism**.

Epoch: a geological time unit (cf. **chronostratigraphy**), of shorter duration than a **period** and itself divisible into **ages**.

Equigranular: a texture in which all the crystals are approximately the same size.

Era: a major geological time unit (cf. **chronostratigraphy**), which is divisible into **periods**.

Euhedral: descriptive of a mineral grain, such as a **phenocryst**, with well-formed crystal faces.

Exsolution: the process whereby an initially homogeneous mineral separates into two distinct and commonly intergrown crystalline phases on cooling without a change in the bulk composition.

Extrusive: descriptive of igneous rocks that have been extruded onto the Earth's surface, rather than being intruded beneath the surface (**intrusive**).

Facies: the characteristic features of a rock unit, including rock-type, mineralogy, texture and structure, which together reflect a particular sedimentary, igneous or metamorphic environment and/or process.

Fault: a fracture in the Earth's **crust** across which the rocks have been displaced relative to each other.

Felsic: descriptive of light-coloured minerals (*fel*dspar/*fel*dspathoid and *si*lica); or of an igneous rock containing substantial proportions of these minerals; the opposite of **mafic**.

Felsite: a field term for glassy and fine-grained **felsic** igneous rocks.

Fissure eruption: a volcanic eruption where **lava** wells up through fissures in the Earth's **crust**. Often involves very fluid **basic lavas**, and can spread over very large areas.

Flexural subsidence: the downward bending of the **lithosphere** due to loading, for example by the weight of sediment (as in a **foreland basin**) or by **tectonic** overthrusting.

Glossary

Flood basalt: a widespread sheet or layer of basaltic **lava** erupted from a fissure-type eruption.

Fluidization: mobilization resulting from passage of a fluid (usually a gas) through a granular solid.

Fluvial: referring to a river environment.

Foidite: a general term for fine-grained igneous rocks in which the **felsic** minerals include more than 60% feldspathoids.

Foidolite: a general term for coarse-grained igneous rocks in which the **felsic** minerals include more than 60% feldspathoids.

Foliation: the planar arrangement of components within a rock.

Foreland basin: a sedimentary **basin** developed by depression of a convergent continental margin due to the weight of sediment accumulating in front of the orogenic belt.

Formation: a **lithostratigraphical** unit, hierarchically higher than 'member' and lower than 'group'. A named 'Formation' represents an assemblage of strata that have a common characteristic useful for mapping.

Fractional crystallization: the process in which the early formed crystals in a **magma** are removed or otherwise prevented from equilibrating with the residual liquid, which consequently becomes progressively more evolved in composition (i.e. more fractionated).

Gabbro: a coarse-grained, **mafic**, **basic** igneous rock (see Figures G.2 and G.3).

GCR: Geological Conservation Review, in which nationally important geological and geomorphological sites were assessed and selected with a view to their long-term conservation as SSSIs.

Glomeroporphyritic: a **porphyritic** rock containing clusters of **phenocrysts**.

Gneiss: a coarse-grained, inhomogenous rock, common in relatively high-grade metamorphic terranes, characterized by banding or layering.

Gneissose: a metamorphic texture, which has a 'stripy' appearance due to the segregation of the component minerals into compositionally distinct lenses.

Graben: an elongate, down-faulted crustal block, commonly with a marked topographic expression.

Granite: a coarse-grained, **felsic**, **acid** igneous rock (see Figure G.2).

Granoblastic: a metamorphic texture in which recrystallization has formed essentially equidimensional crystals.

Granulite facies: the temperature and pressure conditions typical of high-temperature and moderate- to high-pressure regional metamorphism.

Group: a **lithostratigraphical** unit consisting of one or more **formations**, important for local and regional **lithostratigraphical** correlation.

Hanging wall: the upper side of an inclined **fault** or other dislocation.

Harzburgite: a **peridotite** consisting mainly of olivine and orthopyroxene (see Figure G.4).

Hawaiian eruption: a type of eruption characterized by the flow of basaltic **lava** from an eruptive centre or centres without appreciable explosive activity.

Hawaiite: a fine-grained, **mafic**, **intermediate** igneous rock, belonging to the **alkali basalt** suite (see Figures G.1, G.5 and G.6).

Hornfels: a well-baked, hard, splintery rock resulting from thermal (contact) metamorphism.

Hyaloclastite: a **pyroclastic** rock composed of angular fragments of glass, formed when **magma** is rapidly quenched and shattered on entering water.

Hybridization: the intermixing of two or more **magmas**, which crystallize as a single rock, commonly having a heterogeneous texture and complex mineralogy.

Hydroclastic: descriptive of fragmentation of **magma** or hot rock by its interaction with water (see also **hydrovolcanic** and **phreatomagmatic**).

Hydromagmatic: descriptive of processes driven by the interaction of **magma** with water.

Hydrothermal alteration: changes in mineralogy and chemistry in rocks resulting from the reaction of hot water with pre-existing minerals (cf. **metasomatism**).

Hydrovolcanic: descriptive of volcanic processes driven by the interaction of **magma** with water.

Hypabyssal: descriptive of an igneous intrusion, or its rock, emplaced at a depth intermediate between **plutonic** and volcanic.

Incompatible elements: trace elements that are not readily accepted into the crystal structure of common rock-forming minerals during the crystallization of **magma** and hence are concentrated preferentially into the remaining liquid. They are also concentrated in the first liquids produced during **partial melting**.

Intermediate: descriptive of igneous rock that is transitional in chemical composition between **acid** and **basic** (see Figure G.5).

Intrusive: descriptive of igneous rocks that have been intruded into older rocks beneath the Earth's surface, rather than being extruded onto the surface (**extrusive**).

Joint: a fracture in a rock across which there has been no noticeable displacement. Common types of joints in igneous rocks are cooling joints, formed through thermal contraction as the **magma** cools.

Juvenile: descriptive of volcanic fragments that have been derived directly from **magma**.

Laccolith: an igneous intrusion, roughly circular in plan and concordant with the structure of the **country rock**; it generally has a flat floor, a shallow domed roof and a **dyke**-like feeder beneath its thickest point.

Lamprophyre: the name used for a distinctive group of largely **hypabyssal** rocks characterized by abundant **phenocrysts** of **mafic** minerals, with **felsic** minerals confined to the groundmass.

Lapilli-tuff: a **pyroclastic** rock in which 25–75% of the **clasts** are between 2 and 64 mm in diameter (lapilli), and are set in a finer-grained matrix.

Lava: molten rock at the Earth's surface (contrast with **magma**).

Lava tube: a hollow space beneath the solidified surface of a **lava**, formed by the draining out of molten **lava** after the **crust** had formed.

Laterite: a red subsoil, rich in hydrous oxides of iron and/or aluminium and commonly with kaolinite and silica that develops as a residual product of weathering in tropical and subtropical climates.

Leucocratic: descriptive of light-coloured igneous rocks containing few **mafic** minerals.

Lherzolite: a **peridotite** consisting mainly of olivine, clinopyroxene and orthopyroxene (see Figure G.4).

Lithosphere: the outer layer of the solid Earth, including the **crust** and upper part of the **mantle**, which forms tectonic plates above the **asthenosphere**.

Lithostratigraphy: the stratigraphical subdivision and correlation of rocks based on their lithology. Units are named according to their perceived rank in a formal hierarchy, namely supergroup, **group**, **formation**, **member** and **bed**.

Maar: a broad, low-rimmed volcanic crater formed by collapse within a shallow cone produced by **phreatic** or **phreatomagmatic** eruptions. Generally composed of less **juvenile** material than a **tuff-ring**. Commonly contains a lake, also termed a maar.

Mafic: descriptive of dark-coloured minerals, rich in *ma*gnesium and/or iron (*Fe*), or an igneous rock containing substantial proportions of these minerals, mainly amphibole, pyroxene or olivine; the opposite of **felsic**.

Magma: molten rock beneath the Earth's surface.

Magma chamber: a large body of **magma** that has accumulated within the Earth's **crust** or upper **mantle**.

Mantle: part of the interior of the Earth, beneath the **crust** and above the core.

Mass-flow: the transport, down slope under the force of gravity, of large, coherent masses of sediment, **tephra** or rock; commonly assisted by the incorporation of water, ice or air.

Megacryst: any crystal in a crystalline rock that is very much larger than the surrounding groundmass.

Mélange: a chaotic rock unit, characterized by a lack of internal continuity of contacts between component blocks and including fragments of a wide range of composition and size.

Melanocratic: descriptive of dark-coloured igneous rocks rich in **mafic** minerals.

Member: a **lithostratigraphical** unit, hierarchically higher than 'bed' and lower than '**formation**'.

Mesocratic: descriptive of igneous rocks intermediate between **leucocratic** and **melanocratic** in colour.

Mesostasis: the groundmass in an igneous rock.

Meta: prefix added to any rock name to indicate a metamorphosed variety, e.g. metabasalt is a metamorphosed **basalt**.

Metaluminous: degree of alumina-saturation in igneous rocks in which the molecular proportion of Al_2O_3 is greater than that of $Na_2O + K_2O$, but less than that of $Na_2O + K_2O + CaO$.

Metasomatism: a process involving fluids that introduce or remove chemical constituents from rock thus changing its chemical and mineralogical composition without melting.

Mid-ocean ridge: a continuous median mountain range within the oceans along which new oceanic **crust** is generated by volcanic activity.

Mid-ocean ridge basalt (MORB): a type of **tholeiitic basalt**, generated at **mid-ocean ridges**. A worldwide, voluminous **basalt** type widely used as a fundamental standard for comparative geochemistry.

Miospore: a fossil spore or pollen grain that is less than 200 microns in diameter.

Moho (=Mohorovicic Discontinuity): the boundary surface within the Earth below which there is an abrupt increase in seismic velocity; marks the base of the **crust** above the underlying **mantle**. Geophysical and petrological criteria define slightly different positions for the boundary.

Monchiquite: an **alkaline** variety of **lamprophyre**, similar to **camptonite** except that the groundmass is feldspar-free, being composed almost entirely of glass and feldspathoids.

Mugearite: a fine-grained, **mafic**, **intermediate** igneous rock, belonging to the **alkali basalt** suite (see Figures G.1, G.5 and G.6).

Namurian Series: a **chronostratigraphical** division; the lowermost **series** of the **Silesian** (Upper Carboniferous) **sub-System** in Europe, dated at 327–315 Ma. It follows the **Visean Series** and precedes the **Westphalian Series**.

Neck: the feeder 'pipe' of an ancient volcano, which has been infilled with collapsed material from the surface **vent** and commonly intruded by further **magma** to form a **plug**, after the cessation of eruption. Exposed due to subsequent erosion.

Norm: a recalculation of the chemical composition of an igneous rock to obtain a theoretical mineralogical ('normative') composition; useful for classification purposes and for comparison with experimental studies of **magma** crystallization.

Ocean island basalt (OIB): a compositionally diverse type of **basalt**, ranging from **tholeiitic** to **alkali basalt**, characteristic of within-plate oceanic settings.

Orogenesis: crustal thickening following the collision of tectonic plates and resulting from magmatism, folding, thrusting and accretion, leading to regional uplift and mountain building.

Pahoehoe: **basalt lava** with a smooth, ropy surface.

Palaeosol: an ancient or 'fossilized' soil.

Palaeozoic Era: a geological time division (**era**; cf. **chronostratigraphy**), ranging from 545 to 248 million years ago. The **Carboniferous** and **Permian periods** occur at the end of this **era**.

Partial melting: the incomplete melting of a rock to produce a **magma** that differs in composition from the parent rock.

Pegmatitic: textural description of an area within an igneous rock that is notably more coarsely crystalline and commonly forming **veins** and **dykes** (contrast with **aplitic**).

Peléan: a volcanic eruption characterized by gaseous ash clouds associated with the growth and collapse of volcanic domes.

Peperite: a **breccia** characterized by isolated blocks and lobes of igneous rock, commonly chilled and mixed with **fluidized** host sediment; typically present at the margins of high-level **sills** intruded into water-bearing sediment.

Peralkaline: the degree of alumina-saturation in igneous rocks in which the molecular proportion of Al_2O_3 is less than that of $Na_2O + K_2O$.

Peraluminous: the degree of alumina-saturation in igneous rocks in which the molecular proportion of Al_2O_3 is greater than that of $Na_2O + K_2O$.

Peridotite: a coarse-grained, **ultramafic**, **ultrabasic** igneous rock consisting predominantly of olivine with varying amounts of orthopyroxene and clinopyroxene (see Figures G.3 and G.4).

Period: a geological time unit (cf. **chronostratigraphy**), of shorter duration than an **era** and itself divisible into **epochs**.

Permian Period: a geological time division (**period**; cf. **chronostratigraphy**), ranging from about 290 until 248 million years ago. It follows the **Carboniferous Period** and precedes the Triassic Period.

Petrogenesis: the origin and evolution of rocks.

Petrography: the study of the mineralogy, texture and systematic classification of rocks, especially under the microscope.

Petrology: the study of the origin, occurrence, structure and history of rocks; includes **petrography** and **petrogenesis**.

Phenocryst: a crystal in an igneous rock that is larger than those of the groundmass, usually having crystallized at an earlier stage.

Phonolite: a fine-grained, **felsic**, **silica-under-saturated** igneous rock containing significant amounts of feldspathoid minerals (see Figures G.1 and G.5).

Phreatic: descriptive of a volcanic eruption or explosion of steam, not involving **juvenile** material, that is caused by the expansion of groundwater due to an underlying igneous heat source.

Phreatomagmatic: descriptive of explosive volcanic activity caused by the contact of **magma** with large volumes of water, producing intensely fine ash and abundant steam.

Phreatoplinian: a rare type of explosive volcanic eruption and its deposits produced by **phreatomagmatic** processes (contrast with **plinian**).

-phyric: as in 'plagioclase-phyric', a **porphyritic** rock containing **phenocryst**s of plagioclase.

Picrite: a term originally used to describe a variety of **dolerite** or **basalt** extremely rich in olivine and pyroxene. Now defined chemically as a group name for rocks with SiO_2 < 47%, total alkalis < 2% and MgO > 18%.

Pillow lava: subaqueously erupted **lava**, usually basaltic in composition, comprising an accumulation of smooth pillow shapes and **lava tubes** produced by rapid chilling.

Playa: a flat plain on the coast or at the centre of an inland drainage basin found in arid areas.

Plinian: a type of explosive volcanic eruption and its deposits; **magma** is fragmented through the release of magmatic gas and released at high velocity to form an eruption column that extends high into the Earth's atmosphere.

Plug: the solidified remains of a cylindrical intrusion of **magma**, commonly **intrusive** into, or associated with, a volcanic **neck**.

Pluton: an intrusion of igneous rock, emplaced at depth in the Earth's **crust**.

Plutonic: descriptive of igneous rocks formed at depth in the Earth's **crust**.

Poikilitic: a textural term for an igneous rock in which small crystals of one mineral are enclosed within a larger crystal of another mineral.

Porphyritic: a textural term for an igneous rock in which larger crystals (**phenocrysts**) are set in a finer-grained or glassy groundmass.

Porphyroblast: a large, well-formed crystal that grew *in situ* during metamorphic recrystal-lization and typically encloses finer-grained crystals that formed earlier.

Porphyry: a field term for an igneous rock that contains **phenocrysts** within a fine-grained groundmass of indeterminate composition; usually preceded by a mineral qualifier indicating the type of **phenocryst** present, e.g. feldspar porphyry.

Protolith: the source rock from which an igneous rock was formed, most commonly by melting.

Proximal: near to the source.

Pseudomorph: a replacement product, composed either of a single mineral or an assemblage of minerals, that retains the distinctive overall shape of the parent crystal.

Pumice: light-coloured **pyroclast** of generally **acid**, highly vesicular, glass foam.

Pyroclast: a fragment (**clast**) ejected from a volcano; the terms ash, lapilli, and **block** or **bomb** are used to describe pyroclasts that are respectively less than 2 mm, 2–64 mm and more than 64 mm in diameter.

Pyroclastic: descriptive of unconsolidated deposits (**tephra**) and rocks that form directly by explosive ejection from a volcano.

Pyroclastic breccia: a rock comprising predominantly angular **pyroclasts** with an average size greater than 64 mm in diameter.

Pyroclastic fall deposit: tephra deposited by fall-out from a volcanic eruption cloud.

Pyroclastic flow: a volcanic avalanche; a hot density current comprising **pyroclasts** and gases, erupted as a consequence of the explosive disintegration of **magma** and/or hot rock; also describes the deposit from this eruption.

Pyroclastic surge: similar to a **pyroclastic flow** but turbulent and less dense.

Pyroxenite: a coarse-grained, **ultramafic** igneous rock consisting predominantly of orthopyroxene and clinopyroxene, with lesser amounts of olivine in varying proportions (see Figures G.3 and G.4).

Radiometric age: the age in years calculated from the decay of radioactive elements.

Red beds: a collective term applied to continental sedimentary successions that are predominantly red in colour owing to the presence of iron oxides and hydroxides formed in a highly oxidizing environment.

Restite: the material remaining after **partial melting**.

Glossary

Rhyolite: a fine-grained, **felsic**, **acid** igneous rock (see Figures G.1, G.5 and G.6).

RIGS: Regionally Important Geological/geomorphological Sites.

Rifting: the thinning, and rupture along **faults**, of the **lithosphere** under extensional stress, commonly accompanied by upwelling of hot material from the **asthenosphere** below.

Scoriaceous: descriptive of **lavas** that are very highly vesiculated, giving them a 'clinkery' appearance.

Seismic profile: a cross-section of the **lithosphere**, constructed by creating artificial earthquakes using explosives or other vibrating devices, and then recording the vibrations that pass through the Earth to an array of instruments at a range of distances along a pre-determined line.

Series: a **chronostratigraphical** unit; it comprises all the rocks formed during an **epoch** and can be divided into **stages**.

Serpentinization: **hydrothermal alteration** of **ultramafic** rocks in which the **mafic** minerals are replaced by a range of hydrous secondary minerals, collectively known as 'serpentine'.

Shearing: the deformation of a rock body by the sliding of one part relative to another part, in a direction parallel to their plane of contact.

Sheet flood: a broad expanse of rapidly moving water and debris, not confined to a channel and usually of short duration due to rapid run-off in an arid area.

Silesian sub-System: a **chronostratigraphical** division; equivalent to the Upper Carboniferous in Europe, dated at 327–290 Ma. It is preceded by the **Dinantian sub-System**, and comprises the **Namurian**, **Westphalian** and **Stephanian** series.

Silica-saturation: a measure of the amount of silica available to form the major mineral components of an igneous rock, usually calculated from the **norm**. Silica-oversaturated rocks may contain free silica as quartz; silica-undersaturated rocks may contain feldspathoids in addition to feldspars.

Silicic: alternative term to **acid**.

Sill: a tabular body of igneous rock, originally intruded as a sub-horizontal sheet and generally concordant with the **bedding** or **foliation** in the **country rocks**.

Slickensides: linear grooves and ridges formed on a fault surface as rocks move against each other along the fault plane.

Spheroidal weathering: a type of weathering commonly found in **mafic** and **ultramafic** rocks; also known as 'onion-skin' weathering, because it leads to the formation of a flaky, weathered zone around a central, unweathered, spherical core.

Spherulite: a spherical mass of acicular crystals, commonly feldspar, radiating from a central point; commonly found in glassy **silicic** volcanic rocks as a result of **devitrification**.

Stage: a **chronostratigraphical** unit; it comprises all the rocks formed during an **age**, and is usually taken to be the smallest standard unit.

Stephanian Series: a **chronostratigraphical** division; the uppermost **series** of the **Silesian** (Upper Carboniferous) **sub-System** in Europe, dated at 303–290 Ma. It follows the **Westphalian Series** and precedes the **Permian Period**.

Stock: a small, discordant igneous **intrusion**, usually sub-cylindrical and with steep margins.

Stoping: the emplacement of **magma** by detaching pieces of **country rock** which either sink through or are **assimilated** by the **magma**.

Stratovolcano: a cone-shaped volcano with a layered internal structure.

Strike-slip: see **transcurrent**.

Strombolian: type of volcanic eruption and its deposits characterized by continuous small explosive 'fountains' of fluid basaltic **lava** from a central crater.

Subduction: the process of one **lithospheric** plate descending beneath another during plate convergence.

Syenite: a coarse-grained, **felsic**, **intermediate** igneous rock (see Figure G.2).

System: a **chronostratigraphical** unit; it comprises all the rocks formed during a **period**, and can be divided into **series**.

Tectonic: referring to the movements and deformation of the **crust** on a large scale.

Tectonic inversion: a change in the relative elevation of a block of **crust** (e.g. a **basin** becomes a basement high or vice versa), brought about by the reversal of movement direction along structures such as **faults**, due to a change in regional forces.

Tephra: an unconsolidated accumulation of **pyroclasts**.

Terrane: a fault-bound body of oceanic or continental **crust** having a geological history that is distinct from that of contiguous bodies.

Glossary

Thermal subsidence: subsidence caused by the sinking of the **lithosphere** as it thickens and cools through heat conduction to the surface, after the end of a period of extension and active **rifting**.

Tholeiitic: descriptive of a suite of **silica-oversaturated** igneous rocks, characterized chemically by strong iron enrichment relative to magnesium during the early stages of evolution of the **magma**; formed in extensional within-plate settings, at constructive plate margins and in island arcs.

Tonstein: a term used, especially in central Europe, for thin beds of kaolin-rich clay in coal-bearing strata, possibly of **volcaniclastic** origin (see **bentonite**).

Tournaisian Series: a **chronostratigraphical** division; the lowermost **series** of the **Dinantian** (Lower Carboniferous) **sub-System** in Europe, dated at 354–342 Ma. It follows the Devonian Period and precedes the **Visean Series**.

Trachyte: a fine-grained, **felsic**, **intermediate** igneous rock (see Figures G.1, G.5 and G.6).

Transcurrent (or **strike-slip**): a large-scale, steeply dipping **fault** or shear, along which the movement is predominantly horizontal. Movement may be either left-lateral (sinistral) or right-lateral (dextral).

Transgression: used herein to refer to the point where a **sill** 'steps up' or 'steps down', in changing from one stratigraphical horizon to another.

Transitional basalt: a **basalt** that is intermediate between an **alkali basalt** and a tholeiite.

Transpression: crustal shortening as a result of oblique compression across a **transcurrent** fault or shear zone.

Transtension: crustal extension as a result of oblique tension across a **transcurrent** fault or shear zone leading to localized rifts or **basins**.

Trap topography: descriptive of the typical terrain found on predominantly basaltic **lava** fields, in which layers of resistant **lava** form cliffs or steep slopes, separated by flat or gently sloping ledges representing more easily weathered material. The ledges form either on the tops and bottoms of flows, or on interflow sedimentary and **pyroclastic** rocks.

Tuff: a rock comprising **pyroclasts** with an average grain size less than 2 mm.

Tuff-breccia: a **pyroclastic** rock in which between 25 and 75% of the **pyroclasts** are greater than 64 mm in diameter.

Tuffisite: an **intrusive tuff**, which can be formed by the mechanical breakdown of rocks close to a rock fracture, due to the passage of volcanic gasses.

Tuffite: a tuffaceous sedimentary rock, i.e. one that contains a significant proportion (25–75%) of **pyroclastic** fragments in addition to sedimentary **clasts**.

Tuff-ring: a shallow cone of **pyroclastic** deposits formed by **phreatic** or **phreato-magmatic** eruptions. Generally composed of a higher proportion of **juvenile** materials than a **maar** volcano and lacking the broad collapse crater.

Turbidite: a clastic rock formed through deposition from subaqueous sediment-laden density currents (turbidity currents) that move swiftly down slope under the influence of gravity.

Ultrabasic: descriptive of an igneous rock with a silica content less than that of **basic** rocks (less than 45% SiO_2).

Ultramafic: descriptive of an igneous rock in which dark-coloured minerals (amphibole, pyroxene, olivine) comprise more than 90% of the rock.

Variscan Orogeny: a period of **orogenesis** that occurred during the **Carboniferous Period** and affected rocks in south-west England, south Wales and southern Ireland.

Vein: a term frequently used for an intrusion of igneous rock, commonly irregular, which is narrower than a **dyke** or a **sill**, i.e. a few cm wide or less. This contrasts with general usage, e.g. for mineral veins that can be of any width.

Vent: that part of a volcano at which the **lava** and/or **pyroclastic** rocks are erupted onto the surface.

Vesicle: a gas bubble cavity, usually in a **lava** or shallow intrusion.

Visean Series: a **chronostratigraphical** division; the uppermost **series** of the **Dinantian** (Lower Carboniferous) **sub-System** in Europe, dated at 342–327 Ma. It follows the **Tournaisian Series** and precedes the **Namurian Series**.

Vitroclastic: descriptive of a **pyroclastic** rock characterized by fragments of glass.

Volcaniclastic: generally applied to a clastic rock containing mainly material derived from volcanic activity, but without regard for its origin or environment of deposition (includes **pyroclastic** rocks and sedimentary rocks containing volcanic debris).

Volcanotectonic fault: **fault** along which the displacement occurred through sub-surface movement of **magma** or during its eruption.

Vug: a cavity in a rock, with a lining of crystalline minerals.

Websterite: a **pyroxenite** consisting mainly of orthopyroxene and clinopyroxene with little olivine (see Figure G.4).

Wehrlite: a **peridotite** consisting mainly of olivine and clinopyroxene (see Figure G.4).

Welded tuff: a glass-rich **pyroclastic** rock in which the grains have been welded together because of heat and volatiles retained by the particles and the weight of the overlying material (not synonymous with ignimbrite though many ancient ignimbrites are welded).

Westphalian Series: a **chronostratigraphical** division; the middle **series** of the **Silesian** (Upper Carboniferous) **sub-System** in Europe, dated at 315–303 Ma. It follows the **Namurian Series** and precedes the **Stephanian Series**.

Xenocryst: a crystal, like a **phenocryst**, but which is foreign to the igneous rock in which it is found.

Xenolith: a rock fragment that is foreign to the igneous rock in which it is found.

Zeolites: a group of hydrous alumino-silicate minerals formed at relatively low temperatures, particularly during the later stages of cooling of volcanic rocks.

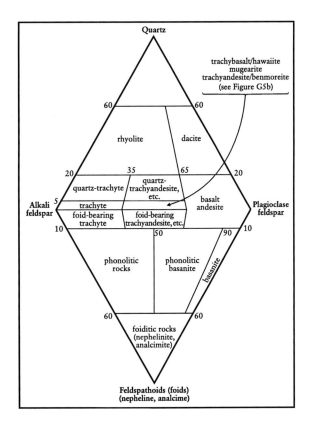

Figure G.1 The classification of fine-grained felsic and mafic crystalline igneous rocks, based upon their felsic mineral content. The distinction between basalt and andesite and between trachybasalt and trachyandesite is based on the composition of the plagioclase feldspar present. For divisions of the trachyandesite + trachybasalt fields, see Figure G.5b.

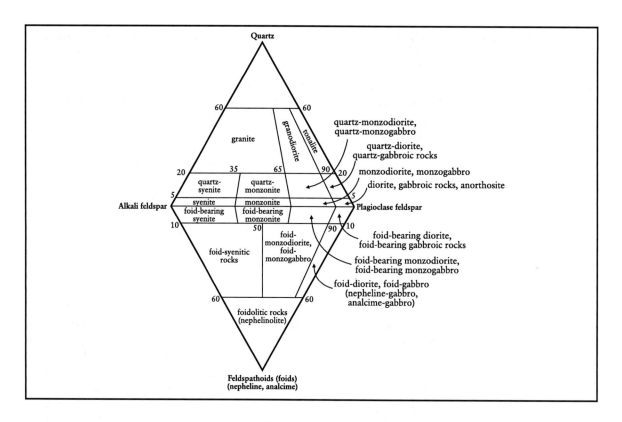

Figure G.2 The classification of coarse-grained felsic and mafic crystalline igneous rocks, based upon their felsic mineral content. The distinction between gabbroic rocks and diorite is based upon the composition of the plagioclase feldspar present. Medium-grained rocks are named by attaching the prefix 'micro', for example microsyenite. However, in this volume and commonly elsewhere, dolerite is used as a synonym for micro-gabbro.

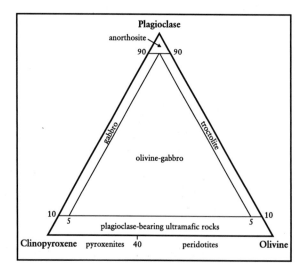

Figure G.3 The more detailed classification of coarse-grained mafic crystalline igneous rocks, falling in the gabbroic rocks field of Figure G.2, based upon their plagioclase, olivine and clinopyroxene content. Note that other varieties of gabbroic rock, containing orthopyroxene, do not occur in this essentially alkaline igneous province, except as lower crustal xenoliths (see Chapter 1).

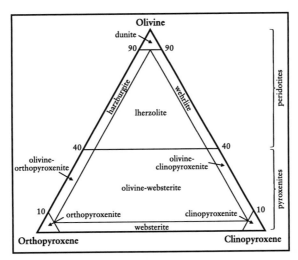

Figure G.4 The classification of coarse-grained crystalline ultramafic rocks, based upon their olivine, orthopyroxene and clinopyroxene content.

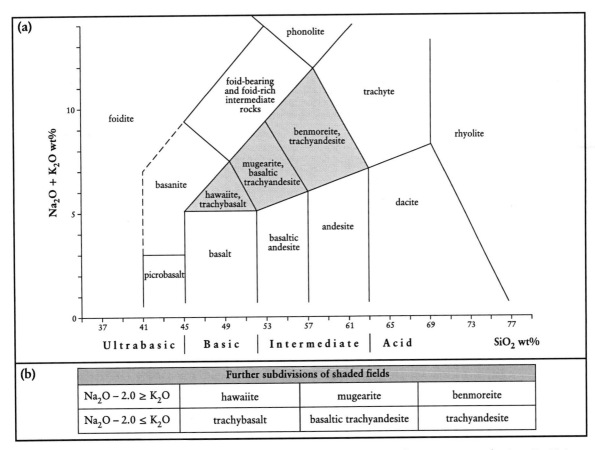

Figure G.5 The most usual chemical classification of fine-grained crystalline igneous rocks (e.g. Le Maitre, 2002), used when it is not possible to classify according to their mineralogy due to very fine grain size. Note that alteration can result in the loss or addition of highly mobile elements such as sodium (Na) and potassium (K), with consequent changes in silica (SiO_2) and inaccuracies in classification. (a) Total alkalis ($Na_2O + K_2O$) versus silica (SiO_2). (b) Rocks in the shaded area of (a) can be subdivided according to their Na_2O/K_2O ratio. However, most Dinantian igneous rocks of Great Britain fall close to the dividing line between sodic and potassic affinities and hence are difficult to classify. In much of the older literature (before *c.* 1975), without the benefit of analyses, the terms 'trachybasalt' and 'trachyandesite' are commonly used in a general sense for both sodic and potassic types.

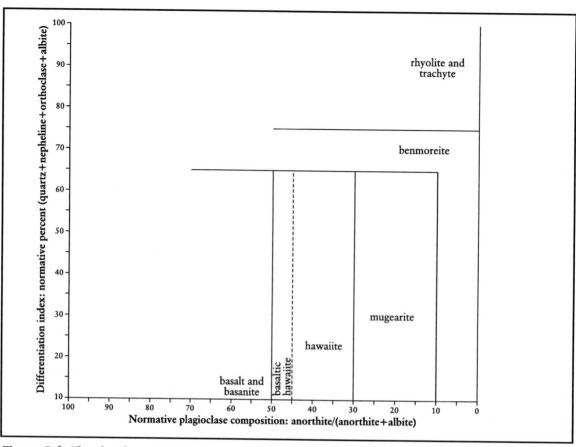

Figure G.6 The classification of fine-grained crystalline igneous rocks that is most commonly used in geo-chemical studies of Carboniferous and Permian igneous rocks of Great Britain. Modified by Macdonald (1975) after Coombs and Wilkinson (1969).

Table G.1 Local nomenclature of basic igneous rocks of Carboniferous and Permian age in Scotland, as used on Geological Survey maps and in most literature since 1928. Now being replaced by more-standard termi-nology based on dominant phenocrysts and, where possible, the chemical composition. (pl = plagioclase, ol = olivine, cpx = clinopyroxene, fetiox = iron-titanium oxides.)

Basalt type of MacGregor (1928)	Phenocrysts		Chemical classification after Macdonald (1975)	Type locality
	abundant	may be present in lesser amounts		
Macroporphyritic (phenocrysts > 2mm)				
Markle	pl	± ol, fetiox	pl ± ol ± fetiox-phyric hawaiite, basaltic hawaiite or basalt	Markle Quarry, East Lothian
Dunsapie	pl + ol + cpx	± fetiox	ol + cpx + pl ± fetiox-phyric basaltic hawaiite or ol + cpx + pl-phyric basalt	Dunsapie Hill, Edinburgh (neck intrusion)
Craiglockhart	ol + cpx		ol ± cpx-phyric picrobasalt or basanite	Craiglockhart Hill, Edinburgh (flow)
Microporphyritic (phenocrysts < 2mm)				
Jedburgh	pl	± ol, fetiox	pl ± ol ± fetiox-phyric hawaiite, basaltic hawaiite or in some cases basalt	Little Caldon, Stirling-shire (plug). Also in Jedburgh area
Dalmeny	ol	± cpx, pl	ol ± cpx-phyric basalt	Dalmeny Church, West Lothian (flow)
Hillhouse	ol + cpx		ol ± cpx-phyric basalt or basanite	Hillhouse Quarry, West Lothian (sill)

Index

Note: Page numbers in **bold** and *italic* type refer to **tables** and *figures* respectively

Index

Index

Index

Index

Index

White trap/whin 158, 178–9,
184–5, 188–90, *189*, *192*,
193–5, 222, 229, 273
  Midland Valley Sill-complex
225, 244
  Whin Sill-complex 229, 249,
252, 254
Wydon GCR site **13**, 275–7, *275*

Xenocrysts 33–4
  almadine-pyrope garnets 32
  clinopyroxene 27, 29
  quartz 72, 104
  sanidine 58
  see also Megacrysts;
    Xenoliths
Xenoliths
  cognate (autoliths) 28
  crustal sources 31–3, 48, 51,
53, 55, 155, 165, 184, 312,
315–16
  cumulates 31, 163
  distribution **161**
  host magmas 28
  local derivation 33
  localities of occurrence 28
  megacrysts 33–4, 154, 156,
159, **161**, 163, 165, 185
  sources
    upper crust 33, 48, 53
    middle crust 32–3, 48, 51,
53

lower crust 28, 29, 31–2,
48, 51, 53, 55, 155, 165,
185, 212
upper mantle 9, 22–3,
28–31, 48, 53–5, 104,
154–6, 165, 184–5,
296–9, 315–16
Xenoliths (constituents) 9,
28–34, 48, 51–5, 92–3, 303–4
  anorthosite 32
  composite wehrlite–
lherzolite 30, 163
  dunite 93
  feldspathic 33
  glimmerite 210, *212*
  gneiss *30*, 53
    mafic gneiss 32
    quartzo-feldspathic gneiss
32
  granite 52
  harzburgite 297, 315
    spinel harzburgite 29, 296
  lherzolite 29, 30, 128, 297,
298, 315
    garnet lherzolite 22, 23,
26, 33–4, 55
    spinel lherzolite 26, 29,
53–4, 109, 163, 210,
213, 297, 315
  mantle-derived material 9,
28, 296, 312, 315–16
  meta-anorthosite 31

meta-quartz-diorite 31
metadiorite 31
metagabbro 31
metamorphic rocks 152,
163, 211, 212
metatonalite 31
peridotite 29, *29*, 30–1,
53–4, 116, 297, 315
pyroxenite 29–31, *30*, 33,
161, 163, 212, *212*
  biotite pyroxenite 31,
163, 312
  clinopyroxenite 29, 31, 54
  garnet pyroxenite 29, 163
  kaersutite pyroxenite 31,
33, 210
  olivine pyroxenite 210,
212
sedimentary rocks 92–4,
313
syenitic (anorthoclasites) 34,
165
trachybasalt, analcime-
hornblende trachybasalt
63
ultramafic rocks 29–30, 54,
108, 210, 297, 312–15
websterite 29, 163
wehrlite 29, 31, 54, 161,
163, 210, 212

Yoredale Series 250